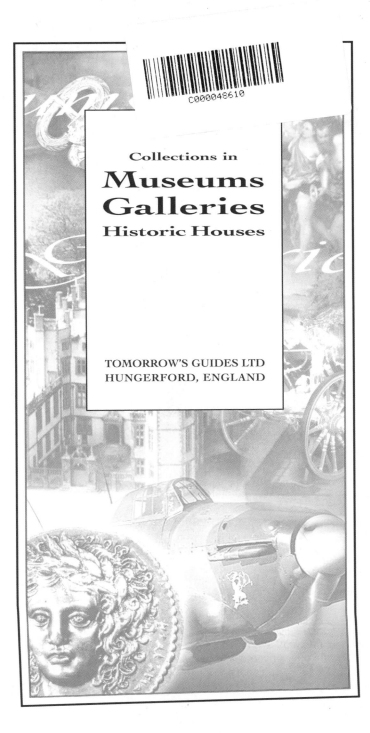

Collections in

Museums
Galleries
Historic Houses

TOMORROW'S GUIDES LTD
HUNGERFORD, ENGLAND

Acknowledgements

We are indebted to curators, owners and their staff who have provided us with profiles and photographs of their wonderful and diverse collections from over 1600 museums, art galleries, historic houses and sites.

Publisher: Davina Ludlow
Sales Director: Geoffrey Snell
Editor: Victoria Rowlands
Assistant Editor: Rowan Fitzpatrick
Production: Oli Blackwell
Mapping & Imaging: Phil Cory
Design: Zai Khan

This edition edited and designed by:

Tomorrow's Guides
PO Box 7677, Hungerford RG17 0FX
Subscription sales Tel: 0800 387342
sales@tomorrows.co.uk
www.tomorrows.co.uk

Distribution in the UK by Portfolio

Printed in Spain

Second edition 2003

© Tomorrow's Guides Ltd 2003

ISBN 1 85890 035 2

Foreword

In my first two years as Chairman of Resource, the Council for Museums, Archives and Libraries, I have had the extraordinary pleasure of visiting a large number of museums, galleries and historical houses throughout the UK.

Lord Evans of Temple Guiting
Photo Richard H Smith

The variety and depth of collections on public display in the United Kingdom is unrivalled. We are the envy of Europe and yet most of us have little knowledge of this huge quantity and geographic spread of places and collections available to us.

I have been struck by both the quantity and quality of museums, galleries, houses and sites, extending from the great collections in our National Museums & Galleries to the fine collections of the Cecil Higgins Art Gallery in Bedford, to the glories of Hadrian's Wall, the delights of the collection at Harewood House and, at the other end of the country, Truro's Royal Cornwall Museum.

This publication draws together comprehensive listings information and maps that will contribute to raising the profile of many lesser known sites and institutions and provide greater detail to cover wider audiences.

The galleries, houses and museums listed here and the people that look after and interpret them for us are a vital part of our cultural well-being. It is these places and these things which inspire our creativity and sense of exploration. They provide us with experiences that can enrich, make sense of and change our lives. They can help ground our modern society in its history and traditions and help build a thriving cultural economy.

This slim volume has a great role to play, in widening our horizons, and widening the audiences who will enjoy and discover the heritage around us.

Matthew Evans
Chairman of Resource

Contents

Contents

Introduction

Welcome to the 2003 edition of 'Collections in Museums, Galleries, Historic Houses'. We were delighted with the response to our first edition and we are indebted to all of the contributors for their support.

We would also like to thank those of you who have taken the time to contact us with comments and recommendations and as you will see many of those suggestions have been included within the book.

In this, our Second Edition, we have again included many of the greatest treasures in the world which are exhibited in both British and Irish museums and art galleries. The stately homes and historic country houses featured have superb collections of fine pictures, furniture and decorative art. We are also highlighting more forthcoming Exhibitions and Events than in our previous edition, which we believe will be of particular interest to our readers.

The curators, owners and their staff have provided us with a wealth of information, profiles and photographs of their wonderful and diverse collections from over 1600 museums, art galleries, historic houses and sites - and now many, including our national museums and art galleries, have free entry for everyone.

Our book caters for all ages and will assist you in finding whatever you are looking for. Refer to the three indexes at the back of the book to search by Classification, Town or Name of Entry. There are 32 different and specialist classifications ranging from Anthropology to Victoriana (listed on page 11).

If there are any museums, art galleries or historic houses that you feel have been omitted and should be listed, please email us on editor@tomorrows.co.uk or return the report form at the back of the book, and we will add them to the 2004 edition to be published in November 2003.

And finally, we would like to thank all of you who have bought this book, whether for the first time or as a previous purchaser. We do hope you enjoy visiting some of the places listed and we look forward to receiving your comments and recommendations through the year.

Davina Ludlow
Publisher

How to use

Finding the right Museum, Gallery, Historic House
We have divided the publication into England, Scotland, Wales, Ireland, Isle of Man and Channel Islands. Each section has its own colour coding. The maps on pages 8-9 detail the Areas/Counties for each Country, and the contents (pages 4-5) provide a page reference to each Area/County, where you will find a more detailed map showing Map References for Museums, Art Galleries and Historic Houses listed within that Area/County. You should use these Map References to locate Museums etc within the Town or Area that you wish to visit. Also refer to the quick reference indexes at the back which provide page references by Classification, Town and, if you are looking for a particular Museum, by Name.

Sequence of Entries
The listings within each Area (i.e North Wales) or within each County (i.e Cumbria) are sequenced by Town Name. Multiple listings within the same town are shown in alphabetical order.

Profiles
Each entry has a profile of its Collection/s written by the Museum's Curator (or in some cases its owner).

Opening Times
The periods of the year, the days of the week and opening times (24 hour clock) are provided.

Admission Charges
Admission charges for England, Scotland, Wales, Northern Ireland, Isle of Man and the Channel Islands are shown in British £, and for Ireland in Euros (€).

Key to Symbols

☜ Guided or Private Tours	☕ Café or Refreshments
♿ Disabled Access (Please check for exact details)	🍴 Restaurant
🎁 Gift Shop or Sales Point	🚗 Car Parking

Ireland Counties Map

UK Counties Map

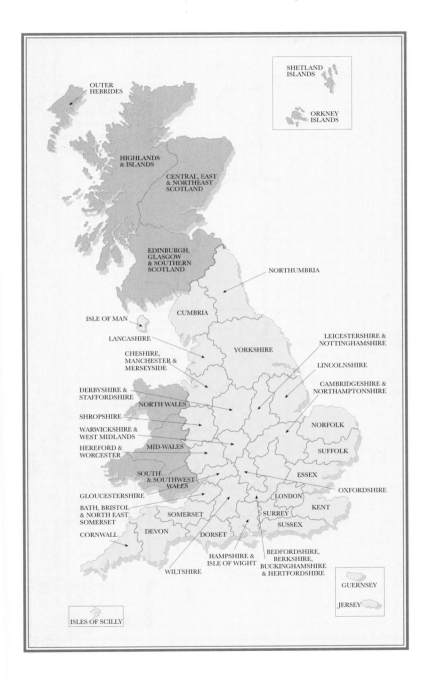

UK Railways Network

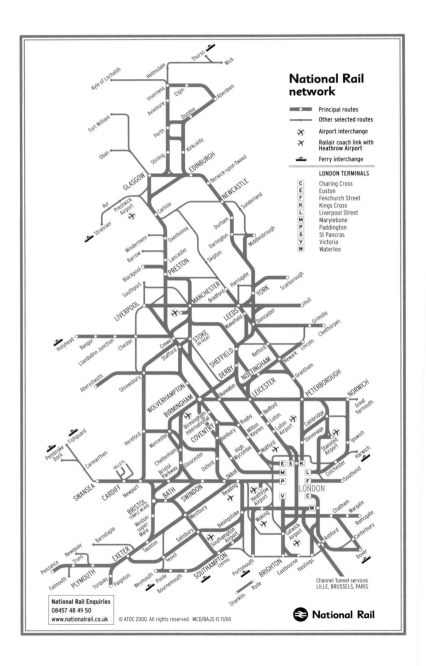

National Rail network

Principal routes
Other selected routes
✈ Airport interchange
✈ Railair coach link with Heathrow Airport
⛴ Ferry interchange

LONDON TERMINALS
- C — Charing Cross
- E — Euston
- F — Fenchurch Street
- K — Kings Cross
- L — Liverpool Street
- M — Marylebone
- P — Paddington
- S — St Pancras
- V — Victoria
- W — Waterloo

Channel Tunnel services
LILLE, BRUSSELS, PARIS

National Rail Enquiries
08457 48 49 50
www.nationalrail.co.uk   © ATOC 2000. All rights reserved. MCD/BAJS-1S 11/00

National Rail

How to use

Locations
Each listing has a brief description of its location as well as a Map Reference which is shown on the Map at the start of each Area/County.

Exhibitions & Events 2003
The dates and subject matter are listed for Exhibitions and Events scheduled to take place during 2003 in many of the major Museums, Galleries and Historic Houses listed.

Indexes
At the back of the book there are quick reference indexes by Classification (see key below), Town Name and Entry Name.

Feedback
There is a Report Form on page 448 and this should be used to let us know about Museums etc that you visit (we value your comments, good or bad), also to advise us of any Collections that are not listed in our book that you feel should be listed. Feedback is essential for the integrity of our book.

www.tomorrows.co.uk
Visit our website to order copies of this book and our other publications. Also for information on our Museum & Galleries website which is scheduled to be on-line in Spring 2003.

Key to Classifications
see Classifications Index on page 413

Anthropology	Jewellery	Railway
Archaeological	Literature & Libraries	Religion
Art Galleries	Maritime	Roman
Arts, Crafts & Textiles	Military & Defence	Science - Earth
China, Glass & Ceramics	Mills - Water & Wind	& Planetary
Communications	Multicultural	Sculpture
Egyptian	Music & Theatre	Sporting History
Fashion	Natural History	Stately Homes
Geology	Oriental	Toy & Childhood
Health & Medicine	Palaces	Transport
Horticultural	Police, Prisons & Dungeons	Victoriana

Bath, Bristol & Northeast Somerset

Bristol, the largest university city in the southwest of England with its beautiful cathedral, is an industrial and commercial centre with a long history of maritime adventure and commerce and housing a wealth of historic treasures.

The jewel of this lovely region is undoubtedly Bath, built on hills rising steeply from the River Avon. This delightful city, a spa centre since Roman times, became a centre of fashion and manners during the eighteenth century. The tradition and history of this region is innovatively and fascinatingly revealed to the visitor through a wealth of fine galleries, museums and displays.

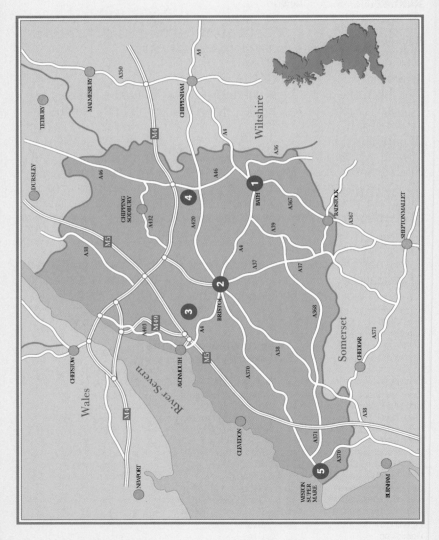

The Red Map References should be used to locate Museums etc on the pages that follow

Bath, Bristol & Northeast Somerset

American Museum in Britain

Claverton Manor, Bath BA2 7BD   Tel: 01225 460503   Fax: 01225 469160
Email: amibbath@aol.com   Web: www.americanmuseum.org

Conkey's Tavern

The American Museum shows in a series of 18 period rooms how Americans lived between the late 17th and mid 19th centuries. There are galleries devoted to Folk Art and to an extensive textile collection. The grounds contain an arboretum of American trees and shrubs as well as a replica of part of the garden at Mount Vernon, George Washington's Virginia home.

Opening Times: 22 Mar to 2 Nov Tue to Sun 14:00-17:00. 22 Nov to 14 Dec Tue to Sun 13:00-16:00. Closed Mon.
Admission: Adult £6.00, Child £3.50, OAP £5.50.
Location: Two miles south east of Bath   Map Ref: 1

Bath Abbey Heritage Vaults

13 Kingston Buildings, Bath BA1 1LT   Tel: 01225 422462
Email: laj@heritagevaults.fsnet.co.uk

A pageant of the Abbey's past from the 8th century to the present day in words and pictures, sights and sounds.

Opening Times: Daily 10:00-16:00, closed Xmas & New Year and Good Friday.
Admission: Adult £2.50, Child Free, OAP/Student £1.50.   Location: In the centre of Bath, alongside Bath Abbey.   Map Ref: 1

Bath Postal Museum

8 Broad Street, Bath BA1 5LJ   Tel / Fax: 01225 460333   Email: info@bathpostalmuseum.org
Web: www.bathpostalmuseum.org

Postboy 18th/19th century

We illustrate 4,000 years of communication from clay-mail to e-mail. This time-line includes exhibitions on the Romans and the Victorians, an essential ingredient in school curricula. Four computer games demonstrate how the post was 'carried' then and in medieval times. Constantly playing videos plus an international airmail room showing early aviation films, a reconstructed 1930s post office and special displays will intrigue the visitor.

Opening Times: Mon to Sat 11:00-17:00.   Admission: Adult £2.90, Child/Concession £1.50, OAP £2.40.   Location: In town centre, one minute walk from General Post Office.   Map Ref: 1

Beckford's Tower & Museum

Lansdown Road, Bath BA1 9BH   Tel: 01225 422212/460705   Fax: 01225 481805
Email: beckford@bptrust.demon.co.uk   Web: www.bath-preservation-trust.org.uk

The recently restored Tower, built in 1827 for William Beckford, boasts a spiral staircase and elegant Belvedere offering panoramic views. It contains a museum collection, with paintings, prints, models and art objects, illustrating Beckford's life and interests.

Opening Times: Easter to end Oct Sat Sun & BH 10:30-17:00.   Admission: Adult £2.50, Child/OAP £2.00, Family £6.00.   Location: One and a half miles north from Bath centre on Lansdown Road towards the racecourse.   Map Ref: 1

Building of Bath Museum

Countess of Huntingdon's Chapel, The Vineyards, Bath BA1 5NA   Tel: 01225 333895
Fax: 01225 445473   Email: cathryn@bathmuseum.co.uk   Web: www.bath-preservation-trust.org.uk

Situated in the beautiful Gothic chapel built in 1765 is the complete guide to how Georgian Bath was conceived and built. The exhibition is illustrated with a number of models, artefacts, paintings and touch screen computer.

Opening Times: 15 Feb to 30 Nov, Tue to Sun & BH 10:30-17:00. Closed 1 Dec to 14 Feb.
Admission: Adult £4.00, Child £1.50, Concession £3.00.   Location: Short walk from Bath Town Centre on The Paragon which runs parellel with Lansdown and Walcot Street.   Map Ref: 1

Bath, Bristol & Northeast Somerset

Holburne Museum of Art

Great Pulteney Street, Bath BA2 4DB   Tel: 01225 466669   Fax: 01225 333121
Email: holburne@bath.ac.uk   Web: www.bath.ac.uk/holburne

This jewel in Bath's crown was once the Georgian Sydney Hotel, whose glittering society Jane Austen watched from her house opposite. It displays the treasures collected by Sir William Holburne: superb English and continental silver, porcelain, maiolica, glass and Renaissance bronzes. The Picture Gallery contains works by Turner, Guardi, Stubbs and other artists plus portraits of Bath society by Thomas Gainsborough.

Opening Times: Mid Feb to Mid Dec Tue to Sat 10:00-17:00, Sun 14:30-17:30. Admission: Adult £4.50, Child

The Holburne Museum of Art by Ray Williams

£1.50, OAP £4.00, Family £9.00, Residents of Bath & NE Somerset £2.50.   Location: Five minutes walk from town centre.   Map Ref: 1

Museum of Bath at Work

Campden Works, Julian Road, Bath BA1 2RH   Tel / Fax: 01225 318348
Email: mobaw@hotmail.co.uk   Web: www.bath-at-work.org.uk

Stories of working life in Bath, of Bath stone and building industry, Victorian ironmongers, mineral water factory and engineering works, furniture making and car factory. Temporary exhibitions.

Opening Times: Apr to Nov daily, Nov to Apr Sat & Sun 10:00-17:00. Admission: Adult £3.50, Concession £2.50, Family £10.00. Location: North of city centre, five minutes walk. Map Ref: 1

Museum of Costume

Assembly Rooms, Bennett Street, Bath BA1 2QH   Tel: 01225 477785
Fax: 01225 477743   Email: costume_bookings@bathnes.gov.uk
Web: www.museumofcostume.co.uk

One of the most prestigious and extensive collections of its kind. Displays include over 150 dressed figures illustrating the changing styles in fashionable dress for men, women and children from the late 16th century to the present day. The modern collection contains work by many of the world's top designers. Free personal audio guides.

Opening Times: Daily 10:00-16:30, last exit 17:00. Closed 25-26 Dec. Admission: 2002 Adult £5.00, Child £3.50, OAP £4.00, Family £14.00. Group rates and Saver tickets with Roman Baths are available. Location: Ten

A display in the 18th Century Gallery

minute walk from city centre, 15 minute walk from bus and railway stations.   Exhibitions & Events 2003 : 11 Dec to 4 Nov: Modern Times - People and Dress in the 1920s.   Map Ref: 1

Museum of East Asian Art

12 Bennett Street, Bath BA1 2QJ   Tel: 01225 464640
Fax: 01225 461718   Email: museum@east-asian-art.freeserve.co.uk   Web: www.east-asian-art.co.uk

A unique museum housing a fine collection of objects from all over East Asia, ranging in date from circa 5000 BC to the present day. The exquisite collection includes Chinese ceramics and metalware, Japanese lacquer and a range of south east Asian ceramics, as well as some outstanding examples of Chinese jade.

Opening Times: Tue to Sat 10:00-17:00, Sun 12:00-17:00, some BH. Closed Mon, Xmas & New Year. Admission: Adult £3.50, Child (under 12) £1.00, OAP £3.00. Location: Upper town area of city; just off The Circus. 20 minutes walk from railway/bus station.

Gilt bronze statue of a standing monk with begging bowl

Exhibitions & Events 2003 : 4 Feb to 6 Apr: Animals in Chinese Art, 15 Apr to 22 Jun: The Chinese Feast, 1 Jul to 14 Sep: The World in Blue and White, 23 Sep to 11 Jan: Death and Burial.   Map Ref: 1

Bath, Bristol & Northeast Somerset

No 1 Royal Crescent

Bath BA1 2LR Tel: 01225 338727 Fax: 01225 481850 Email: admin@bptrust.demon.co.uk
Web: www.bath-preservation-trust.org.uk

The Lady's Bedroom

A grand town house of the late 18th century accurately restored and furnished with authentic furniture, paintings and carpets. On the ground floor are the study and dining room and on the first floor a lady's bedroom and drawing room. In the basement is a period kitchen and a museum shop.

Opening Times: Mid-Feb to end Oct Tue to Sun 10:30-17:00, Nov Tue to Sun 10:30-16:00. Closed Good Friday, open BH. Admission: Adult £4.00, Child/Concession/Student £3.50, Family £10.00, Schools £2.50, Groups £3.00 . Location: Central.   Map Ref: 1

Roman Baths

Pump Room, Stall Street, Bath BA1 1LZ Tel: 01225 477785 Fax: 01225 477743
Email: romanbaths_bookings@bathnes.gov.uk Web: www.romanbaths.co.uk

Great Bath, Roman Baths

The Roman Baths contain the remains of one of the greatest religious spas in the ancient world and a fine Roman museum. Bath's unique thermal springs rise at the heart of the site. It is the most popular visitor attraction in the West Country and is among the UK's major heritage sites. Free audio tours are available in seven languages.

Opening Times: Jan to Feb & Nov to Dec 09:30-16:30, Mar to Jun & Sep to Oct 09:00-17:00, Jul to Aug 09:00-21:00. Last exit 1/2 hour after closing. Closed 25-26 Dec. Admission: 2002 Adult £8.00, Child £4.60, OAP £7.00, Family £20.50. Group rates and saver tickets with

Museum of Costume are available. Location: City centre.   Map Ref: 1

Victoria Art Gallery

Bridge Street, Bath BA2 4AT Tel: 01225 477233 Fax: 01225 477231
Email: victoria_enquiries@bathnes.gov.uk Web: www.victoriagal.org.uk

The permanent collection at the
Victoria Art Gallery

Bath and North East Somerset's art gallery, housing a substantial permanent collection in addition to major touring exhibitions. Paintings by Gainsborough, Turner and Sickert hang in the recently refurbished Upper Gallery and are described on free audio guides. Decorative arts newly on display include collections of pottery, porcelain, glass and watches.

Opening Times: Tue to Fri 10:00-17:30, Sat 10:00-17:00, Sun 14:00-17:00. Closed BH. Admission: Free.
Location: City centre.   Map Ref: 1

William Herschel Museum

19 New King Street, Bath BA1 2BL Tel: 01225 311342/446865 Fax: 01225 446865
Web: www.bath-preservation-trust.org.uk

Home of 18th century astronomers William and Caroline Herschel. A charming Georgian townhouse furnished in the style of the period, includes workshop where Herschel made telescopes and discovered the planet Uranus in 1781. Collection of astronomical and musical instruments. 'Star Vault' attraction showing astronomy programmes. Delightful Georgian garden.

Opening Times: 10 Feb to 30 Nov Mon to Fri 14:00-17:00, Sat & Sun 11:00-17:00.
Admission: Adult £3.50, Child £2.00, Family £7.50. Bath Pass Scheme & Bath Preservation Trust Museums Concession.   Location: Six minutes walk from central bus and railway stations, near city centre.
                                                                                    Map Ref: 1

BRISTOL

Arnolfini

🐦 ❀ ⤢ **ARNOLFINI**

16 Narrow Quay, Bristol BS1 4QA   Tel: 0117 929 9191   Fax: 0117 925 3876
Email: arnolfini@arnolfini.demon.co.uk   Web: www.arnolfini.demon.co.uk

Arnolfini is one of Europe's leading centres for the contemporary arts with an international reputation for presenting new and innovative work. Arnolfini presents international developments and emerging trends in visual art through one-person and group exhibitions, commissions and projects. The Programme draws attention to important British artists at the early stage of their career and presents timely exhibitions by major international artists.

Photo: Woodley and Quick

Opening Times: Exhibitions - Mon to Wed, Fri & Sat 10:00-19:00, Thu 10:00-21:00, Sun & BH Mon 12:00-19:00. Closed Xmas, New Year & Good Friday. In Summer 2003 a major refurbishment will be undertaken. Though the building will be closed for 18 months, Arnolfini will still be programming arts events around Bristol. Please phone ahead to confirm. Admission: Free.
Location: Located on the harbourside, near to the town centre, 15 minute walk from Bristol Temple Meads Railway Station.   Map Ref: 2

At-Bristol Ltd

♿ ❀ ⤢ ❀ 🚂

Anchor Road, Harbourside, Bristol BS1 5DB   Tel: 0845 345 1235   Fax: 0117 915 7200
Email: information@at-bristol.org.uk   Web: www.at-bristol.org.uk

At-Bristol brings science, nature and art to life. It consists of Explore, an interactive science centre; Wildwalk, a journey through the history of life on Earth; and the IMAX Theatre, showing giant-screen films.

Opening Times: Daily 10:00-18:00. Admission: Adult from £6.50, Child from £4.50, Concession from £5.50. Location: On Bristol's harbourside in the city centre.   Map Ref: 2

Blaise Castle House Museum

❀ 🚂

Henbury Road, Henbury, Bristol BS10 7QS   Tel: 0117 903 9818   Fax: 0117 903 9820
Email: general_museum@bristol-city.gov.uk   Web: www.bristol-city.gov.uk/museums

Steeped in history and set in beautiful parkland, discover everyday objects from times past including kitchen and laundry equipment; sumptuous costume and accessories; a Victorian school room; Victorian baths; model trains, dolls and toy soldiers and more.

Opening Times: Apr to Oct Sat to Wed 10:00-17:00. Admission: Free.   Map Ref: 3

Bristol City Museum & Art Gallery

♿ ❀ ⤢ **Bristol Museums & Art Gallery**

Queens Road, Bristol BS8 1RL   Tel: 0117 922 3571   Fax: 0117 922 2047
Email: general_museum@bristol-city.gov.uk   Web: www.bristol-city.gov.uk/museums

Be amazed by countless, wonderful objects. Some of the treasures include: minerals and fossils; Egyptian galleries; Far Eastern art; wildlife galleries; archaeology; ceramics and glass; seven galleries of art. Temporary exhibitions and special events are held throughout the year.

Opening Times: Daily 10:00-17:00. Admission: Free.
                                                                           Map Ref: 2

'La Belle Dame/Sans Merci' Frank Dicksee 1902

Bath, Bristol & Northeast Somerset

Bristol Industrial Museum

Princes Wharf, Wapping Road, Bristol BS1 4RN   Tel: 0117 925 1470   Fax: 0117 929 7318
Email: general_museums@bristol-city.gov.uk   Web: www.bristol-city.gov.uk/museums

Bringing the past to life. Discover loads of things to see and do. The Museum's exhibits based on Bristol's rich industrial past include: The story of the Port of Bristol's trading past and present; Bristol's involvement in transatlantic slave trade; Bristol-made cars, buses, bicycles and motorbikes; how printing and packaging was made; how the aircraft industry developed in the city, with real aircraft and engines.

Opening Times: Apr to Oct Sat to Wed 10:00-17:00. Nov to Mar Sat & Sun 10:00-17:00.   Admission: Free.

Tobacco and Aircraft - two of
Bristol's major industries

Map Ref: 2

British Empire & Commonwealth Museum

Clock Tower Yard, Temple Meads, Bristol BS1 6QH   Tel: 0117 9254 980   Fax: 0117 9254 983
Email: staff@empiremuseum.co.uk   Web: www.empiremuseum.co.uk

The permanent galleries chart the history of the British Empire and Commonwealth. The galleries use material from the museum's vast collections ranging from uniforms and other costume to ethnographic material, photographs, film and oral history collections.

Opening Times: Closed until Autumn 2002. Please phone for opening times.   Location: Near Templemeads Station, one minute walk from the station.

Map Ref: 2

Georgian House

7 Great George Street, Bristol BS1 5RR   Tel: 0117 921 1362   Email: general_museum@bristol-city.gov.uk   Web: www.bristol-city.gov.uk/museums

The Georgian House is an exquisite example of a town house of about 1790. The house is furnished to illustrate life both above and below stairs.

Opening Times: Apr to Oct Sat to Wed 10:00-17:00.   Admission: Free.

Map Ref: 2

Red Lodge

Park Row, Bristol BS1 5LJ   Tel: 0117 921 1360   Email: general_museum@bristol-city.gov.uk
Web: www.bristol-city.gov.uk/museums

Red Lodge is an Elizabethan house built around 1590, with the city's last surviving suite of 16th century rooms. There is also an impressive Tudor-style knot garden.

Opening Times: Apr to Oct Sat to Wed 10:00-17:00.   Admission: Free.

Map Ref: 2

SS Great Britain

Great Western Dock, Gas Ferry Road, Bristol BS1 6TY   Tel: 0117 926 0680   Fax: 0117 925 5578   Email: enquiries@ss-great-britain.com   Web: www.sss-great-britain.com

The SS Great Britain, Brunel's masterpiece of ship design and engineering, is housed in the original 'Great Western Dock' in which she was built in 1843. The ship is the world's first great ocean liner - before she was built, long distance sea voyages that were made on wooden sailing ships were dangerous and unpredictable. Sea travel took a great leap forward when famous Victorian engineer Isambard Kingdom Brunel applied his remarkable skill to the problem. The design of Brunel's SS Great Britain embodied so many innovative engineering ideas. She was the largest ship of her day and the first screw-propelled iron passenger liner; in fact the ship is really the forerunner of all modern ships. A major programme of works, supported by the Heritage Lottery Fund, is now underway at the ship allowing you to see conservation in action. For more details please email or call the ship at the address below. When she is in port admission also includes a visit to The Matthew - a replica of John Cabot's 15th century ship that sailed the Atlantic. Your ticket also includes the Maritime Heritage Centre, exhibiting a collection that portrays the history of shipbuilding in Bristol.

Opening Times: Apr to Oct 10:00-17:30, Nov to Mar 10:00-16:30.   Admission: Adult £6.25, Child/Student £3.75, OAP £5.25, Family (2 adults and 2 children) £16.50.   Map Ref: 2

Bath, Bristol & Northeast Somerset

Dyrham Park

near Chippenham SN14 8ER   Tel: 01179 372501   Fax: 01179 371353
Email: dyrhampark@ntrust.org.uk   Web: www.nationaltrust.org.uk

17th century mansion was built in the baroque style between 1692 and 1704 by William Blathwayt secretary of state to William III. Fine collection of paintings and delftware.

Opening Times: House, Park & Gardens - 28 Mar to 2 Nov.   Admission: Adult £7.90, Child £3.90, Family £19.50, National Trust Members Free.   Map Ref: 4

The Helicopter Museum

The Heliport, Locking Moor Road, Weston-super-Mare BS24 8PP   Tel: 01934 635227
Fax: 01934 645230   Email: office@helimuseum.fsnet.co.uk
Web: www.helicoptermuseum.co.uk

Britain's only helicopter museum is a fascinating place to visit with many rare and unique helicopters on display under cover. Group/school visits welcome by prior arrangement. Restoration hangar, adventure play area, open cockpit days and sight-seeing flights.

Opening Times: Apr to Oct Wed to Sun 10:00-18:00, Nov to Mar 10:00-16:00. Open daily for BH, Easter and summer school holidays.   Admission: Adult £3.95, Child £2.75, OAP £3.25, Family (2 adults and 2 children) £11.00, Concessions for groups.   Location: Museum is on A368/A371, three miles from Weston-super-Mare seafront. Approx one and a half miles from junction 21 on M5.   Map Ref: 5

North Somerset Museum

Burlington Street, Weston-super-Mare BS23 1PR   Tel: 01934 621028   Fax: 01934 612526
Email: museum.service@n-somerset.gov.uk   Web: www.n-somerset.gov.uk/museum

Victorian museum featuring galleries of archaelogy, social and natural history, The Seaside Gallery and the unique Clara's Cottage make up the static displays. Exhibitions, Peoples Collection, events and seminars make this a very popular attraction.

Opening Times: Mon to Sat 10:00-16:30.   Admission: Adult £3.50, Child £1.50, OAP £2.50, Family £8.00.   Location: Town centre, five minutes walk from all car parks.   Map Ref: 5

Bedfordshire, Berkshire, Buckinghamshire & Hertfordshire

These four counties encapsulate much of the English way of life. At the very heart of the country and surrounding the capital, the region was the culmination of ancient tracks and trade routes, the Ridgeway and the Icknield Way, dating back to the Bronze Age. The Romans too in their turn left their road building mark. In a country of magnificent medieval castles, this area being so close to the country's heart felt safe from invaders and as a consequence, what it lacks in military architecture it more than makes up for with its glorious domestic architecture.

The marks indelibly stamped on these four counties by their early occupants are thankfully well recorded in their splendid museums and heritage centres.

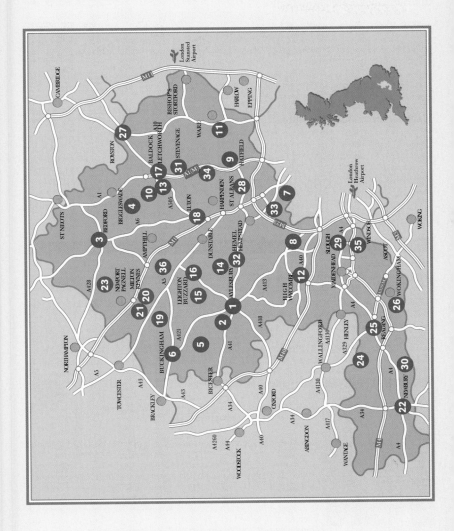

The Red Map References should be used to locate Museums etc on the pages that follow

Beds, Berks, Bucks & Herts

AYLESBURY *Bucks*

Buckinghamshire County Museum
& The Roald Dahl Children's Gallery

Church Street, Aylesbury HP20 2QP   Tel: 01296 331441   Fax: 01296 334884
Email: museum@buckscc.gov.uk   Web: www.buckscc.gov.uk/museum

You really can awaken your senses at this award-winning museum with its innovative touchable displays, exciting programme of family exhibitions, and regular events and activities. Let your imagination run wild.

Opening Times: Mon to Sat 10:00-17:00, Sun 14:00-17:00. On school days the Dahl Gallery is reserved for school use only until 15:00. Admission: Bucks County Museum - Free. Roald Dahl Children's Gallery: Adult £3.50, Child £2.75. Location: In the old part of Aylesbury near the town centre, three minutes walk from bus station.   Map Ref: 1

Buckinghamshire Railway Centre

Quainton Road Station, Quainton, Aylesbury HP22 4BY   Tel: 01296 655450   Fax: 01296 655720   Web: www.bucksrailcentre.org.uk

A working steam railway museum with a large collection of vintage steam/diesel locomotives, carriages and wagons, and small relics. Steam train rides most weekends. Miniature railway, gift and bookshop, refreshment room.

Opening Times: Apr to Oct Wed to Sun 10:30-16:30. Steam trains on Sun & BH. Also Jun to Aug Wed. Admission: Adult £4.50, Child/OAP £3.50, Under 5s Free. Location: Off A41 Aylesbury to Bicester Road, seven miles north west of Aylesbury.   Map Ref: 2

Waddesdon Manor - The Rothschild Collection

Waddesdon, Aylesbury HP18 0JH   Tel: 01296 653226   Fax: 01296 653208
Web: www.waddesdon.org.uk

Waddesdon Manor (built 1874-89) is a magnificent French Renaissance-style chateau, housing The Rothschild Collection of art treasures, a superb cellar of Rothschild wines, and surrounded by spectacular grounds.

Opening Times: House: 2 Apr to 2 Nov Wed to Sun & BH Mon 11:00-16:00. Grounds: 5 Mar to 21 Dec Wed to Sun & BH Mon 10:00-17:00. Admission: House & Grounds: Adult £11.00, Child £8.00, National Trust Members Free. Grounds only: Adult £4.00, Chld £2.00, National Trust Members Free. Location: On A41 between Aylesbury and Bicester.   Map Ref: 2

BEDFORD

Bedford Museum

Castle Lane, Bedford MK40 3XD   Tel: 01234 353323   Fax: 01234 273401
Email: bmuseum@bedford.gov.uk   Web: www.bedfordmuseum.org

Embark on a fascinating journey through the human and natural history of North Bedfordshire. Go back in time to visit the delightful rural room sets and the Old School Museum.

Opening Times: Tue to Sat 11:00-17:00, Sun & BH Mon 14:00-17:00. Closed Good Friday, Xmas & New Year. Admission: Adult £2.10, Child/OAP/Concession Free. Annual ticket £8.40. Location: Close to two town centre car parks and a short walk from Allhallows Bus Station and the Midland Road Railway Station.   Map Ref: 3

Entrance Hall, Victorian Mansion

Cecil Higgins Art Gallery

Castle Lane, Bedford MK40 3RP   Tel: 01234 211222
Fax: 01234 327149   Email: chag@bedford.gov.uk
Web: www.cecilhigginsartgallery.org

Housed in an elegantly converted and extended Victorian mansion, the Gallery is home to one of the most outstanding fine and decorative art collections outside London. A remarkable collection of British and European watercolours from the 18th to the 20th centuries and international prints from Impressionism to the present. Ceramics and glass from the Renaissance to the 20th century, with particular focus on 18th century porcelain, Whitefriars glass and ceramics of the Art & Crafts movement. Authentically reconstructed Victorian room settings, including the William Burges Room, a complete Gothic experience. Thomas Lester lace collection and changing

20

Beds, Berks, Bucks & Herts

exhibitions, programme events, lectures and workshops for all ages.

Opening Times: Tue to Sat 11:00-17:00, Sun & BH Mon 14:00-17:00. Admission: Adult £2.10, Child/Concession Free. Location: Centre of Bedford, just off the Embankment. Exhibitions & Events 2003 : Please ring for current exhibition programme.   Map Ref: 3

'Norham Castle, Summer's Morn' 1798 by J M W Turner

Elstow Moot Hall

Church End, Elstow, Bedford MK42 9XT   Tel: 01234 266889   Fax: 01234 228531
Email: garyfuller1@ntlworld.com

Collection of furniture dating from the 17th century display of Bedfordshire lace and straw plait. Also John Bunyan book collection, many in foreign languages.

Opening Times: Apr to Sep Tue to Thu, Sun and BH 13:00-16:00. Admission: Adult £1.00, Child/Concession 50p, Group - 30 Adults £20.00, 30 Child/Concession £10.00.
Location: Approximately three miles from Bedford Town Centre.   Map Ref: 3

John Bunyan Museum

Bunyan Meeting Free Church, Mill Street, Bedford MK40 3EU   Tel / Fax: 01234 213722
Email: bmeeting@dialstart.net

Walk through the life and times of the famous 17th century preacher, pastor and author of The Pilgrim's Progress. The collection includes copies of John Bunyan's most celebrated work in over 170 languages.

Opening Times: 4 Mar to 25 Oct Tue to Sat 11:00-16:00. Closed Good Friday.
Admission: Free   Location: Near town centre, just off the High Street.   Map Ref: 3

BIGGLESWADE *Beds*

Shuttleworth Collection

Old Warden Aerodrome, Biggleswade SG18 9EA   Tel: 01767 627288

A collection of historic aeroplanes kept in flying condition housed in eight hangars in a quiet countryside setting on an established all-grass runway. Flying displays during summer months.

Opening Times: Daily Apr to Oct 10:00-17:00, Nov to Mar 10:00-16:00. Closed Xmas & New Year. Admission: Adult £6.00, Child Free. Flying Display Day £10.00, Event Day £7.50, Military Pageant Adult £15.00.   Location: Three miles west of A1 at the Biggleswade roundabout, nearest railway station - Biggleswade.   Map Ref: 4

BUCKINGHAM

Claydon House

Middle Claydon, Buckingham MK18 2EY   Tel: 01296 730349   Fax: 01296 738511
Email: tcdgen@smtp.ntrust.org.uk   Web: www.nationaltrust.org.uk

National Trust property with family museum containing mementoes of Florence Nightingale, military uniforms, weapons, costume and musical instruments. Exhuberant Rococo and Chinoiserie style throughout. Second hand bookshop.

Opening Times: Apr to Oct Sat to Wed 13:00-17:00. Admission: Adult £4.40, Child £2.20, Family £11.00, National Trust Members Free   Location: Four and a half miles from Winslow, seven miles from Buckingham.   Map Ref: 5

The Old Gaol Museum

Market Hill, Buckingham MK18 1JX   Tel: 01280 823020

One of the first purpose bulit county gaols in England, now a museum proudly displaying aspects of historical Buckingham.

Opening Times: Mon to Sat 10:00-16:00. Admission: Adult £1.50, Child/Concession £1.00.
Location: One minute walk from town centre car park.   Map Ref: 6

Bushey Museum & Art Gallery

Bushey Museum & Art Gallery
Rudolph Road, Bushey WD23 3HW   Tel: 020 8420 4057
Fax: 020 8420 4923   Email: busmt@bushey.org.uk
Web: www.busheymuseum.org

An award-winning community museum telling the unique story of Bushey from the earliest times to the present day. Art galleries and special displays show two hundred years of art teaching and practice in Bushey from the early watercolours of the Monro Circle to the social realism and portraiture of the Herkomer Art School, to the animal painting of Lucy Kemp-Welch and Marguerite Frobisher Schools.

Opening Times: Thu to Sun 11:00-16:00. Admission: Free.
Location: Just off Bushey High Street.   Map Ref: 7

Walk into History at
The Chiltern Open Air Museum

Chiltern Open Air Museum
Newland Park, Gorelands Lane, Chalfont St Giles HP8 4AD
Tel: 01494 871117   Fax: 01494 872774
Email: coam@netscape.net Web: www.coam.org.uk

Chiltern Open Air Museum consists of more than 30 historic buildings which were all rescued from demolition and are representative of the built heritage of the Chilterns. Visitors are able to roam the museum's 45 acre woodland and parkland site at their leisure and explore the buildings. Brick making, straw plaiting, candle making and rag rug making are just some of the hands-on activities that take place throughout the season .

Opening Times: 31 Mar to 31 Oct daily 10:00-17:00.
Admission: Adult £6.00, Child £3.50, Concession £5.00, Family (2 adult and 2 children) £16.50. Location: One mile off the A413 at Chalfont St Giles in Buckinghamshire.   Map Ref: 8

Milton's Cottage
Deanway, Chalfont St Giles HP8 4JH   Tel: 01494 872313   Email: info@miltonscottage.org
Web: www.miltonscottage.org

Probably the finest collection of Milton 17th century 1st editions in the world. Milton memorabilia and civil war artefacts. All housed in the 16th century grade I listed cottage to which he escaped from the plague in 1665.

Opening Times: 1 Mar to 31 Oct Tue to Sun 10:00-13:00 & 14:00-18:00. Closed Mon except BH.
Admission: Adult £3.00, Child £1.00, Group (20+) £2.00. Location: Centre of village.
Map Ref: 8

Mill Green Museum & Mill
Mill Green, Hatfield AL9 5PD   Tel: 01707 271362   Email: museum@welhat.gov.uk
Web: www.welhat.gov.uk

An 18th century watermill, restored to working order, with a museum in the adjoining miller's house complete with Victorian kitchen. The museum also features regular special exhibitions and events.

Opening Times: Tue to Fri 10:00-17:00 Sat, Sun & BH 14:00-17:00. Closed Mon.
Admission: Free. Location: In hamlet of Mill Green. One mile from Hatfield railway station.
Map Ref: 9

Stondon Museum
Station Road, Lower Stondon, Henlow SG16 6JN Tel: 01462 850339 Fax: 01462 850824
Email: enquiries@transportmuseum.co.uk Web: www.transportmuseum.co.uk

Beds, Berks, Bucks & Herts

Largest private collection in the country, covering one hundred years of motoring, plus military vehicles, fire engines etc, even a full size replica of Captain Cook's ship, 'Endeavour'.

Opening Times: Daily 10:00-17:00. Closed Xmas. Admission: Adult £5.00, Child £2.50, OAP £4.00, Family £13.00. Group rates available, please pre-book. Location: Off A600 Hitchin - Bedford road, four miles from Hitchin. Map Ref: 10

HERTFORD

Hertford Museum
18 Bull Plain, Hertford SG14 1DT Tel: 01992 582686
Fax: 01992 534797 Email: info@hertfordmuseum.org
Web: www.hertfordmuseum.org

Located in 17th century town house with attractive Jacobean style garden. Century old collections of local and social history, geology, archaeology, photographs and fine art, changing exhibitions, events and activity room for schools.

Opening Times: Tue to Sat 10:00-17:00. Admission: Free. Location: Town centre. Exhibitions & Events 2003 : 3 Mar to 31 May: At Home with the Romans, 5 Apr to 10 May: Hertford Car Rally Exhibition, Jun to Jul: Garden Exhibition - focusing on the museum's own Jacobean style garden, Aug to Nov: Pride in our Past, Faith in our Future. Hertford Museum centenary. Map Ref: 11

HIGH WYCOMBE *Bucks*

Hughenden Manor
Valley Road, High Wycombe HP14 4LA Tel: 01494 755573 Fax: 01494 474284

Home of Benjamin Disraeli from 1848 to 1881. Most of his furniture, pictures and books remain. A collection of personal memorabilia is also shown.

Opening Times: 3 Apr to 3 Nov Wed to Sun 13:00-17:00. Open Good Friday & BH.
Admission: Adult £4.40, Child £2.20, Family £11.00. Garden: Adult £1.50, Child 75p.
Location: One and a half miles north of High Wycombe on A4128. Map Ref: 12

Wycombe Museum
Priory Avenue, High Wycombe HP13 6PX Tel: 01494 421895 Fax: 01494 421897
Email: enquiries@wycombemuseum.demon.co.uk Web: www.wycombe.gov.uk/museum

Friendly local museum set in 18th century house with attractive grounds. Modern displays include interactive exhibits and children's activities. Collections include historic Windsor chairs from the Chiltern's traditional furniture industry.

Opening Times: Mon to Sat 10:00-17:00 & Sun 14:00-17:00. Closed BH. Admission: Free.
Location: Five minute walk from High Street. ten minute walk from bus station, two minute walk from railway station. Map Ref: 12

HITCHIN *Herts*

Hitchin Museum & Art Gallery
Paynes Park, Hitchin SG5 1EW Tel: 01462 434476 Fax: 01462 431316
Email: caroline.frith@nhdc.gov.uk Web: www.north-herts.gov.uk

Hitchin Museum is housed in a beautiful Georgian town house build by George Kershaw in 1825, who ran a coaching service between the town and London. In this historical setting we tell the story of Hitchin's past through imaginative displays. Explore Hitchin's industrial and domestic life, contemplate the clothes people have worn for the last 170 years and fabulous art collection. Keepers of the Herts Yeomanry on permanent display.

Opening Times: Mon, Tue, Thur to Sat 10:00-17:00. Closed Wed, Sun & BH. Admission: Free.

Hitchin Museum & Art Gallery

Location: 20 minute walk from Hitchin Railway Station situated next door to Hitchin Library, two minute walk from Market Place. Map Ref: 13

Ford End Watermill

Station Road, Ivinghoe Tel: 01582 600391

The only working watermill in Buckinghamshire with its original machinery. Built in 1700s, it has all the atmosphere of a small corn mill of the late 1800s. Stone ground wholemeal flour for sale on milling days.

Opening Times: 21 Apr, 4, 5* & 11* 26* May, 1 & 8 Jun, 6 & 13* Jul, 3, 10 & 25* Aug, 7 & 14 Sep, all 14:30-17:30. * = milling days. Admission: Adult £1.20, Child 40p. Location: Four miles from Tring, nine miles from Aylesbury, seven miles from Dunstable.   Map Ref: 14

Ascott House

Ascott Estate Office, Wing, Leighton Buzzard LU7 0PS Tel: 01296 688242 Fax: 01296 681904 Email: paf@ascottestate.co.uk

Originally a half timbered Jacobean farmhouse, Ascott was bought in 1876 by the De Rothschild family and considerably transformed and enlarged. It now houses a quite exceptional collection of fine paintings, Oriental porcelain and English and French furniture.

Opening Times: House & Gardens: 2-30 Apr & 6 Aug to 13 Sep daily except Mon 14:00-18:00. Gardens: 1 May to 31 Jul every Wed & last Sun in month 14:00-18:00.18 & 25 Sep. Admission: House & Gardens: Adult £5.60, Child £2.80. Gardens: Adult £4.00, Child £2.00 National Trust Members Free. Location: Half a mile east of Wing, two miles south west of Leighton Buzzard on A418.   Map Ref: 15

Leighton Buzzard Railway

Pages Park Station, Billington Road, Leighton Buzzard LU7 4TN Tel: 01525 373888 Fax: 01525 377814 Email: info@buzzrail.co.uk Web: www.buzzrail.co.uk

A working passenger railway, using the line of the narrow-gauge Leighton Buzzard Light Railway, built in 1919 to carry sand trains. Displays of photographs and actual locomotives and rolling stock. Regular working displays.

Opening Times: Mar to Oct Sun & BH weekends, extra days Jul & Aug. Admission: Adult £5.50, Child £2.00, Under 2s Free, OAP £4.50. Location: On A4146 Hemel Hempstead road, near roundabout with A505 from Dunstable and A5.   Map Ref: 16

First Garden City Heritage Museum

296 Norton Way South, Letchworth, Garden City SG6 1SU Tel: 01462 482710 Fax: 01462 486056 Email: fgchm@letchworth.com Web: www.letchworth.com

This museum tells the story of Letchworth, the First Garden City and the history of the Garden City Movement. Permanent displays of paintings, photographs, arts and crafts style furniture are complemented by a fascinating temporary exhibition programme.

Opening Times: Mon to Sat 10:00-17:00. Admission: Non-Resident £1.00, Resident 50p, Under 16s Free. Location: Two minutes from town centre and multi-storey car parks.
                                        Map Ref: 17

Letchworth Museum & Art Gallery

The Broadway, Letchworth SG6 3PF Tel: 01462 685647 Fax: 01462 481879 Email: letchworth.museum@north-herts.gov.uk Web: www.north-herts.gov.uk

Manor Farm, Norton, oil on canvas, c.1912 (William Ratcliffe)

Letchworth Museum opened in 1914 to house the collections of the Letchworth Naturalists Society, but since then has expanded greatly. The attractive downstairs Natural History Gallery shows local wildlife in realistic settings, including the famous Letchworth black squirrel. The Archaeology Gallery upstairs displays fascinating Celtic and Roman collections, while the Art Gallery is home to a wide range of temporary exhibitions.

Opening Times: Mon to Sat 10:00-17:00. Closed Wed, Sun & BH. Admission: Free. Location: Near Broadway Cinema, next door to Letchworth Library, five minutes walk from railway station.   Map Ref: 17

Beds, Berks, Bucks & Herts

Luton Museum & Gallery

♿ 🔵 📷 🚗

Wardown Park, Luton LU2 7HA   Tel: 01582 746722
Email: museum.gallery@luton.gov.uk
Web: www.luton.gov.uk/enjoying/museums

French Needle lace fllounce c.170

The collections present the story of the people of Luton from earliest times to the present century. Highlights include a spectacular hoard of Roman gold coins, wonderful Saxon jewellery, the nationally important lace collection and the straw plait and hat collections, and the Bedfordshire and Hertfordshire Regimental Gallery. The brand new Luton Life Galleries will open at the start of 2003.

Opening Times: Tue to Sat 10:00-17:00, Sun 13:00-17:00.
Admission: Free.   Location: Situated in beautiful Wardown Park, one mile north of town centre, Bus 24 & 25. Follow brown signs.   Exhibitions & Events 2003 : 4 Feb to 16 Mar: Journey of the Senses - sculpture by international artist Jan Neidoljadlo, 10 May to 22 Jun: Annual Luton Art Exhibition, 12 Jul to 2 Nov: Plantastic! The weird and wonderful world of plants, 15 Nov to 1 Feb: New Horizons Quilt Exhibition - work by the renowned quilters group, New Horizons.   Map Ref: 18

Stockwood Craft Museum & Gardens & Mossman Collection

♿ 🔵 📷 🚗

Stockwood Park, Farley Hill, Luton LU1 4BH   Tel: 01582 738714
Email: museum.gallery@luton.gov.uk   Web: www.luton.gov.uk/enjoying/museums

The Favourite Omnibus c.1850
on display in the Mossmam Collection

The Craft Museum collections focus on the rural life, crafts and trades of Bedfordshire. In the Mossman Building, visitors can enjoy the largest collections of horse-drawn vehicles on public display in Britain. In addition, the Transport Gallery brings the story into the 20th century with vintage cars, bicycles and a model of Luton's trams.

Opening Times: Apr to Oct Tue to Sat 10:00-17:00, Sun 10:00-18:00. Nov to Mar Sat to Sun 10:00-15:45.
Admission: Free.   Location: In Stockwood Country Park, five minutes drive from junction 10 of the M1, Buses 1 & 4 from Park Square, town centre five minutes.   Map Ref: 18

Bletchley Park

📧 ♿ 🔵 📷 ♿ 🚗

The Mansion, Wilton Avenue, Bletchley, Milton Keynes MK3 6EB   Tel: 01908 640404
Fax: 01908 274381   Email: majenkins@bletchleypark.org.uk   Web: www.bletchleypark.org.uk

Bletchley Park, also known as 'Station X', was home to the famous codebreakers of the Second World War and the birthplace of modern computing and communications. Historic buildings, exhibitions and tours.

Opening Times: Mar to Dec Sat, Sun & BH 10:30-17:00.   Admission: Adult £6.00, Concession/ Child £5.00, Under 8s Free.   Location: Two minutes from Bletchley Railway Station. Map Ref: 19

Milton Keynes Gallery

📧 ♿

900 Midsummer Boulevard, Milton Keynes MK9 3QA   Tel: 01908 676900   Fax: 01908 558308
Email: mkgallery@mktgc.co.uk   Web: www.mkweb.co.uk/mkg

This successful new contemporary art gallery offers 8-10 solo and group exhibitions a year, presenting all media, including painting, sculpture, photography, printmaking and installation. There are regular talks, tours and weekend and holiday activities for children. Recorded information (01908) 558307.

Opening Times: Tue to Sat 10:00-17:00, Sun 11:00-17:00. Closed Mon & BH.   Admission: Free.   Location: City Centre.   Map Ref: 20

MILTON KEYNES *Bucks (continued)*

Milton Keynes Museum

Stacey Hill Farm, Southern Way, Wolverton, Milton Keynes MK12 5EJ   Tel: 01908 316222
Fax: 01908 319148   Email: mkmuseum@mkmuseum.org.uk   Web: www.mkmuseum.org.uk

Victorian/Edwardian room settings, schoolroom and nursery provide a link with times past. The Shopping Street is now open. In the Hall of Transport the restored Wolverton to Stony Stratford Tramcar provides an eye-catching centre piece. Jessie the shire horse can be seen working in the extensive grounds.

Opening Times: Easter to Oct Wed to Sun 12:30-16:30. Also BH Mon & Spring half term.
Admission: Adult £3.50, Concession £2.50, Family £8.00.   Location: Five minutes by car from Milton Keynes Station or Wolverton Station.   Map Ref: 21

NEWBURY *Berks*

West Berkshire Museum
 Museum
The Wharf, Newbury RG14 5AS   Tel: 01635 30511   Fax: 01635 38535
Email: heritage@westberks.gov.uk   Web: www.westberks.gov.uk

West Berkshire Museum is situated in two historic buildings in the heart of Newbury. The 17th century Cloth Hall and 18th century granary overlooking the Kennet & Avon Canal house fascinating displays of local history and archaeology, decorative arts, costume and rural crafts. There are galleries devoted to the Civil War battles of 1643 and 1644 and the history of Greenham Common.

Opening Times: Apr to Sep Mon to Fri 10:00-17:00, Sat 10:00-16:30. Oct to Mar Mon to Sat 10:00-16:00. Closed Wed except school holidays. Closed Sun and BH.

West Berkshire Museum

Admission: Free.   Location: Town centre, five minute walk from bus and railway station.   Map Ref: 22

OLNEY *Bucks*

The Cowper and Newton Museum

Orchard Side, Market Place, Olney MK46 4AJ   Tel: 01234 711516   Fax: 0870 164 0662
Email: cnm@mkheritage.co.uk   Web: www.cowperandnewtonmuseum.org

Home of 18th century poet and letter-writer, William Cowper. Artefacts of Cowper and former slave trader, John Newton, author of 'Amazing Grace'. Period gardens. Collections of bobbin lace, dinosaur bones and local history.

Opening Times: 1 Mar to 23 Dec Tue to Sat 10:00-13:00 & 14:00-17:00. Also Sun in June, Jul & Aug 14:00-17:00, BH 10:00-17:00. Closed Good Friday.   Admission: Adult £3.00, Child £1.50, Concession £2.00, Family £7.50. Group/Tour rates available. Garden only £1.00.   Location: In south east corner of Market Place in centre of Olney on A509. Five miles from junction 14 off M1.
Map Ref: 23

READING *Berks*

Basildon Park

Lower Basildon, Reading RG8 9NR   Tel: 0118 9843040   Fax: 0118 9841267
Email: tbdgen@smtp.ntrust.org.uk   Web: www.nationaltrust.org.uk/regions/thameschilterns

An 18th century Palladian mansion set in 400 acres of parkland, contains fine plasterwork, an important collection of furniture and paintings, a decorative shell room and Graham Sutherland's studies for the tapestry 'Christ in Glory'.

Opening Times: 23 Mar to 3 Nov Wed to Sun, BH Mon & Tue 4 Jun 12:00-17:30.
Admission: Adult £4.40, Child £2.20, Family £11.00.   Location: On A329 between Pangbourne and Streatley, one mile walk from Pangbourne Station.   Map Ref: 24

Museums • Galleries • Historic Houses

Please let us know of any collections that are not listed in this guide that you feel should be listed. E-mail us on *editor@tomorrows.co.uk*
or return the Report Form on page 448

Beds, Berks, Bucks & Herts

Museum of Reading
The Town Hall, Blagrave Street, Reading RG1 1QH   Tel: 0118 939 9800
Web: www.readingmuseum.org.uk

Excellent collections of archaeology including Roman Silchester, Reading Abbey, art and natural history. Now featuring 12 hands-on galleries.

Opening Times: Tue to Sat 10:00-16:00, Thu 10:00-19:00, Sun & BH Mon 11:00-16:00. Closed Mon.   Admission: Free.   Location: In town centre, two minutes from railway station.

Map Ref: 25

REME Museum of Technology
Isaac Newton Road, Arborfield Garrison, Reading RG2 9NJ   Tel / Fax: 0118 9763375
Email: reme-museum@gtnet.gov.uk   Web: www.rememuseum.org.uk

Reflective of the skills and training REME has employed since 1942. Displays include avionics, aeronautical instruments, control equipment, optics, radar and radios. The museum exhibition hall displays 19 specialist vehicles, a helicopter and an education area.

Opening Times: Mon to Thu 09:00-16:30, Fri 09:00-16:00, Sun 11:00-16:00. Closed Xmas & New Year.   Admission: Adult £3.00, Child £2.00, OAP/Concession £2.50, Family £8.00, Group rates available, School visits please enquire and book in advance.   Location: Off Biggs Lane, three miles from Wokingham in Berkshire countryside.

Map Ref: 26

Rural History Centre (incorporating Museum of English Rural Life)
The University of Reading, Whiteknights, Reading RG6 6AG   Tel: 0118 3788661   Fax: 0118 9751264   Email: r.d.brigden@reading.ac.uk   Web: www.ruralhistory.org

A national collection with public displays relating to the farming, rural industries and country life of the last 200 years. The library and resident collections of photographs and archives may be viewed by appointment.

Opening Times: Tue to Sat 10:00-13:00 14:00-16;30. Closed Xmas & New Year.
Admission: Adult £1.00, Child/student Free, OAP/Concession 75p.   Location: Two miles south east from Reading Town Centre, on the University Campus.

Map Ref: 25

Royston & District Museum
Lower King Street, Royston SG8 5AL   Tel: 01763 242587

Local history and archaeology. Changing Exhibitions. Excellent ceramic collection covering late 19th and 20th century.

Opening Times: Wed, Thu & Sat 10:00-16:45. From 1 Sun in Mar to last Sun in Oct additional opening Sun & BH Mon 14:00-16:45. Closed Xmas & New Year.   Admission: Free. Groups by appointment.   Location: Five minutes from railway station, ten minutes from bus station. Car parking within two minutes.

Map Ref: 27

Clock Tower
Market Place, St Albans AL3 5DR   Tel: 01727 751810   Fax: 01727 859919
Email: c.green@stalbans.gov.uk   Web: www.stalbansmuseums.org.uk

Built between 1403 and 1412 this four-staged tower is the only Medieval town belfry in England. Its fine bell has also survived almost 600 years of use.

Opening Times: Easter to Oct Sat, Sun & BH 10:30-17:00.   Admission: 30p.   Location: In town centre.

Map Ref: 28

De Havilland Aircraft Heritage Centre
(inc the Mosquito Aircraft Museum)

PO Box 107, Salisbury Hall, London Colney, St Albans AL2 1EX Tel: 01727 822051 Fax: 01727 826400 Web: www.dehavillandmuseum.co.uk

A secret wartime site waiting to be discovered by you. Home of the prototype Mosquito. On display there is a variety of de Havilland aircraft, ranging from Tiger Moth to modern military and civil jets including various sections. A working museum. Comprehensive collection of de Havilland engines and memorabilia.

Opening Times: First Sun in Mar to last Sun in Oct, Tue to Thu & Sat 14:00-17:00, Sun & BH 10:30-17:00.
Admission: Adult £5.00, Child/OAP £3.00, Family £13.00.
Groups by arrangement. Location: Junction 22 of M25, follow signs (near St Albans). Map Ref: 28

de Havilland Aircraft Heritage Centre

Hypocaust

Verulamium Park, St Michaels, St Albans AL3 4SW Tel: 01727 751810 Fax: 01727 859919
Email: d.thorold@stalbansmuseums.org.uk Web: www.stalbansmuseums.org.uk

The hypocaust building presents in situ an original Roman mosaic and its underfloor heating system. It was once part of a large house.

Opening Times: Mon to Sat 10:00-17:00, Sun 14:00-17:00. Admission: Free. Location: In Verulamium Park, opposite Verulamium Museum. Map Ref: 28

Kingsbury Watermill Museum

St Michaels Village, St Albans AL3 4SJ Tel: 01727 853502

Elizabethan Watermill on three floors with working waterwheel. Fine display of milling machinery and comprehensive selection of 19th century dairy and farming implements. Pottery, gift shop and Waffle House Restaurant.

Opening Times: Mon to Sat 10:00-18:00 Sun & BH 11:00-18:00. Winter closing time 17:00.
Admission: Adult £1.10, Child 60p, Concession 75p. Location: Ten minute walk from town centre. Map Ref: 29

Museum of St Albans

Hatfield Road, St Albans AL1 3RR Tel: 01727 819340 Fax: 01727 837472
Email: a.wheeler@stalbans.gov.uk Web: www.stalbansmuseums.org.uk

The story of historic St Albans from the departure of the Romans to the present day. Also home to the Saloman Collection of craft tools. Regular exhibitions and wildlife garden.

Opening Times: Mon to Sat 10:00-17:00, Sun 14:00-17:00. Admission: Free. Location: Five minutes walk from town centre, ten minutes walk from railway station. Map Ref: 28

The Roman Theatre of Verulamium

Bluehouse Hill, St Albans AL3 6AH Tel: 01727 835035 Email: stalbans@strutlandparker.co.uk
Web: www.romantheatre.co.uk

The Roman Theatre of Verulamium was built in 140 AD as a theatre with a stage, rather than an amphitheatre. The current ruins were found in 1847 but were not fully excavated until 1930-1935.

Opening Times: Daily all year - summer 10:00-17:00, winter 10:00-16:00. Admission: Adult £1.50, Child 50p, Concession £1.00, Under 5s Free. Location: On the western outskirts of St Albans, just off the A4147 and on the road known as Bluehouse Hill. Map Ref: 28

Verulamium Museum

St Michaels, St Albans AL3 4SW Tel: 01727 751810 Fax: 01727 859919
Email: a.coles@stalbans.gov.uk Web: www.stalbansmuseums.org.uk

Discover the life and times of a major Roman city, set in attractive parkland. Nearby Roman theatre, walls, hypocaust. Demonstrations by Roman soldiers every second weekend of the month.

Opening Times: Mon to Sat 10:00-17:00, Sun 14:00-17:30. Admission: Adult £3.20 Child/Concession £1.85 Family £8.05 Location: Ten minutes from St Albans City Centre Map Ref: 28

Beds, Berks, Bucks & Herts

SILCHESTER *Berks*

Calleva Museum

Bramley Road, Silchester RG7 2LU   Tel: 0118 9700825

Calleva Museum is unmanned and gives a pictorial record of life in Roman times. The museum acts as an information point.

Opening Times: Daily 09:30 to dusk.   Admission: Free.   Location: In the village of Silchester, Bramley Road.   Map Ref: 30

SLOUGH *Berks*

Slough Museum

278/286 High Street, Slough SL1 1NB   Tel / Fax: 01753 526422
Email: info@sloughmuseum.co.uk   Web: www.sloughmuseum.co.uk

Slough has a unique and fascinating history stretching back thousands of years. The museum traces this history in its exhibition 'A Journey Through Time', telling the story of Slough from mammoths to the modern day. Work by local groups is on display in the temporary exhibition room and there are lots of special activities for schools, children and families.

Opening Times: Wed to Sat 11:30-16:00.
Admission: Free.   Location: East end of Slough High Street, ten minutes walk from train/bus station.

Horlicks has been made in Slough since 1906

Map Ref: 29

STEVENAGE *Herts*

Stevenage Museum

St Georges Way, Stevenage SG1 1XX   Tel: 01438 218881   Fax: 01438 218882
Email: museum@stevenage.gov.uk   Web: www.stevenage.gov.uk/museum

The main galleries focus on the history of the town, from the Stone Age right up to the present day. Frequently changing exhibitions on a wide range of topics.

Opening Times: Mon to Sat 10:00-17:00, Sun 14:00-17:00. Closed BH.   Admission: Free.
Location: Three minutes walk from town centre.   Map Ref: 31

TRING *Herts*

The Walter Rothschild Zoological Museum

Akeman Street, Tring HP23 6AP   Tel: 020 7942 6171   Fax: 020 7942 6150
Web: www.nhm.ac.uk/museum/tring

Once the private collection of Lionel Walter, 2nd Baron Rothschild, now part of The Natural History Museum. More than 4000 mounted specimens of animals in a unique Victorian setting. The Discovery Room on the first floor is a hands-on interactive centre that encourages a sense of wonder about the natural world.

Opening Times: Mon to Sat 10:00-17:00, Sun 14:00-17:00.   Admission: Free.   Exhibitions & Events 2003 : A changing programme of exhibitions - please phone for details.   Map Ref: 32

WATFORD *Herts*

Watford Museum

194 High Street, Watford WD17 2DT   Tel: 01923 232297   Fax: 01923 224772
Email: museum@artsteam-watford.co.uk   Web: www.hertsmuseums.org.uk

Watford Museum tells the story of Watford and its people from the earliest times to the present. Special exhibitions of printing and brewing and regularly changing temporary exhibitions offer something for everyone.

Opening Times: Mon to Fri 10:00-17:00, Sat 10:00-13:00 & 14:00-17:00. Closed Sun & BH.
Admission: Free.   Location: Near town centre, five minute walk from Harlequin Shopping Centre.   Map Ref: 33

Beds, Berks, Bucks & Herts

Shaw's Corner
 ♿

Ayot St Lawrence, Welwyn AL6 9BX   Tel / Fax: 01438 820307
Email: shawscorner@ntrust.org.uk   Web: www.nationaltrust.org.uk/shawscorner

An arts and crafts inspired house, home to playwright and socialist G Bernard Shaw for over 40 years. The rooms are much as he left them, a faithful reflection of pre-war furniture and decoration.

Opening Times: 2 Apr to 2 Nov Wed to Sun & BH Mon. House - 13:00-17:00 (last admission 16:30). Garden - 12:00-17:30.   Admission: Adult £3.60, Child £1.80, Family (2 adults and 3 children) £9.00, National Trust Members Free.   Location: A1(M) junction 4, five miles Welwyn Garden City, five miles Harpenden. Two miles north west of Wheathampstead.   Map Ref: 34

Museum of Eton Life

Eton College, Windsor SL4 6DW   Tel: 01753 671177   Fax: 01753 671265
Email: visits@etoncollege.org.uk   Web: www.etoncollege.com

School Yard, Eton College

The Museum of Eton illustrates the history and function of Eton College. There is a short video which depicts life and work of the school today. A visit to the Museum usually follows a guided tour of the College although it is open to visitors who do not take a tour.

Opening Times: 27 Mar to 22 Apr & 28 Jun to 2 Sep 10:30-16:30. 23 Apr to 27 Jun & 3 Sep to 5 Oct 14:00-16:30.   Admission: Ordinary entrance £3.70, Guided tours £4.70.   Location: 15 minutes walk from Windsor.
Map Ref: 35

Town & Crown Exhibition
♿

Royal Windsor Information Centre, 24 High Street, Windsor SL4 1LH   Tel: 01753 743918
Fax: 01753 743917   Email: museum.collections@rbwm.gov.uk   Web: www.rbwm.gov.uk

Small display of Windsor history from its origins as a hilltop fort through to Victorian times.

Opening Times: Daily as per Tourist Centre opening hours.   Admission: Free.   Map Ref: 35

Key to Classifications
see Classifications Index on page 413

Anthropology	Jewellery	Railway
Archaeological	Literature & Libraries	Religion
Art Galleries	Maritime	Roman
Arts, Crafts & Textiles	Military & Defence	Science - Earth
China, Glass & Ceramics	Mills - Water & Wind	& Planetary
Communications	Multicultural	Sculpture
Egyptian	Music & Theatre	Sporting History
Fashion	Natural History	Stately Homes
Geology	Oriental	Toy & Childhood
Health & Medicine	Palaces	Transport
Horticultural	Police, Prisons & Dungeons	Victoriana

Beds, Berks, Bucks & Herts

Windsor Castle   ♿ 🐾

Windsor SL4 1NJ   Tel: 020 7321 2233   Fax: 020 7930 9625
Email: information@royalcollection.org.uk   Web: www.royal.gov.uk

The largest and oldest occupied castle in the world, encapsulates 900 years of British history and is furnished with some of the finest works of art from the Royal Collection.

Opening Times: Mar to Oct 09:45-17:15 (last admission 16:00), Nov to Feb 09:45-16:15 (last admission 15:00).   Admission: Adult £11.50, Under 17s £6.00, OAP/Student £9.50, Family (2 adults and 3 children) £29.00.   Location: Windsor, Berkshire.   Map Ref: 35

Woburn Abbey   🍃 ♿ 🐾 ♨ 🚂

Woburn MK17 9WA   Tel: 01525 290666   Fax: 01525 290271
Email: enquiries@woburnabbey.co.uk   Web: www.woburnabbey.co.uk

Woburn Abbey has been home to the Dukes of Bedford for almost 450 years. Over the centuries the Russell family have, with their love of art, created one of the finest private collections in England. There are paintings by Van Dyck, Gainsborough, Reynolds and Velazquez. 21 views of Venice by Canaletto can be seen in the Venetian Room in the Private Apartments. The Vaults contain beautiful porcelain from France, Japan, Germany, England and China, including the famous Sevres dinner service given to the 4th Duchess by Louis XV. The 3,000 acre deer park contains nine species of deer and there are two gift shops, a pottery and an Antique Centre with 40 shops.

Woburn Abbey

Racing Room at Woburn Abbey

Opening Times: 23 Mar to 28 Sep Mon to Fri 11:00-16:00, Sat & Sun 11:00-17:00. Open 1 Jan to 22 Mar and 4 to 26 Oct weekends only.   Admission: Adult £8.50, OAP £7.50, Child £4.00. Group Adult £7.00, Group OAP £6.00, Group Child £3.00.   Location: Woburn Village one mile distance, Flitwick Railway Station five miles. No local transport available.   Exhibitions & Events 2003 : Jan to Oct: Exhibition 'A Singular Couple' depicting the lives of Herbrand the 11th Duke of Bedford and his wife Mary, 'The Flying Duchess', 7/8 Jun: Woburn Garden Show, 16/17 Aug: De Havilland Moth Club Rally, 7/8 Sep: Craft Fair.   Map Ref: 36

Cambridgeshire & Northamptonshire

Cambridgeshire, which includes the Soke of Peterborough and the Isle of Ely, boasts a wealth of historic sites and spectacular buildings. Northamptonshire, 'the county of spires and squires', is primarily a farming county.

Both Cambridgeshire and Northamptonshire can be considered to be counties of personalities, their stories carefully preserved in collections of memorabilia.

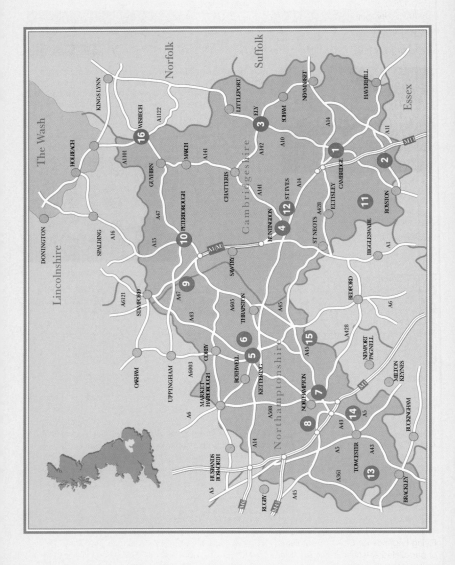

The Red Map References should be used to locate Museums etc on the pages that follow

Cambridgeshire & Northamptonshire

Cambridge & County Folk Museum

2/3 Castle Street, Cambridge CB3 0AQ Tel: 01223 355159 Email: info@fokmuseum.org.uk
Web: www.folkmuseum.org.uk

The museum is housed in a superb late 15th century timber-framed building. The displays reflect the everyday life of the people of Cambridge and the surrounding county from 1700 to the present day.

Opening Times: Apr to Sep Mon to Sat 10:30-17:00, Sun 14:00-17:00. Oct to Mar Tue to Sat 10:30-17:00, Sun 14:00-17:00. Admission: Adult £2.50, Child 75p, Concession £1.50.
Location: Near the town centre, a five minute walk from central shopping area and two minutes drive from M11.   Map Ref: 1

Fitzwilliam Museum

Trumpington Street, Cambridge CB2 1RB Tel: 01223 332900 Fax: 01223 332923
Email: fitzmuseum-enquiries@lists.cam.ac.uk Web: www.fitzmuseum.cam.ac.uk

Magnificent permanent collection including antiquities from Ancient Egypt, Greece and Rome, sculpture, furniture and paintings by artists such as Titian, Canaletto, Constable, Monet and Picasso. Guided tours, concerts, gallery talks and other events. Details on www.fitzmuseum.cam.ac.uk. For disabled access please phone 01223 332937 in advance.

Claude Monet 'Poplars' © The Fitzwilliam Museum, University of Cambridge

Opening Times: Tue to Sat 10:00-17:00, Sun 14:15-17:00, Easter Mon 21 Apr. Closed Mon & Good Friday, Xmas & New Year. Admission: Free. Location: Near town centre.   Map Ref: 1

Imperial War Museum Duxford

Cambridge CB2 4QR Tel: 01223 835000 Fax: 01223 837267
Email: duxford@iwm.org.uk Web: www.iwm.org.uk

Europe's premier aviation museum stands on a wartime airfield and is home to a unique and fascinating collection of aircraft and military exibits. This historic airfield was built during the First World War and played an important role in the Battle of Britain during the Second World War. Much of the airfield is preserved as it was during the early 1940s, including the hangars and the Battle of Britain Operations Room. Duxford also has one of the finest collections of tanks, military vehicles and artillery in the country and features the Normandy Experience and Monty exhibitions.

Photo credit John M Dibbs

There are 200 aircraft on display including the legendary Spitfire, Lancaster, Concorde and the amazing SR-71 Blackbird spy plane which flew on the edge of space. Over 50 working historic aircraft are based at Duxford and regularly take to the sky over the Museum. The recent re-configured award winning American Air Museum located at Duxford houses the largest collection of US aircraft outside of America including the beautifully restored B-24 Liberator. The American Air Museums stands as a memorial to the 30,000 US airmen who gave their lives while flying from British bases, including Duxford, during the Second World War.

Opening Times: 17 Mar to 27 Oct 10:00-18:00 (summer) 10:00-16:00 (winter). Closed Xmas. Admission: Please telephone 01223 835000 for details. Prices vary on Air Show days, Children under 12 must be accompanied by an adult. Location: Off junction 10 on M11, near Cambridge. Exhibitions & Events 2003 : Imperial War Museum Duxford plays host to four Air Shows in 2003, 4 May: May Air Display - Britain's first major air show of the year, 12 & 13 Jul: Flying Legends Air Show - Established as the 'warbird' show in Europe, bringing together an unparralleled selection of classic fighters, 6 & 7 Sep: Duxford 2003 Air Show - Stunning action for the whole family marking the centenary of flight, 12 Oct: Autumn Air Show - The perfect chance to see you favourites before winter, featuring many Duxford based aircraft. For further details see the website www.iwm.org.uk or call the hotline on 01223 499301.   Map Ref: 2

Kettle's Yard
🕊 🕮 **KETTLE'S YARD**

Castle Street, Cambridge CB3 0AQ   Tel: 01223 352124   Fax: 01223 324377
Email: mail@kettlesyard.cam.ac.uk   Web: www.kettlesyard.co.uk

Interior of Kettle's Yard

Kettle's Yard is a house with a permanent collection and a Gallery showing a changing programme of exhibitions. Founded by Jim Ede, once a curator at the Tate Gallery, it was intended as a 'refuge of peace and order, of the visual arts and music'. Works of art by Ben and Winifred Nicholson, Christopher Wood, Alfred Wallis, Barbara Hepworth, Constantin Brancusi and Henri Gaudier-Brzeska.

Opening Times: House: 19 Apr to 25 Aug Tue to Sun 13:30-16:30, 26 Aug to 18 Apr Tue to Sun 14:00-16:00. Gallery: Tue to Sun 11:30-17:00.   Admission: Free.

Location: Near town centre.   Map Ref: 1

Scott Polar Research Institute Museum
♿ 🕮

Lensfield, Cambridge CB2 1ER   Tel: 01223 336540   Fax: 01223 336549
Web: www.spri.cam.ac.uk

Displays include materials from the Antarctic expeditions of Robert Falcon Scott and Sir Ernest Shackleton, and the Arctic expeditions of Sir John Franklin and others searching for the 19th century.

Opening Times: Mon to Fri 14:00-16:00.   Admission: Free.   Location: Ten minutes walk from railway station and central bus station.   Map Ref: 1

Sedgwick Museum of Geology
🕮

Dept of Earth Sciences, Downing Street, Cambridge CB2 3EQ   Tel: 01223 333456

Fossils and minerals, mounted skeletons, important local displays, historical material. Major new displays opening early summer 2002.

Opening Times: Mon to Fri 09:00-13:00 and 14:00-17:00, Sat 10:00-13:00. Closed Xmas and Easter.   Admission: Free.   Location: Near town centre, two minutes walk from bus station.
Map Ref: 1

University Museum of Archaeology & Anthropology
♿

Downing Street, Cambridge CB2 3DZ   Tel: 01223 333516   Fax: 01223 333517
Email: cumaa@hermes.cam.ac.uk   Web: www.cumaa.archanth.cam.ac.uk

The collections and their associated photographic and archival material are of outstanding research and historical value; they cover the ethnography and pre-history of the world together with local archaeology. The museum is an important national resource in archaeology and anthropology.

Opening Times: Tue to Sat 14:00-16:30, closed Sun, Mon & BH.   Admission: Free.
Location: City centre.   Map Ref: 1

University Museum of Zoology at Cambridge
♿

Downing Street, Cambridge CB2 3EJ   Tel: 01223 336650   Fax: 01223 336679
Email: umzc@zoo.cam.ac.uk   Web: www.zoo.cam.ac.uk/museum

Spectacular displays of internationally important zoological specimens, including fossils, dinosaurs, mammal skeletons, birds, beautiful shells and a huge whale. Temporary exhibitions throughout the year.

Opening Times: Mon to Fri 10:00-13:00 & 14:00-16:45. Closed Xmas & Easter.
Admission: Free.   Location: City centre.   Map Ref: 1

Museums • Galleries • Historic Houses

Please let us know of any collections that are not listed in this guide that you feel should be listed. E-mail us on *editor@tomorrows.co.uk* or return the Report Form on page 448

Cambridgeshire & Northamptonshire

Whipple Museum of the History of Science

Free School Lane, Cambridge CB2 3RH   Tel: 01223 330906   Fax: 01223 334554   Email: hps-whipple-museum@lists.cam.ac.uk   Web: www.hps.cam.ac.uk/whipple/

The Whipple Museum is a pre-eminent collection of scientific instruments and models, dating from the Middle Ages to the present. Microscopes and telescopes, sundials, early slide rules, pocket electronic calculators, teaching and demonstration apparatus, as well as laboratory equipment are included in this outstanding collection. Part of the Department of History and Philosophy of Science, it plays an important role in the Department's teaching and research.

The main gallery of the Whipple Museum

Opening Times: Mon to Fri 13:30-16:30. Closed Sat, Sun & BH. Please check beforehand as the Museum is not always open during the University vacations.   Admission: Free.   Location: In town centre.

Map Ref: 1

Oliver Cromwell's House

29 St Marys Street, Ely CB7 4HF   Tel: 01353 662062   Fax: 01353 668518   Email: tic@eastcambs.gov.uk   Web: www.eastcambs.gov.uk

Cromwell's family home from 1636. Period rooms, exhibitions and displays tell the story of Ely's most famous resident.

Opening Times: Summer daily 10:00-17:30, winter Mon to Fri & Sun 11:00-16:00, Sat 11:00-17:00.   Admission: Adult £3.50. Wide range of concessions available.   Location: In heart of conservation area, 300 yards from cathedral.

Map Ref: 3

Stained Glass Museum

South Triforium, The Cathedral, Ely CB7 4DL   Tel: 01353 660347   Fax: 01353 665025   Email: stainedglass@lineone.net   Web: www.stainedglassmuseum.org

A unique museum with an exhibition of stained glass from 1240 to the present. The exhibition contains examples of stained glass from all over Britain and explains the history of the craft.

Opening Times: Mon to Fri 10:30-17:00, Sat 10:30-17:30 (winter 10:30-17:00), Sun 12:00-18:00 (winter 12:00-4:30). Closed Xmas & New Year and Good Friday.   Admission: Adult £3.50, Child (over 12)/Concession £2.50. Group rates available.   Location: In the centre of city, ten minute walk from the railway station.

Map Ref: 3

Cromwell Museum

Grammar School Walk, Huntingdon PE29 3LF   Tel: 01480 375830   Fax: 01480 459563   Email: cromwellmuseum@cambridgeshire.gov.uk   Web: http://edweb.camcnty.gov.uk/cromwell

The collection includes many portraits, personal objects, books and documents, which illustrate the man, his family and his significance.

Opening Times: Apr to Oct Tue to Fri 11:00-13:00 & 14:00-17:00, Sat & Sun 11:00-13:00 &14:00-16:00. Nov to Mar Tue to Fri 13:00-16:00, Sat 11:00-13:00 & 14:00-16:00, Sun 14:00-16:00.   Admission: Free.   Location: Centre of Huntingdon, opposite All Saints Church, next to the market place. Five minute walk from Central Bus Station, ten minute walk from railway station.

Map Ref: 4

The Manor

Hemingford Grey, Huntingdon PE28 9BN   Tel: 01480 463134   Fax: 01480 465026   Email: diana_boston@hotmail.com   Web: www.greenknowe.co.uk

Built about 1130, reputedly the oldest continuously inhabited house in Britain. House contains Lucy Boston's patchwork collection and famous for her Green Knowe books. Garden with topiary, roses and herbaceous borders.

Opening Times: House: by appointment except May. May guided tours daily 11:00 & 14:00. Garden: 11:00-17:00 (dusk in winter).   Admission: Adult £4.00, Child £1.50, OAP £3.50. Garden only: Adult £2.00, Child 50p.

Map Ref: 4

Alfred East Gallery

Sheep Street, Kettering NN16 0AN   Tel: 01536 534274   Email: museum@kettering.gov.uk
Web: www.kettering.gov.uk

Works by late 19th/early 20th century artists, including Sir Alfred East, Thomas Cooper Gotch and members of the Newlyn School, plus a programme of temporary and touring exhibitions.

Opening Times: Mon to Sat 09:30-17:00. Closed Sun & BH.   Admission: Free.   Location: In town centre, by library and Tourist Information Centre.   Map Ref: 5

Boughton House

Kettering NN14 1BJ   Tel: 01536 515731   Fax: 01536 417255
Email: lit@boughtonhouse.org.uk   Web: www.boughtonhouse.org.uk

Northamptonshire home of the Duke of Buccleuch and Queensberry. A superb collection of paintings, furniture, tapestries, needlework, carpets, porcelain, arms and silver.

Opening Times: Aug to Sep, Park from 13:00-17:00, House from 14:00-16:30
Admission: House & Grounds: Adult £6.00, Child/OAP £5.00. Grounds only: Adult £1.50,
Child/OAP £1.00.   Location: Off the A43, three miles north of Kettering.   Map Ref: 6

Manor House Museum

Sheep Street, Kettering NN16 0AN   Tel: 01536 534219   Fax: 01536 534370
Email: museum@kettering.gov.uk   Web: www.kettering.gov.uk

Collections reflecting the history of Kettering Borough from pre-historic times to the modern day. Also monthly living history events.

Opening Times: Mon to Sat 09:30-17:00. Closed Sun & BH.   Admission: Free.   Location: In town centre, next to Tourist Information Centre.   Map Ref: 5

Abington Museum

Abington Park, Park Avenue South, Northampton NN1 5LW   Tel: 01604 631454   Fax: 01604 238720   Email: museums@northampton.gov.uk   Web: www.northampton.gov.uk/museums

Once a 15th century manor house, the museum includes Northamptonshire's military history - at home and abroad, Northampton life from the cradle to the grave, and a 19th century fashion gallery.

Opening Times: Mar to Oct Tue to Sun 13:00-17:00, Nov to Feb Tue to Sun 13:00-16:00.
Admission: Free.   Location: Under ten minute journey from town centre, situated in Abington Park.   Map Ref: 7

Althorp

The Stables, Althorp, Northampton NN7 4HQ
Tel: 01604 770107   Fax: 01604 770042
Email: mail@althorp.com   Web: www.althorp.com

Next to the House lies the honey-coloured stable block, a truly breathtaking building that at one time accommodated up to 100 horses and 40 grooms. This is the setting for the Exhibition celebrating the life and work of Diana, Princess of Wales and honouring her memory after her death. The freshness and modernity of the facilities are a unique tribute to a woman who captivated the world in her all-too-brief existence.

The Saloon, Althorp House

Opening Times: 1 Jul to 30 Sep daily 10:00-17:00. Closed 31 Aug.
Admission: Pre-booked rates: Adult £10.50, Child £5.50 (under 5s Free), OAP £8.50, Family (2 adults and 3 children) £26.50.
Location: Located seven miles west of Northampton.   Map Ref: 8

| Guided or Private Tours | Disabled Access | Gift Shop or Sales Point | Café or Refreshments | Restaurant | Car Parking |

Cambridgeshire & Northamptonshire

Northampton Central Museum & Art Gallery

♿ ⬡

Guildhall Road, Northampton NN1 1DP   Tel: 01604 238548   Fax: 01604 238720   Email: museums@northampton.gov.uk
Web: northampton.gov.uk/museums

The Museum houses a collection of boots and shoes, the largest in the world. Also on display; Northampton's history, decorative arts - Oriental and British ceramics, Italian 15th to 18th century paintings and British art.

Opening Times: Mon to Sat 10:00-17:00, Sun 14:00-17:00. Admission: Free. Location: Situated in town centre, five minute walk from bus station.   Map Ref: 7

PETERBOROUGH *Cambs*

Nene Valley Railway

♿ ⬡ ▱ 🚃

Wansford Station, Stibbington, Peterborough PE8 6LR   Tel: 01780 784444
Fax: 01780 784440   Web: www.nvr.org.uk

Thomas and Britannia at Nene Valley Railway

A large collection of British and continental locomotives and carriages are available for viewing on site, many of which are used to run the train service. For lovers of steam both young and old, visit Britain's International Steam Railway for a great day out. Travelling between Wansford and Peterborough the seven and a half mile of track passes through the heart of the picturesque 500 acre Ferry Meadows Country Park. There is a small museum and a second-hand railway bookshop hou-sed in a railway carriage at Wansford Station. Visit the restored Southern Railway Travelling Post Office carriage where letters and parcels can be sorted by visitors. NVR is the home of 'Thomas' the childrens favourite engine. Talking Timetable 01780 784404.

All the sights & sounds of the golden age of steam come alive at Nene Valley

Opening Times: Sun from Jan, weekends from Apr to Oct, Wed from May, plus other mid-week services in summer. Santa Specials end Nov and throughout Dec.
Admission: Adult £10.00, Child £4.00, OAP £6.00, Family (2 adults and 3 children) £20.00.
Special fares apply for Santa Specials and Thomas.   Location: Wansford Station, off southbound carriageway of A1 at Stibbington - west of Peterborough.   Exhibitions & Events 2003 : Special Events throughout 2003.   Map Ref: 9

Peterborough Museum & Art Gallery

🦕 ♿ ⬡ 🚃

Priestgate, Peterborough PE1 1LF   Tel: 01733 343329   Fax: 01733 341928
Email: museum@peterborough.gov.uk   Web: www.peterboroughheritage.org.uk

Exhibitions of the permanent collection covering the history and community of Peterborough. Collections include local archaeology, social history and geology. Unique collections of Jurassic marine reptiles and French Napoleonic prisoner of war craft work. Changing historical and art exhibition programme, plus events and activities at weekends.

Opening Times: Sat 10:00-17:00, Sun & BH 12:00-16:00, Tue to Fri 12:00-17:00 (termtime) 10:00-17:00 (school holidays). Closed Mon, Xmas & New Year. Admission: Free. Small charge for some events or exhibitions.   Location: City centre, just off Main Street, within five minutes walk of both railway and bus stations.   Map Ref: 10

Cambridgeshire & Northamptonshire

Peterborough Sculpture Trust

c/o 12 Burghley Road, Peterborough PE1 2QB   Tel: 01733 755545

Sculpture by major artists of the last 25 years, including Gormley and Caro.

Opening Times: Year round.   Admission: Free.   Location: 20 minutes walk from city centre.
The Sculpture Park is on either side of the one kilometre long Rowing Lake.   Map Ref: 10

Railworld

Oundle Road, Peterborough PE2 9NR   Tel / Fax: 01733 344240   Web: www.railworld.net

Railworld's exhibition centre and museum highlights modern trains worldwide and environmental concerns. Railworld's model railway is impressive. Railworld also has 'Age of Steam' exhibits, flower beds and 'Stephenson' the cat!

Opening Times: Mar to Oct daily 11:00-16:00, Nov to Feb Mon to Fri 11:00-16:00. Xmas & New
Year by appointment.   Admission: Adult £3.00, Child £2.00, Concession £2.50, Family £8.00.
Location: Near city centre, 15 minute walk from bus and railway station.   Map Ref: 10

ROYSTON *Cambs*

Wimpole Hall & Home Farm

THE NATIONAL TRUST

Wimpole Hall, Arrington, Royston SG8 0BW   Tel: 01223 207257
Fax: 01223 207838   Email: aweusr@smtp.ntrust.org.uk   Web: www.wimpole.org

The finest country house in Cambridgeshire, see over thirty rooms including the Library, plunge bath and basements. Enjoy walks around the landscaped park. Home Farm with a historical farmyard where you can see and feed some of our rare breeds of cattle, sheep, pigs and poultry. Also Pets Corner, Adventure Playground and Mini Tractors.

Opening Times: Hall: Mar to Nov Tue to Thu, Sat & Sun 13:00-17:00. Farm: Mar to Nov Tue to Thu, Sat & Sun 10:30-17:00. Nov to Mar Sat & Sun 11:00-16:00. Admission: Hall: Adult £6.20, Child £2.80. Farm: Adult £4.90, Child £2.80. Garden: Adult £2.50, Child Free. Estate: Adult £9.00, Child £4.50.   Location: Eight miles

Wimpole Hall viewed across the parterre
- Olga Damant/The National Trust

south west of Cambridge off A603. Junction 12 of M11.   Map Ref: 11

ST IVES *Cambs*

Norris Museum

The Broadway, St Ives PE27 5BX   Tel: 01480 497314

History of Huntingdonshire: fossils and dinosaurs, archaeology, history, the Civil War, Fen skating, art gallery with regular special exhibitions.

Opening Times: May to Sep Mon to Fri 10:00-13:00 & 14:00-17:00, Sat 10:00-12:00 & 14:00-
17:00, Sun 14:00-17:00. Oct to Mar Mon to Fri 10:00-13:00 & 14:00-16:00, Sat 10:00-12:00.
Admission: Free.   Location: West end of town centre, beside the river and near the parish
church.   Map Ref: 12

SULGRAVE *Northants*

Sulgrave Manor

Manor Road, Sulgrave, Banbury OX17 2SD   Tel: 01295 760205   Fax: 01295 768056
Email: sulgrave-manor@talk21.com   Web: www.sulgravemanor.org.uk

A Tudor manor house and gardens, the ancestral home of George Washington. Well known for the excellence of the guided tours and the quality of the special events.

Opening Times: 1 Apr to 30 Oct 14:00-17:30. Closed Mon and Fri, except BH.
Admission: Adult £5.00, Child £2.50. Garden only £2.50.   Location: In the village of Sulgrave,
seven miles from M40 junction 11.   Map Ref: 13

Guided or Private Tours	Disabled Access	Gift Shop or Sales Point	Café or Refreshments	Restaurant	Car Parking

Cambridgeshire & Northamptonshire

Canal Museum

Stoke Bruerne, Towcester NN12 7SE   Tel: 01604 862229   Fax: 01604 864199

An old cornmill housing a colourful collection depicting 200 years of inland waterways, situated in a rich historical site by the busy Grand Union Canal.

Opening Times: Easter to Oct daily 10:00-17:00, Oct to Easter Tue to Sun 10:00-16:00. Closed Xmas.   Location: Village four miles from junction 15 of M1.   Map Ref: 14

Irchester Narrow Gauge Railway Museum

Little Irchester Country Park, Wellingborough NN9   Tel: 01234 750469
Email: irchester@kingstonray.freeserve.co.uk   Web: www.ingrt.freeuk.com/

A narrow gauge railway museum, with operating locomotives. A total of four steam, four diesel and over 30 items of rolling steel.

Opening Times: Sun and BH, 10:00-17:00 (Winter 10:00-16:00).   Admission: Free.
Location: Irchester Country Park, one mile from Wellingborough.   Map Ref: 15

Wisbech & Fenland Museum

Museum Square, Wisbech PE13 1ES   Tel: 01945 583817   Fax: 01945 589050
Email: wisbechmuseum@beeb.net

A purpose built Victorian Museum, dating from 1847, with much of its original fittings and charm. Decorative art, ceramics, archaeology, natural history, geology, fossils, social history, egyptology, ethnography and numismatics. Exhibition on The Fenland, and Thomas Clarkson and his campaign to abolish slavery.

Opening Times: Summer Tue to Sat 10:00-17:00, winter Tue to Sat 10:00-16:00.   Location: At centre of town's Georgian Crescent, opposite Wisbech Castle and next to St Peter's Church.
                                                                              Map Ref: 16

Chester, a port until silting-up forced it to relinquish its sea trade to its neighbour Liverpool, is a city of great age, remarkable charm and some of the finest half-timbered buildings in the world. Manchester, despite dating back to the Roman era, is predominantly Victorian, and in Liverpool, though the days of the great ocean going liners have gone, much of the associated architecture remains.

Nearly 80 museums, galleries and historic houses combine to display the military, shipping and industrial history of this region.

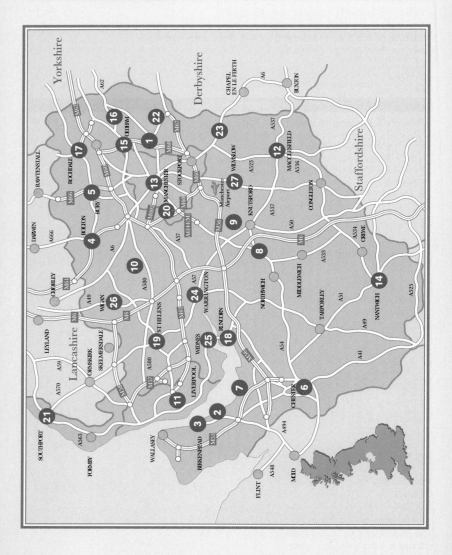

The Red Map References should be used to locate Museums etc on the pages that follow

Central Art Gallery   ♿ ■

Old Street, Ashton-under-Lyne OL6 7SF   Tel: 0161 342 2650

The Central Art Gallery is on Old Street in Ashton-under-Lyne. The first floor of this fine Victorian Gothic building provides three excellent galleries. A varied programme of temporary exhibitions has been established featuring a wide range of work including paintings, sculptures and textiles from regional artists and touring exhibitions.

Opening Times: Tue, Wed & Fri 10:00-17:00 Thur 13:00-19:30 Sat 09:00-12:30 & 13:00-16:00.
Admission: Free.   Location: Five minutes walk from Ashton railway and bus station.

Map Ref: 1

Museum of the Manchesters: Social & Regimental History   ♿ ■ 🚌

Town Hall, Ashton-under-Lyne OL6 6DL   Tel: 0161 342 3078

Museum displays feature the experience of 'Women At War' and the 'Home Front', the trenches of the First World War and computer interactives. You can also enjoy the fine collection of weapons and uniforms.

Opening Times: Mon to Sat 10:00-16:00.   Admission: Free.   Location: Two minute walk from Ashton-under-Lyne railway and bus stations.   Map Ref: 1

Portland Basin Museum   🗳 ♿ ■ 📷 🚌

Portland Place, Ashton-under-Lyne OL7 0QA   Tel: 0161 343 2878   Fax: 0161 343 2869
Email: jo.edwards@mail.tameside.gov.uk   Web: www.tameside.gov.uk

Portland Basin Museum is the centre piece of the recently rebuilt Ashton Canal Warehouse, now looking much as it did in 1834 when it was first built. This historic building houses exciting displays, describing the social and industrial history of Tameside and its people.

Opening Times: Tue to Sun 10:00-17:00. Closed Mon except BH.   Admission: Free.

Map Ref: 1

Lady Lever Art Gallery   🗳 ♿ ■ 📷 🚌

Port Sunlight Village, Lower Road, Bebington, Wirral
CH62 5EQ   Tel: 0151 478 4136   Fax: 0151 478 4140
Web: www.ladyleverartgallery.org.uk

The jewel in the crown of the garden village of Port Sunlight, housing the magnificent personal collection of the first Lord Leverhulme. Built by the soap magnate and philanthropist in 1922, the gallery includes Pre-Raphaelites, paintings by Turner and Constable alongside 18th century furniture, ceramics, Wedgewood, sculpture, tapestries and Napoleonic memorabilia.

Lady Lever Art Gallery   Opening Times: Mon to Sat 10:00-17:00, Sun 12:00-17:00. Closed
23-26 Dec & 1 Jan. Admission: Free. Location: Signposted from
A41 New Chester Road. Bebington railway station.   Map Ref: 2

Port Sunlight Heritage Centre   🗳 ♿ ■

95 Greendale Road, Port Sunlight, Bebington, Wirral CH62 4XE   Tel: 0151 644 6466
Fax: 0151 645 8973   Web: www.portsunlightvillage.com

Port Sunlight Heritage Centre explores the fascinating story about the village and its community. Old photographs and early film footage depict a quality of life for residents unimaginable in most 19th century industrial communities.

Opening Times: Mon to Fri 10:00-16:00, Sat & Sun (Apr to Oct) 10:00-16:00, (Nov to Mar)
11:00-16:00. Closed Xmas. Admission: Small admission charge. Group discount.
Location: 20 minutes by road or rail from Chester and Liverpool.   Map Ref: 2

Cheshire, Manchester & Merseyside

Birkenhead Priory & St Marys Tower

Priory Street, Birkenhead CH41 5JH   Tel: 0151 666 1249

Scheduled ancient monument, site of monastery founded 1150; small museum on site and remains of St Mary's Parish Church - tower now dedicated to those lost on HMS Thetis in 1939.

Opening Times: Jan to Mar & Nov to Dec Tue to Sun 12:00-16:00, Apr to Oct Tue to Sun 13:00-17:00. Closed Mon except BH. Admission: Free. Location: Five minute walk from Woodside Ferry/Hamilton Square.   Map Ref: 3

Egerton Bridge

Shore Road, Birkenhead

Working Bascule Bridge on docks network affording views of docks and River Mersey. Film interpretation of history of docks.

Opening Times: Jan to Mar & Nov to Dec Sat & Sun 12:00-16:00, Apr to Oct Sat & Sun 13:00-17:00. School holidays Tue to Sun 13:00-17:00. Admission: Free. Location: Tram ride from Woodside Ferry.   Map Ref: 3

Shore Road Pumping Station

Hamilton Street, Birkenhead CH41 6DN   Tel: 0151 650 1182

Grasshopper Steam Engine built to extract water from railway tunnel under River Mersey. Audio visual presentation on history of tunnel and railway.

Opening Times: Jan to Mar, Nov & Dec Sat & Sun 12:00-16:00, Apr to Oct Sat & Sun 13:00-17:00. School Holidays Tue to Sun 13:00-17:00. Admission: Free. Location: One minute walk from Woodside Ferry/Hamilton Square.   Map Ref: 3

Williamson Art Gallery & Museum

Slatey Road, Birkenhead CH43 4UE   Tel: 0151 652 4177   Fax: 0151 670 0253

Large but unintimidating gallery and museum with excellent picture and maritime displays, and active exhibition programme.

Opening Times: Tue to Sun 10:00-17:00. Closed Mon except BH. Admission: Free.
Location: 20 minute walk from Birkenhead Park or Birkenhead Central Stations; five minute drive from town centre.   Map Ref: 3

Wirral Museum - Birkenhead Town Hall

Hamilton Street, Birkenhead CH41 5BR   Tel: 0151 666 4010

Refurbished Victorian Town Hall still being developed as local history museum and access point for archives service.

Opening Times: Tue to Sun 10:00-17:00. Closed Mon except BH. Admission: Free.
Location: One minute walk from Hamilton Square Station.   Map Ref: 3

Bolton Museum, Art Gallery & Aquarium

Le Mans Crescent, Bolton BL1 1SE   Tel: 01204 332211   Fax: 01204 332241
Email: museums@bolton.gov.uk   Web: www.boltonmuseums.org.uk

'The Perspective of Idleness', E. Wadsworth (1930)

Bolton Museum, Art Gallery and Aquarium is one of the largest regional art galleries in the North West, housing an impressive collection of fine and decorative art dating from the 18th to the 20th century. This includes watercolours and drawings, a prominent collection of modern British art prints, along with 20th century sculpture and contemporary ceramics. The Museum has recently purchased the Thomas Moran painting 'Nearing Camp on the Upper Colorado River' after a national campaign. The Museum has extensive collections of Egyptology, ethnography, natural, local and industrial history, with examples of machinery and working models. The Natural History department includes the Wildlife on your Doorstep Gallery and an award winning, interactive Wildlife Study Centre and dinosaurs. The art gallery has a constantly changing programme of events and exhibitions. The aquarium is heavily involved in conservation and has a highly specialised breeding

Cheshire, Manchester & Merseyside

Thomas Moran, Nearing Camp,
Evening on the Upper Colorado River, 1882

programme. It features a wide variety of species of fish from around the world, some now extinct in their natural habitat. The education department plays a prominent and important role in the Museum's success and works closely with schools and other groups, particularly in subject areas included in the national curriculum.

Opening Times: Mon to Sat 10:00-17:00. Closed Sun & BH. Admission: Free. Location: Town centre, behind town hall, five minutes from train and bus stations. Exhibitions & Events 2003 : 15 Nov to 11 Jan: Homes of Football:, 18 Jan to 22 Feb: Nicholas Pace 'Unatural Habitat', 8 Mar to 20 Apr: Memory & Makers, 3 May to 14 Jun: 'Three Halves' Contemparय art project interpreting the Cotton Industry, 21 Jun to 30 Aug: Celebratring Boxes Tullie House Touring Exhibition, 8 Nov to 10 Jan 2004: War Memorial.

Map Ref: 4

Bury Art Gallery & Museum

Moss Street, Bury BL9 0DR Tel: 0161 253 5878 Fax: 0161 253 5915
Email: artgallery@bury.gov.uk Web: www.bury.gov.uk/culture.htm

Spring Morning: Haverstock Hill, George Clausen

Discover world-famous paintings by Turner and Constable and sample the best of Victorian art. Love or hate the lively changing exhibitions of contemporary art. Stroll down 'Paradise Street' in the museum and remember. Don't miss the family-friendly 'Art Trolley' and hands-on activities - all this in a beautiful Edwardian building that's a work of art in itself.

Opening Times: Tue to Sat 10:00-17:00.
Admission: Free. Location: Bury Town Centre, two minute walk from bus/tram interchange. Exhibitions & Events 2003 : 25 Jan to 5 Apr: Contrasts - Pairs of pictures from Bury's collections with something to say about each other, 8 Mar to 3 May: Wriggly Stories - Fun for under 5s and their grown ups inspired by Victorian paintings, 10 May to 12 Jul: A Plea to Somewhere Else - Contemporary art exploring issues of exile and refuge. Map Ref: 5

Fusiliers Museum (Lancashire)

Wellington Barracks, Bolton Road, Bury BL8 2PL Tel / Fax: 0161 764 2208
Email: rrflhq@aol.com Web: www.thefusiliers.org.uk

The museum contains uniforms, arms, medals, records, military art and regimental silver dating from 1688 to present day. Artefacts are also held of General Wolfe, Napoleon and General Robert Ross of Bladenburg.

Opening Times: Daily except Wed & Sun 09:30-16:30. Admission: Adult £2.00, Child Free, OAP £1.00. Location: One mile from town centre on the Bolton Bury Road (A58). Bus service from Bury Interchange/Metroline. Map Ref: 5

Cheshire Military Museum

The Castle, Chester CH1 2DN Tel / Fax: 01244 327617
Web: www.chester.ac.uk/militarymuseum

An attractive and interesting exhibition depicting the history of four famous regiments and their military connection with the county of Cheshire.

Opening Times: Daily 10:00-17:00. Location: From town centre, follow castle signs. We are the left wing building of Greek Revival Castle buildings, next to the Crown Court. Map Ref: 6

| Guided or Private Tours | Disabled Access | Gift Shop or Sales Point | Café or Refreshments | Restaurant | Car Parking |

43

Face to face with yesterday

Grosvenor Museum

27 Grosvenor Street, Chester CH1 2DD
Tel: 01244 402008 Fax: 01244 347587
Email: s.rogers@chestercc.gov.uk
Web: www.chestercc.gov.uk/heritage/museum/home.html

The museum to visit for the 21st century family. Step-free access to ground floor. Fascinating audio-visual introduction to the city's history. Unique Roman cemetery with world-renowned tombstone collection. Paintings by local artists. Work from Chester's silversmiths. Period rooms in a townhouse. Cheshire's wildlife. Temporary exhibitions. Interactives. Keeper-guided video tours of first floor galleries. Computerised collections.

Opening Times: Mon to Sat 10:30-17:00, Sun 14:00-17:00.
Admission: Free. There is a charge for guided tours.
Location: Near town centre and drop-off point for open bus tours.
Map Ref: 6

Boat Museum

South Pier Road, Ellesmere Port CH65 4FW   Tel: 0151 355 5017   Fax: 0151 355 4079
Email: bookings@thewaterwaystrust.org   Web: www.boatmuseum.org.uk

The Boat Museum is situated on the Shropshire Union Canal

Set within a historic dock complex, see the world's largest floating collection of canal craft. A video sets the scene while eight indoor exhibitions tell the history of canals. Together with four period cottages, power hall, blacksmiths forge, shop, cafe, free parking, disabled access, boat trips (seasonal).

Opening Times: Apr to Oct daily 10:00-17:00. Nov to Mar Sat to Wed 11:00-16:00. Closed Thu & Fri.
Admission: Adult £5.50, Child £3.70, Concession £4.30, Family £16.50. Group rates available. Location: Just off J9 M53. Ten minute walk from railway station, 15 minute walk from central bus station.   Map Ref: 7

Tabley House Stately Home

Tabley House, Knutsford WA16 0HB   Tel: 01565 750151   Fax: 01565 653230
Email: inquiries@tableyhouse.co.uk   Web: www.tableyhouse.co.uk

The finest Palladian House in the north west, containing fascinating Leicester family memorabilia, furniture by Chippendale, Gillow and Bullock, and the first collection of English paintings ever made, shown in the State Rooms.

Opening Times: Apr to end Oct Thu, Fri, Sat, Sun and BH 14:00-17:00. Admission: Adult £4.00, Child/Student £1.50. Location: Rural, two and a half miles west of Knutsford (M6 J19)
Map Ref: 8

Tatton Park

Knutsford WA16 6QN Tel: 01625 534400 Fax: 01625 534403
Email: tatton@cheshire.gov.uk Web: www.tattonpark.org.uk

Music Room

Magnificent grounds, superb gardens, lakes, a Neo-classical mansion and Tudor Old Hall make Tatton Park one of England's greatest country estates. Step into the enchanted gardens where you will find exotic trees and plants from all over the world. Visit the Mansion with its collection of art treasures and original furniture by Gillows of Lancaster. There is a working farm with rare breeds.

Opening Times: Mansion: 13:00-16:00 (guided tours 12:00 & 12:15). Tudor Old Hall: Sat & Sun guided tours 12:00-16:00. Admission: Per attraction: Adult £3.00, Child £2.00, Family £8.00. Saver Tickets (any two attractions) Adult £4.60, Child £2.60, Family £12.80. Park entry £3.80.   Location: Three miles from Knutsford station.   Map Ref: 9

LEIGH *Gtr Man*

Turnpike Gallery   ♿ 🚜

Civic Square, Leigh WN7 1EB   Tel: 01942 404469   Fax: 01942 404447
Email: turnpikegallery@wiganmbc.gov.uk   Web: www.wiganmbc.gov.uk

The gallery presents contemporary art through exhibitions, projects, residencies, arts outreach and education. The exhibition programme reflects the broad variety of current visual arts practice by regional, national and international artists.

Opening Times: Mon, Thu & Fri 09:30-17:30, Tue 10:00-17:30, Wed 09:30-17:00, Sat 10:00-15:00. Closed Sun & BH.   Admission: Free.   Location: In town centre, three minute walk from bus station.   Map Ref: 10

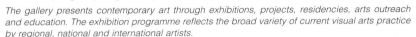

LIVERPOOL *Merseyside*

Conservation Centre   📧 ♿ 🎁 ☕   N M G M

Whitechapel, Liverpool L1 6HZ   Tel: 0151 478 4999
Fax: 0151 478 4990
Web: www.conservationcentre.org.uk

The award-winning Conservation Centre is dedicated to the preservation of precious items, from ceramics and paintings to textiles and sculpture. It is the only centre of its kind to open its doors to the public revealing the fascinating techniques with its weekly studio tours.

Opening Times: Mon to Sat 10:00-17:00, Sun 12:00-17:00. Closed 23-26 Dec & 1 Jan.   Admission: Free.   Location: Lime Street Station and Queen Square bus station - five minute walk.
Map Ref: 11

Croxteth Hall & Country Park   ∘   📧 ♿ 🎁 ☕ 🚜

Croxteth Hall Lane, West Derby, Liverpool L12 0HB   Tel: 0151 228 5311   Fax: 0151 228 2817
Web: www.croxteth.uk

The Hall depicts the lifestyle of the Earl and family, where visitors can appreciate an Edwardian country house with character figures of the family and of the servants working below stairs. Over 100 paintings, family portraits and sporting pictures. No visit to the Earl's estate would be complete without also visiting the Victorian walled garden and home farm which contains rare breeds.

Opening Times: Apr to Oct 10:30-17:00.   Admission: Hall & Farm: Adult £2.00, Child/OAP £1.18. Walled Garden: Adult £1.18, Child/OAP 67p.   Location: Six miles from the city centre.
Map Ref: 11

HM Customs & Excise National Museum   📧 ♿ 🎁 ☕   N M G M

Merseyside Maritime Museum, Albert Dock, Liverpool L3 4AQ   Tel: 0151 478 4499
Fax: 0151 478 4590   Web: www.customsmuseum.org.uk

Enter into the intriguing world of customs and excise. This surprising museum demonstrates how the battle against smuggling is undertaken by sniffer dogs and customs officers, from uncovering endangered species to drugs and replica goods. Meet some of the museum's colourful characters, including Mother Redcap, spot suspect travellers and learn about the latest technology used by customs officers.

HM Customs & Excise
National Museum endangered species

Opening Times: Mon to Sun 10:00-17:00. Closed 23-26 Dec & 1 Jan.   Admission: Free.   Location: James Street Station ten minute walk.   Map Ref: 11

Liverpool Central Library

William Brown Street, Liverpool L3 8EW   Tel: 0151 233 5845   Fax: 0151 233 5886
Email: refhum.central.library@liverpool.gov.uk   Web: www.liverpool.gov.uk

Major public library service, with superb collection of rare illustrated books, fine bindings, craft printing etc. Permanent display in historic Picton Library, visitors may view other items from Hornby and Oak Collections by appointment.

Opening Times: Mon to Thu 09:00-20:00, Fri 09:00-19:00, Sat 09:00-17:00, Sun 12:00-16:00. Closed BH. Admission: Free. Location: Two minute walk from Lime Street main line and Merseyrail station. Close to Liverpool Museum and Walker Art Gallery.   Map Ref: 11

Liverpool Museum

William Brown Street, Liverpool L3 8EN   Tel: 0151 478 4399   Fax: 0151 478 4322
Web: www.liverpoolmuseum.org.uk

A popular family destination, exploring the secrets of the natural world and the mysteries of outer space. A truly world class museum with important and diverse collections covering archaeology, ethnology and the natural and physical science. Liverpool Museum is currently undergoing extensive building improvements and refurbishments. The project will see the museum double in size with new attractions like The Bug House and The Exploration Zone. Expected completion date - late 2004.

Opening Times: Mon to Sat 10:00-17:00, Sun 12:00-17:00. Closed 23-26 Dec & 1 Jan. Admission: Free.
Location: Lime Street train station five minute walk.   Exhibitions & Events 2003 : To 23 Feb: Teddy Bear Story - 100 years of teddies.   Map Ref: 11

Merseyside Maritime Museum

Albert Dock, Liverpool L3 4AQ   Tel: 0151 478 4499   Fax: 0151 478 4590
Web: www.merseysidemaritimemuseum.org.uk

Liverpool's seafaring heritage brought to life in the historic Albert Dock. The museum's collections reflect the international importance of Liverpool as a gateway to the world, including the city's role in the transatlantic slave trade and emigration, the merchant navy and the Titanic. During the summer visitors can also explore the adjacent ships and quaysides.

Opening Times: Mon to Sun 10:00-17:00. Closed 23-26 Dec & 1 Jan. Admission: Free. Location: James Street train and Paradise Street bus station - ten minute walk.

Merseyside Maritime Museum - Titanic display

Exhibitions & Events 2003 : To 24 Feb: Blue Funnel to China, From 10 Jul: Liverpool at War - includes displays in the museum as well as on the ships and quaysides, and vehicles used in the Liverpool Blitz will be on display in the Great Western Railway Building throughout the summer.   Map Ref: 11

Museum of Liverpool Life

Pier Head, Liverpool L3 1PZ   Tel: 0151 478 4080   Fax: 0151 478 4090
Web: www.museumofliverpoollife.org.uk

The Museum of Liverpool Life celebrates the unique character of this vibrant city and its contribution to national life from Brookside to the Grand National. Recently expanded to include three new galleries, City Lives exploring the richness of Liverpool's cultural diversity, The River Room featuring life around the River Mersey and City Soldiers telling the story of the Kings Regiment.

Opening Times: Mon to Sun 10:00-17:00. Closed 23-26 Dec & 1 Jan Admission: Free. Location: James Street train station and Paradise Street bus station - ten minute walk.   Exhibitions & Events 2003 : To 23 Feb: Indian

Museum of Liverpool Life, River Room

Presence, From May: Wartime Garden - to tie in with the 'Liverpool at War' exhibition at the Maritime Museum, From May: 1940s House - also to tie in with 'Liverpool at War'.   Map Ref: 11

Cheshire, Manchester & Merseyside

Sudley House
Mossley Hill Road, Mossley Hill, Liverpool L18 8BX
Tel: 0151 724 3245   Web: www.sudleyhouse.org.uk

The former home of Victorian ship builder George Holt, housing his personal collection of 18th and 19th century British art. A charming gallery with works by Turner, Gainsborough, Lord Leighton and Holman Hunt. Many of the original Victorian features of the building survive, including tiles, ceramics, stained glass and wallpaper.

Opening Times: Mon to Sat 10:00-17:00, Sun 12:00-17:00. Closed 23-26 Dec & 1 Jan. Admission: Free. Location: Mossley Hill train and bus stop ten minute walk.   Map Ref: 11

Tate Liverpool
Albert Dock, Liverpool L3 4BB   Tel: 0151 702 7400   Fax: 0151 702 7401
Email: liverpoolinfo@tate.org.uk   Web: www.tate.org.uk/liverpool/

Experience for free the national collection of modern art on three floors of galleries, all with stunning views across the historic Albert Dock and River Mersey. Temporary exhibitions featuring internationally renowned artists are shown in the top floor galleries.

Opening Times: Tue to Sun 10:00-17:50. Closed Mon (except BH), 24-26 Dec, 31 Dec & 1 Jan & Good Friday. Admission: Free to Tate Collection; charges for special exhibitions. Location: 5 minute walk from city centre, ten minute walk from Lime Street Station.

Exterior of Tate Liverpool, Photo Roger Sinek   Map Ref: 11

University of Liverpool Art Gallery
3 Abercromby Square, Liverpool L69 3BX   Tel: 0151 794 2347/8   Fax: 0151 794 2343
Email: artgall@liv.ac.uk

Fine and decorative art from the University collections is displayed in an elegant Georgian house. Works by JMW Turner, Wright of Derby, Burne-Jones, Augustus John, Epstein, Freud and Frink.

Opening Times: Mon to Fri 12:00-16:00. Closed Aug BH & weekends. Admission: Free.
Location: Ten minute walk from city centre.   Map Ref: 11

The Walker
William Brown Street, Liverpool L3 8EL   Tel: 0151 478 4199   Fax: 0151 478 4190
Web: www.thewalker.org.uk

The national gallery of the North, the Walker is one of the finest art galleries in Europe housing outstanding collections spanning from 1300 to the present day. Especially rich in European Old Masters, Victorian and Pre-Raphaelite pictures and modern British works. A major refurbishment in 2002 has enabled the Walker to host must-see exhibitions in the new temporary exhibition galleries.

Opening Times: Mon to Sat 10:00-17:00, Sun 12:00-17:00. Closed 23-26 Dec & 1 Jan. Admission: Free.

The Walker, Rembrandt Room   Location: Lime Street Railway Station and Queen Square bus station - five minute walk. Exhibitions & Events 2003 : 24 Jan to 30 Mar: Henry VIII Revealed, 17 Oct to 18 Jan: Dante Gabriel Rossetti.   Map Ref: 11

Museums • Galleries • Historic Houses

Please let us know of any collections that are not listed in this guide that you feel should be listed. E-mail us on *editor@tomorrows.co.uk* or return the Report Form on page 448

Cheshire, Manchester & Merseyside

Macclesfield Silk Museums

Heritage Centre, Roe Street, Macclesfield SK11 6UT   Tel: 01625 613210/612045   Fax: 01625 617880   Web: www.silk-macclesfield.org

Tells the fascinating story of silk which links Macclesfield, once the centre of the English silk industry, with China and the Far East through an AV programme, costume, textiles and models.

Opening Times: Mon to Sat 11:00-17:00, Sun & BH 13:00-17:00. Closed Xmas & New Year.
Admission: Admission charge.   Location: In town centre - five minutes walk from bus and railway station.   Map Ref: 12

Paradise Mill & The New Silk Museum

Park Lane, Macclesfield SK11 6TJ   Tel: 01625 612045   Fax: 01635 612048   Web: www.silk-macclesfield.org

Working silk mill until 1981 and today the top floor is a living museum. Knowledgeable guides demonstrate the silk processes on the restored 26 hand jacquard silklooms and ancillary equipment. Room sets depict life in the 1930s. New extended displays in restored former School of Art.

Opening Times: Mar to Oct daily 11:00-17:00. Closed Xmas & New Year.
Admission: Admission charge.   Location: Town centre - five minutes walk from bus and railway stations.   Map Ref: 12

West Park Museum

Prestbury Road, Macclesfield   Tel: 01625 619831   Web: www.silk-macclesfield.org

Established in 1898 it houses a small but interesting collection of Egyptian antiquities, fine and decorative art and a gallery devoted to works of local born artist Charles Tunnicliffe.

Opening Times: Apr to Oct Tue to Sun & BH 13:30-16:30. Nov to Mar Tue to Sun 13:00-16:00.
Closed Xmas & New Year.   Admission: Free.   Location: On outskirts of town located in public park.   Map Ref: 12

Gallery of Costume

Platt Hall, Wilmslow Road, Rusholme, Manchester M14 5LL   Tel: 0161 224 5217

Gallery of Costume

The Gallery of Costume is an elegant 18th century textile merchant's house, housing Manchester's extraordinary collection of clothing and fashion accessories. The collection gives a fascinating insight into styles of dress from the 17th century to the present day.

Opening Times: Mar to Oct Tue to Sun 10:00-17:00, Nov to Feb Tue to Sun 10:00-16:00. Closed Mon (except BH).
Admission: Free.   Location: Platt Fields Park, Wilmslow Road, Rusholme, South Manchester.   Map Ref: 13

Gallery of Costume, Platt Hall. Photo by Len Grant

Heaton Hall

Heaton Park, Prestwich, Manchester M25 5SW   Tel: 0161 773 1231

Heaton Hall

Heaton Hall is a magnificent 18th century neo-classical country house set in 650 acres of rolling parkland. The Hall is now Grade I listed and its interiors have been beautifully restored to reflect late 18th and early 19th century life in Heaton.

Opening Times: 30 Mar to 29 Sep Thu to Sun & BH Mon. Times may vary. Please phone 0161 235 8888 for details.
Admission: Free.   Location: In Heaton Park, off Middleton Road, near Prestwich north of the city centre.

Heaton Hall, photo by Len Grant   Map Ref: 13

Imperial War Museum North

Trafford Wharf Road, Trafford Park, Manchester M17 1HH   Tel: 0161 836 4000
Fax: 0161 836 4012   Email: info@iwmnorth.org.uk   Web: www.iwm.org.uk

Imperial War Museum North © Len Grant

Opened in July 2002, Imperial War Museum North offers a new way of understanding war and conflict and the impact it has on all our lives. In the stunning aluminium-clad building - the first in the UK by international architect Daniel Libeskind - visitors will enjoy a multi-sensory experience expressing how war affects everything it touches. The Museum utilises the world-famous collections of the Imperial War Museum with a number of new display techniques. The Big Picture uses the sound and photography archive to immerse visitors in a spectacular audio-visual show using over 60 projectors. Interactors are on hand to discuss objects from the TimeStacks with visitors and the Timeline tells the story of the 20th century. 'Silos' pick out themes for further study - Women and War, Commonwealth, Legacy, Experience, Impressions and Science - and a number of iconic objects such as a Harrier Jump-Jet, a Trabant estate car and a T34 Tank are highlights in the breathtaking gallery. The Special Exhibition Gallery shows exhibitions on the themes of war and conflict, as well as the first show which looks at the building itself.

Opening Times: Daily 10:00-18:00.   Admission: Free.   Location: Two miles from Manchester City Centre at the Quays, Trafford Park.   Exhibitions & Events 2003 : Apr to Sep: 'In The Mood' exhibition.   Map Ref: 13

John Rylands University Library of Manchester

150 Deansgate, Manchester M3 3EH   Tel: 0161 834 5343   Fax: 0161 834 5574
Email: danielle.shields@man.ac.uk   Web: www.rylibweb.man.ac.uk/spcoll

The John Rylands Library is one of the finest examples of Neo-Gothic architecture in Europe, housing a spectacular collection of printed books, manuscripts and archives. Public library with regular exhibitions.

Opening Times: Mon to Fri 10:00-17:15, Sat 10:00-13:00. Closed Sun, BH, Xmas/New Year period, Easter weekend.   Admission: Free (public tours each Wednesday 12:00 £1 a head). Location: In town centre, few minutes walk from several train stations, metrolink stops (tram) and bus stops.   Map Ref: 13

The Lowry

Pier 8, Salford Quays, Manchester M5 2AZ   Tel: 0161 876 2020   Fax: 0161 876 2021
Email: info@thelowry.com   Web: www.thelowry.com

The City Gallery

The Lowry features the work of LS Lowry, Salford's most famous son and one of the most popular of all English painters. Changing exhibitions explore the Lowry collection along with a wide range of contemporary and historical art from Britain and abroad. The Deck and The Promenade spaces have solo and group exhibitions by significant regional, national and international artists and photographers.

Opening Times: Sat 10:00-19:30 Sun to Wed 11:00-17:00 Thu & Fri 11:00-19:30. Please ring to check times as Galleries may close between exhibitions.

Admission: Free.   Location: In the heart of Salford Quays, five minutes walk from Broadway tram stop.   Map Ref: 13

Manchester Art Gallery

Moseley Street, Manchester M2 3JL   Tel: 0161 235 8888

Manchester Art Gallery opened in May 2002 after a £35 million transformation. The Gallery houses one of the UK's finest art collections in spectacular surroundings. Six centuries of British art, including some wonderful 19th century Pre-Raphaelite works, alongside fine examples of Dutch and Italian paintings. The Gallery is also renowned for its collection of decorative art. A lively special exhibitions programme showcases the best in British and international art and design. Also since the re-opening - The Gallery of Craft and Design, The Clore Interactive Gallery, and The Manchester Gallery.

Manchester Art Gallery

Opening Times: Tue to Sun 10:00-17:00. Closed Mon (except BH).   Admission: Free.
Location: Manchester City Centre.   Map Ref: 13

Manchester Jewish Museum

190 Cheetham Hill Road, Manchester M8 8LW   Tel: 0161 834 9879
Fax: 0161 834 9801   Email: info@manchesterjewishmuseum.com
Web: www.manchesterjewishmuseum.com

The Museum, set in a beautifully restored Grade II* listed Spanish and Portuguese synagogue building, tells the history of the Jewish community in Manchester and Salford over the past 250 years. Our education and outreach programme won the 1998 Sandford Award and is much in demand. The shop sells educational materials, books and gifts.

Opening Times: Mon to Thu 10:30-16:00, Sun 10:30-17:00. Closed 1 Jan, 17, 34 & 24 Apr, 28 Sep, 6, 12 & 19 Oct, 24 & 25 Dec and at 13:00 on 16 Apr & 5 Oct.

Admission: Adult £3.65, Concession £2.75, Family £8.95.   Location: Half a mile from Manchester Victoria and Metrolink Station.   Exhibitions & Events 2003 : 1 Apr: Passover Seder Demonstration - 19:30, 30 Mar, 27 Apr: Heritage Trails - 14:00, 25 May, 29 Jun: Heritage Trails - 14:00, 27 Jul, 24 Aug: Heritage Trails - 14:00, 21 Sep, 26 Oct: Heritage Trails - 14:00.

Map Ref: 13

The Manchester Museum

The University of Manchester, Oxford Road, Manchester M13 9PL   Tel: 0161 275 2634
Fax: 0161 275 2676

The Manchester Museum has just undergone a major £19.5 million refurbishment which has created new galleries with hundreds of fascinating displays, a temporary exhibition programme, a new Discovery Centre with hands-on exhibits, a café, shop and disabled access to all areas. It amazing collections, containing six million items, provide a window on the world from Peru to Japan, from Egypt to North America.

Opening Times: Mon to Sat 10:00-17:00, Sun & BH 11:00-16:00. Please ring for Christmas opening.
Admission: Free.   Location: One mile south of Manchester City Centre on the campus of the University of Manchester.   Map Ref: 13

Manchester United Museum & Tour Centre

Sir Matt Busby Way, Old Trafford, Manchester M16 0RA   Tel: 0870 442 1994   Fax: 0161 868 8861   Email: tours@manutd.co.uk   Web: www.manutd.com

Ryan Giggs - one of our regular temporary exhibitions

Manchester United's new museum was opened by the legendary Pele in April 1998. Filling three floors of Old Trafford's massive North Stand, the museum outlines Manchester United's history from 1878 to the present day. Displays include the magnificent Trophy Room, the history of United, a special display on the Munich Air Disaster, kit and equipment, fans, the Legends Gallery and the new Treble Exhibition. There is also a changing programme of temporary exhibitions throughout the year. Explore the interactive Man-U-Net and find out about every player to have made a first team appearance for the club. Take a virtual tour of Old Trafford and go behind the scenes at one of the world's most famous stadiums. Add your own distinctive style of commentary to match action as Martin Tyler gives you tips in our commentary booth. Visit our audio-visual theatre and see 'Backstage at The Theatre of Dreams'. Listen to United fans describing their experiences watching United in our Fanzone. Pop into our Legends Cafe for a quick snack or into the Red Cafe for something more substantial. After visiting the Museum, why not go on a tour and see the pitch, sit in the dugout, enter the changing rooms and walk down the players' tunnel?

Ruud van Nistelrooy - A British record transfer to United

Opening Times: Daily 09:30-17:00, tours daily 09:40-16:30. Admission: Museum - Adult £5.50, Child/OAP £3.75, Family £15.50. Museum & Tour - Adult £8.50, Child/OAP £5.75, Family £23.50, Under 5s Free. Location: Five minute walk from Old Trafford Metro Station, which is accessible from Piccadilly Train Station in Manchester. Events 2003 : Ring for details.   Map Ref: 13

The Museum of Science and Industry in Manchester

Liverpool Road, Castlefield, Manchester M3 4FP   Tel: 0161 832 2244/1830 24hr   Fax: 0161 833 1471   Email: marketing@msim.org.uk   Web: www.msim.org.uk

Based in the building of the world's oldest passenger railway station

The Museum of Science and Industry in Manchester is one of the world's biggest and most impressive science museums. Bursting with entertaining galleries and amazing exhibits, the Museum tells the compelling story of Manchester. Highlights include: historic locomotives and incredible aircraft, thunderous cotton machinery and huge steam mill engines, interactive exhibits and Special Exhibitions, including Dinosaurs - they're back! and Star Trek: Federation Science.

Opening Times: Daily 10:00-17:00. Closed 24-26 Dec. Admission: Free entry to permanent collections, charge for Special Exhibitions. Location: City centre location, nearest railway station, Deansgate is five minutes walk. Nearest Metrolink station, G-Mex is five minutes walk.   Map Ref: 13

Museum of Transport - Greater Manchester

Boyle Street, Cheetham, Manchester M8 8UW   Tel / Fax: 0161 205 2122   Web: www.gmts.co.uk

Over 85 vehicles mainly buses relating to over a century of road public transport in Greater Manchester. Small exhibits and archives.

Opening Times: Wed, Sat, Sun & BH 10:00-17:00. Admission: Adult £3.00, Concession £1.75, Under 5s Free. Location: One and a half miles north of Victoria Station, five minute walk from Woodlands Road Metrolink. Exhibitions & Events 2003 : 23 Feb: Morris Minor Event, 29 & 30 Mar: Spring Transport Festival, 11 May: The Bury Centenary Event, 14 & 15: Accessible Transport

Cheshire, Manchester & Merseyside

Weekend, 7 Sep: The Annual Trans Lancs Rally, 13 & 14 Sep: Civic Trust Heritage Open Days, 5 Oct: Rover Car Club Event, 11 & 12 Oct: Salford 100, 16 Nov: Citroen Car Club Event, 6 & 7 Dec: Christmas Cracker Festival. Map Ref: 13

Peoples History Museum

🐿 🕭 ● ⬚ 🚂

P H **People's History Museum**

Bridge Street, Manchester M3 3ER   Tel: 0161 839 6061   Fax: 0161 839 6027   Email: info@peopleshistorymuseum.org.uk
Web: www.peopleshistorymuseum.org.uk

National Union of Railwaymen banner, Wakefield branch, about 1920

The People's History Museum is the only national museum in Britain dedicated to people's history, it celebrates the triumphs and struggles of everyday people. Watch the first Match of the Day, visit the Co-op shop, play your favourite vinyl on the jukebox and try your hand at sweated labour. The Head Office of the museum houses the Textile Conservation Centre which specializes in the conservation of banners in both the museums own collection nationally.

Opening Times: Tue to Sun 11:00-16:30. Closed Mon (except BH) & Good Fridays. Admission: Adult £1.00, Child/OAP/Student/Concession Free, Free to all on Fri. Location: Easy walking distance from city centre.
Gartside Street multi-storey car park next door. Ten minute walk from Deansgate Train Station.
Map Ref: 13

The Whitworth Art Gallery

🐿 🕭 ● ⬚ 🚂   The Whitworth Art Gallery

The University of Manchester, Oxford Road, Manchester M15 6ER
Tel: 0161 275 7450   Fax: 0161 275 7451   Email: whitworth@man.ac.uk
Web: www.whitworth.man.ac.uk

Situated in Whitworth Park to the south of Manchester city centre, the Whitworth Art Gallery is internationally famous for its collections of art and design. The Whitworth's collection includes an outstanding range of prints and drawings, one of the great collections of British watercolours, and excellent work by modern and contemporary artists. In addition to this, the Whitworth is home to the finest collections of textiles and wallpapers outside the Victoria and Albert Museum in London. A changing programme of special exhibitions designed to complement the permanent collection runs throughout the year.

'Sudden Shower at Ohashi Bridge'
Utagawa Hiroshige 1797-1858

Opening Times: Mon to Sat 10:00-17:00, Sun 14:00-17:00. Admission: Free. Location: Approx one and a half miles south of Manchester City Centre, in Whitworth Park (Oxford Road), opposite Manchester Royal Infirmary. Exhibitions & Events 2003 : 24 Jan to 27 Apr: Lee Miller: Photographic Witness, 16 May to 3 Aug: Editions Alecto: Original Graphics, Mulitple Originals 1960-1981, 22 Aug to 31 Oct: Thomas Jones, 21 Nov to Feb 04: Flexible 4: Identities. Map Ref: 13

Wythenshawe Hall

● 🚂

Wythenshawe Park, Northenden, Manchester M23 0AB   Tel: 0161 998 2331

Wythenshawe Hall. Photo by Len Grant

Wythenshawe Hall is a striking half-timbered Tudor house with fine oak-panelled interiors, set in its own beautiful gardens. The Hall was the home of the Tatton family for nearly four hundred years and its long history includes a dramatic role in the events of the English Civil War. A visit to the Hall today gives a fascinating insight into the changing history of this part of Manchester.

Opening Times: 30 Mar to 29 Sep Thu to Sun & BH 10:00-17:00. Times may vary please phone 0161 235 8888 for details. Admission: Free. Location: Five miles south of city centre in Wythenshawe Park, B5167.
Map Ref: 13

Cheshire, Manchester & Merseyside

Nantwich Museum   ♿ ●

Pillory Street, Nantwich CW5 5BQ   Tel: 01270 627104   Email: nantwich.museum@virgin.net

A fascinating insight into the history of the ancient market town of Nantwich together with a cheese making room and a modern Millennium Gallery for temporary exhibition.

Opening Times: Apr to Sep Mon to Sat 10:30-16:30, Oct to Mar Tue to Sat 10:30-16:30.
Admission: Free.   Location: Near town centre.

Map Ref: 14

Gallery Oldham

Greaves Street, Oldham OL1 3DL   Tel: 0161 911 4853   Fax: 0161 911 4669
Email: ecs.galleryoldham@oldham.gov.uk   Web: www.galleryoldham.org.uk

This fine and decorative art collection of mainly British artists was first established by Victorian industrial philanthropists and now includes work by modern and contempory artists. Large collection of objects representing Oldham people's lives from the industrial era of cotton and engineering. Extensive natural history collection of mainly local plants, geology, insects and birds reflects historic local passion for scientific study.

Opening Times: Mon to Sat 10:00-17:00.
Admission: Free.   Location: In Oldham Town Centre behind library, two minutes from bus station, five minutes from Oldham Mumps Station.   Exhibitions & Events 2003 : Mar & Apr: Words - Hayward Gallery Touring Exhibition, Mar to Jun: From Palettes to Pixels, May to Sep: By the Sea, May to Jul: Art of Noises, May to Sep: Classical Illusions, Oct to Nov: Picasso: Histoire Naturelle, Dec to Apr: William Stott of Oldham.

Map Ref: 15

Saddleworth Museum & Art Gallery

High Street, Uppermill, Oldham OL3 6HS   Tel: 01457 874093   Fax: 01457 870336
Email: museum-curator@saddleworth.net   Web: www.museum.saddleworth.net

Set in a beautiful location beside the Huddersfield narrow canal, Saddleworth Museum charts 3000 years of history in this ancient Yorkshire parish, set in the foothills of the Pennines. Refreshments for tours by arrangement.

Opening Times: Mar to Oct Mon to Sat 10:00-17:00, Sun 12:00-17:00. Nov to Feb Mon to Sun 13:00-16:00.   Admission: Adult £2.00, Child/OAP £1.00, Family £4.00.   Location: In the centre of Uppermill village, eight miles from Oldham on A670.

Map Ref: 16

Rochdale Pioneers Museum or Toad Lane Museum

31 Toad Lane, Rochdale OL12 0NU   Tel: 01706 524920   Email: museum@co-op.ac.uk
Web: www.co-op.ac.uk/toad_lane.htm

The home of the worldwide co-operative movement. In 1844 the Rochdale Pioneers opened their store selling pure food at fair prices and honest weights and measures. See how your ancestors did their shopping.

Opening Times: Tue to Sat 10:00-16:00, Sun 14:00-16:00.   Admission: Adult £1.00, OAP/Student 50p, Family £2.00.   Location: Situated in the Toad Lane Conservation Area at the rear of the Rochdale Exchange Shopping Precinct on Hunters Lane.

Map Ref: 17

Norton Priory Museum & Gardens

Tudor Road, Manor Park, Runcorn WA7 1SX   Tel: 01928 569895   Fax: 01928 589743
Email: info@nortonpriory.org   Web: www.nortonpriory.org

Unique and beautiful site incorporating atmospheric museum, excavated Priory remains, sculpture trail, peaceful and relaxing two and a half acre walled garden and the awe inspiring St Christopher statue, now housed in its own gallery.

Opening Times: Apr to Oct Mon to Fri 12:00-17:00, Sat, Sun & BH 12:00-18:00. Nov to Mar daily 12:00-16:00. Closed Xmas & New Year.   Admission: Adult £3.95, Concession £2.75, Family £10.00, Under 5s Free.   Location: Less than 30 minutes by car from Chester, Liverpool and Manchester. Close to junction 11 of M56.

Map Ref: 18

Cheshire, Manchester & Merseyside

The World of Glass

Chalon Way East, St Helens WA10 1BX Tel: 08707 444 777 Fax: 01744 616 966
Email: info@worldofglass.com Web: www.worldofglass.com

The World of Glass is constructed on a historic site, which incorporates a Grade II* listed Victorian glassmaking furnace. The centre also houses the Pilkington Glass Collection and St Helen's Council Social History Collection.

Opening Times: Daily 10:00-17:00 except Mon. Closed Xmas & New Year. Admission: Adult £5.00, Child £3.60, Under 5s Free, Concession £3.60. Group rates available.
Location: Situated in the heart of St Helens, just a five minute walk from the bus and railway station. Excellent access by road from junction 7 on M62. Map Ref: 19

Ordsall Hall Museum

332 Ordsall Lane, Ordsall, Salford M5 3AN Tel: 0161 872 0251 Fax: 0161 872 4951
Email: admin@ordsallhall.org Web: www.ordsallhall.org

Grade I listed Tudor Manor House with black and white timbers, and 600 years of history, including a part in the gunpowder plot. Educational visits, guided tours and temporary exhibitions.

Opening Times: Mon to Fri 10:00-16:00, Sun 13:00-16:00. Admission: Free. Location: Five minutes walk from Exchange Quay Metrolink. Map Ref: 20

Salford Museum & Art Gallery

Peel Park, Crescent, Salford M5 4WU Tel: 0161 736 2649 Fax: 0161 745 9490
Email: salford.museum@salford.gov.uk Web: www.salfordmuseum.org

A traditional reconstructed Victorian Street with shops, workshops and houses - plus a Victorian Gallery. Most exhibitions here look forward rather than back, showcasing the work of both young British artists and international culture.

Opening Times: Mon to Fri 10:00-16:45, Sat & Sun 13:00-17:00. Admission: Free.
Location: Situated on the A6 near the Greater Manchester motorway network, five minutes. Map Ref: 20

Atkinson Art Gallery

Lord Street, Southport PR8 1DH Tel: 01704 533133 Fax: 0151 934 2109
Web: www.seftonarts.co.uk

Permanent collection of 19th and 20th century works, including LS Lowry, John Piper and Henry Moore. Temporary exhibition programme, including contemporary artists.

Opening Times: Mon to Wed & Fri 10:00-17:00, Thu & Sat 10:00-13:00. Closed BH. Admission: Free.
Location: In town centre, next to library. Map Ref: 21

Breton Dining Room by Sir William Russell Flint (1880-1969)

Botanic Gardens Museum

Churchtown, Southport PR9 7NB Tel: 01704 227547 Fax: 01704 224112
Web: www.seftonarts.co.uk

Local history galleries, Victorian room with toy display and costume, natural history gallery. Temporary exhibition programme.

Opening Times: Tue to Fri 11:00-15:00, Sat & Sun 14:00-17:00, BH 12:00-16:00, closed following Fri. Admission: Free. Location: In Churchtown to north of Southport. Map Ref: 21

Guided or Private Tours	Disabled Access	Gift Shop or Sales Point	Café or Refreshments	Restaurant	Car Parking

Cheshire, Manchester & Merseyside

Astley Cheetham Art Gallery

Trinity Street, Stalybridge SK15 2BN   Tel: 0161 338 2708

Astley Cheetham Art Gallery originally operated as a lecture hall but developed into an art gallery when J F Cheetham bequeathed his collection of paintings to the town in 1932. The collection includes Italian paintings from the 14th and 15th centuries and works from British masters such as Cox and Burne-Jones.

Opening Times: Mon to Wed & Fri 10:00-12:30 & 13:00-17:00 Sat 09:00-12:30 & 13:00-17:00.
Admission: Free. Location: Two minutes from bus station.   Map Ref: 22

Lyme Park

Disley, Stockport SK12 2HA   Tel: 01663 762023   Fax: 01663 765035   **THE NATIONAL TRUST**
Email: mlyrec@smtp.ntrust.org.uk   Web: www.nationaltrust.org.uk

Lyme Hall and Cage

Originally a Tudor house, Lyme was transformed by the Venetian architect Leoni into an Italianate palace. Some of the Elizabethan interiors survive and contrast dramatically with later rooms. The state rooms are adorned with Mortlake tapestries, Grinling Gibbons wood-carvings and an important collection of English clocks. The 17 acre Victorian garden boasts impressive bedding schemes, a sunken parterre, an Edwardian rose garden, Jekyll-style herbaceous borders, reflection lake, a ravine garden and Wyatt conservatory. The garden is surrounded by a medieval deer park of almost 1400 acres of moorland, woodland and parkland, containing an early 18th century hunting tower. Lyme appeared as 'Pemberley' in the BBC's adaptation of the Jane Austen novel Pride and Prejudice. Lyme also featured in Granada's production of the Forsyte Saga.

Winter at Lyme Hall

Opening Times: House: 1 Apr to 28 Oct Fri to Tue 13:00-17:00. BH Mon 11:00-17:00. For other opening times please contact us. Admission: House & Garden: Adult £5.50, Family £12.00. House: £4.00, Garden: £2.50. Park: £3.50 per car. National Trust Members Free.
Location: Entrance on A6, six and a half miles south east of Stockport, nine miles north west of Buxton. Disley Station half a mile from park entrance.
Exhibitions & Events 2003 : Please telephone for details   Map Ref: 23

Warrington Museum & Art Gallery

Bold Street, Warrington WA1 1JG   Tel: 01925 442392   Fax: 01925 442399
Email: museum@warrington.gov.uk   Web: www.warrington.gov.uk/museum

The Earth's History Gallery

Warrington Museum & Art Gallery combines a Victorian 'cabinet of curiosities' charm with state-of-the-art temporary exhibition galleries. Displays feature a wealth of material on the natural world, local history, fine art and treasures from ancient civilisations and distant continents. Many galleries feature free hands-on activities for younger visitors. Lively temporary exhibition programme - ring for details.

Opening Times: Mon to Fri 10:00-17:30, Sat 10:00-17:00. Closed Sun & BH. Admission: Free. Location: Town centre location, five minute walk from Bank Quay station.
                                                                          Map Ref: 24

Catalyst

Gossage Building, Mersey Road, Widnes WA8 0DF   Tel: 0151 420 1121   Fax: 0151 495 2030
Email: info@catalyst.org.uk   Web: www.catalyst.org.uk

Cheshire, Manchester & Merseyside

Catalyst has hands-on exhibits relating to chemistry and the everyday products of the chemical industry. Winner of 13 major awards: history, science and technology. Science fuses with fun at Catalyst.

Opening Times: Tue to Fri 10:00-17:00, Sat & Sun 11:00-17:00, BH Mon & Mon in school holidays. Closed Xmas & New Year. Admission: Adult £4.65, Child £3.40, Concession £3.95, Family £13.95. Group rates available. Location: Widnes, Junction 12 of M56, junction 7 of M62, nearest railway station Widnes.
Map Ref: 25

Wigan Pier

Trencherfield Mill, Wigan WN3 4EF   Tel: 01942 323666   Fax: 01942 701927
Email: wiganpier@wiganmbc.gov.uk   Web: www.wiganpier.net

The Wigan Pier Experience
set on the Leeds-Liverpool Canal

Opie's Museum of Memories at the Wigan Pier Experience. The Robert Opie collection had been assembled to reflect the remarkable story of domestic life in Britain since the industrial revolution. By displaying the actual products, brands, posters, magazines, toys, televisions and royal souvenirs of each era, along with the advertisments and images that reflect fashion and design, it is possible to gain a sense of ever changing culture and lifestyle through which our parents and grandparents lived. The Museum of Memories not only tells the incredible story of our consumer society but also revives our own memories, placing us in the context of history, of which we are all part of. The Way We Were Heritage Centre takes you back to the strict days of Victorian Britain; experience the hardship, social lives and in, some instances the entertaining times of people of Wigan in 1900. See for example what they did on holiday during 'wakes week', walk through our mine, witness the Maypole colliery diaster. Visitors never forget our Victorian

Let us take you back in time
at the Wigan Pier Experience

schoolroom - you will meet the schoolmaster and participate in choir practice; you may even be the bell monitor or 'lice' inspector. At Wigan Pier Experience we will provide you and your family with the opportunity to take a journey through yesteryear.

Opening Times: Mon to Thu 10:00-17:00, Sat & Sun 11:00-17:00. Closed Fri, 25-26 Dec & New Year's Day. Admission: Adult £7.50, Child £5.95, Concession £5.95, Group 20+ £4.95. Location: Signposted from all major road networks. Near town centre, five minute walk from Wigan Train Station. Exhibitions & Events 2003 : Please telephone for details.
Map Ref: 26

Quarry Bank Mill & Styal Estate

Styal, Wilmslow SK9 4LA   Tel: 01625 527468   Fax: 01625 539267
Email: msyrec@smtp.ntrust.org.uk   Web: www.quarrybankmill.org.uk

Working water powered cotton mill, with its estate village, farm and woodland. See a Spinning Jenny, a mule, and Lancashire looms in action. Original Apprentice House and garden - see how pauper children were fed, worked and slept. Purchase unique Styal Calico from the shop.

Opening Times: Easter to Sep daily 10:30-17:30, Oct to Mar Tue to Sun 10:30-17:00. Admission: Mill: Adult £5.00, Concession £3.40. Mill & Apprentice House: Adult £6.50, Concession £3.70. National Trust Members Free. Location: Ten minutes drive from Wilmslow and Manchester Airport.
Map Ref: 27

Cornwall is truly a county of romance with its tales of King Arthur who legend has it was born in Tintagel. The River Tamar, in separating the county from the rest of England, successfully preserves the distinct Cornish character.

Museums and Galleries admirably record Cornwall's social history, its association with the sea, smuggling and piracy, its magnetic appeal to artists, its mining past and mineral collections and its living plant collection.

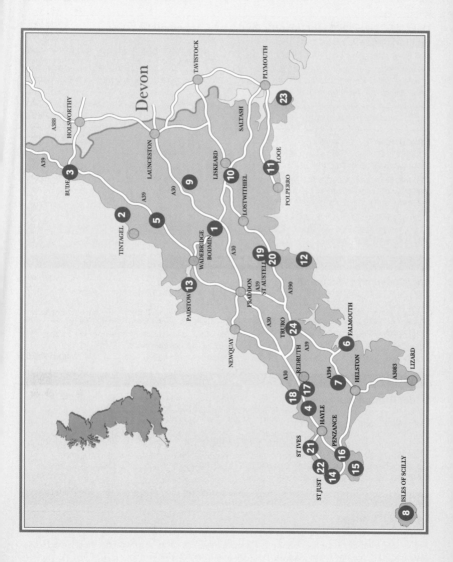

The Red Map References should be used to locate Museums etc on the pages that follow

Cornwall & Isles of Scilly

Bodmin Town Museum

Mount Folly, Bodmin PL31 2HQ   Tel: 01208 77067   Fax: 01208 79268
Email: bodmin.museum@ukonline.co.uk

Local history museum with exhibits and text from medieval times to the 1950s, featuring Bodmin Moor, agriculture, law and order, trades and occupations, transport, Victorian domestic life and costume, World Wars I & II.

Opening Times: Apr to Sep daily 10:30-16:30, Oct 10:30-14:30. Closed Sun & BH.
Admission: Free.   Location: Town centre, two minute walk from car parks.   Map Ref: 1

Duke of Cornwalls Light Infantry Regimental Museum
(Military Museum Bodmin)

The Keep, Bodmin PL31 1EG   Tel / Fax: 01208 72810   Email: dclimus@talk21.com

Covers military history from the capture of Gibraltar in 1704 up to World War II. Fascinating displays of weapons, pictures, uniforms and documents - including General George Washington's Bible 'taken' by the Regiment in 1777.

Opening Times: Mon to Fri (and Sun in Jul & Aug) 09:00-17:00.   Admission: Adult £2.00, Child 50p.   Location: Bodmin.   Map Ref: 1

Pencarrow

Bodmin PL30 3AG   Tel / Fax: 01208 841369   Email: pencarrow@aol.com
Web: www.pencarrow.co.uk

Historic Georgian house and Grade II star listed garden; still owned and lived in by the family. Superb collection of paintings, furniture, porcelain and some antique dolls. Gold Award for Best Property in UK.

Opening Times: 30 Mar to 30 Oct Sun to Thu 11:00-17:00.   Admission: Adult £6.00, Child £3.00, Group discount available.   Location: Four miles north west of Bodmin, signed off A389 and B3266 at Washaway.   Map Ref: 1

The Museum of Witchcraft

The Harbour, Boscastle PL35 0HD   Tel: 01840 250111   Email: museumwitchcraft@aol.com
Web: www.museumofwitchcraft.com

The world's largest collection of Witchcraft related artefacts. This unique museum (now 50 years old) is one of the most popular in Cornwall.

Opening Times: Easter to Halloween Mon to Sat 10:30-18:00, Sun 11:30-18:00.
Admission: Adult £2.00, Child/OAP £1.00.   Location: Boscastle Harbour.   Map Ref: 2

Bude-Stratton Museum

Lower Wharf, Bude EX23 8LG   Tel / Fax: 01288 353576   Email: theclerk@bude-stratton.gov.uk
Web: www.bude-stratton.gov.uk

Old photographs, models and an audio-visual presentation tell the story of the canal and the ships that used it.

Opening Times: Good Friday to Sep daily 12:00-17:00.   Admission: Adult 50p, Child Free, OAP 25p.   Location: On Bude's canalside.   Map Ref: 3

Trevithick Cottage

Penponds, Camborne TR14 0QG   Tel: 01209 612154   Fax: 01209 612142

Home of the famous Cornish engineer, Richard Trevithick. Now a private house owned by the National Trust, but one room contains portraits and memorabilia.

Opening Times: Apr to Oct Wed 14:00-17:00.   Admission: Donations of £1.00 invited.
Location: Take Barriper Road after leaving Camborne towards Helston. Turn right into Penponds at the School - cottage is first on right.   Map Ref: 4

Cornwall & Isles of Scilly

British Cycling Museum

The Old Station, Camelford PL32 9TZ   Tel / Fax: 01840 212811   Web: www.chycor.co.uk/

The British Cycling Museum is the foremost display of cycling history from 1818 to present day with over 400 various machines and the largest display of cycling memorabilia on show.

Opening Times: Sun to Thu 10:00-17:00. Admission: Adult £2.50, Child £1.50.
Location: One mile north of Camelford on B3266.   Map Ref: 5

North Cornwall Museum & Gallery

The Clease, Camelford PL32 9PL   Tel / Fax: 01840 212954
Email: camelfordtlc@eurobell.co.uk

The museum shows many aspects of life in North Cornwall from 50-100 years ago. The gallery has monthly changing exhibitions by artists and craftsmen.

Opening Times: Apr to Sep Mon to Sat 10:00-17:00. Closed Sun. Admission: Adult £2.00, Child £1.00, OAP/Concession £1.50.   Location: Just off the A39 in Camelford at southern end of town, opposite free car park.   Map Ref: 5

Falmouth Art Gallery

Muncipal Buildings, The Moor, Falmouth TR11 2RT   Tel: 01326 313863   Fax: 01326 318608   Email: info@falmouthartgallery.com   Web: www.falmouthartgallery.com

Falmouth Art Gallery is one of the leading art galleries in the South West. Its permanent collection features works by major British artists including Sir Frank Brangwyn, Sir Edward Coley Burne-Jones, Sir Alfred Munnings, Henry Scott Tuke and Dame Laura Knight. The gallery's most famous work is 'The Lady of Shallot' by John William Waterhouse, which is known throughout the world. The gallery also puts on a varied temporary exhibitions programme, showing major one person shows, touring and mixed themed exhibitions.

John T Richardson, The Bar Pool, Falmouth signed and dated 1912, oil on canvas

Opening Times: Mon to Sat 10:00-17:00.Admission: Free.
Location: On the Moor, above the library Exhibitions &
Events 2003 : Please telephone for details.   Map Ref: 6

National Maritime Museum Cornwall

Discovery Quay, Falmouth TR11 3QY   Tel: 01326 313388   Fax: 01326 317878   Email: enquiries@nmmc.co.uk   Web: www.nmmc.co.uk

Opened in 2002, National Maritime Museum Cornwall is a brand new state-of-the-art museum set in a landmark new building on Falmouth's waterfront. It offers you an outstanding experience whatever your age or interest. Enjoy a wide range of interactive displays and demonstrations, explore Cornwall's unique maritime heritage and discover an unrivalled range of boats - including many in active use on the water.

Opening Times: Wed to Sun until Feb, then daily.
Summer 10:00-18:00, Winter 10:00-17:00.

The Landmark Museum on the waterfront

Admission: Adult £5.90, Child/OAP £3.90, Family £15.50.
Location: On Waterfront, near town centre, five minutes walk from train station.   Map Ref: 6

Pendennis Castle

Falmouth TR11 4LP   Tel: 01326 316594

Pendennis Castle formed part of a chain of castles built by Henry VIII along the south coast as protection against attack from France. Pendennis has been adapted over the years to meet changing defence requirements. The collection provides a survey of coastal defence cannon from the 18th to 20th centuries.

Opening Times: Apr to Sep daily 10:00-18:00, Oct daily 10:00-17:00, Nov to Mar daily 10:00-16:00. Closed Xmas & New Year. Admission: Adult £4.20, Child £2.10, Concession £3.20.
Location: On Pendennis Head, Cornwall, one mile south east of Falmouth.   Map Ref: 6

Cornwall & Isles of Scilly

Poldark Mine & Heritage Complex

Poldark Mine, Wendron, Helston TR13 0ER   Tel: 01326 573173   Fax: 01326 563166

18th century tin mine and museum explaining early tin recovery and the fascinating story of the Cornish overseas. Set in attractive surroundings complete with craft workshops and family entertainments.

Opening Times: Easter to 1 Nov daily 10:00-18:00, last mine tour 16:00.   Admission: Site: Free, Tour: Adult £5.75, Child £3.75, Family £15.50.   Location: Two miles from Helston on the B3297.   Map Ref: 7

Isles of Scilly Museum

Church Street, St Mary's, Isles of Scilly TR21 0JT   Tel / Fax: 01720 422337
Email: info@iosmuseum.org   Web: www.iosmuseum.org

Collections feature local history and archaeology, particularly ships and the sea. Extensive exhibitions on shipwrecks, birds and local flora. Exhibitions on special topics during summer.

Opening Times: Easter to Oct daily 10:00-16:30. Also 19:30-21:00 (weekdays) Whitsun to Sep. Winter Mon to Sat 10:00-12:00.   Admission: Adult £2.00, Child 50p, OAP £1.00.   Location: In Church Street, Hugh Town ten minute walk from harbour.   Map Ref: 8

Daphne Du Maurier's Smugglers at Jamaica Inn

Jamaica Inn Courtyard, Bolventor, Launceston PL15 7TS   Tel: 01566 86025

Tableaux in light and sound from the book 'Jamaica Inn.' Some history of the Du Maurier family and smuggling history, ancient and modern.

Opening Times: Easter to Oct daily 10:00-17:00, high season 10:00-19:00.   Admission: Adult £2.50, Child/OAP £2.00. Group rates available.   Location: In the village of Bolventor. Half way between Launceston and Bodmin, short distance from A30.   Map Ref: 9

Potters Museum of Curiosity

Jamaica Inn Courtyard, Bolventor, Launceston PL15 7TS   Tel / Fax: 01566 86838
Email: jamaicainn@eclipce.co.uk   Web: www.pottersjamaicainn.com

Unique collection, established in 1861 by founder Walter Potter, of Victorian taxidermy and weird and wonderful curiosities from all over the world, includes weapons, toys, fossils, smoking memorabilia, etc.

Opening Times: Daily Nov, Dec, Feb & Mar 11:00-16:00, Apr to Jun & Sep 10:00-17:00, Jul & Aug 10:00-19:00.   Admission: Adult £2.50, Child/OAP £2.00, Family £6.95, Groups £1.50. Location: Just off A30, halfway between Launceston and Bodmin.   Map Ref: 9

John Southern Wildlife Art Gallery

Dobwalls, Liskeard PL14 6HB   Tel: 01579 320325   Fax: 01579 321345

Original watercolours and limited edition prints by Steven Townsend - Artist of the Year 1999. Also the largest and most comprehensive permanent display of limited edition prints by Carl Brenders in the UK, supported by the work of Robert Bateman, Antony Gibbs, Matthew Hillier, Terry Isaac and Daniel Smith.

Opening Times: Daily 10:30-16:00. Closed Xmas & New Year.   Admission: Free.   Location: Adjacent to Dobwalls Adventure Park.   Map Ref: 10

Cornwall & Isles of Scilly

LOOE

The Old Guildhall Museum ♿ ⚫

c/o The East Looe Town Trust, The Guildhall, Fore Street, East Looe PL13 1BP   Tel: 01503 263709   Fax: 01503 265674

The museum is housed in a 15th century listed building which retains the old magistrates benches, cells and stocks. Models of boats, local history, smuggling, lifeboat logs, fishing, minerals and porcelain.

Opening Times: Easter week, then Sun to Fri 11:30-16:30 end of May to Sep including BH Sat.   Admission: Adult £1.50, Child 50p. Special rates for school parties.   Location: Near town centre and the beach.   Map Ref: 11

MEVAGISSEY

Mevagissey Folk Museum ⚫

East Quay, Mevagissey PL26 6PP   Tel: 01726 843568   Email: ronforder@talk21.com

Located in an 18th century boat builders (1745) with the original lath insitu. Three floors of artefacts, with an excellent display of photos taken throughout the last century. Also on display are larger exhibits such as the apple crusher the cider press and a Cornish kitchen complete with clome oven. Twice voted one of the best small museums in Cornwall.

Opening Times: Good Friday to end Oct Mon to Fri 11:00-17:00, Sat & Sun 10:00-13:00. Admission: Adult £1.00, Child 50p. Location: Town Quay.   Map Ref: 12

PADSTOW

Prideaux Place

Padstow PL28 8RP   Tel: 01841 532411   Fax: 01841 532945   Email: office@prideauxplace.fsnet.co.uk

Beautiful Home of the Prideauz-Brune family for over 400 years. Surrounding by gardens, wooded grounds and overlooking the deer park. An international film and television location in recent years.

Opening Times: 20 to 24 Apr & 11 May to 9 Oct Sun to Thu. Grounds & Tearoom: 12:30-17:00.   House: 13:30-16:00.   Admission: House & Grounds: Adult £6.00, Child £2.00. Grounds: Adult £2.00, Child £1.00.   Location: Just off main B3276 Padstow to Newquay Road.   Map Ref: 13

PENZANCE

Geevor Tin Mine

Pendeen, Penzance TR19 7EW   Tel: 01736 788662   Fax: 01736 786059   Email: pch@geevor.com   Web: www.geevor.com

Mining museum, largest preserved mining site in UK. Guided underground tour, spectacular coastal setting. Support for educational/study groups.

Opening Times: Apr to Sep 09:00-17:00, Nov to Feb 09:00-16:00. Closed Sat (unless a BH) & Sun in winter season.   Admission: Adult £6.00, Student £3.50, OAP £5.50, Family £16.00.   Location: In Pendeen, on B3066 road from St Ives to Lands End, six miles from Penzance (bus/railway station).   Map Ref: 14

Museum of Submarine Telegraphy

Porthcurno, Penzance TR19 6JX   Tel / Fax: 01736 810966

The submarine cable that landed on Porthcurno beach in 1870 was the start of a world spanning telegraph system that led to Porthcurno becoming the largest cable station in the world.

Opening Times: 25 Mar to 3 Nov Sun to Fri & BH Sat 10:00-17:00, Jul & Aug Sun to Sat 10:00-17:00. Jan to Mar & Nov to Dec Sun & Mon 10:00-16:00. Closed Xmas & New Year.   Admission: Adult £4.00, Concession £3.50, Student £2.50, Family £10.50.   Location: At Porthcurno, take A30 from Penzance towards Land's End.   Map Ref: 15

Newlyn Art Gallery

New Road, Newlyn, Penzance TR18 5PZ   Tel: 01736 363715   Fax: 01736 331578   Email: newlyn@newlynartgallery.freeserve.co.uk
Web: www.newlynartgallery.co.uk

Newlyn Art Gallery showing the Newlyn Society of Artists Critic's Choice - 2001

Newlyn Art Gallery is one of the South West's leading contemporary art organisations, showing work by local, national and international artists. As an educational charity the gallery's education programme encourages a better understanding and enjoyment of the work on show. The programme includes talks, discussion sessions, workshops and projects for the widest cross section of the community as possible.

Opening Times: Mon to Sat 10:00-17:00 (including BH).
Admission: Free.   Map Ref: 16

Pendeen Lighthouse

Pendeen, Penzance TR19 7ED   Tel: 01736 788418   Fax: 01736 786059

Built in 1900, this dramatically positioned lighthouse is open with its Engine Room containing the last surviving 12 inch siren in England.

Opening Times: 29 Mar to 4 Apr, 3 to 9 May, 26 to 31 May, Jul & Aug Sun to Sat 11:00-17:00.
Admission: Adult £2.00, Concession £1.50, Student £1.00, Family £5.00.   Location: Signed
from B3306 St Just to St Ives road in Pendeen village.   Map Ref: 14

Penlee House Gallery & Museum

PENLEE HOUSE
Gallery & Museum

Penlee Park, Morrab Road, Penzance TR18 4HE   Tel: 01736 363625
Fax: 01736 361312   Email: info@penlee-house.demon.co.uk   Web: www.penleehouse.org.uk

Penlee House Gallery & Museum, Penzance, is an elegant gallery set within a Victorian house and park. Changing exhibitions mainly feature famous 'Newlyn School' artists (1880-1930), including Stanhope and Elizabeth Forbes, Walter Langley, Harold Harvey and 'Lamorna' Birch. The museum features 5,000 years of the history of Penwith. There is an excellent café and shop.

Opening Times: May to Sep Mon to Sat 10:00-17:00, Oct to Apr Mon to Sat 10:30-16:30. Admission: Adult £2.00, Child Free, Concession £1.00. Location: Situated in
Penlee Park, a short walk from town centre and seafront.   Map Ref: 16

The Pilchard Works

Tolcarne, Newlyn, Penzance TR18 5QH   Tel: 01736 332112   Fax: 01736 332442
Email: nick@pilchardworks.co.uk   Web: www.pilchardworks.co.uk

Text, photographs and artefacts combine in this 'working museum'. Sole producers of salted, pressed pilchards using traditional methods. Visitors can taste the product, draw their own stencils and talk to production staff.

Opening Times: Apr to Oct Mon to Fri 10:00-18:00. Last admission 17:00. Admission: Adult
£3.25, Child £1.95, OAP £2.95, Family £10.00. Location: 50 yards upstream from Newlyn
Bridge.   Map Ref: 16

Trinity House National Lighthouse Centre

The Former Buoy Store, Wharf Road, Penzance TR18 4BN   Tel: 01736 360077

The job of lighthouse keeper has gone, but items once found in daily use including lamps, clocks, engines, uniforms, fog signals, furniture and some major optics removed from lighthouses, form this collection.

Opening Times: Apr to Oct daily 10:30-16:30. Admission: Adult £3.00, Child £1.00,
OAP/Student £2.00, Family £6.00. Location: Penzance Harbourside - five minute walk from
main car parks.   Map Ref: 16

Cornwall & Isles of Scilly

Camborne School of Mines Geological Museum & Art Gallery

University of Exeter, Redruth TR15 3SE Tel: 01209 714866 Fax: 01209 716977
Email: scamm@csm.ex.ac.uk Web: www.geo-server.ex.ac.uk

The museum features an extensive collection of rocks which is continuously updated by international geological research at CSM. There are also displays on the history and future of mining in Cornwall.

Opening Times: Mon to Fri 10:00-16:00. Admission: Free. Location: Next to Camborne Pool, Redruth College, 20 minutes walk from Camborne or Redruth station. Map Ref: 17

Cornish Mines & Engines & Cornwall Industrial Discovery Centre

Poo1, Redruth TR15 3NP Tel / Fax: 01209 315027

The gateway to Cornwall's industrial past: including the Discovery Centre with a stunning audio visual presentation; Taylor's 1892 90' single cylinder pumping engine; Michell's 1887 winding or 'whim' engine.

Opening Times: Jan to Mar Fri 11:00-16:00, 25 Mar to 3 Nov Sun To Fri 11:00-17:00, Aug Sun to Sat 11:00-17:00, Nov to Mar by arrangement (01209 210900). Admission: Adult £5.00, Concession £4.60, Student £3.00, Family £13.00. Location: At Pool, two miles west of Redruth on both sides of A3047. Map Ref: 17

Tolgus Tin

c/o Cornish Gold Site, Portreath Road, Redruth TR16 4HN Tel: 01209 215185 Fax: 01209 219786

One of two tin streaming works in Cornwall, contains Cornish stamps driven by waterwheel and one of the last round frames.

Opening Times: Jan to Mar Sun 10:30-16:00, Mon to Wed 09:30-17:00. Apr to Oct Sun & BH Sat 10:30-16:00, Mon to Fri 09:30-17:00. Nov to Mar Sun to Wed 10:00-16:00.
Admission: Adult £2.25, Concession £1.75, Student £1.50, Family £6.50. Location: From A30 take B3300 to Portreath. On the site of the Cornish Goldcentre. Map Ref: 18

Cornwall's Museum of The Clay Country

Carthew, Wheal Martyn, St Austell PL26 8XG Tel / Fax: 01726 850362

26 acre museum of the china clay industry. Comprises industrial and social history items. Photographic collections. Features two water wheels, sand and mica drags, settling pits, pan kiln, transport etc.

Opening Times: Apr to Oct daily 10:00-17:00, Nov to Mar daily 11:00-16:00. Admission: Adult £5.00, Child £3.00, OAP £4.00, Family £13.00. Group rates available. Location: Two miles north of St Austell B3274. Map Ref: 19

Key to Classifications

see Classifications Index on page 413

Anthropology	Jewellery	Railway
Archaeological	Literature & Libraries	Religion
Art Galleries	Maritime	Roman
Arts, Crafts & Textiles	Military & Defence	Science - Earth
China, Glass & Ceramics	Mills - Water & Wind	& Planetary
Communications	Multicultural	Sculpture
Egyptian	Music & Theatre	Sporting History
Fashion	Natural History	Stately Homes
Geology	Oriental	Toy & Childhood
Health & Medicine	Palaces	Transport
Horticultural	Police, Prisons & Dungeons	Victoriana

ST AUSTELL *(continued)*

Eden Project

Bodelva, St Austell PL24 2SG Tel: 01726 811900 Fax: 01726 811912
Web: www.edenproject.com

An unforgettable experience in a breathtaking epic location. Eden is a gateway into the fascinating world of plants and people and a vibrant reminder of how we need each other for our mutual survival. Its home is a dramatic global garden the size of thirty football pitches, nestling like a lost world in a crater overlooking St Austell Bay. One of its giant conservatories is a majestic rainforest cathedral, the other is host to the fruits of the Mediterranean and the flowers of South Africa and California. Outside in the landscaped grounds you will find tea and lavender, sunflowers and hemp. It is a place to tell a hundred plant stories from cocoa and coffee to bananas and rubber. From plants and medicine to plants in construction, from paper and wine and from perfume to brewing. Wherever you are in the world you will instantly recognise this spectacular place with its stunning architecture and breathtaking living plant collection as the Eden Project, Cornwall, UK.

Opening Times: 31 Mar to 2 Nov 10:00-18:00 (last entry 5pm), 4 Nov to 30 Mar 10:00-16:30 (last entry 3pm). Closed 24-25 Dec. Admission: Adult £9.80, Child £4.00, OAP £7.50, Family £23.00. Location: Near St Austell. Follow brown tourism signs from A390, A30 and A391. Exhibitions & Events 2003 : Please check website for details.   Map Ref: 20

ST IVES

Penwith Galleries

Back Road West, St Ives TR26 1NL Tel: 01736 795579

Mixed exhibitions and one man shows all year.

Opening Times: Tue to Sat 10:00-13:00 14:30-17:00. Admission: Adult 50p. Location: Near town centre.   Map Ref: 21

St Ives Museum

Wheal Dream, St Ives TR26 1PR Tel: 01736 796005

A 'real' museum, in which every facet of St Ives' fascinating history is represented in its many collections, from which old and young can glean and learn of the past. These include: art, blacksmith, boat building, Cornish kitchen, crysede, farming, fire brigade, fishing, geology, Hain Steamship Company, lifeboat, lighthouses, mining, photographs, police, railway, shipwrecks, toys, Victorian clothes, wartime memorabilia.

Opening Times: 14 Apr to 1 Nov, Mon to Fri 10:00-17:00, Sat 10:00-16:00. Closed Sun & Good Friday. Location: Near harbour quay.   Map Ref: 21

St Ives Society of Artists

Norway Gallery, Old Mariners Church, Norway Sq, St Ives TR26 1NA Tel: 01736 795582
Email: gallery@stivessocietyofartists.com Web: www.stivessocietyofartists.com

Art works in this gallery are largely traditional and representational. Members submit new work each year for inclusion in the Exhibition. Paintings sold are replaced by others, therefore the Exhibition is continuous but changing.

Opening Times: Mid Mar to early Nov Mon to Sat & BH Sun 10:00-16:30. Admission: Adult 25p, Child Free. Location: Close to harbour - behind The Sloop Inn car park. In the Old Mariners Church.   Map Ref: 21

| Guided or Private Tours | Disabled Access | Gift Shop or Sales Point | Café or Refreshments | Restaurant | Car Parking |

Cornwall & Isles of Scilly

Tate St Ives

St IVES

Porthmeor Beach, St Ives TR26 1TG   Tel: 01736 796226   Fax: 01736 794480   Web: www.tate.org.uk

Alfred Wallis, The Blue Ship c. 1934

Tate St Ives opened in 1993 and offers a unique introduction to modern art, where paintings and sculpture can be seen in the surroundings which inspired many of them. The gallery presents changing displays from the Tate Collection focusing on the post-war modern movement for which St Ives is famous, there are also major exhibitions of work by contemporary artists. Tate St Ives also manages the Barbara Hepworth Museum and Sculpture Garden in St Ives, which offers a remarkable insight into the work and outlook of one of Britain's most important 20th century sculptors.

Opening Times: Mar to Oct daily 10:00-17:30, Nov to Feb Tue to Sun 10:00-16:30. Admission: Adult £4.25, Child Free, Concession £2.50, OAP Free.
Location: Situated by Porthmeor Beach close to town centre. Exhibitions & Events 2003 : To 26 Jan: Real Life - Video installations by Susan Hiller, Steve McQueen, Gillian Weaving, Tracey Emin, Gilbert & George, Sam Taylor Wood and Mark Wallinger, 8 Feb to 11 May: Painting not Painting - Terry Frost, Jim Lambie, Victoria Morton, Julie Roberts and Richard Slee, 8 Feb to 25 Jan 04: Pier Art Centre Collection at Tate St Ives, 24 May to 12 Oct: Barbara Hepworth Centenary Exhibition.

Barbara Hepworth, Sea Form (Porthmeor) 1958

Map Ref: 22

Mount Edgcumbe House & Country Park

Mount Edgcumbe House, Cremyll, Torpoint PL10 1HZ   Tel: 01752 822236

Mount Edgcumbe House, Cornwall

Sir Richard Edgcumbe of Cotehele built a new home in his deer park at Mount Edgcumbe in 1547-53. It is now beautifully furnished with family possessions, including paintings by Sir Joshua Reynolds, Gerard Edema and William van der Velde, Irish bronze age horns, 16th century tapestries and 18th century Chinese and Plymouth porcelain. Exhibitions include April to June - Lenckewicz prints. August to September Robin Armstrong Wildlife Artist.

Opening Times: 29 Mar to 29 Sep Wed to Sun & BH 11:00-16:30. Admission: Adult £4.50, Child £2.25, Concession £3.50. Group advanced booking (min 10) £3.50. Location: Across the river from Plymouth by passenger ferry (10 mins). By car - Torpoint Ferry or Tamar Bridge (A374, B3247 follow brown signs).

Map Ref: 23

Royal Cornwall Museum

River Street, Truro TR1 2SJ   Tel: 01872 272205   Fax: 01872 240514   Email: enquiries@royal-cornwall-museum.freeserve.co.uk   Web: www.royalcornwallmuseum.org.uk

Nationally important collection of Cornish minerals, Cornish archaeology and local history, paintings, ceramics, Greek, Roman and Egyptian archaeology, and a regular temporary exhibition progamme. Many activities for children and families, especially in holidays.

Opening Times: Mon to Sat 10:00-17:00, closed Sun and BH. Admission: Adult £4.00, Child free, OAP/Student £2.50. Location: Near town centre on A390 past the railway station. Exhibitions & Events 2003 : To 1 Mar: Peter Freeman, 8 Mar to 10 May: John Hedgecoe, 24 May to 12 Jul: Ray Exworth, Jul to Sep: Summer Exhibition for families - phone for details, 27 Sep to 22 Nov: Monet & Daubigny on tour from the National Gallery.

Map Ref: 24

Cumbria

To many, Cumbria is synonymous with the Lake District, with its amazing variety of scenery contained within a relatively small area. South Cumbria, sandwiched between the Lake District and the Yorkshire Dales has its history recorded in the art and literature of William Turner and John Ruskin. On the west coast a succession of ports once exported coal and in the north the county town, Carlisle, stands guard over the flat lands leading to the Scottish boarder, its castle for centuries a bastion against the marauding Scots.

Cumbria lays claim to some outstanding museums including collections of its literary, artistic, boating and military history.

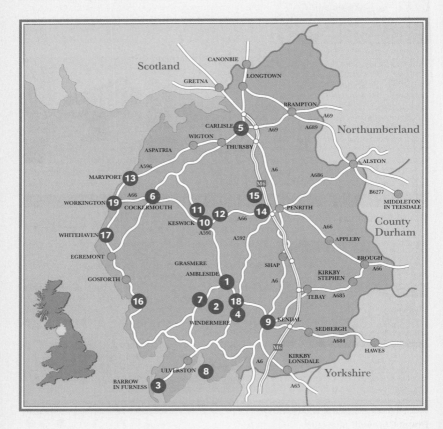

The Red Map References should be used to locate Museums etc on the pages that follow

Cumbria

Armitt Library & Museum of Ambleside

Rydal Road, Ambleside LA22 9BL   Tel: 015394 31212   Fax: 015394 31313
Email: mail@armitttrust.fsbusiness.co.uk   Web: www.armitt.com

2000 years of local history from Romans to Beatrix Potter's watercolours. Hands-on activities for all the family.

Opening Times: Daily 10:00-17:00. Closed Xmas & Boxing Day.   Admission: Adult £2.50, Concession £1.80, Family £5.60.   Location: Two mins from Tourist Information Centre.
Map Ref: 1

Beatrix Potter Gallery

THE NATIONAL TRUST

Main Street, Hawkshead, Ambleside LA22 0NS   Tel: 01534 36355
Fax: 01534 36187   Email: rhabpg@smtp.ntrust.org.uk   Web: www.nationaltrust.org.uk

A unique collection of Beatrix Potter's work. The gallery has the largest collection of her published work, including most of the original watercolour illustrations and manuscripts from the 'Peter Rabbit' series of little books. Annually, a selection of Potter's work is displayed in the gallery, which were formerly the offices of her husband's solicitors' practice and is set within the picturesque village of Hawkshead.

Opening Times: 29 Mar to 29 Oct Sat to Wed 10:30-16:00.   Admission: Adult £3.00, Child £1.50, Family £7.50.   Location: Main Street - Hawkshead, close to car park.   Map Ref: 2

Beatrix Potter Gallery

Hill Top

Near Sawrey, Hawkshead, Ambleside LA22 0LF   Tel: 015394 36269   Fax: 015394 36811
Email: rpmht@smtp.ntrust.org.uk   Web: www.nationaltrust.org.uk

Beatrix Potter wrote many of her famous children's stories in this little 17th century house and it has been kept exactly as she left it, complete with her furniture and china.

Opening Times: 29 Mar to 29 Oct daily except Thur & Fri (open Good Friday). Please phone to check times.   Admission: Adult £4.50, Child £1.00, Family £10.00.   Location: Two miles south of Hawkshead, in hamlet of Near Sawrey, behind the Tower Bank Arms.   Map Ref: 2

The Dock Museum

North Road, Barrow-in-Furness LA14 2PW   Tel: 01229 894444   Fax: 01229 811361
Email: rlitten@barrowbc.gov.uk   Web: www.dockmuseum.org.uk

Spectacular new permanent exhibition 'Shipbuilders To The World'; fine collection of ship models, social and industrial history and fine art gallery. The waterfront site has an adventure playground and walkways linked to Cumbria's Coastal Way.

Opening Times: Apr to Oct Tue to Fri 10:00-17:00, Sat & Sun 11:00-17:00. Nov to Mar Wed to Fri 10:30-16:00, Sat & Sun 11:00-16:30.   Admission: Free.   Location: One mile from town centre. 15 minute walk from railway station.   Exhibitions & Events 2003 :   12 Apr to 7 May: Blitz: Barrow at War, 14 Jun to 27 Aug: Work by the fantasy artist Anne Sudworth, 4 Oct to 4 Jan: Dive: The

The Dock Museum has a fully landscaped waterfront site

Best of British Submarines.   Map Ref: 3

Furness Abbey

Barrow-in-Furness LA13 0TJ   Tel: 01229 823420

Furness Abbey was once the richest Cistercian abbey in England. The remains of the earlier monastery can still be seen. The museum contains an exhibition and a wealth of stonework from the abbey.

Opening Times: Apr to Sep daily 10:00-18:00, Oct daily 10:00-17:00, Nov to Mar daily 10:00-16:00. Closed Xmas & New Year.   Admission: Adult £3.20, Child £1.60, Concession £2.40.   Location: One and a half miles north of Barrow-in-Furness, on minor road off A590.   Map Ref: 3

Cumbria

Blackwell - The Arts & Crafts House

Bowness-on-Windermere LA23 3JR Tel: 015394 46139 Fax: 015394 88486
Email: info@blackwell.org.uk Web: www.blackwell.org.uk

Designed by MH Baillie Scott as a holiday home, Blackwell has survived intact with many original details - stained glass windows, carved oak panelling, iron work, stone carving and decorative plasterwork. Changing exhibitions.

Opening Times: Feb to Dec daily 10:00-17:00. Winter closing 16:00. Admission: Adult £4.50, Child £2.50, Family £12.00. Location: On B5360, one and a half miles south of Bowness-on-Windermere.   Map Ref: 4

Carlisle Cathedral Treasury Museum

Carlisle Cathedral, Castle Street, Carlisle CA3 8TZ Tel: 01228 548151 Fax: 01228 547049
Email: office@carlislecathedral.org.uk Web: www.carlislecathedral.org.uk

A display of Cathedral and Diocesan silver and treasures, illustrating the story of Christians in Cumbria through the centuries.

Opening Times: Daily 08:30-16:30. Admission: Donation of £1.00. Location: In town centre, ten minutes walk from main railway station and bus station.   Map Ref: 5

Guildhall Museum

Greenmarket, Carlisle Tel: 01228 534781 Fax: 01228 810249
Email: enquiries@tullie-house.co.uk Web: www.tulliehouse.co.uk

The Guildhall is a half-timbered house on the corner of the Greenmarket and Fisher Street. It was given to the city by Richard De Redeness and was long used as the meeting place of the town's eight medieval Trade Guilds. Four of the Guilds survive today and continue to meet annually in the building on Ascension Day.

Opening Times: Apr to Oct Tue to Sun 12:00-16:30. Closed Mon except BH. Admission: Free. Location: Located in the city's pedestrianised area at the southern end of Fisher Street, close to Carlisle Visitor Centre.   Map Ref: 5

Guildhall Museum

Museum of the Border Regiment
& Kings Own Royal Border Regiment

Queen Marys Tower, The Castle, Carlisle CA3 8UR Tel: 01228 532774
Fax: 01228 521275 Email: RHQ@kingsownborder.demon.co.uk
Web: www.armymuseums.org.uk

The Museum relates the history of Cumbria's County Infantry Regiment, local Militia and Volunteer units from 1702 to the present day and is located in Carlisle Castle, a superb medieval fortress founded in 1092, which has been the home of the Regiment since 1873. The displays on two floors include uniforms, weapons, equipment, medals, silver, pictures, memorabilia and much more.

Opening Times: Apr to Sep Mon to Sun 09:30-18:00, Oct Mon to Sun 10:00-17:00, Nov to Mar Mon to Sun 10:00-16:00. Closed Xmas & New Year. Admission: Included in entry charge to castle - Adult £3.40, Child £1.70, Concession £2.60. Location: North side of city centre, ten minutes from railway station. Adjacent car park Devonshire Walk on the west side of the Castle, disabled parking in the Castle.   Map Ref: 5

Gateway, Carlisle Castle c.1835

	&#9855;	&#9632;	&#9971;		&#128667;
Guided or Private Tours	Disabled Access	Gift Shop or Sales Point	Café or Refreshments	Restaurant	Car Parking

CARLISLE (continued)

Tullie House Museum & Art Gallery

Railway Area, Border Gallery

Castle Street, Carlisle CA3 8TP   Tel: 01228 534781   Fax: 01228 810249
Email: enquiries@tullie-house.co.uk   Web: www.tulliehouse.co.uk

The Bishops Stone,
Border Reiver Pathway

Tullie House combines the features of historic house and modern Museum. Old Tullie House is a 17th century town house of character, with a fine classical façade overlooking a herb garden. Inside are some early features - including Jacobean staircase and panelled Drawing Room. The latter displays key artworks by the Pre-Raphaelites; other rooms feature portraits and fine paintings and a childhood gallery. The modern Border Galleries show Carlisle's exciting history and wildlife. There is a wealth of objects from prehistoric and Roman times (complete with reconstruction of Hadrian's Wall). Inter-actives include Roman writing and artillery. The spectacular Reivers audio-visual presentation brings to life the lawless Borders of the Middle Ages; the railway story is told by the 'station announcer'. Local wildlife - complete with badger sett - is seen under a domed ceiling with changing light and sound. The New Rotunda viewing platform affords striking views of Carlisle Castle and opened in 2001 with the excitingly different Millennium Gallery. This celebrates unique aspects of Carlisle's collections and includes a stunning display of minerals from Cumbria/N Pennines, set on cast glass; rare archaeology (with transforming 'Peppers Ghost' interactive); local paintings and costume. The walls feature Carlisle building styles and also tell stories.

Opening Times: Nov to Mar Mon to Sat 10:00-16:00, Sun 12:00-16:00. Apr to Oct Mon to Sat 10:00-17:00, Sun 12:00-17:00 Closed Xmas. Admission: Adult £5.00, Child £2.50, Concession £3.50, Family £14.00. Exhibitions & Events 2003 : 9 Nov to 5 Jan: Georgina Follett - acclaimed jeweller, 11 Jan to 16 Mar: Picturesque - contemporary artists exploring landscape, 22 Mar to 18 May: Air Guitar, 17 May to 14 Sep: 1980s Show, 24 May to 13 Jul: Paul Scott, 19 Jul to 27 Sep: Aspects of Childhood, 4 Oct to 16 Nov: Blue Streak and Landscape Photographs, 19 Oct to 5 May: The Hills are Alive (Cumbrian mountain wildlife), 22 Nov to 17 Jan: Northern Potters.   Map Ref: 5

COCKERMOUTH

Cumberland Toy & Model Museum

Banks Court, Market Place, Cockermouth CA13 9NG   Tel: 01900 827606
Email: rod@toymuseum.co.uk   Web: www.toymuseum.co.uk

This national award winning museum has many visitor operated exhibits including Hornby Trains, Scalextric Cars and Lego. Come and re-live your childhood.

Opening Times: Feb to Nov 10:00-17:00. Dec to Jan times vary, please phone.
Admission: Adult £3.00, Child £1.50, OAP £2.60, Group rates for parties of 10+.
Location: Market Place. Follow signs from car parks.   Map Ref: 6

CONISTON

Brantwood

Coniston LA21 8AD   Tel: 015394 41396   Fax: 015394 41263
Email: enquiries@brantwood.org.uk   Web: www.brantwood.org.uk

The former home of John Ruskin, Brantwood presents and explores the various themes that interested him throughout his life - art, the environment, geology, architecture and society.

Opening Times: Mid Mar to mid Nov daily 11:00-17:30, mid Nov to mid Mar Wed to Sun 11:00-16:30. Admission: Adult £4.50, Child £1.00, Student £3.00, Family £10.00. Garden only £2.00.
Location: On the east side of Coniston Water, two and a half miles from the village of Coniston.   Map Ref: 7

Cumbria

The Ruskin Museum

Yewdale Road, Coniston LA21 8DU   Tel: 015394 41164   Fax: 015394 41132
Email: vmj@ruskinmuseum.com   Web: www.ruskinmuseum.com

Sunset at Herne Hill through the smoke of London, 1886, watercolour John Ruskin

The Ruskin Museum, Coniston's award-winning 'cabinet of curiosities' introduces a local story as old as the hills which copper-bottomed the fleet and slate-roofed the world; celebrates the life, art and radical ideas of John Ruskin, 'one of those rare men who think with their hearts'; honours heroic Speed Ace Donald Campbell and Bluebird.

Opening Times: Easter/1 Apr to Oct daily 10:00-17:30, Nov to Mar Wed to Sun 10:30-15:30. Admission: Adult £3.50, Child £1.75, Family £9.00. Group rates available. Location: Near village centre, on Yewdale Road, three minute walk from main car park and Tourist Information

Centre.   Exhibitions & Events 2003 : 12/13 Apr, 7/8 May, 14/15 Jun, 10/11 Sep, 11/12 Oct: Each two-day, non-residential, practical courses - How to Make Ruskin Lace - taught by world expert, Elizabeth Prickett. Please phone for details   Map Ref: 7

Holker Hall

Cark-in-Cartmel, Grange-over-Sands LA11 7PL   Tel: 015395 58328   Fax: 015395 58378
Email: publicopening@holker.co.uk   Web: www.holkerhall.co.uk

Discover the beauty and elegance of Holker Hall without the confines of ropes or barriers to restrict your viewing. Relax in 25 acres of National Award Winning Garden. Stroll through the formal gardens and thrill at the unique and rare treasures they offer. Treat yourself to a special lunch or afternoon tea in the Courtyard Café or picnic in the grounds. Children will delight at the adventure playground. Plants from our nursery, unique gifts and specialty products all hand selected by Lady Cavendish are available in our gift shop.

Opening Times: 25 Mar to 2 Nov 10:00-18:00, last admission 16:30. Admission: Adult £8.75. Child £5.00, £25.75. Location: Follow brown tourism signs from A590 from Barrow or junction 36 of M6. Exhibitions & Events 2003 : 30 May to 1 Jun: Holker Garden Festival, 5 Jul: Shakespeare's Romeo & Juliet, Aug: Lakeland Motor Museum 25th Anniversary, 29 Aug: Opera, Barbara of Saville, 30 Aug: Gala on Impressario.   Map Ref: 8

Lakeland Motor Museum

Holker Hall and Gardens, Cark-in-Cartmel, Grange-over-Sands LA11 7PL   Tel / Fax: 015395 58509

A nostalgic reminder of transport and horticultural bygones appealing to all ages and offering a truly astonishing insight into our forefathers' inventiveness and dexterity. Over 20,000 exhibits including The Campbell Legend Bluebird Exhibition.

Opening Times: Easter to end Oct Sun to Fri 10:30-16:45. Admission: Motor museum and gardens: Adult £7.50, Child £4.50. Location: On B5278 near Grange-over-Sands.   Map Ref: 8

Abbot Hall Art Gallery

Abbot Hall, Kendal LA9 5AL   Tel: 01539 722464   Fax: 01539 722494
Email: info@abbothall.org.uk   Web: www.abbothall.org.uk

A fine Georgian house containing a growing collection of modern art. The ground floor rooms contain furniture by Gillows of Lancaster and painting by Kendal born artist George Romney. Changing exhibitions.

Opening Times: Feb to Dec Mon to Sat 10:30-17:00. Winter closing 16:00. Location: Junction 36 of M6, Kendal is ten minutes drive. Nearest station: Oxenholme.   Map Ref: 9

Cumbria

Kendal Museum

Station Road, Kendal LA9 6BT   Tel: 01539 721374   Fax: 01539 737976
Email: info@kendalmuseum.org.uk   Web: www.kendalmuseum.org.uk

Displays of archaeology and natural history, both local and global. With examples of lakeland flora and fauna, the museum charts developments from pre-historic times through Roman, Medieval and Victorian and into the 21st century.

Opening Times: Feb to Dec Mon to Sat 10:30-17:00. Winter closing 16:00.   Location: Junction 36 on M6, ten minutes drive. Nearest station: Kendal.   Map Ref: 9

Levens Hall

Kendal LA8 0PD   Tel: 015395 60321   Fax: 015395 60669
Email: email@levenshall.fsnet.co.uk   Web: www.levenshall.co.uk

Levens Hall is an Elizabethan mansion, home of the Bapot family, containing fine panelling, plasterwork and period furniture. World famous topiary gardens laid out by Monsieur Beaumont

Opening Times: Gardens: Sun to Thu 10:00-17:00, House: Sun to Thu 12:00-17:00. Closed Fri & Sat.   Map Ref: 9

Museum of Lakeland Life

Abbot Hall, Kendal LA9 5AL   Tel: 01539 722464   Fax: 01539 722494
Email: info@lakelandmuseum.org.uk   Web: www.lakelandmuseum.org.uk

Real objects and displays tell the story of Cumbria's history - from the age of 18th century yeoman farmers, through Georgian and Victorian periods and into living memory.

Opening Times: Feb to Dec daily 10:30-17:00. Winter closing 16:00.   Admission: Please phone for details.   Location: Junction 36 of M6, ten minutes drive to Kendal. Nearest station: Oxenholme.   Map Ref: 9

Cars of The Stars Motor Museum

Standish Street, Keswick CA12 5HH   Tel: 0176787 73757   Fax: 0176787 72090
Web: www.carsofthestars.com

This world famous museum features vehicles from television and film, including Chitty Chitty Bang Bang, Batmobiles, Herbie, A-Team van, Del Boy's yellow Reliant, FAB 1, Back to the Future, James Bond's Aston Martin and many more. A souvenir shop and famous autographs. Definitely not to be missed!

Opening Times: Easter to end Nov daily 10:00-17:00. Also open Feb half term and weekends in Dec. Admission: Adult £3.00, Child £2.00. Discount of 10% on parties of 20+.   Location: In town centre. 100 yards from car park, five minutes walk from bus station.   Map Ref: 10

Delorean - Back to the Future

Cumberland Pencil Museum

Southey Works, Greta Bridge, Keswick CA12 5NG   Tel: 017687 73626   Fax: 017687 74679
Email: museum@acco-uk.co.uk   Web: www.pencils.co.uk/

The pencil story; from the discovery of graphite to the present day method of pencil manufacture. Told through exhibitions and a video presentation. Including a techniques video, world's longest pencil, gift shop.

Opening Times: 09:30-16:00. Closed Xmas & New Year.   Admission: Adult £2.50, Child/OAP £1.25, Family £6.25.   Location: 300 yards west of town centre.   Map Ref: 10

Keswick Museum & Art Gallery

Fitz Park, Station Road, Keswick CA12 4NF   Tel: 017687 73263   Fax: 017687 80390
Email: keswick.museum@allerdale.gov.uk   Web: www.allerdale.gov.uk

Keswick's Victorian museum is full of surprises: the amazing musical stones played by Royal Command, the 500 year old cat and a stunning collection of crystals. Art exhibitions monthly.

Opening Times: 1 Apr to 31 Oct daily 10:00-16:00.   Admission: Adult £1.50, Child/Concession 50p, Groups 10% discount on 10 or more.   Location: In Fitz Park, on Station Road, five minutes walk from town centre, follow brown and white signs for 'Museum & Art Gallery'.   Map Ref: 10

Cumbria

Mirehouse

Underskiddaw, Keswick CA12 4QE   Tel / Fax: 017687 72287   Email: info@mirehouse.com
Web: www.mirehouse.com

Living family home which has passed by descent for three hundred years. Remarkable group of 19th century friendships illustrated by manuscripts and portraits: Tennyson, Wordsworth, Southey, Carlyle, Fitzgerald, Constable and Francis Bacon Collection from his biographer James Spedding.

Opening Times: Gardens & Tearoom: Apr to Oct daily 10:00-17:30. House: Apr to Oct Sun & Wed 14:00-17:00 (last entry 16:30), also Fri in Aug. Groups by appointment throughout year. Admission: Gardens & Lakeside Walk: Adult £2.00, Child £1.00. House & Gardens: Adult £4.00, Child £2.00.   Location: Three and a half miles north of Keswick on A591. Excellent rural bus service.   Map Ref: 11

Threlkeld Quarry & Mining Museum

Threlkeld Quarry, Threlkeld, Keswick CA12 4TT   Tel: 017687 79747
Email: coppermaid@aol.com   Web: www.golakes.co.uk   www.earthlines.com

The finest mining museum in the north of England - realistic mine tour of 45 minutes pure history and adventure. Excavators and locomotives, we have the 'lot'.

Opening Times: Mar to Oct daily 10:00-17:00.   Admission: Museum: Adult £2.50. Mine Tour: £3.00.   Location: Keswick - four miles on A66 Penrith/Keswick Road.   Map Ref: 12

Maryport Maritime Museum

1 Senhouse Street, Shipping Brow, Maryport CA15 6AB   Tel: 01900 813738

Comprehensive display on the maritime traditions of Maryport including the origins of the famous White Star Line.

Opening Times: Mon to Sat 10:00-13:00 & 14:00-16:30. Closed Sun.   Location: Listed building on the edge of harbour.   Map Ref: 13

The Senhouse Roman Museum

Sea Brows, Maryport CA15 6JD   Tel / Fax: 01900 816168
Email: romans@senhouse.freeserve.co.uk   Web: www.senhousemuseum.co.uk

The museum houses the Netherhall Collection, one of the largest collections of Roman altars from a single site in Britain. Many fine religious sculptures, including the mysterious 'Serpent Stone'.

Opening Times: Apr to end Jun Tue, Thu, Fri to Sun 10:00-17:00, Jul to end Oct daily 10:00-17:00. Nov to end Mar Fri to Sun 10:30-16:00.   Admission: Adult £2.50, Child 75p. Group rates available.   Location: Set on low lying cliffs overlooking Maryport harbour.   Map Ref: 13

Dalemain Historic House & Garden

Penrith CA11 0HB   Tel: 01768 486450   Fax: 01768 486223   Email: admin@dalemain.com
Web: www.dalemain.com

Mediaeval Tudor and Georgian house, home to Hasell family since 1679. Fascinating interiors, delightful gardens, rare plants, old fashioned roses, free parking, restaurant and tearoom, gift shop - plant sales.

Opening Times: 23 Mar to 13 Oct Sun to Thu. House: 11:00-16:00, Garden, Tearoom & Gift Shop: 10:30-17:00.   Admission: House & Garden: £5.50, Garden: £3.50.   Location: Between Penrith and Ullswater.   Map Ref: 14

Hutton-In-The-Forest

Penrith CA11 9TH   Tel: 017684 84449   Fax: 017684 84571   Email: hutton-in-the-forest@talk21.com

Historic house and gardens, based on a medieval pole tower, with substantial additions in 17th, 18th and 19th centuries; collections of portraits, tapestries, ceramics and furniture. Surrounded by beautiful gardens and woodland.

Opening Times: 18 Apr to 28 Sep Thu, Fri, Sun & BH 12:30-16:00.   Admission: Adult £4.50, Child £2.50, Family £12.00.   Location: On B5305, two and a half miles north west of M6 junction 41.   Map Ref: 15

Cumbria

Muncaster Castle Gardens & Owl Centre

Muncaster Castle, Ravenglass CA18 1RQ   Tel: 01229 717614   Fax: 01229 717010
Email: info@muncaster.co.uk   Web: www.muncaster.co.uk

Home to the Pennington family for 800 years. Muncaster is a genuine treasure trove of art and antiques including Henry VI's drinking bowl. The rich furnishings and decor include some fine Elizabethan furniture and embroidery. A walk through the castle brings you seven centuries of glorious history including portraits by famous artists and beautiful tapestries.

Opening Times: Mar to Nov daily 10:30-18:00. Castle open Sun to Fri 12:00-17:00. Admission: Please telephone for prices. Location: One mile south of Ravenglass on the A595. Exhibitions & Events 2003
: May: Fantasia of Rhododenrons, Apr & Sep: Study Days. Please Call for details.   Map Ref: 16

The Beacon

West Strand, Whitehaven CA28 7LY   Tel: 01946 592302   Fax: 01946 598150
Email: thebeacon@copelandbc.gov.uk   Web: copelandbc.gov.uk

Home to Whitehaven's museum, The Beacon also offers the world's first Met Office Weather Gallery and an attractive programme of exhibitions throughout the year.

Opening Times: Easter to Oct Tue to Sun 10:00-17:30. Nov to Mar 10:00-16:30. School & BH open Mon. Admission: Adult £4.25, Child/Concession £2.80, OAP £3.50, Family £12.70. Group rates available. Location: On harbourside.   Map Ref: 17

Windermere Steamboats & Museum

Rayrigg Road, Windermere LA23 1BN   Tel: 015394 45565   Fax: 015394 48769
Email: steamboat@ecosse.net   Web: www.steamboat.co.uk

Large collection of Victorian/Edwardian launches and motor boats in spectacular lakeside setting. Cruises on steam launches. Swallows & Amazons exhibition. 'Model Boats - You Too Can Do It!' exhibition.

Opening Times: 15 Mar to 26 Oct daily 10:00-17:00. Admission: Adult £3.50, Child £2.00, Family £8.50. Group rates available. Location: Half a mile north of Bowness-on-Windermere on A592.   Map Ref: 18

Helena Thompson Museum

Park End Road, Workington CA14 4DE   Tel: 01900 326255

Costume, ceramics of 18th and 19th century. Social history and photographic archive of Workington town and industries.

Opening Times: Mon to Sat 10:00-16:00. Admission: Free. Location: Opposite Workington Hall and Curwen Park overlooking the Irish Sea.   Map Ref: 19

Derby, famous for its Royal Crown Derby porcelain as well as its Rolls-Royce engines, has a fine cathedral and despite its industrial heart fine scenery is never far away. Staffordshire too offers quite remarkable contrasts. Within a short distance of the busy county town of Stafford lies Cannock Chase, over 20,000 acres of glorious heath and woodland.

Here was the cradle of the Industrial Revolution and the creative expertise and heritage of these two counties is clearly reflected in their fine museums and art galleries and from mills, and mining to potteries and brewing.

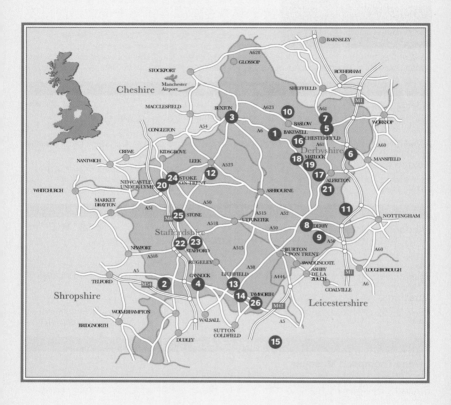

The Red Map References should be used to locate Museums etc on the pages that follow

Derbyshire & Staffordshire

BAKEWELL *Derbys*

Haddon Hall

Bakewell DE45 1LA   Tel: 01629 812855   Fax: 01629 814379   Email: info@haddonhall.co.uk
Web: www.haddonhall.co.uk

This magnificent Medieval and Tudor manor house provides a popular location for film and television productions. The beautiful terraced rose gardens remain one of the chief glories of Haddon.

Opening Times: 1 Apr to 30 Sep daily 10:30-17:00, Oct Thu to Sun 10:30-16:30.
Admission: Adult £7.50, Child £3.75, Concession £6.25.   Location: Bakewell.   Map Ref: 1

BISHOP'S WOOD *Staffs*

Boscobel House

Brewood, Bishop's Wood ST19 9AR   Tel: 01902 850244

Restored to its appearance in Victorian times, Boscobel House was originally a 17th century hunting lodge. The House has panelled rooms, secret hiding places and pretty gardens and provided refuge for King Charles II from Cromwell's troops.

Opening Times: Mar to Sep daily 11:00-18:00, Oct daily 11:00-17:00, Nov Wed to Sun 11:00-16:00. Closed 1 Dec to 28 Mar 2004.   Admission: Adult £4.40, Child £2.20, Concession £3.30, Family £11.00.   Location: On minor road from A41 to A5, eight miles north west of Wolverhampton.   Map Ref: 2

BUXTON *Derbys*

Buxton Museum & Art Gallery

Terrace Road, Buxton SK17 6DA   Tel: 01298 24658   Fax: 01298 79394
Email: buxton.museum@derbyshire.gov.uk   Web: www.derbyshire.gov.uk

Explore the wonders of the Peak through seven time zones revealing the geology, archaeology and history of the Peak District. Enjoy our busy programme of temporary art and craft exhibition.

Opening Times: Tue to Fri 09:30-17:30, Sat 09:30-17:00. Also from Easter to 30 Sep Sun & BH Mon 10:30-17:00. Closed Mon.   Admission: Downstairs: Free. Upstairs: Adult £1.00, Concession 50p, Family £2.00. Prices subject to change.   Location: Near Town Hall, ten minutes from train station.   Map Ref: 3

CANNOCK *Staffs*

Museum of Cannock Chase

Valley Road, Hednesford, Cannock WS12 5TD   Tel: 01543 877666   Fax: 01543 428272
Email: museum@cannockchasedc.gov.uk   Web: www.museumofcannockchase.co.uk

Small museum occupying ex-colliery site. Illustrates history of Cannock Chase from medieval hunting forest to coalfield community. Collections comprise social history, domestic and industrial artefacts.

Opening Times: Easter to Sep daily 11:00-17:00. Oct to Easter Mon to Fri 11:00-16:00.
Admission: Free except for guided parties.   Location: Near Hednesford centre on A460 to Rugeley, ten minutes from station.   Map Ref: 4

CHESTERFIELD *Derbys*

Chesterfield Museum & Art Gallery

St Marys Gate, Chesterfield S41 7TD   Tel: 01246 345727
Email: museum@chesterfieldbc.gov.uk

Taking the 'Story of Chesterfield' as its theme the museum shows how the town has become the place it is today, by looking at different aspects of its history.

Opening Times: Mon, Tue, Thu, Fri, Sat 10:00-16:00. Closed Wed & Sun and Xmas & New Year.
Admission: Free.   Location: The museum is located on St Mary's Gate close to the parish church (Crooked Spire), easy walking distance of car parks and railway station.   Map Ref: 5

| Guided or Private Tours | Disabled Access | Gift Shop or Sales Point | Café or Refreshments | Restaurant | Car Parking |

Derbyshire & Staffordshire

Hardwick Hall, Gardens & Park

Doe Lea, Chesterfield S44 5QJ   Tel: 01246 857488/850430   Fax: 01246
854200   Email: hardwickhall@ntrust.org.uk

THE NATIONAL TRUST

*The Long Gallery containing
the famous Gideon Tapestries*

Set high on a hill in North East Derbyshire, spectacular 405 year old Hardwick, the home of Bess of Hardwick. One of the greatest Elizabethan houses, surviving almost unchanged to date. The Hall contains one of Europe's best collections of furniture, embroideries and tapestries. Surrounded by four walled courtyards, aromatic garden and famous herb garden. Enjoy great walks around the ponds.

Opening Times: 29 Mar to 26 Oct. Hall: Wed, Thu, Sat, Sun, BH Mon & Good Friday 12:30-17:00. Garden: daily except Tue 11:00-17:30. Admission: Adult £6.60, Child £3.30, Family £16.50, National Trust Members Free.

Location: Near junction 29 on the M1, follow with Brown Tourist Signs.   Map Ref: 6

Revolution House

High Street, Old Whittington, Chesterfield   Tel: 01246 345727
Email: museum@chesterfieldbc.gov.uk

Originally an alehouse, this 17th century thatched cottage was the site of a meeting between local noblemen involved in the Revolution of 1688.

Opening Times: Good Friday to end Sep daily 10:00-16:00, 13 Dec to 24 Dec & 27 Dec to 31 Dec daily 10:00-16:00. Admission: Free. Location: In the centre of Old Whittington village near the 'Cock & Magpie'. Regular bus service from Chesterfield.   Map Ref: 7

DERBY

Derby Industrial Museum

The Silk Mill, Silk Mill Lane, off Full Street, Derby DE1 3AF   Tel: 01332 255308   Fax: 01332 716670   Email: david.fraser@derby.gov.uk   Web: www.derby.gov.uk/museums

The museum is housed in Derby's historic Silk Mill. Built circa 1720 as one of Britain's first factories. Displays feature local industries, including railway engineering and Rolls Royce aero engines.

Opening Times: Mon 11:00-17:00, Tue to Sat 10:00-17:00, Sun & BH 14:00-17:00. Closed Xmas & New Year break. Admission: Free. Location: Beside the River Derwent, five minutes walk from bus station, 25 minutes walk from railway station.   Map Ref: 8

Derby Museum & Art Gallery

The Strand, Derby DE1 1BS   Tel: 01332 716659   Fax: 01332 716670
Email: david.fraser@derby.gov.uk   Web: www.derby.gov.uk/museums

The Ceramics Gallery

The museum houses internationally important collections of Derby porcelain and major paintings by Joseph Wright of Derby (1734-97). Derbyshire wildlife and geology feature in a splendid series of natural settings and hands-on exhibits. Other galleries are devoted to local regiments, local archaeology, Bonnie Prince Charlie's visit to Derby during the 1745 uprising, and to exciting temporary exhibitions.

Opening Times: Mon 11:00-17:00, Tue to Sat 10:00-17:00, Sun & BH 14:00-17:00. Closed Xmas & New Year break. Admission: Free. Location: In city centre, ten minutes walk from bus station, 25 minutes walk from railway station.   Map Ref: 8

Donington Grand Prix Collection

Donington Park, Castle Donington, Derby DE74 2RP   Tel: 01332 811027
Fax: 01332 812829   Email: enquiries@doningtoncollection.co.uk
Web: www.doningtoncollection.com

DERBY *(continued)*

The Mclaren Hall, featuring the World's largest collecion of McLaren F1 cars

Take a lap around the Donington Grand Prix Collection, which is the world's largest collection of Grand Prix racing cars. Featuring over 130 cars within five halls and described by a number of visitors as 'a gold mine to motor racing heritage'. The collection features the world's largest collection of McLaren Formula One cars on public display and also cars such as Ferrari, Jordan, Williams, BRM and Vanwalls. Driven by such famous names as Senna, Nuvolari, Moss, Hill and Fangio. Also there are drivers' helmets and memorabilia covering every wall within the collection.

1955 Lancia D50 Ferrari - the newest arrival within the Collection

Opening Times: Daily 10:00-17:00, last admission 16:00.
Admission: Adult £7.00, Child £2.50, Student/OAP £5.00, Family (2 adults and 3 children) £14.00, Group discount available.
Location: Two miles from junction 23A M1/M42. Exhibitions & Events 2003 : A number of anniversaries are celebrated to commemorate racing drivers and cars.   Map Ref: 9

Pickfords House Museum
41 Friar Gate, Derby DE1 1DA   Tel: 01332 255363   Fax: 01332 716670
Email: david.fraser@derby.gov.uk   Web: www.derby.gov.uk/museums

A fine Georgian town house built in 1770 by local architect, Joseph Pickford, as his home. Displays include period rooms circa 1800, historic costume and an 18th century style garden.

Opening Times: Mon 11:00-17:00, Tue to Sat 10:00-17:00, Sun & BH 14:00-17:00. Closed Xmas & New Year break. Admission: Free. Location: 25 minutes from railway station by foot, ten minutes walk from bus station.   Map Ref: 8

Regimental Museum of the 9th/12th Royal Lancers (Prince of Wales's)
City Museum & Art Gallery, The Strand, Derby DE1 1BS   Tel: 01332 716656   Fax: 01332 716670

Information panels, audio system and items relating to the history of the Regiment and its predecessors from 1715 to Bosnia. Displays include a reconstruction stable. 9th/12th Lancers archives and photos are available by appointment.

Opening Times: Mon 11:00-17:00, Tue to Sat 10:00-17:00, Sun 14:00-17:00. Admission: Free.
Location: Town centre, 15 minute walk from railway station.   Map Ref: 8

Royal Crown Derby Visitor Centre
194 Osmaston Road, Derby DE23 8JZ   Tel: 01332 712800   Fax: 01332 712899
Web: www.royal-crown-derby.co.uk

Superb collection of Royal Crown Derby porcelain from earliest origins circa 1750 to present day. Highlights include Raven Room Collection incorporating works of most renowned artists. Also Factory Tours and Demonstrations.

Opening Times: Mon to Sat 09:30-17:00, Sun 10:30-16:30. Closed Xmas. Admission: Factory Tour including Visitor Centre Adult £4.95, Visitor Centre Adult £2.95, Concession £2.75.
Location: One mile outside Derby Town Centre.   Map Ref: 8

HOPE VALLEY *Derbys*

Eyam Museum
Hawkhill Road, Eyam, Hope Valley S32 5QP   Tel / Fax: 01433 631371
Web: www.eyam.org.uk

The display covers the 1665/6 outbreak of bubonic plague in Eyam. The collection includes local documents, fossils and minerals, archaeological material and many local photographs.

Opening Times: 25 Mar to 2 Nov Tue to Sun & BH 10:00-16:30. Admission: Adult £1.50, Child/Concession £1.00, Family £4.25. Location: Opposite main car park in Hawkhill Road, Eyam.   Map Ref: 10

Derbyshire & Staffordshire

Erewash Museum

High Street, Ilkeston DE7 5JA   Tel: 0115 907 1141   Fax: 0115 932 9264
Email: museum@erewash.gov.uk   Web: www.erewash.gov.uk

Local and social history collections plus regular events and exhibitions. Period kitchen and scullery. Suitable for all ages.

Opening Times: Feb to Dec Tue, Thu, Fri, Sat & BH 10:00-16:00.   Admission: Free.
Location: Near town centre.   Map Ref: 11

Cheddleton Flint Mill

Leek Road, Cheddleton, Leek ST13 7HL   Tel: 01782 502907
Web: www.ex.ac.uk/~akoutram/cheddleton-mill/index.htm

Two water mills, complete with wheels. Shows the process of grinding flint for the pottery industry. Panels tell the story of the materials used in pottery manufacture. Allow an hour.

Opening Times: Sat & Sun 13:00-17:00. Open most weekdays 10:30-17:00. Closed Xmas & New Year. Admission: Free, but donations most welcome. Location: Cheddleton village on A520, three miles south of Leek.   Map Ref: 12

Lichfield Heritage Centre

Market Square, Lichfield WS13 6LG   Tel: 01543 256611   Fax: 01543 414749
Email: smc@lichfieldheritage.org.uk   Web: www.lichfieldheritage.org.uk

The Staffordshire Millenium Tapestries on display within exciting new exhibition. Audio visuals, Treasury, Muniment room, Social History Gallery. Children's favorite - the fun way to learn history - follow the Mouse Trail.

Opening Times: Mon to Sat 10:00-17:00, Sun 10:30-17:00. Closed 25-26 Dec & New Year's Day. Last admission 16:00. Admission: Adult £3.50, Child £1.00, Under 5s Free, Concession £2.50, Booked Groups £2.50, Family £8.00. Location: Inside Church building on main Market Square in town centre.   Map Ref: 13

Samuel Johnson Birthplace Museum

Breadmarket Street, Lichfield WS13 6LG   Tel: 01543 264972   Fax: 01543 414779
Email: sjmuseum@lichfield.gov.uk   Web: www.lichfield.gov.uk/sjmuseum

The birthplace of Dr Samuel Johnson now houses a splendid museum dedicated to the life, work and personality of one of England's greatest writers and most fascinating characters.

Opening Times: Apr to Sep daily 10:30-16:30. Oct to Mar daily 12:00-16:30. Admission: Adult £2.20, Child/Concession £1.30, Family £5.80. Location: City centre, location overlooking Market Place.   Map Ref: 13

Staffordshire Regiment Museum

Whittington Barracks, Lichfield WS14 9PY   Tel: 0121 311 3229   Fax: 0121 311 3205
Email: museum@rhqstaffords.fsnet.co.uk   Web: www.armymuseums.org.uk

History of the Regiment and its forebears since 1705. Good collections of medals (including British & Victoria Cross sets), uniforms and weapons. Hands on area and quizzes for children. 100 metres of outdoor World War I trench, two World War II Anderson shelters. Key stage 2 and 3 education, archive (booking only).

Opening Times: Year round Tue to Fri 10:00-16:30. Apr to Oct Sat, Sun & BH 12:30-16:30. Closed Xmas & New Year. Admission: Adult £2.00, Concession £1.00, Under 5s Free, Family £5.00, Group £1.00. Members of MOD (Army), Regimental Association Free. Location: On A51 between Lichfield and Tamworth. Between main barracks and golf club.   Map Ref: 14

Wall Roman Site & Museum (Letocetum)

Watling Street, Wall, Lichfield WS14 0AW   Tel: 01543 480768

Wall was once a staging-post on Watling Street, with a bath house and guest house where travellers could stay overnight. The museum houses a display of Romano-British finds from the site including pottery, jewellery, coins and metalwork.

Opening Times: Apr to Sep daily 10:00-18:00, Oct daily 10:00-17:00 Admission: Adult £2.60, Child £1.30, Concession £2.00. National Trust Members Free. Location: Off A5 at Wall near Lichfield.   Map Ref: 15

Derbyshire & Staffordshire

Caudwell's Mill & Craft Centre

Rowsley, Matlock DE4 2EB   Tel / Fax: 01629 734374   Web: www.caudwellsmill.museum.com

The only complete Victorian water turbine-powered roller flour mill in the country. Powered by the River Wye, four floors of fascinating machinery demonstrate how wheat was turned into flour. With traditional craft workshops and gallery.

Opening Times: Apr to Oct daily 10:00-17:30, Nov to Mar Sat & Sun 10:00-16:30.
Admission: Craft Centre Free. Mill, Adult £3.00, Child £1.00, OAP £2.50.   Location: In Rowsley village on the main A6 between Matlock and Bakewell. On bus routes with stops immediately outside the mill.   Map Ref: 16

Crich Tramway Village

Crich, Matlock DE4 5DP   Tel: 0870 75 TRAMS/87267   Fax: 01773 852326
Email: info@tramway.co.uk   Web: www.tramway.co.uk

Derbyshire's award-winning family attraction where you can enjoy unlimited tram rides in a recreated village street, plus play areas, shops, tearooms and lots, lots more. A relaxing day out for all the family!

Opening Times: 8 to 23 Feb, weekends in Mar, 29 Mar to 2 Nov, weekends in Nov & Dec.
Admission: Adult £7, Child £3.50, OAP £6.00, Family £19.00.   Location: Six miles from Matlock, eight miles from junction 28 on M1.   Map Ref: 17

Peak District Mining Museum & Temple Mine

The Pavilion, Matlock Bath, Matlock DE4 3NR   Tel: 01629 583834
Email: mail@peakmines.co.uk   Web: www.peakmines.co.uk

Depicting mining in Derbyshire since Roman times, Wills founder engine, Howie mineral collection, rag and chain pump, informative displays. Temple mine shows insight into mineral mining with spacious well lit tunnels.

Opening Times: Apr to Oct daily 10:00-17:00, Nov to Mar daily 11:00-15:00. Closed Xmas.
Admission: Museum or Mine: Adult £2.50, Child/OAP £1.50, Family £6.00. Joint Ticket: Adult £4.00, Child/OAP £2.50, Family £9.00. Group rates available.   Location: Adjacent A6 Matlock Bath.   Map Ref: 18

Sir Richard Arkwrights Cromford Mill

Cromford Mill, Mill Lane, Cromford, Matlock DE4 3RQ   Tel / Fax: 01629 823256

Visit the world's first successful water powered cotton spinning mill. Tours available daily and exhibitions. Part of the Derwent Valley Mills, having achieved World Heritage status in Dec 2000.

Opening Times: Daily 9:00-17:00. Closed Xmas.   Admission: No charge to the site. Tours - Adult £2.00, Concession £1.50.   Location: Off the A6 Derby to Buxton Road, located on the outside of the village of Cromford.   Map Ref: 19

Borough Museum & Art Gallery

Brampton Park, Newcastle-under-Lyme ST5 0QP   Tel: 01782 619705   Fax: 01782 626857   Email: nulmuseum@newcastle-staffs.gov.uk   Web: www.newcastle-staffs.gov.uk/museum.htm

Chemist, Victorian Street Scene

Newcastle's long history can be traced through the Roman period, its medieval castle, Royal Charters and industries. All of these and more are represented in the museum's permanent displays. The art gallery includes local artists, travelling exhibitions and a frequently changing programme of exhibitions, which means that there is always something new to see in both the main art gallery and the small gallery.

Opening Times: Mon to Sat 10:00-17:30, Sun 14:00-17:30.   Admission: Free.   Location: In Brampton Park on Brampton Road (A527), just 1/2 mile from Newcastle Town Centre and three miles from junction 15 of the M6.   Map Ref: 20

Derbyshire & Staffordshire

Midland Railway Centre

Butterley Station, Ripley DE5 3QZ   Tel: 01773 747674   Fax: 01773 510721
Email: info@midlandrailwaycentre.co.uk

'Midday Midlander' Sunday lunch train departs from Butterley Station

Large collection of railway locomotives and rolling stock. Operating standard gauge railway (three and a half miles) and narrow gauge railway (one mile). Farm Park, Country Park, Demonstration Signal Box, Victorian Railwayman's Church and much more.

Opening Times: Daily 10:00-16:00. Trains run weekends throughout the year, Wed Apr to Oct & school holidays. Admission: Adult £7.50, OAP £6.50, Child £3.50, under 3s free. Location: On B6179, one mile north of Ripley, signposted from A38.   Map Ref: 21

The Princess Royal Class Locomotive Trust

West Shed, Midland Railway Centre, Swanwick Junction, Ripley DE5 3QZ   Tel: 01773 747471
Fax: 01335 346546   Email: prclt@whitehouseconstruction.co.uk   Web: www.prclt.co.uk

The Duchess of Sutherland

Steam locomotives on display together with historical 21' gauge locos and small exhibits museum. No 46203 'Princess Margaret Rose', No 6233 'Duchess of Sutherland', 80098 & 80080 British railway standard tank locos workshops, museum, display in 'The West Shed'.

Opening Times: Daily 10:30-16:30. Admission: Free. Location: Adjacent to Swanwick Junction, Midland Railway Centre.   Map Ref: 21

Ripley Castle

Ripley HG3 3AY   Tel: 01423 770152   Fax: 01423 771745
Email: enquiries@ripleycastle.co.uk   Web: www.ripleycastle.co.uk

Ripley Castle stands at the heart of a delightful estate village with lakes, deer park and Victorian walled garden.

Opening Times: Sep to May Tue, Thu, Sat, Sun 10:30-15:00. Jun to Aug daily. Admission: Adult £5.50, Child £3.00, OAP £4.50.   Location: A61 north of Harrogate (three miles).   Map Ref: 21

Ancient High House

Greengate Street, Stafford ST16 2JA   Tel: 01785 619131   Fax: 01785 619132
Email: ahh@staffordbc.gov.uk   Web: www.staffordbc.gov.uk

England's largest timber-framed townhouse contains a collection of mainly 18th and 19th century domestic furnishings displayed in room settings. Also rare 18th century wallpaper discovered during recent restoration.

Opening Times: Mon to Sat 10:00-17:00. Admission: Free (charges may apply per event). Location: In the town centre.   Map Ref: 22

Shire Hall Gallery

Market Square, Stafford ST16 2LD   Tel: 01785 278345

Paintings, prints by Staffordshire artists. Contemporary jewellery.

Opening Times: Mon to Sat 09:30-17:00. Closed Sun & BH.   Admission: Free. Location: Centre of town, next to Guildhall Shopping Centre.   Exhibitions & Events 2003 : For Exhibitions and Events please telephone for details.   Map Ref: 22

Derbyshire & Staffordshire

Shugborough Estate

Millford, Stafford ST17 0XB   Tel: 01889 881388   Fax: 01889 881323
Email: shugborough.promotions@staffordshire.gov.uk
Web: www.staffordshire.gov.uk/shugborough

Shugborough is the ancestral home of the fifth Earl of Lichfield, who as Patrick Lichfield is known worldwide as a leading photographer. The 18th century Mansion House contains a fine collection of ceramics, silver, paintings and French furniture. Part of the house continues to be lived in by the Earl and his family. Visitors can enjoy the 18 acre Grade I listed historic garden and a unique collection of neo-classical monuments by James 'Athenian' Stuart. Other attractions include the original servants' quarters. The working laundry, kitchens, brewhouse and coach houses have all been lovingly restored. Costumed guides can show how the servants lived and worked over 100 years ago. Shugborough Park Farm is a Georgian farmstead that features an agricultural museum, working corn mill and rare breeds centre. The livestock are all historic breeds and in the farmhouse visitors can see brick bread ovens in operation and butter and cheese making in the dairy. The annual programme of events ranges from seasonal craft fairs to the delights of candlelit evenings, and a Victorian street market of spectacular firework displays. Teachers will be pleased to note that there is an extensive educational programme available for children of all ages with an attractive selection of adult tours and demonstrations. There is something for everyone on the Shugborough Estate.

Cherubs in The Rose Garden

Opening Times: Mar to Oct Tue to Sun 11:00-17:00. Open BH Mon.
Admission: Telephone (01889) 881388 for details.   Location: Three miles from Stafford.
Exhibitions & Events 2003 : Please telephone for details.   Map Ref: 23

Stafford Castle Visitor Centre

staffordˇ castLe

Newport Road, Stafford ST16 1DJ   Tel: 01785 257698
Email: castlebc@btconnect.com   Web: www.staffordbc.gov.uk

Try on armour and costume, see finds from the archaeological dig at Stafford Castle, watch a video describing the history of the site. Visit the ruined remains of this motte and bailey castle.

Opening Times: Apr to Oct Tue to Sun & BH Mon 10:00-17:00. Nov to Mar Tue to Sun & BH Mon 10:00-16:00.
Admission: Free. Charges may apply for events.
Location: Five minutes by car from the town centre.
Stafford Castle   Map Ref: 22

Ford Green Hall

Ford Green Road, Smallthorne, Stoke-on-Trent ST6 1NG   Tel: 01782 233195

17th century timber-framed yeoman farmhouse complete with period herb garden. The hall is furnished with textiles, ceramics and furniture. Events programme throughout the year including children's activities every holiday. The hall is licensed for weddings, and children's parties are available. Changing displays and touring exhibitions. Family friendly with interactives for children. Disabled access to ground floor. Situated next to a nature reserve.

(continued on next page)

STOKE-ON-TRENT *Staffs (continued)*

Opening Times: Sun to Thu 13:00-17:00. Admission: Admission charge. Location: Ten minutes from Hanley (city centre). Exhibitions & Events 2003 : 16 Feb 03: Meet a Ford Green Hall Servant Canal ware painting demo, 17 to 20 Feb: Children's craft activities, 16 Mar: Friends' event talk: Woman in the 17th century. Map Ref: 24

Gladstone Pottery Museum

Uttoxeter Road, Longton, Stoke-on-Trent ST3 1PQ
Tel: 01782 311378/319232
Email: gladstone@stoke.gov.uk Web: www.stoke.gov.uk/gladstone

Last remaining Victorian pottery factory complete with traditional bottle ovens. Live demonstrations and audio-visual tours show visitors the skills of the potteries. The museum also has the new Flushed with Pride - Story of the Toilet exhibition, which contains the most comprehensive collection of historic toilets in the world. Gladstone also has the nationally recognised collection of decorated tiles now redisplayed in our new Tile Gallery.

Opening Times: Daily 10:00-17:00. Admission: Adult £4.95, Child £3.50, Concession/OAP £3.95, Family £14.00. Location: Longton, Stoke-on-Trent. Two minutes off A50, ten minutes junction 15 of M6.
Map Ref: 24

Gladstone Pottery Museum Yard

The Potteries Museum & Art Gallery

Bethesda Street, Hanley, Stoke-on-Trent ST1 3DW Tel: 01782 232323
Fax: 01782 232500 Email: museums@stoke.gov.uk
Web: www.stoke.gov.uk/museums

Welcome to the home of the world's finest collection of Staffordshire ceramics. We also own the most comprehensive collection of 20th century studio and industrial pottery. With over 650,000 objects, The Potteries Museum & Art Gallery collections are designated of national and international importance. Discover the story of Stoke-on-Trent's people, products and landscapes through imaginative displays of local history, archaeology, geology and wildlife. Explore the rich collections of paintings, prints, drawings, costume and glass in the Art Gallery and Changing Fashions displays. From ancient Roman pots to a Mark XVI Spitfire; from a Staffordshire Wallaby to our famous slipware owl jug; from a Rodin bronze to a popular dolls' house - there is something here for everyone! Enjoy hands-on exhibits, touch-screen computers and a lively programme of holiday activities, talks, tours and workshops. Expert opinion is available through our public enquiry service.

Opening Times: Mar to Oct Mon to Sat 10:00-17:00, Sun 14:00-17:00. Nov to Feb Mon To Sat 10:00-16:00, Sun 13:00-16:00. Admission: Free. Location: In the city centre, within the cultural quarter, one mile from railway station, four miles from junction 15, M6. Exhibitions & Events 2003 : Until 2 Feb: Minton Masterpieces, Until 2 Mar: Open 02, 1 Feb to 30 Mar: Because It Is There, 15 to 16 Feb: The Romans Return, 7 to 16 Mar: National Science Week : Alien Worlds, 22 Mar to 22 Jun: Landscapes : A Tate Partnership Exhibition, 29 Mar to 18 May: The Really Real : The Art of David Gleeson, 12 Apr to 1 Jun: Beyond the Blue : Microscopic Patterns of Willow, 12 Apr to 1 Jun: The Hothouse, 1 May to 2 Jun: Museums & Galleries Month 2003, 14 Jun to 5 Oct: An Archaeological Alphabet, 5 Jul to 31 Aug: 146th Royal Photographic Society International Print Exhib, 13 Sep to 2 Nov: Richard Slee - Show 5, 25 Oct to 18 Jan: Ceramic, Culture, Innovation, 29 Nov to 1 Feb: Open 03. Map Ref: 24

Guided or Private Tours	Disabled Access	Gift Shop or Sales Point	Café or Refreshments	Restaurant	Car Parking

Derbyshire & Staffordshire

Spode Museum & Visitor Centre

Church Street, Stoke-on-Trent ST4 1BX   Tel: 01782 744011   Fax: 01782 744220
Email: visitorcentre@spode.co.uk   Web: www.spode.co.uk

Museum Gallery part of Visitor Centre housing a selection of items produced by Spode from 1770 up to the present day. Contact the Visitor Centre for special exhibitions and more details.

Opening Times: Jan to Dec Mon to Sat 09:00-17:00, Sun 10:00-16:00. Closed 25-26 Dec & New Year.   Admission: Adult £2.75, Child/OAP £2.25, Under 5s Free.   Location: Town centre, ten minute walk from Stoke-on-Trent railway station.   Map Ref: 24

STONE *Staffs*

Izaak Walton's Cottage

Worston Lane, Shallowford, Stone ST15 0PA   Tel: 01785 760278/619619
Fax: 01785 760278 Email: izaakwaltonscottage@staffordbc.gov.uk
Web: www.staffordbc.gov.uk

Izaak Walton, author of 'The Compleat Angler' once owned this charming cottage. There is an Anglers Museum in this 16th century half timbered building, and the splendid rose and herb gardens are a delight to visit.

Opening Times: Apr to Oct Wed to Sun 13:00-17:00.
Admission: Free, charges may apply for events.
Location: Ten minutes by car from Stafford.   Map Ref: 25

The Cottage is set in picturesque gardens

TAMWORTH *Staffs*

Tamworth Castle

The Holloway, Ladybank, Tamworth B79 7NA   Tel: 01827 709629   Fax: 01827 709630
Email: heritage@tamworth.gov.uk   Web: www.tamworth.gov.uk/tamworthleisure

Dramatic Norman castle with later additions houses furnished room displays plus 'Tamworth Story' and Norman exhibitions. Reputedly haunted by two lady ghosts. With clothes to try on, rubbings and two free quizzes, there's lots to interest children.

Opening Times: 15 Feb to 31 Oct Tue to Sun 12:00-17:15. Last admission 16:30. Please telephone for winter opening times.   Admission: Admission charge.   Location: In town centre, five minute walk from central bus stops, ten minutes from the railway station.   Map Ref: 26

Devon

Devon is a county of great seafarers. It was from the fine natural harbour of Plymouth that the Pilgrim Fathers sailed to the New World, and it was from here that Sir Francis Drake and Sir John Hawkins sailed to confront the mighty Spanish Armada. Between the coasts the county is dominated by lofty brooding Dartmoor and the north of the county includes a part of Exmoor where moorland meets the sea. Exeter, the county town has a magnificent Norman cathedral holding the remarkable Anglo-Saxon Exeter book.

Devon's many excellent museums, mills and historic houses cover all aspects of the regions maritime history, its local industries and social history including 'Dartmoor Life'.

The Red Map References should be used to locate Museums etc on the pages that follow

Devon

Arlington Court

THE NATIONAL TRUST

Arlington, Barnstaple EX31 4LP   Tel: 01271 850296

Arlington Court North Devon

Arlington Court, a National Trust mansion situated in peaceful gardens surrounded by parklands and woods and miles of walks. Previously owned by Rosalie Chichester, the house is full of fascinating collections. The working stables have horses, carriages driving school and the Trust's carriage collection.

Opening Times: 23 Mar to 3 Nov daily except Tue 10:30-17:00. Admission: Adult £5.60, Child £2.60, Groups £4.80. Location: On A39, eight miles north of Barnstaple.   Map Ref: 1

Museum of Barnstaple & North Devon

The Square, Barnstaple EX32 8LN   Tel: 01271 346747

Story of North Devon from pre-history to 1930s. Tarka Centre depicting river life and woodland life. Undersea room with replica mammals and fish around North Devon coast. Temporary exhibitions, seven centuries of pottery.

Opening Times: Tue to Sat 10:00-16:30. Closed Sun, Mon & BH. Admission: Free. Location: By the Long Bridge and Clock Tower.   Map Ref: 2

The Burton Art Gallery & Museum

MUSEUM ART GALLERY

Kingsley Road, Bideford EX39 2QQ   Tel: 01237 471455 Fax: 01237 473813   Web: www.burtonartgallery.co.uk

North Devon Shipware Jugs 19th century

North Devon Slipware, model of Bideford Long Bridge 1280-1925, Delft ware, Napoleonic bone ship models, history of Bideford personalities. Paintings by Hubert Coop, Clausen, Fisher, E Aubrey Hunt, Reynolds, Ackland/Edwards collection etc plus contemporary national and local artists. Craft Gallery with work by regional craft artists.

Opening Times: Easter to end Oct Tue to Sat 10:00-17:00, Sun 14:00-17:00. Nov to Easter Tue to Sat 10:00-16:00 Sun 14:00-16:00. BH 10:00-17:00. Closed Mon. Admission: Free. Some special exhibitions Adult £1.00, Concession 50p. Location: Near town centre, in Victoria Park, opposite coach park.
                                                                  Map Ref: 3

Devon Guild of Craftsmen

Riverside Mill, Bovey Tracey TQ13 9AF   Tel: 01626 832223 Fax: 01626 834220 Email: devonguild@crafts.org.uk Web: www.crafts.org.uk

The South West's leading gallery and craft showrooms with work selected from around 240 designer/makers. Top touring and themed shows in Grade II listed Riverside Mill.

Opening Times: Daily 10:00-17:30. Closed Xmas Day & New Years Day. Admission: Free admission to all exhibitions and facilities. Location: In the centre of Bovey Tracey, only two miles off A38, Exeter to Plymouth road.   Map Ref: 4

Craft Shop, Devon Guild of Craftsmen

| Guided or Private Tours | Disabled Access | Gift Shop or Sales Point | Café or Refreshments | Restaurant | Car Parking |

Devon

Brixham Heritage Museum & History Society

Bolton Cross, Brixham TQ5 8LZ   Tel: 01803 856267   Email: mail@brixhamheritage.org.uk
Web: www.brixhamheritage.org.uk

*The museum exhibits Brixham's heritage: the fishing industry, Reverend Lyte (Abide With Me),
Victorian Life, World War II, interactive displays, model of former town railway, Napoleonic forts at
Berry Head with exhibits of museum's archeological 'digs'.*

Opening Times: Mid Feb to Easter 10:00-13:00. Easter to end Oct Mon to Fri 10:00-17:00, Sat
10:00-13:00. Admission: Adult £1.50, Child 50p, OAP £1.00, Family £3.50. Location: Near
town centre, one minute walk from central bus station.   Map Ref: 5

The Golden Hind Museum Ship

The Quay, Brixham Harbour, Brixham TQ5 8AW   Tel: 01803 856223
Email: postmaster@goldenhind.co.uk   Web: www.goldenhind.co.uk

*Relive Drake's incredible voyage of 1577 aboard this full sized replica. The ship gives a
fascinating insight into life aboard in the 16th century. Registered for civil weddings.*

Opening Times: Mar to Oct daily 10:00-16:00, Jul to Aug 09:00-22:00. Admission: Adult
£2.00, Child/OAP £1.50. Location: Brixham Habour.   Map Ref: 5

Bicton Park Botanical Gardens and Countryside Museum

East Budleigh, Budleigh Salterton EX9 7BJ   Tel: 01395 568465   Fax: 01395 568374
Email: info@bictongardens.co.uk   Web: www.bictongardens.co.uk

*Bicton Park is a magical blend of 18th century tranquillity
and modern-day facilities for all the family. The
magnificently landscaped grounds provide a kaleidoscope
of colour through the seasons. Fragrant borders,
manicured lawns, majestic woodlands, reflective lakes and
rippling streams form a scene of peaceful grandeur that
has existed for almost 300 years. The Grade I listed
gardens originated in the 1730s when the Italian Garden
was laid out in the formal style of Versailles designer Andre
le Notre. Outstanding among the glasshouses is the high-
domed 19th century Palm House, several years older than*
the palm house at Kew, it has been fully restored as a home for tropical and subtropical plants,
including Bicton's own orchid. A tour of the 63 acre park, either on foot or aboard the narrow-
gauge Bicton Woodland Railway, reveals many fascinating features. There is a Secret Garden near

*the quaint old Hermitage summerhouse, some amazing
seashells in the American Garden's Shell House, and a
large collection of agricultural and horticultural
implements, including traction engines, in the Countryside
Museum. Drought tolerant plants bloom in the sunny
Mediterranean Garden, while shade-lovers flourish in the
Stream Garden. Rare conifer trees grow in the Pinetum,
near which there are play areas for children.*

Opening Times: Summer 10:00-18:00, winter 10:00-
17:00. Closed Xmas Day. Admission: Adult £4.95, Child
£2.95, Concession £3.95, Family £12.95.   Map Ref: 6

Coldharbour Mill Working Wool Museum

Coldharbour Mill, Uffculme, Cullompton EX15 3EE   Tel: 01884 840960   Fax: 01884 840858
Email: info@coldharbourmill.org.uk   Web: www.coldharbourmill.org.uk

*The 200 year old waterside mill houses working spinning and weaving machines, steam engines
restored to their former glory and the biggest embroidery in the world. Picnic areas and gardens.*

Opening Times: Mar to Dec daily 10:30-17:00, Feb Mon to Fri, please telephone for details.
Admission: Adult £5.50, Child £2.50, Family £15.00. Location: Five minutes drive off junction
27 of M5, in village of Uffculme.   Map Ref: 7

Devon

Killerton House

Broadclyst, Exeter EX5 3LE   Tel: 01392 881345

THE NATIONAL TRUST

Elegant 18th century house with costume collection. 18 acre garden with original plantings from the plant hunters, laid out by Veitch, woodland and open parkland.

Opening Times: 9 Mar to 2 Sep 11:00-17:00. Closed Tue (Mon & Tue in Mar). Aug daily 11:00-17:00.
Admission: House & Garden: Adult £5.40, Child £2.70. Garden: Adult £3.90, Child £1.95. National Trust Members Free. Location: Six miles from Exeter off B3181.

Map Ref: 8

Powderham Castle

Kenton, Exeter EX6 8LQ   Tel: 01626 890243   Fax: 01626 890729
Email: castle@powderham.co.uk   Web: www.powderham.co.uk

Family home of the Earl of Devon. Castle dates back to 1391 and has been in the family for over 600 years. Magnificent state rooms, 17th and 18th century fine furniture, china, paintings. Guided tours throughout the day. Beautiful location in ancient deer park overlooking the Exe Estuary, with tranquil gardens and woodland walks to enjoy.

Opening Times: 26 Mar to 3 Nov Sun to Fri 10:00-17:30.
Admission: Adult £6.45, Child £2.95, OAP £5.95.
Location: Kenton village on A379, eight miles outside Exeter.

Map Ref: 9

Royal Albert Memorial Museum

Queen Street, Exeter EX4 3RX   Tel: 01392 665858

From archaeology to zoology this fine building holds outstanding collections of local and national importance and presents a range of exciting displays. Archaeology and Local History Galleries present finds from c.500,000 years ago to the end of the Middle Ages, including a Roman mosaic a reproduction of a Roman bathhouse. Superlactives abound in the Natural History displays, animals from all around the globe including the largest and tallest land mammals - elephant and giraffe - as well as exotic birds and butterflies, sea urchins and starfish. The effect geology has had on the landscape and people of Devon is explored in the Geology at Work Gallery. Three galleries of world cultures present thousands of amazing objects from all

around the globe including exceptional Pacific and North West Coast material from the early voyages of Captain Cook. The museum also presents regular themed exhibitions of works from the Fine Art collection. The Museum shop stocks fascinating items from all over the world and the friendly, licensed café serves snacks, simple meals and a delicious selection of cakes and biscuits.

Opening Times: Mon to Sat 10:00-17:00. Closed BH.
Admission: Free. Location: In Queen Street, just off high street in Exeter City Centre. Central Station is 100m away. St David's Station is ten minutes walk or short bus/taxi ride.   Exhibitions & Events 2003 : To 2 Feb: Devon Landscapes, 8 Dec to 2 Feb: Visions from the Golden Land - Burma and the Art of Lacquer, 15 Dec to 23 Feb: Exeter Engraved, 9 Feb to 13 Apr: At the Sign of the Rainbow, 11 Feb to 23 Feb: Walking with Dinosaurs and Beasts, 16 Feb to 13 Apr: The Eye That Never Sleeps, 2 Mar to 22 Jun: Clouds, 20 Apr to 15 Jun: Notorious, 20 Apr to 8 Jun: St Ives Artists, 22 Jun to 14 Sep: Lets Face It, 5 Oct to 4 Jan: Land, Love, Labour and Livestock - The Artist's View.

Map Ref: 10

Devon

Topsham Museum

25 The Strand, Topsham, Exeter EX3 0AX   Tel: 01392 873244   Email: museum@topsham.org
Web: www.devonmuseums.net/topsham

Museum situated in 17th century furnished house overlooking Exe Estuary. Exhibits include history of maritime and wildlife around Topsham with multi-media presentations. 2003 Exhibition - Topsham's Burning. The story of the Topsham Fire Service.

Opening Times: Apr to Oct Mon, Wed, Sat & Sun 14:00-17:00.   Admission: Free. Membership subscription £5.00 annually.   Location: 300 yards from Topsham Quay - terminus of the 'T' bus from centre of Exeter.   Map Ref: 11

EXMOUTH

World of Country Life

Sandy Bay, Exmouth EX8 5BU   Tel: 01395 274533   Fax: 01395 273457
Email: worldofcountrylife@hotmail.com   Web: www.worldofcountrylife.co.uk

Vintage vehicles, motorcycle collection, steam engines, vintage farm machinery, Victorian street, working models, play areas, farm animals, pets centre, owl displays, safari deer train, quad bikes, crazy golf.

Opening Times: Easter to end Oct daily 10:00-17:00.   Admission: Adult £6.00, Child £5.00, OAP £5.00, Family £20.00.   Location: Just ten miles from junction 30 on M5. Follow A376 Exmouth/Sandy Bay.   Map Ref: 12

GREAT TORRINGTON

Dartington Crystal

Linden Close, Great Torrington EX38 7AN
Tel: 01805 626242   Fax: 01805 626263
Email: tours@dartington.co.uk   Web: www.dartington.co.uk

Dartington Crystal is internationally famous for beautiful, handmade, contemporary glassware and is dedicated to innovative designs. Visitors to the factory site will be fascinated to watch the highly skilled craftsmen on a unique factory tour. Discover the history of glass and Dartington Story in the popular Visitor Centre. Finally, be tempted by the dazzling collection of glass for sale (the biggest glass shop in the country), many seconds at fantastic prices!

Opening Times: Mon to Fri 09:00-17:00, Sat 10:00-17:00, Sun 10:00-16:00 (Factory tour closed weekends). For Xmas, New Year & BH please phone for details.   Admission: Adult £4.00, Child £2.00, OAP £3.00, Family £12.00.   Location: In centre of Torrington. Turn off A386, opposite church, down School Lane 500 metres.   Map Ref: 13

Torrington Museum & Archive

Town Hall Building, The Square, Great Torrington EX38 8HN   Tel: 01805 624324

Local bygones, local industries and personalities, 17th to 20th century portrait collection, extensive family archive, domestic and agricultural equipment, features on Thomas Fowler (inventor of Thermosyphon and calculator) and Keble Martin of Concise British Flora fame.

Opening Times: May to Sep daily 11:00-16:00, Sat 11:00-13:30.   Admission: Free.
Location: In Town Hall building, The Square.   Map Ref: 13

Museums • Galleries • Historic Houses

Please let us know of any collections that are not listed in this guide that you feel should be listed. E-mail us on *editor@tomorrows.co.uk* or return the Report Form on page 448

Devon

South American Pottery explored by M G Palmer, first curator

Ilfracombe Museum

Runnymede Gardens, Wilder Road, Ilfracombe EX34 8AF
Tel: 01271 863541   Email: ilfracombe@devonmuseums.net
Web: www.devonmuseums.net

A fascinating collection started in 1932 by Mervyn G Palmer who collected in South America for the British Museum. Be amazed by the variety of displays, some slightly old fashioned but popular: Granny's attic, childhood memories, butterflies, beetles, bats, ethnography, Lundy Island, ship to shore radio, yesterday's domestic luxuries, Victorian costume and trinkets, Ilfracombe railway and paddle steamer history and lots more.

Opening Times: Apr to Oct daily 10:00-17:00, Nov to Mar Mon to Fri 10:00-13:00. Admission: Adults £1.50, Child 50p, OAP/Concessions £1.00. Location: Next to Landmark Theatre on sea front.   Map Ref: 14

Cookworthy Museum

The Old Grammar School, 108 Fore Street, Kingsbridge TQ7 1AW   Tel: 01548 853235
Email: wcookworthy@talk21.com

Discover the story of Kingsbridge in our 17th century school room, complete walk in Victorian kitchen, Edwardian pharmacy, large farm gallery in walled garden. With everything from costumes to carts this lively museum provides something for all the family.

Opening Times: 31 Mar to Sep Mon to Sat 10:30-17:00, Oct 10:30-16:00. Local Heritage Resource Centre open throughout the year. Admission: Adult £2.00, Child 90p, OAP £1.50, Family £5.00, Group £1.50 per person, child 45p. Location: 100 metres up Fore Street from Cookworthy Road car park.   Map Ref: 15

Dingles Steam Village

Dingles Steam Village, Milford, Lifton PL16 0AT   Tel: 01566 783425   Fax: 01566 783584
Email: richard@dinglesteam.co.uk   Web: www.dinglesteam.co.uk

Working heritage machinery. Road and industrial steam engines, early road signs, fairground history, vintage cars, lorries, tractors, motorcycles.

Opening Times: Jun to Sep Mon to Thu & weekends in school summer holiday 10:30-17:30.
Admission: Adult £6.00, Child/OAP £4.50, Family £19.50. Location: Rural west Devon.
Map Ref: 16

Museum of Dartmoor Life

Museum Courtyard, 3 West Street, Okehampton EX20 1HQ   Tel: 01837 52295
Fax: 01837 659330   Email: dartmoormuseum@eclipse.co.uk
Web: museumofdartmoorlife.eclipse.co.uk

Housed on three floors in an early 19th century mill, this lively museum tells the story of how people have lived, worked and played on and around Dartmoor through the centuries. It shows how the moorland has shaped their lives just as their work has shaped the moorland. In the Cranmere Gallery, temporary exhibitions feature local history, art and crafts.

Opening Times: Easter to Oct Mon to Sat 10:00-17:00, plus Sun Jun to Sep 10:00-16:30. Winter opening please telephone 01837 52295. Admission: Adult £2.00, Child/Student £1.00, OAP £1.80, Family £5.60. Group/School rates available. Location: Centre of Okehampton, next door to The White Hart Hotel.   Map Ref: 17

Devon

Elizabethan House

32 New Street, Plymouth PL1 2NA   Tel: 01752 304774

This rare survival of a sea captain's or merchant's house in the centre of Elizabethan Plymouth is 400 years old. The house retains most of its original architectural features and the rooms contain period furniture.

Opening Times: 28 Mar to 29 Sep Wed to Sun & BH 10:00-17:00. Admission: Adult £1.60, Child 60p. Location: Situated in the historic Barbican, follow brown tourism signs from city centre.   Map Ref: 18

Merchants House

33 St Andrews Street, Plymouth   Tel: 01752 304774

The largest and finest merchant's house of the 16th and 17th centuries left in Plymouth. Recently restored, it contains fascinating displays that bring the city's history to life. The exhibits include a Victorian schoolroom, a Plymouth Blitz exhibition, photographs of old Plymouth and the Park Pharmacy Shop.

Opening Times: Easter to end of Sep Tue to Fri 10:00-17:30, Sat & BH 10:00-17:00.
Admission: Adult £1.10, Child 60p. Location: Off Royal Parade near St Andrew's Church.
Follow signs.   Map Ref: 18

Plymouth City Museum & Art Gallery

Drake Circus, Plymouth PL4 8AJ   Tel: 01752 304774

The building has been a focal point of the city since 1910, and miraculously survived the Second World War Blitz. It holds important works of art including the Cottonian Collection, featuring paintings by Joshua Reynolds, the Plymouth artist, works by the Newlyn School, Maritime Paintings, Plymouth Silver and Porcelain. Natural History is also well represented. Tales from the City is a special exhibition involving 1000 people telling the story of 20th century Plymouth in their own words.

Opening Times: Tue to Fri 10:00-17:30, Sat & BH Mon 10:00-17:00. Admission: Free. Location: Near the city centre, opposite the university. Five minutes walk from the railway station.   Map Ref: 18

Saltram House

Plympton, Plymouth PL7 1UH   Tel: 01752 333500   Fax: 01752 336474
Email: dsaltr@smtp.ntrust.org.uk   Web: www.nationaltrust.org.uk

Saltram contains fine period furniture, china and pictures - including many portraits by Reynolds, four rooms decorated with original Chinese wallpaper. The house starred as Norland Park in the film Sense and Sensibility.

Opening Times: 24 Mar to 30 Sep Sat to Thu (open Good Friday) 12:00-16:30, 1 Oct to 3 Nov Sat to Thu 11:30-15:30. Admission: House & Gardens: Adult £6.00, Child £3.00, Under 5s Free, Family £15.00. Garden only £3.00. Location: Two miles west of Plympton, three and a half miles east of Plymouth City Centre, between A38 and A379.   Map Ref: 19

Smeatons Tower

The Hoe, Plymouth PL1 2PA   Tel: 01752 600608

The former Eddystone Lighthouse built in 1759 currently undergoing conservation and redisplay as the lighthouse would have been around the mid 19th century.

Opening Times: Tue to Sat 10:00-16:00. Admission: Adult £2.00, Child £1.00. Location: On Plymouth Hoe, five minutes walk from city centre.   Map Ref: 18

Morwellham Quay Museum

MORWELLHAM QUAY
HISTORIC PORT & COPPER MINE

Morwellham, Tavistock PL19 8JL   Tel: 01822 832766   Fax: 01822 833808
Email: enquiries@morwellham-quay.co.uk   Web: www.morwellham-quay.co.uk

Devon

See, they do know how to work! Children of all ages enjoy recreating the 1860s

The greatest copper port in Queen Victoria's empire lies 23 miles inland. The Tamar ketch 'Garlandstone' is moored at the quay; original cottages, shops and hostelry. 1860s costumed staff welcome visitors and host guided tours. Explore one of the copper mines travelling by tram deep underground. In grounds extending to 150 acres enjoy carriage rides; a visit to the farm; the wildlife reserve. Live the history - wear Victorian fashion. Activities throughout the day.

Opening Times: 25 Mar to 3 Nov daily 10:00-17:30. 4 Nov to 29 Mar daily 10:00-16:30. Admission: Main Season: Adult £8.90, Child £6.20, Family £26.00, Senior £7.80. Winter: Adult £5.00, Child £3.00, Senior £4.00. Location: Valley adjacent River Tamar, approx two miles from railway, four miles from Tavistock. Map Ref: 20

TIVERTON

Tiverton Museum of Mid-Devon Life

Beck's Square, Tiverton EX16 6PJ   Tel: 01884 256295   Email: tivertonmus@eclipse.uk Web: www.tivertonmuseum.org.uk

Large regional museum with collections of mid-Devon social history including agriculture, farm equipment, wagons and carts and GWR memorabilia, including Loco 1442 'Tivvy Bumper'. 15 galleries and display areas.

Opening Times: Feb to Xmas Mon to Fri 10:30-16:30, Sat 10:00-13:00. Admission: Adult £3.50, Child £1.00, OAP £2.50, Family £8.00. Group rates available. Location: Near to the town centre and bus station. Map Ref: 21

TORQUAY

Torquay Museum

529 Babbacombe Road, Torquay TQ1 1HG   Tel: 01803 293975 Fax: 01803 294186

Torquay Museum

Schoolgroup viewing the Japanese man-flying kite

Torquay Museum re-opened last year after extensive lottery funded improvements. New galleries include the Devon Farmhouse, re-designed Agatha Christie Exhibition celebrating Torquay's most famous daughter and the exciting and innovative Time Ark Gallery with interactives for children. See the giant replica of a Japanese man-flying kite in the entance hall. Also archaeology, including Kents Cevern material, natural history, geology, local history, Victoriana, world adornment, ancient Egyptians and wartime photography of Torquay. New local studies centre is open two days per week for local history research. Holiday activities and events.

Opening Times: Mon to Sat 10:00-17:00, Sun (Easter to Oct) 13:30-17:00. Admission: Adult £3.00, Child £1.50, OAP £2.00, Family £7.50. Location: Six minutes walking from clocktower at bottom of Torwood Street (near harbour). 32 bus stop outside. Map Ref: 22 13

Torre Abbey Historic House & Gallery

The Kings Drive, Torquay TQ2 5JE   Tel / Fax: 01803 293593   Email: torre-abbey@torbay.gov.uk   Web: www.torre-abbey.org.uk

Founded as a monastery in 1196, the present appearance of Torre Abbey dates from 1741-3, when it was remodelled by the Cary family. As well as nationally important monastic remains,

Devon

today's visitors can see over 20 historic rooms, which contain Devon's largest art gallery together with mementoes of crime writer Agatha Christie. Teas are served in the Victorian kitchen.

Opening Times: 1 Apr to 1 Nov daily 09:30-18:00. 2 Nov to Easter open to Groups by appointment only. Admission: Adult £3.50, Child £1.70, OAP/Student £3.00, Family £7.75. Location: On Torquay sea front, next to the Riviera Centre. Map Ref: 22

Torre Abbey, West Wing

TOTNES

Totnes Costume Museum
Bogan House, 43 High Street, Totnes TQ9 5NP

Themed costume exhibition, changed annually. Collection holds examples of fashionable clothing for men, women and children - 18th, 19th and 20th century. Displayed in one of the most interesting Tudor merchants' houses in Totnes.

Opening Times: 27 May to end Sep Tue to Fri 11:00-17:00. Oct by appointment. Admission: Adult £1.75, Child 75p, Concession £1.25, Family £3.50. Location: Centre of town, opposite Market Square. Map Ref: 23

Totnes Elizabethan Museum
70 Fore Street, Totnes TQ9 5RU   Tel / Fax: 01803 863821   Email: totnes.museum@virgin.net

Grade I Elizabethan Merchant's House c.1575. Collections cover local history, archaeology, crafts, industries, clocks, costumes etc. Also room devoted to computer pioneer Charles Babbage and his inventions.

Opening Times: Apr to Oct Mon to Fri 10:30-17:00. Other times by appointment. Admission: Adult £1.50, accompanied Child 25p, OAP/Student/Concession £1.00, Totnes residents (with proof) Free. Location: In main street, very central. Map Ref: 23

UMBERLEIGH

Cobbaton Combat Collection
Chittlehampton, Umberleigh EX37 9RZ   Tel: 01769 540 740   Fax: 01769 540 141 Email: info@cobbatoncombat.co.uk   Web: www.cobbatoncombat.co.uk

Over 60 mainly World War II vehicles and artillery pieces, plus thousands of smaller items. All undercover, including Home Front building. Militaria and souvenir shop, NAAFI cafeteria, disabled facilities, outdoor children's play vehicles.

Opening Times: Easter to end Oct daily 10:00-17:00 Nov to end Mar weekdays 10:00-16:00. Admission: Adult £4.25, Child £2.75, OAP £3.75. Location: Six miles south east of Barnstaple, eight miles west of South Molton. Map Ref: 24

YELVERTON

Buckland Abbey
Yelverton PL20 6EY   Tel: 01822 853607   Fax: 01822 855448 Email: dbamcx@smtp.ntrust.co.uk   Web: www.nationaltrust.org.uk

THE NATIONAL TRUST

Tucked away in its own secluded valley above the River Tavy, Buckland was originally a small but influential Cistercian monastery. The house has rich associations with Sir Francis Drake and contains much interesting memorabilia. There are exhibitions of seven centuries of history at Buckland, as well as a magnificent monastic barn, craft workshop, herb garden and delightful estate walks.

Buckland Abbey, Drake's former home, from the south-west

Opening Times: Nov to 12 Apr Sat & Sun 14:00-17:00 (closed Xmas to mid Feb), 12 Apr to end Oct daily except Thu 10:30-17:30. Admission: House & Garden: Adult £5.00, Child £2.50. Garden: Adult £2.50, Child £1.20. Party: Adult £3.90, Child £1.90 (15 or more). Location: Six miles south of Tavistock, 11 miles north of Plymouth. Map Ref: 25

Dorset has great literary connections, there being few parts of the county that Thomas Hardy has not lovingly written about. It is renowned for its beautiful countryside, but can also lay claim to some delightful seaside towns. Poole, once the haunt of pirates and smugglers, was developed as a major port in the 13th century.

The county is rich in history and has a wonderfully wide and comprehensive selection of exhibitions, displays and demonstrations portraying its diverse heritage as well as subjects from Dinosaurs to Tutankhamun.

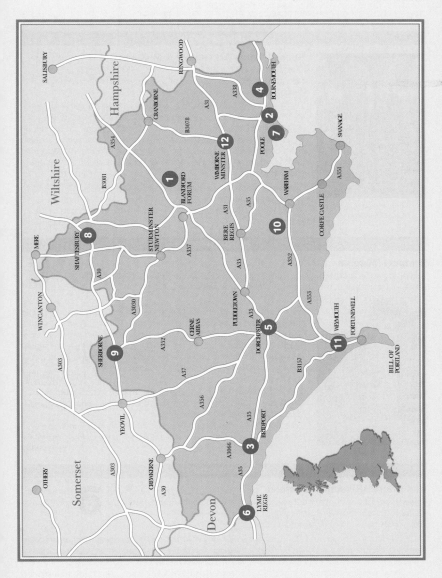

The Red Map References should be used to locate Museums etc on the pages that follow

Dorset

BLANDFORD CAMP

Royal Signals Museum

Blandford Camp DT11 8RH   Tel: 01258 482248   Fax: 01258 482084   Email: royalsignals
Web: www.royalsignals.army.org.uk/museum

Interactive communications, science and technology. Plus a unique series of hands-on exhibitions featuring Enigma, SOE and Elite Special Forces. Prize winning Fun and Discovery trails for children.

Opening Times: All year Mon to Fri 10:00-17:00, end of Feb to Oct also Sat & Sun 10:00-16:00. Closed 2 weeks Xmas.   Admission: Adult £4.50, Child £2.50, OAP £3.50, Family £11.00.
Location: On Blandford Camp, follow the signs from A354 Bypass and bring some form of ID.
Map Ref: 1

BOURNEMOUTH

The Russell-Cotes
Art Gallery & Museum

Russell-Cotes Art Gallery & Museum

East Cliff, Bournemouth BH1 3AA   Tel: 01202 451858
Fax: 01202 451851   Email: kathy.walker@bournemouth.gov.uk
Web: www.russell-cotes.bournemouth.gov.uk

The Art Gallery and Museum is a Victorian villa, built and furnished by Sir Merton and Lady Annie Russell-Cotes and gifted to the town in 1908. The Victorian house is of architectural and historic importance with a remarkable interior, which houses a diverse collection of British fine art and ethnographic objects. Additional art galleries were built in the 1920s to house more of the founder's collections.

Opening Times: Tue to Sun 10:00-17:00. Closed Mon, Good Friday and 25 Dec.   Admission: Free.   Location: On the cliff top overlooking the sea. Five minute walk from the town centre to the east.
Map Ref: 2

BRIDPORT

Bridport Museum

South Street, Bridport DT6 3NR   Tel: 01308 458703/422116   Fax: 01308 458704
Email: s.hunt@westdorset-dc.gov.uk   Web: www.westdorset-dc.gov.uk

From Romans to ropemaking. The development of Bridport is told from its Saxon origins to the present day. The history of the world-famous rope and net industry is covered, along with stories of local people and events. Finds from a nearby Roman hillfort are on display. Temporary exhibitions show the extensive fine art and photograph collections.

Opening Times: Apr to Oct Mon to Sat 10:00-17:00. Closed Sun.
Admission: Adult £2.00, accompanied Child Free, unaccompanied Child 50p.   Location: In town centre.
Exhibitions & Events 2003 : Bridport Museum will be marking the 750th Anniversary of the First Royal Charter to be granted to the town with a special exhibition.
Map Ref: 3

CHRISTCHURCH

Red House Museum & Gardens
  Hampshire County Council

Quay Road, Christchurch BH23 1BU   Tel: 01202 482860   Fax: 01202
481924   Email: musmjh@hants.gov.uk
Web: www.hants.gov.uk/museum/redhouse

The Red House Museum and Gardens (once a Georgian Workhouse) is the setting for outstanding displays of local social and natural history. Highlights include an interactive archaeology gallery, a display of Arthur Romney Green furniture in a 1930s room setting and a reconstruction of a local 19th century High Street taxidermist. Special exhibitions of contemporary and traditional art and an ever changing garden make every visit a new one.

Dorset

Opening Times: Tue to Sat 10:00-17:00, Sun 14:00-17:00. Open spring and summer BH Mon. Admission: Adult £1.50, Concession 80p, Family £3.50. Free to residents of Hants & Dorset C.C. and Christchurch Borough. Location: Near town centre and Christchurch Priory, close to Quay.

Exhibitions & Events 2003 : 18 Jan to 2 Mar: Exploring Space - interactive exhibition for families, 8 Mar to 20 Apr: Heart and Matter - the illustations to Graham Green and Raymond Chandler by Geoff Grandfield, 3 May to 22 Jun: The Chosen Letter - created and creative shapes, 7 to 22 Jun: In the Garden - Arts in the Garden - with a watercolour challenge

The Red HouseMuseum and Gardens.   Map Ref: 4

DORCHESTER

Dinosaur Museum

Icen Way, Dorchester DT1 1EW Tel: 01305 269880   Fax: 01305 268885
Email: info@dinosaur-museum.org.uk Web: www.dinosaur-museum.org.uk

Explore the enthralling pre-historic world of dinosaurs through actual fossils, skeletons, and life-size dinosaur reconstructions combined with hands-on, video and computer displays at this award-winning museum. The museum's innovative and friendly approach mean it was voted one of Britain's top ten Hands-On Museums and make it a must for all families. It's frequently featured on national television.

Opening Times: Apr to Oct daily 09:30-17:30, Nov to Mar daily 10:00-16:30. Closed 24-26 Dec. Admission: Adult £5.50, Child £3.95, Under 4s Free, OAP/Student £4.75, Family £15.95.

Tyrannosaurus rex

Location: In centre of town - follow pedestrian signposts from car parks. Exhibitions & Events 2003 : 18 Apr to 21 Apr: The Great Dinosaur Egg Hunt at the Dinosaur Museum.   Map Ref: 5

Dorset County Museum

High West Street, Dorchester DT1 1XA Tel: 01305 262735 Fax: 01305 257180
Email: dorsetcountymuseum@dor-mus.demon.co.uk Web: www.dorsetcountymuseum.org

Free audio-guides cover 60 key exhibits. Enjoy walking on the royal mosaic floors in the magnificent Victorian Hall. Visit the newly opened Dorchester Gallery depicting Dorchester's history from six thousand years ago to today. Other galleries include Archaeology (illustrating the life of Maiden Castle), Geology, Natural History and The Dorset Writers Gallery.

This houses the largest collection of Thomas Hardy memorabilia in the world, and includes

Roman Mosaic Floors

a reconstruction of the Max Gate Study. There is a variety of children's trails and interactives, making it a museum for all the family.

Opening Times: Nov to Apr Mon to Sat 10:00-17:00, May to Oct daily 10:00-17:00. Open most BH.

Interactive in the Thomas Hardy Gallery

Admission: Adult £3.75, Child £1.75, Concession £2.45, Family £8.95. Location: In middle of town centre.   Map Ref: 5

Guided or Private Tours	Disabled Access	Gift Shop or Sales Point	Café or Refreshments	Restaurant	Car Parking

Dorset Teddy Bear Museum

Antelope Walk, Dorchester DT1 1BE   Tel: 01305 263200   Fax: 01305 268885
Email: info@teddybearhouse.co.uk   Web: www.teddybearhouse.co.uk

Visit Edward Bear and his extended family of human-sized teddy bears in their Edwardian style home, then marvel at bears from throughout the last century displayed in atmospheric settings.

Opening Times: Daily 09:30-17:00. Closed 25-26 Dec. Admission: Adult £2.95, Child £1.95, Family £8.95. Location: In centre of Dorchester, pedestrian signposted from car parks.
Map Ref: 5

The Keep Military Museum

1 Bridport Road, Dorchester DT1 1RN   Tel: 01305 264066   Fax: 01305 250373
Email: keep.museum@talk21.com   Web: www.keepmilitarymuseum.org

A military museum housing the artefacts of the Infantry and Yeomanry regiments of Devon and Dorset, housed in a Grade II listed building.

Opening Times: Apr to Sep Mon to Sat 09:30-17:00, Sun (Jul to Aug) 10:00-16:00. Oct to Mar Tue to Sat 09:30-17:00. Admission: Adult £3.00, Child/OAP £2.00. Group/Family rates available. Location: On the junction of Bridport Road and High West Street at the top of the town.
Map Ref: 5

Old Crown Court & Cells

58/60 High West Street, Dorchester DT1 1UZ   Tel: 01305 252241   Fax: 01305 257039
Email: tourism@westdorset-de.gov.uk   Web: www.westdorset.com

The Court is famous for the trial of the Tolpuddle Martyrs in 1834. Experience four centuries of gruesome crime and punishment in a setting little changed over the years. Stand in the dock and sit in the dimly lit Cells where prisoners waited for their appearance before the judge.

1. Old Crown Court, Dorchester.
©West Dorset District Council

Opening Times: Court Room & Cells: 21 Jul to 12 Sep Mon to Fri 14:00-16:00, (excluding BH) & Wed 10:00-12:00. Court Room only: at other times during office hours. Admission: Charge for Adults, accompanied Under 16s Free. Location: Town centre approx. 300 metres from Top o' Town coach/car park.
Exhibitions & Events 2003 : 19 & 20 Jul: Tolpuddle Martyrs Festival - Commemorating the Martyrs and the Trade Union Movement. Take the chance to visit the Court and Cells. Open Sat 10:00-13:00 & Sun 10:00-13:00, 13 & 14 Sep: Civic Trust Heritage Open Days - Court & Cells open Sat 10:00-17:00 & Sun 14:00-16:00.   Map Ref: 5

Terracotta Warriors Museum

High East Street, Dorchester DT1 1JU   Tel: 01305 266040   Fax: 01305 268885
Email: info@terracottawarriors.co.uk   Web: www.terracottawarriors.co.uk

The only museum devoted to the terracotta warriors - 8th Wonder of the Ancient World - outside of China. See unique museum replicas from China, costumes and armour recreated, and multimedia presentations.

Opening Times: Daily 10:00-17:30. Please phone for winter hours. Closed 25-26 Dec. Admission: Adult £4.75, Child £2.95, Under 5s Free, OAP/Student £3.75, Family £13.95. Location: In centre of Dorchester.
Map Ref: 5

Dorset

The Golden Funerary Mask

Tutankhamun Exhibition   ♿ ▩

High West Street, Dorchester DT1 1UW
Tel: 01305 269571   Fax: 01305 268885
Email: info@tutankhamun-exhibition.co.uk
Web: www.tutankhamun-exhibition.co.uk

Experience the mystery and the wonder of the world's greatest discovery of ancient treasure. Tutankhamun's tomb, treasures, jewels and mummified body are exquisitely recreated through sight, sound and smell. Be at the discovery, explore the ante-chamber and the burial chamber. Finally marvel at the superb facsimilies of Tutankhamun's greatest golden treasures including the golden Funerary Mask and the Harpooner.

Opening Times: Apr to Oct daily 09:30-17:30, Nov to Mar Mon to Fri 09:30-17:00, Sat & Sun 10:00-17:00. Closed 24-26 Dec.
Admission: Adult £5.50, Child £3.95, Under 5s Free, OAP/Student £4.75, Family £15.95.   Location: In centre of Dorchester, pedestrian signposted from car parks.

Map Ref: 5

LYME REGIS

Lyme Regis Philpot Museum

▩ THE AWARD-WINNING
LYME REGIS MUSEUM

Bridge Street, Lyme Regis DT7 3QA   Tel: 01297 443370
Email: info@lymeregismuseum.co.uk   Web: www.lymeregismuseum.co.uk

The museum tells the story of Lyme Regis and its landscape, with award winning displays featuring: early history from prehistoric to civil war; the Cobb harbour and Lyme's involvement with the sea; fossils and geology, and the importance of local personalities such as Mary Anning; Lyme's literary connections from Henry Fielding and Jane Austen to John Fowles.

Lyme Regis Museum 'The Philpot'

Opening Times: Apr to Oct Mon to Sat 10:00-17:00, Sun 11:00-17:00. Nov to Mar Sat 10:00-17:00, Sun 11:00-17:00, weekdays in school holidays. Admission: Adult £1.60, Child 60p, Concession £1.30. Location: In the centre of town facing the sea and beside the Guildhall and tourist information centre. Map Ref: 6

POOLE

Scaplen's Court Museum

High Street, Poole BH15 1BW   Tel: 01202 262600   Fax: 01202 262622
Email: museums@poole.gov.uk   Web: www.poole.gov.uk

Scaplen's Court is part of the museum's education service. It is only open to the general public during the month of August or for special events, which are advertised locally.

Opening Times: Aug Mon to Sat 10:00-17:00, Sun 12:00-17:00.   Admission: Free.
Location: Adjacent to Waterfront Museum, off Poole Quay.   Map Ref: 7

Waterfront Museum   ♿

4 High Street, Poole BH15 1BW   Tel: 01202 262600   Fax: 01202 262622
Email: museums@poole.gov.uk   Web: www.poole.gov.uk

Waterfront Museum tells of Poole's history. Displays include a street scene, Roman occupation, trade with Newfoundland, the Studland Bay Wreck and more. Poole Local History Centre offers research facilities on the history of the town.

Opening Times: Apr to Oct Mon to Sat 10:00-17:00, Sun 12:00-17:00. Nov to Mar Mon to Sat 10:00-15:00, Sun 12:00-15:00.   Admission: Free.   Location: Adjacent to Poole Quay
Map Ref: 7

SHAFTESBURY

Shaftesbury Abbey Museum & Garden   ♿ ▩

Park Walk, Shaftesbury SP7 8JR   Tel / Fax: 01747 852910
Email: anna@shaftesburyabbey.fsnet.co.uk   Web: www.shaftesburyabbey.co.uk

Dorset

In the heart of this historic hill top town, only a short distance from the famous Gold Hill, are the excavated foundations of the Abbey church, once the most important Benedictine community for women in the country.

Opening Times: Apr to Oct daily 10:00-17:00. Admission: Adult £2.00, Child 60p, OAP £1.50. Location: Five minutes from town centre. Map Ref: 8

Shaftesbury Town Museum
Gold Hill, Shaftesbury SP7 8JW Tel: 01747 852157

Special items reflecting life in Shaftesbury, domestically and agriculturally with some civic items. Two floors with special displays each year.

Opening Times: Easter to end Oct daily 10:30-16:30. Admission: Adult £1.00, Child Free. Location: Top of Gold Hill, behind Town Hall, centre of town. Map Ref: 8

SHERBORNE

Sherborne Castle

New Road, Sherborne DT9 5NR Tel: 01935 813182 Fax: 01935 816727
Email: enquiries@sherbornecastle.com Web: www.sherbornecastle.com

Historic country house built by Sir Walter Raleigh and extended by the Digby family, to whom it still belongs. Fine collections of pictures, English furniture, Oriental and European ceramics representing four hundred years of collecting. Delightful setting in parkland landscaped by Capability Brown. Walks round the lake give views of the deer park and ruined Old Castle.

Opening Times: Apr to Oct daily except Mon & Fri 11:00-16:30. Also open BH. Admission: Gardens: Adult £3.25, Child Free. Castle & Gardens: Adult £6.00, Child Free, OAP £5.50. Location: Near town centre, five minute walk from London/Waterloo to Exeter mainline railway. Map Ref: 9

Sherborne Castle Dorset

WAREHAM

Tank Museum

Bovington, near Wool, Wareham BH20 6JG Tel: 01929 405096 Fax: 01929 405360 Email: davidb@tankmuseum.co.uk Web: www.tankmuseum.co.uk

The Tank Museum houses the world's finest international indoor collection of Armoured Fighting Vehicles; there are 150 vehicles from 26 different countries. Free audio guides available, large car park, outdoor children's play area, large specialist gift and model shop and licensed restaurant. During school holidays the exhibits are brought to life with live demonstrations and Tanks in Action displays throughout the summer.

Opening Times: Daily 10:00-17:00. Closed Xmas. Admission: Please phone for prices. Location: In the village of Bovington, near Wool which is a main-line station from Waterloo. Map Ref: 10

The famous Bovington Tiger

Museums • Galleries • Historic Houses

Please let us know of any collections that are not listed in this guide that you feel should be listed. E-mail us on *editor@tomorrows.co.uk* or return the Report Form on page 448

Dorset

Nothe Fort

Barrack Road, Weymouth DT4 8UF   Tel: 01305 766626

A dramatically restored Victorian fort with ramparts, gun floors and magazines furnished as a museum of coastal defence. 70 rooms of guns, equipment, displays, models, artefact and military memorabilia.

Opening Times: 12 Apr to 27 Apr, 1 May to 30 Sep, 26 Oct to 2 Nov Mon to Sun all year 10:30-17:30 (16:30 winters).   Admission: Adult £3.50, Concessions £2.50.   Location: 15 minute walk from town centre or rowboat ferry from Pavilion.   Map Ref: 11

Weymouth Museum & Exhibition Gallery

Brewers' Quay, Hope Square, Weymouth DT4 8TR
Tel: 01305 777622   Fax: 01305 761680

2003 Exhibition - Come into Our Garden - A Celebration of the 125 years of local gardening by the Broadwey, Upwey and District Horticultural Society, giving an insight into the history and development of gardening through the ages.

Opening Times: Daily 10:00-17:00, except second two weeks in Jan. Admission: Free. Location: Situated at the Brewers Quay Complex. Follow brown signs.   Exhibitions & Events 2003 : Mar 24 to Dec 31: Come into Our Garden.   Map Ref: 11

Statue of George III, stands on a fine Georgian Esplanade

Priest's House Museum & Garden

23/27 High Street, Wimborne Minster BH21 1HR   Tel / Fax: 01202 882533
Email: priestshouse@eastdorset.gov.uk

The Victorian Kitchen

The Priest's House is set in an historic town house. A series of period rooms take the visitor back through the centuries. The Museum tells the story of East Dorset from ancient to modern times. With hands-on activities in the the Victorian schoolroom and Galleries of Childhood and Archaeology - there is plenty to do. The walled garden behind the house is a tranquil retreat in the centre of town. New for 2003 - Costume & Textile Gallery.

Opening Times: 1 Apr to 31 Oct Mon to Sat 10:00-16:30. Admission: Adult £2.50, Child £1.00, OAP/Student £1.90, Family £6.50. Location: Centre of Wimborne town, opposite the Minster.   Map Ref: 12

Essex is well endowed with interesting towns. Colchester, claiming to be Britain's oldest recorded town, has Europe's biggest Norman keep. Ancient Chelmsford is Essex's county town, once a New Town planned in 1199 by the Bishop of London. All of these towns have their stories to tell in a plethora of splendid museums.

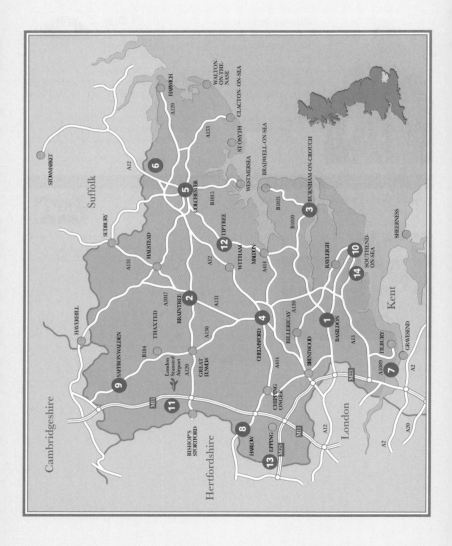

The Red Map References should be used to locate Museums etc on the pages that follow

BASILDON

The Haven Plotlands Museum

Langdon Visitor Centre, Third Avenue, Lower Duton Road, Basildon SS16 6EB Tel: 01268 419103 Fax: 01268 546137 Email: melaniel@essexwt.org.uk Web: www.essexwt.org.uk

Original 1930s Plotland home has been restored. Fully furnished with 1930s style furnishings, memorabilia, kitchen/garden implements. The Haven offers people the chance to enjoy their memories.

Opening Times: Mar to Oct Tue to Sun 13:30-16:30. Other times by arrangement.
Admission: Free; donations appreciated. Location: On a nature reserve. Access by public transport limited.
Map Ref: 1

BRAINTREE

Braintree District Museum

Town Hall Centre, Market Square, Braintree CM7 3YG Tel: 01376 325266 Fax: 01376 344345 Email: jean@bdcmuseum.demon.co.uk

The Victorian Schoolroom

The Museum's Gallery exhibits interpret the diverse local industrial heritage of this area which has a major influence on 20th century life in England and the world, particularly in silks, man-made textiles and metal window design. The natural historian John Ray, who was born in the district, has a gallery devoted to his life and work.

Opening Times: Mon to Sat & BH 10:00-17:00, Oct to Dec Sun 13:00-16:00. Admission: District visitors: Adult £1.00, Concession 50p. All other visitors Adult £2.00, Concession £1.00. Location: Town centre, five minutes from railway station and one minute from bus station.
Map Ref: 2

BURNHAM-ON-CROUCH

Mangapps Farm Railway Museum

Mangapps Farm, Burnham-on-Crouch CM0 8QQ Tel: 01621 784898

Areas of special interest include one of the finest displays of signalling equipment on public view. A large, indoor museum containing comprehensive displays of railway memorabilia of particular East Anglian interest.

Opening Times: Sat, Sun & BH, every day Easter fortnight & Aug 13:00-17:00. Closed Xmas.
Admission: Adult £4.00, Child £2.00, Under 4s Free, OAP £3.00. Location: One mile north Burnham-on-Crouch.
Map Ref: 3

CHELMSFORD

Chelmsford Museum & the Essex Regiment Museum

Oaklands Park, Moulsham Street, Chelmsford CM2 9AQ Tel: 01245 615100 Fax: 01245 611250 Email: oaklands@chelmsfordbc.gov.uk Web: www.chelmsfordmuseums.co.uk

Local history museum featuring 'The Story of Chelmsford' exhibition, natural history, social history, costume, ceramics, early English drinking glasses, coins. The Essex Regiment Museum tells the story of the local county regiment.

Opening Times: Mon to Sat 10:00-17:00. Sun 14:00-17:00 in Summertime, 13:00-16:00 in Wintertime. Closed Good Friday & Xmas. Admission: Free. Location: Three quarters of a mile from town centre.
Map Ref: 4

Museums • Galleries • Historic Houses

Please let us know of any collections that are not listed in this guide that you feel should be listed. E-mail us on *editor@tomorrows.co.uk* or return the Report Form on page 448

Essex

COLCHESTER

Castle Museum

Castle Park, Colchester CO1 1TJ   Tel: 01206 282939   Fax: 01206 282925
Web: www.colchestermuseums.org.uk

A visit to Colchester Castle Museum takes you through 2000 years of some of the most important events in British history. The Castle is the largest keep ever built by the Normans and is constructed on the foundations of Roman Temple of Claudius. An award winning museum featuring hands-on displays and lively events programme.

Opening Times: Mon to Sat 10:00-17:00, Sun 11:00-17:00.   Admission: Adult £4.00, Child £2.70, OAP/Concession £2.70, Family £10.80.
Location: Central off high street, Castle park. Five mins walk from bus station and town railway station. Map Ref: 5

Hollytrees Museum

High Street, Colchester CO1 1UG   Tel: 01206 282940   Fax: 01206 282925
Web: www.colchestermuseums.org.uk

Hollytrees Museum is in a beautiful Georgian town house built in 1718 interpreting 300 years of domestic life with fun and humour in mind. Highlights are the Childhood Gallery and interactive displays.

Opening Times: Mon to Sat 10:00-17:00, Sun 11:00-17:00. Admission: Free. Location: Off high street, in Castle Park five minutes from bus and railway station.   Map Ref: 5

Natural History Museum

All Saint's Church, High Street, Colchester CO1 1DN   Tel: 01206 282941   Fax: 01206 282925
Web: www.colchestermuseums.org.uk

The Natural History Museum offers an interesting perspective on the natural history of Essex from the ice age to the present day, with many hands-on displays, and summer events programme.

Opening Times: Mon to Sat 10:00-17:00, Sun 11:00-17:00. Admission: Free. Location: End of high street five minutes from bus and train station.   Map Ref: 5

Tymperleys Clock Museum

Trinity Street, Colchester CO1 1JN   Tel: 01206 282943   Fax: 01206 282925
Web: www.colchestermuseums.org.uk

Tymperleys has a fine display of Colchester made clocks from the outstanding Mason collection. It is situated in a beautiful restored 15th century timber-framed house with medieval herb garden in the grounds.

Opening Times: May to Oct Tue to Sat 10:00-13:00 & 14:00-17:00. Admission: Free.
Location: Town centre.   Map Ref: 5

DEDHAM

Sir Alfred Munnings Art Museum

Castle House, Dedham CO7 6AZ   Tel: 01206 322127

The home, studios and grounds where Sir Alfred Munnings KCVO PRA lived and worked for 40 years until his death in 1959. A large collection of his works shown in his former home. Annual special exhibition.

Opening Times: Easter Sun to 1st Sun in Oct Wed & Sun 14:00-17:00, also Aug Thu & Sat 14:00-17:00. Groups by appointment. Admission: Adult £3.00, Child 50p, Concession £2.00.
Location: Three quarters of a mile from centre of Dedham.   Map Ref: 6

GRAYS

Thurrock Museum

Thameside Complex, Orsett Road, Grays RM17 5DX   Tel: 01375 382555   Fax: 01375 392666
Email: jcatton@thurrock.gov.uk   Web: www.thurrock.gov.uk/museum

Local history collection from archaeology to social history collections covering the history of Thurrock.

Opening Times: Mon to Sat 09:00-17:00. Closed Sun. Admission: Free. Location: Near town centre, five minutes walk from Grays Railway Station.   Map Ref: 7

Essex

The Museum of Harlow

Muskham Road, Off First Avenue, Harlow CM20 2LF   Tel: 01279 454959   Fax: 01279 626094
Email: tmoh@harlow.gov.uk   Web: www.tmoh.com

The museum, set within its own walled gardens, tells the story of the development of Harlow from its earliest origins 7000 years ago through to the present day.

Opening Times: Tue to Fri 10:00-17:00, Sat 10:00-12:30 & 13:30-17:00.   Admission: Free.
Location: Located at Muskham Road, off First Avenue. Approx one kilometre from Harlow Mill
Station.   Map Ref: 8

Audley End House & Gardens

Audley End, Saffron Walden CB11 4JF   Tel: 01799 522842

Audley End was one of the great wonders of the nation when it was built by the first Earl of Suffolk, Lord Treasurer to James I. Some interiors were remodelled in the 18th century by Robert Adam, and the grounds were landscaped by Capability Brown. Picture collections, comprising family portraits and Old Master paintings, furniture, silver, mounted birds and animals, and more.

Opening Times: Please phone for details.
Admission: House & Grounds: Adult £8.00, Child £4.00,
Concession £6.00, Family £20.00. Grounds only: Adult
£4.00, Child £2.00, Concession £3.00, Family £10.00.

The Chapel

Location: One mile west of Saffron Walden on B1383.   Map Ref: 9

Saffron Walden Museum

Museum Street, Saffron Walden CB10 1JL   Tel / Fax: 01799 510333
Email: museum@uttlesford.gov.uk

Friendly, family-size museum. Winner Best Museum of Social History. Good disabled access. Moccasins, mummy cases, woolly mammoths and 'Wallace The Lion' - something for all ages.

Opening Times: Mar to Oct Mon to Sat 10:00-17:00 Sun & BH 14:00-17:00. Nov to Feb Mon to
Sat 10:00-16:30 Sun & BH 14:00-16:30. Closed 24-25 Dec.   Admission: Adult £1.00, Child
Free, Concession 50p.   Location: Close to Parish Church, castle ruins in grounds.   Map Ref: 9

Prittlewell Priory

Priory Park, Victoria Avenue, Southend-on-Sea   Tel: 01702 342878   Fax: 01702 349806
Email: southendmuseum@hotmail.com   Web: www.southendmuseums.co.uk

12th century Cluniac Priory with later additions, extensively restored in the 1920s, set in an attractive park. Displays focus on the history of the Priory itself, local wildlife and also on the museum's fine collection of radios and televisions (Ekco was a local firm). A fine series of recently restored panel paintings by artist Alan Sorrell are also on show.

Opening Times: Tue to Sat 10:00-13:00 & 14:00-17:00.
Closed Sun, Mon and BH.   Admission: Free.
Location: In Priory Park, 1 kilometre north of town centre.
Map Ref: 10

Prittlewell Priory from the Old World Gardens

Guided or Private Tours	Disabled Access	Gift Shop or Sales Point	Café or Refreshments	Restaurant	Car Parking

Southchurch Hall

Southchurch Hall Close, Southchurch, Southend-on-Sea SS1 2TE   Tel: 01702 467671
Fax: 01702 439806   Email: southendmuseums@hotmail.com
Web: www.southendmuseums.co.uk

Southchurch Hall from the South

A moated early 14th century timber framed manor house set in gardens. It has rooms furnished in medieval, Tudor and Victorian styles. An exhibition room tells the story of the Hall and there are exhibits from excavations near the moat. The museum specialises in historic presentations to school children and also hosts various events, such as open days, during the year.

Opening Times: Tue to Sat 10:00-13:00 & 14:00-17:00 (mornings reserved for schools during term time). Closed Sun, Mon and BH.   Admission: Free.   Location: One kilometre east of town centre, five minutes walk from Southend East Railway Station.

Map Ref: 10

Southend Central Museum & Planetarium

Victoria Avenue, Southend-on-Sea SS2 6EW   Tel: 01702 434449   Fax: 01702 349806
Email: southendmuseums@hotmail.com   Web: www.southendmuseums.co.uk

The new Discovery Centre

The museum has displays of local history, geology and wildlife with special sections on the Thames Estuary and Victorian Life. An imposing feature, dominating the main hall, is the late medieval 'Reynolds' fireplace, originally part of a building in nearby Prittlewell. The museum's Discovery Centre, opened in 2000, is an interactive centre where visitors can handle exhibits. Video microscopes allow visitors to examine a range of specimens, from London Clay fossils to coins and garden pests, in amazing detail. In addition, they

A demonstration in the Discovery Centre

can try and solve problems on topic tables and refer to SID, a rapidly growing database of historic local photographs which has a particularly fine selection of views of Southend from Victorian times to the 1960s. Upstairs, Southend Planetarium allows visitors to sit back and enjoy a forty minute tour of the Universe presented by a guide lecturer. Investigate the scale of Space, details of the Sun and the planets or take a look at the myths and legends of the skies. (Please note that under 5s are not admitted to the planetarium).

Opening Times: Tue to Sat 10:00-17:00, closed Sun, Mon and BH. Planetarium open Wed to Sat at 11:00, 14:00 and 16:00.   Admission: Museum Free. Planetarium Adult £2.25, Child £1.60, OAP £1.60, Group rates on request.   Location: In town centre, next to Southend Victoria Railway Station.   Exhibitions & Events 2003 : 8 Mar to 16 Mar: Science Week, programme of events, 6 Apr: Amphibian Awareness Day, 4 May to 11 May: Local History Week, displays, guided walks etc, 2 Nov to 7 Dec: Essex Salon of Photography.

Map Ref: 10

House on the Hill Museums Adventure

Stansted CM24 8SP   Tel: 01279 813237   Fax: 01279 816391   Web: www.gold.enta.net

A huge range of toys and games from later Victorian times up to the 1970s - about 75,000 exhibits in total.

Opening Times: Daily 10:00-17:00. Closed Xmas & New Year.   Admission: Adult £3.80, Child £2.80, OAP £3.50.   Location: Adjacent to Mountfitchet Castle, in the centre of Stansted village.

Map Ref: 11

TIPTREE

Tiptree Museum

Wilkin & Sons Ltd, Tiptree CO5 0RF Tel: 01621 815407 Fax: 01621 814555 Email: tiptree@tiptree.com Web: www.tiptree.com

Renovated Farm Building at Tiptree

Over 50 years ago John Wilkin grandson of the founder Arthur Charles Wilkin began collecting the paraphernalia of preserve making and Essex village life, storing away pictures, documents and redundant machines. With the opening of the museum in a renovated farm building in 1995, John Wilkin's foresight was at last rewarded and visitors can now see how life was and how the art of jam making has advanced over the years.

Opening Times: Mon to Fri 10:00-17:00. During Jun, Jul & Aug also open Sun 12:00-17:00. Closed Xmas week. Admission: Free. Location: Tiptree is 15 minutes from Colchester and the Jam Factory & Museum is along the B1023 heading towards Tollesbury.

Map Ref: 12

WALTHAM ABBEY

Epping Forest District Museum

39/41 Sun Street, Waltham Abbey EN9 1EL Tel: 01992 716882 Fax: 01992 700427 Email: museum@efdc.fsnet.co.uk Web: www.eppingforestdistrictmuseum.org.uk

The museum tells the story of the people who have lived and worked in this part of West Essex, from the earliest inhabitants to the present. Housed in a building dating to 1520, with a changing programme of temporary exhibitions.

Opening Times: Mon & Fri 14:00-17:00, Sun (1 May to 30 Sep) 14:00-17:00, Tue 12:00-17:00, Sat 10:00-17:00. Wed & Thu Group bookings available. Admission: Free. Location: Near town centre.

Map Ref: 13

WESTCLIFF-ON-SEA

Beecroft Art Gallery

Station Road, Westcliff-on-Sea, Westcliff-on-Sea SS0 7RA Tel: 01702 347418 Fax: 01702 347681 Web: www.beecroft-art-gallery.co.uk

Edward B Seago (1910-1974).
The Doge's Palace, Venice

The gallery's fine collection of over 2,000 works includes a selection of Dutch and Flemish 17th century paintings by artists such as Molenaer, Ruisdael and Berchem. Also represented is a fair selection of 19th century artists including Rossetti, with a fine pencil drawing of model Fanny Cornforth, Constable with an early oil sketch of the Stour valley and Edward Lear with a watercolour of Egypt, 20th century works including paintings by Carel Weight, the Great Bardfield Group and a fine bronze by Jacob Epstein. The local artist Alan Sorrell is well represented by his 'Drawings of Nubia' series depicting a visit to Egypt prior to the building of the Aswan Dam. Of particular interest is the Thorpe Smith Collection of local landscape views, containing paintings, drawings and prints from as early as 1803. A selection of the finest works is always on show. There is a range of temporary exhibitions. Particularly popular are the summer 'Essex Open Exhibition', a selected show open to artists working and living in Essex, and the annual Christmas Show with a range of items suitable for presents.

Dante Gabriel Rossetti
(1828-1882). Fanny Cornforth

Opening Times: Tue to Sat 10:00-13:00 & 14:00-17:00. Closed Sun and Mon, but open at least one Sun during exhibitions. Admission: Free. Location: Ten minute walk from town centre, opposite Cliffs Pavilion. Exhibitions & Events 2003 : 12 Jan to 23 Feb: Andrew Cookson: atmospheric charcoal drawings, 2 Mar to 13 Apr: Southend Art Club Annual Exhibition, 20 Apr to 1 Jun: 'Celebrating Local History', views of Southend over the last 200 years, 22 Jun to 17 Aug: 44th Essex Open Exhibition, 24 Aug to 5 Oct: 'The Art of Fashion' costume and portraits from the gallery collection, 12 Oct to 9 Nov: Southend Schools Exhibition, 16 Nov to 21 Dec: Christmas Exhibition.

Map Ref: 14

Cheltenham, the small spa village, was transformed into an elegant fashionable town in 1788 through the visit of George III and the consequent patronage. Gloucester with its magnificent cathedral, the nave of which is dominated by the largest stained glass window in Britain created in 1349, was once a commercially important port.

The county's museums tell the story of its Arts and Crafts, its Roman occupation, its waterways, railways, the Forest of Dean and its heritage.

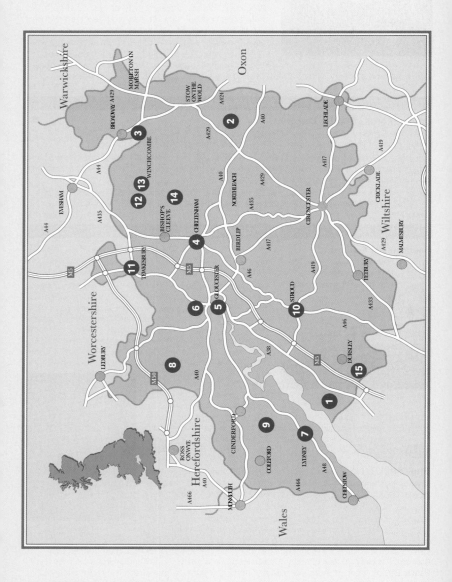

The Red Map References should be used to locate Museums etc on the pages that follow

Gloucestershire

Berkeley Castle

Berkeley GL13 9BQ Tel: 01453 810332 Fax: 01453 512995 Email: info@berkeley-castle.com Web: www.berkeley-castle.com

A romantic Mediaeval castle full of history and treasures, surrounded by Elizabethan terraced gardens and overlooking rolling countryside towards the Severn Estuary. Berkeley Castle has been in possession of the same family for over 800 years, celebrated by Shakespeare, the scene of murder - of a king, breached by the Roundheads in the Civil War, host to Francis Drake, Elizabeth I, and more English kings and queens than we care to count, and is still home to the Berkeley family today.

Berkeley Castle from Queen Elizabeth 1st's Bowling Green. © Jason Ingran

Opening Times: Apr to Sep Wed to Sat 11:00-16:00, Sun 14:00-17:00. Oct Sun 14:00-17:00. Admission: Adult £6.25, Child £3.25, OAP £5.00. Garden & Butterfly House only: Adult £3.00, Child £1.00. Location: South Gloucestershire, just off A38 (half way between Bristol and Gloucester), between junction 13 & 14 of M5. Exhibitions & Events 2003 : Joust - A weekend of Medieval mayhem, never before has a festival of this scale taken place in the UK, not only will there be full contact jousting but you can also witness daring display of weaponary, falconry and archery. www.joust.info. Map Ref: 1

Jenner Museum

Church Lane, Berkeley GL13 9BH Tel: 01453 810631 Fax: 01453 811690 Email: manager@jennermuseum.com Web: www.jennermuseum.com

Georgian country home of Edward Jenner, discoverer of vaccination against smallpox. Portraits, personal possessions and reconstruction of study, vaccination equipment and computerised display explaining modern immunology.

Opening Times: Apr to Sep Tue to Sat 12:30-17:30, Sun 13:00-17:30. Oct Sun only 13:00-17:30. Groups at other times by appointment. Admission: Adult £3.00, Child £1.50, OAP £2.30. Group discounts available. Location: Near Berkeley Town Centre, beside church and castle, one mile from A38 - use junction 14 or 15 of M5. Map Ref: 1

Cotswold Motoring Museum & Childhood Toy Collection

The Old Mill, Bourton-on-the-Water GL54 2BY Tel: 01451 821255 Email: michelle.blackmore@csma.uk.com

Full of exciting memorabilia including classic cars, motorcycles, model aeroplanes, pedal cars and one of the largest collections of metal motoring signs. The museum is also home to Brum, the little yellow car from the children's TV series.

Opening Times: Mar to Oct 10:00-18:00. Admission: Adult £2.95, Child £1.95, Family £8.95. Location: Just off High Street, a short walk from The Green. Map Ref: 2

Snowshill Manor

Snowshill, Broadway WR12 7JU Tel: 01386 852410 Fax: 01386 842822 Email: snowshill@nationaltrust.org.uk Web: www.nationaltrust.org.uk

A Cotswold manor house, containing Charles Paget Wade's extraordinary collection of craftsmanship and design including Samurai armour. A delightful organic garden, shop and restaurant.

Opening Times: 29 Mar to 2 Nov Wed to Sun, BH Mon, also Mon in Jul & Aug 12:00-17:00 (House), 11:00-17:30 (Garden, shop & restaurant). Admission: Adult £6.40, Child £3.20, Family £16.00. Garden, shop & restaurant only Adult £3.60, Child £1.80. Coach and school parties by written appointment only. Location: Two and a half miles south west Broadway off A44 bypass. Map Ref: 3

Cheltenham Art Gallery & Museum

Clarence Street, Cheltenham GL50 3JT   Tel: 01242 237431   Fax: 01242 262334   Email: artgallery@cheltenham.gov.uk
Web: www.cheltenhammuseum.org.uk

Cheltenham's Arts and Craft Movement collection of furniture, textiles, ceramics, carvings, silver and jewellery is recognised as an outstanding collection of international importance. Cheltenham's history is also well represented, and in addition there are paintings spanning four centuries, oriental collections of pottery and costume, archaeological treasures from the neighbouring Cotswolds, as well as a programme of special exhibitions changing regularly throughout the year.

Opening Times: Mon to Sat 10:00-17:20, Sun 14:00-16:20. Closed Easter and BH.   Admission: Free.
Location: Town centre.

Chinese robe and Ceramics

Exhibitions & Events 2003 : Until Feb: Encounters with Africa: Cheltenham's collections revealed, 22 Feb to 6 Apr: A View of China in the 1920s, 22 Feb to 6 Apr:

Piano, case designed by C R Ashbee, made in oak and holly

Cheltenham Camera Club, 12 Apr to 11 May: Cheltenham Schools Art, 17 May to 29 Jun: Honore Daumier: Lithographer Extraordinaire, 17 May to 13 Jul: Contemporary Textile Artists, 19 Jul to 31 Aug: Andy Goldsworthy: Selected photo works, 6 Sep to 26 Oct: Ernest Gimson: Arts & Crafts Designs and Objects, 13 Sep to 17 Nov: Fans, 1 to 23 Nov: Cheltenham Group of Artists, 29 Nov to 11 Jan: Gloucestershire Guild of Craftsmen.   Map Ref: 4

Holst Birthplace Museum

4 Clarence Road, Pittville, Cheltenham GL52 2AY   Tel: 01242 524846   Fax: 01242 580182
Email: holstmuseum@btconnect.com   Web: www.holstmuseum.org.uk

Birthplace of the composer of The Planets, displaying personal memorabilia including his piano. Also a fine period house with rooms illustrating the 'upstairs-downstairs' way of Victorian life. Holst's music is played.

Opening Times: Tue to Sat 10:00-16:00, closed Sun, Mon and some BH. Closed Dec to Jan, except for pre-booked groups.   Admission: Adult £2.50, Concessions £2.00, Family £7.00, special rate for schools.   Location: Ten minute walk from town centre. Near Portland Street car park. Opposite Gateway of Pittville Park.   Map Ref: 4

City Museum & Art Gallery

Brunswick Road, Gloucester GL1 1HP   Tel: 01452 396131   Fax: 01452 410898
Email: city.museum@gloucester.gov.uk   Web: www.mylife.gloucester.gov.uk

The Museum's collections include dinosaurs, fossils, unique Roman remains, stunning Birdlip mirrors, antique furniture, painting and decorative arts. Temporary exhibitions, hands-on displays, children's holiday activities and regular special events.

Opening Times: Tue to Sat 10:00-17:00   Admission: Adults £2.00, Free for all Gloucester City Residents and under 18s.   Location: Five minutes walk from Central Bus Station, near Town Centre   Exhibitions & Events 2003 : Summer 03: The Upright Ape.   Map Ref: 5

Gloucester Folk Museum

99/103 Westgate Street, Gloucester GL1 2PG   Tel: 01452 396467   Fax: 01452 330495
Email: folk.museum@gloucester.gov.uk   Web: www.mylife.gloucester.gov.uk

Grade II Listed Tudor and Jacobean timber-framed buildings with new extensions housing displays on social history, crafts, trades and industries of Gloucester City and County. Regular special exibitions, activities, crafts and an interactive ICT gallery.

Opening Times: Tue to Sat 10:00-17:00   Admission: Adults £2.00, Free for all Gloucester City Residents and under 18s.   Location: Ten minutes walk from Central Bus Station, near Town Centre   Exhibitions 2003 : Summer 03: Beatrix Potter Centenary Exhibition.   Map Ref: 5

Gloucestershire

National Waterways Museum

Llanthony Warehouse, The Docks, Gloucester GL1 2EH   Tel: 01452 318200
Fax: 01452 318202

Museum Entrance and Shop

The collection is designated as being 'of national importance' and includes many artefacts and historic floating exhibits that chart the fascinating 300 year story of our inland waterways. Interactives and touch-screen computers bring history to life as does our working blacksmith forge. From Easter to October you can even take a 45 minute boat trip along the Gloucester and Sharpness Canal.

Opening Times: Daily 10:00-17:00. Closed Xmas Day.
Admission: Adult £5.00, Child/OAP £4.00, Family £12.00-£16.00. Location: Situated in historic docks five minutes from city centre, 15 minutes walk from Gloucester Bus Station and Railway Station.   Map Ref: 5

Nature in Art

Wallsworth Hall, Twigworth, Gloucester GL2 9PA   Tel: 01452 731422   Fax: 01452 730937
Email: ninart@globalnet.co.uk   Web: www.nature-in-art.org.uk

World's first museum dedicated exclusively to art inspired by nature. Fine, decorative and applied art spanning 1500 years from 60 countries in all styles and media. Situated in a fine Georgian mansion.

Opening Times: Tue to Sun & BH 10:00-17:00. Closed Xmas. Admission: Adult £3.60, Child/OAP/Concession £3.00, Under 8s Free. Group rates available.   Location: Two miles north of Gloucester on main A38.   Map Ref: 6

Dean Forest Railway Museum

Norchard Railway Centre, Forest Road, New Mills, Lydney GL15 4ET   Tel / Fax: 01594 845840
Web: www.deanforestrailway.co.uk

General railway artefacts with emphasis on local Forest of Dean area. Also includes working telephone exchange (old restored BT system) for railway system. Story of Severn and Wye railway since 1809. Information (24 hrs) 01594 843423.

Opening Times: Summer daily 11:00-17:00. Winter Wed, Sat & Sun 11:00-16:00. Closed Xmas.
Admission: Free on non-operational days. Operational Days: Adult £5.50, Child £3.50, OAP £4.50. Group rates available. Prices subject to change.   Location: Road: one mile north of Lydney Town Centre on B4234 - off A48, follow brown tourist signs. Rail: 300 yards from Lydney mainline to DFR Lydney Junction.   Map Ref: 7

Shambles Museum

Church Street, Newent GL18 1PP   Tel: 01531 822144

A collection set out as a Victorian town of the 1890s - houses, cottages, shops, trades, around cobbled street, square and cottage garden.

Opening Times: Mid Mar to end Oct Tue to Sun 10:00-17:00. Admission: Adult £3.85, Child £2.25, OAP £3.25. Location: Centre of town.   Map Ref: 8

Dean Heritage Centre

Camp Mill, Soudley, Royal Forest of Dean GL14 2UB   Tel: 01594 824024   Fax: 01594 823711
Email: deanmuse@btinternet.com

Restored mill and pond in a wooded valley. The collection covers the period from pre-history to the present day, reflecting life in the Forest of Dean and rural skills.

Opening Times: Summer: 10:00-17:30. Winter: 11:00-16:30. Closed Winter 02/03.
Admission: Adult £4.00, Child £2.50, OAP £3.50, Family £12.00. Group rates available.
Location: Pretty woodland setting.   Map Ref: 9

Gloucestershire

The world's first lawnmower invented by Edwin Budding, 1830

Museum in the Park

Stratford Park, Stratford Road, Stroud GL5 4AF
Tel: 01453 763394   Fax: 01453 752400
Email: museum@stroud.gov.uk   Web: www.stroud.gov.uk

New family friendly museum in historic parkland setting. Innovative and colourful displays including dinosaurs, Uley Roman Temple, the world's first lawnmower and much more! Temporary exhibition programme and fun museum trails for children of all ages.

Opening Times: Apr to Sep Tue to Fri 10:00-17:00, Sat, Sun & BH 11:00-17:00. Oct to Mar Tue to Fri 10:00-16:00, Sat & Sun 11:00-16:30. Admission: Free. Location: In Stratford Park, ten minute walk from Stroud Town Centre.   Map Ref: 10

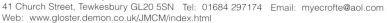

John Moore Countryside Museum

41 Church Street, Tewkesbury GL20 5SN   Tel: 01684 297174   Email: myecrofte@aol.com
Web: www.gloster.demon.co.uk/JMCM/index.html

A natural history collection exhibited in a 15th century house and honouring the prophetic writings on nature conservation of John Moore the writer. Displays of British woodland and wetland wildlife. The impact of people on the natural environment and the need for conservation are explored.

Opening Times: Apr to Oct & BH Tue to Sat 10:00-13:00 & 14:00-17:00. Nov to Mar most Sat plus special Xmas & spring half term 11:00-13:00 & 14:00-16:00. Admission: Adult £1.00, Child 50p, OAP 75p, Group 75p. Location: In the precincts of Tewkesbury Abbey, three minute walk from town centre.   Map Ref: 11

Gloucestershire Warwickshire Railway

The Railway Station, Toddington GL54 5DT   Tel: 01242 621405   Email: enquiries@gwsr.plc.uk
Web: www.gwsr.plc.uk

'Raveningham Hall' and 'Bahamas'
Dixton Cutting, Glos/Warks Railway

The 'Friendly Line in the Cotswolds' operates a round trip of 20 miles from Toddington via Winchcombe to Gotherington (Cheltenham Racecourse - opens April 2003), including the 693 yard Greet Tunnel, one of the longest on a preserved railway. Superb views of the Cotswolds, Malverns and Vale of Evesham. Steam and diesel locomotives. Restored carriages and stations. Locomotives under restoration.

Opening Times: Mar to Nov, Sat & Sun. BH, Apr, Jul & Aug, selected weekdays 10:00-17:00. Dec Sat & Sun Santa Specials. Admission: Adult £9.00, Child £5.50, Under 5s Free, OAP £7.50, Family £24.00. Group rates available. Location: Ten miles east of junction 9 on M5, near the junction of B4077 and B4632. Exhibitions & Events 2003 : 12 Apr: Cheltenham Racecourse extension should be open with two weeks of daily services featuring special guest locomotives, 5/6 Apr, 9/10 Aug: Day out with Thomas, 9 to 11 May: Diesel Galas, 22 Jun, 6 & 20 Jul: Transport Events, 31 Aug: Transport Events, 11/12 Oct: Steam Vintage Gala, 8 Nov: Model Railways, 24 to 26 Oct: Diesel Galas, 29 Dec: Diesel Galas.   Map Ref: 12

Gloucestershire

Hailes Abbey

Winchcombe, near Cheltenham GL54 5PB   Tel: 01242 602398

This Cistercian abbey was built by Richard, Earl of Cornwall in the 13th century, in gratitude for surviving a perilous sea journey. The museum contains an important collection of floor tiles, including early inlaid tiles.

Opening Times: Apr to Sep daily 10:00-18:00, Oct daily 10:00-17:00. Closed in winter.
Admission: Adult £3.00, Child £1.50, Concession £2.30, National Trust Members Free.
Location: Two miles north east of Winchcombe off B4632.   Map Ref: 13

Aerial view of Sudeley Castle and Gardens

Sudeley Castle

Winchcombe GL54 5JD   Tel: 01242 604357/602308
Fax: 01242 602959   Email: marketing@sudeley.org.uk
Web: www.stratford.co.uk/sudeley

Set against the beautiful backdrop of the Cotswold Hills, Sudeley Castle is steeped in history. With Royal connections spanning thousands of years, it has played an important role in the turbulent and changing times of England's past.

Opening Times: Gardens, Grounds, Shop, Exhibition & Plant Centre: 2 Mar to 27 Oct 10:30-17:30. Castle Apartments and St Mary's Church: 23 Mar to 27 Oct 11:00-17:00.   Admission: Castle & Gardens: Adult £6.50, Child £3.50, Family £18.00 Concession £5.50. Gardens & Exhibition: Adult £5.00, Child £2.75, Concession £4.00.   Location: Near Winchcombe, eight miles north east of Cheltenham on the B4632 (A46) or ten miles from junction 9 off the M5.   Map Ref: 14

WOTTON-UNDER-EDGE

Wotton Heritage Centre

The Chipping, Wotton-under-Edge GL12 7AD   Tel: 01453 521541
Email: wottonhs@freeuk.com   Web: www.conygres.co.uk

Local and family history, artefacts from Wotton's crafts and industries, with photographs, postcards, documents, maps and books. Also includes, research facilities, Tourist Information Point and a small shop.

Opening Times: Tue to Fri 10:00-13:00, 14:00-17:00 (16:00 in winter), Sat 10:00-13:00. Some Sun afternoons in summer 14:30-17:00.   Admission: Free, small charge for research facilities.
Location: In main car park.   Map Ref: 15

Hampshire is very much a naval county. The naval dockyard established in Portsmouth's sheltered harbour in the seventeenth century developed enormously during the next century. The county has a strong army tradition too. Winchester, the county town, was the capital of Wessex from the days of Alfred the Great and the capital of the whole of England from the tenth century until the Norman Conquest.

Hampshire and the Isle of Wight have a wealth of specialist museums and galleries together with traditional art galleries.

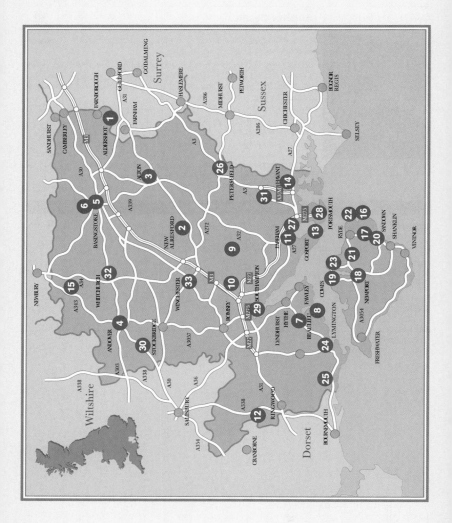

The Red Map References should be used to locate Museums etc on the pages that follow

Hampshire & Isle of Wight

ALDERSHOT

The Airborne Forces Museum

Browning Barracks, Aldershot GU11 2BU   Tel: 01252 349619   Fax: 01252 349203
Email: airborneforcesmuseum@army.mod.uk.net

The collection covers the history of the Parachute Regiment and Airborne Forces from 1940 to the present day.

Opening Times: Daily 10:00-16:30. Admission: Adult £3.00, Child/OAP £1.00. Location: 15 minutes from Aldershot Railway Station.   Map Ref: 1

Aldershot Military Museum

Queens Avenue, Aldershot GU11 2LG   Tel: 01252 314598   Fax: 01252 342942
Email: musmim@hants.gov.uk   Web: www.hants.gov.uk/museum/aldershot

Tells the story of the 'Home of the British Army'. New John Reed Gallery opened in October 2001 with many interactives - climb inside a Scorpion tank turret, try a Victorian soldier's bed, learn to crawl in our training tunnel and more.

Opening Times: Daily 10:00-17:00. Admission: Adult £2.00, Concession £1.00. Location: A short drive from junction 4 of the M3, the A331 and North Camp Railway Station.   Map Ref: 1

Army Medical Services Museum

Keogh Barracks, Ash Vale, Aldershot GU12 5RQ   Tel: 01252 868612   Fax: 01252 868832
Email: museum@keogh72.freeserve.co.uk

The museum tells the story of medical care in the army from 1860 to the present day.

Opening Times: Mon to Fri 10:00-15:30. Closed Sat, Sun & BH. Admission: Free.
Location: Ash Vale, 20 minute walk from Ash Vale Railway Station.   Map Ref: 1

Army Physical Training Corps Museum

Army School of Physical Training, Queen's Avenue, Aldershot GU11 2LB   Tel: 01252 347168
Fax: 01252 340785   Email: regtsec@aptc.org.uk   Web: www.aptc.org.uk

The APTC Museum has been awarded full Museum Gallery Commission Registration. The museum is an APTC and APTC Association facility and is an excellent focal and reference point for 'Corps' personnel.

Opening Times: Mon to Thu 09:30-16:30, Fri 09:30-12:30. Closed Sat & Sun. Admission: Free. Donations welcome. Location: On Queens Avenue, between Aldershot - North Camp entrance via Princes Avenue.   Map Ref: 1

ALRESFORD

Mid Hants Railway - Watercress Line Steam Railway

The Railway Station, Alresford SO24 9JG   Tel: 01962 733810   Fax: 01962 735448
Email: info@watercressline.co.uk   Web: www.watercressline.co.uk

Collection of railway items and archives from pre-1977.

Opening Times: Apr to Sep Sat, Sun, Tue to Thu & BH. Admission: Adult £9.00, Child £2.00, OAP £8.00. Group rates available. Admission to Goods Shed Museum - Free. Location: One minute walk from Alresford village.   Map Ref: 2

Key to Classifications
see Classifications Index on page 413

Anthropology	Jewellery	Railway
Archaeological	Literature & Libraries	Religion
Art Galleries	Maritime	Roman
Arts, Crafts & Textiles	Military & Defence	Science - Earth
China, Glass & Ceramics	Mills - Water & Wind	& Planetary
Communications	Multicultural	Sculpture
Egyptian	Music & Theatre	Sporting History
Fashion	Natural History	Stately Homes
Geology	Oriental	Toy & Childhood
Health & Medicine	Palaces	Transport
Horticultural	Police, Prisons & Dungeons	Victoriana

Hampshire & Isle of Wight

ALTON

Allen Gallery

 Hampshire County Council

Church Street, Alton GU34 2BW   Tel: 01420 82802   Fax: 01420 84227
Email: musmtc@hants.gov.uk   Web: www.hants.gov.uk/museum/allen

The Allen Gallery houses an outstanding collection of ceramics, nearly 1900 items dating from 1250 to the present day. Highlights include the unique Elizabethan Tichborne spoons. A range of delightful watercolours and oil paintings by local artist William Herbert Allen are also on display. There is an exciting programme of temporary exhibitions, a comfortable coffee lounge and a delightful walled garden behind the gallery.

Opening Times: Tue to Sat 10:00-17:00.   Admission: Free.
Location: Town centre.   Exhibitions & Events 2003 : 11 Jan to 15 Mar: The Rural Tradition: Wessex watercolours by W H Allen (1863-1943), 22 Mar to 19 Apr: 150 Years of the Letterbox, 26 Apr to 23 Aug: Invaders: Solve the Ancient Mystery in this interactive exhibition.   Map Ref: 3

Nursery Rhyme tiles in the ceramics collection

Curtis Museum

 Hampshire County Council

High Street, Alton GU34 1BA   Tel: 01420 82802   Fax: 01420 84227
Email: musmtc@hants.gov.uk   Web: www.hants.gov.uk/museum/curtis

One of the finest local history collections in Hampshire, exploring 100 million years of history. The wonderful array of objects includes the celebrated Roman cup found near Selborne and the impressive Anglo Saxon Alton buckle. The Gallery of Childhood is packed with toys, children's books and dolls dating back to the 18th century. Displays include prehistoric tools, local Roman pottery, Saxon burials, hop picking and brewing and local celebrities.

The renowned Anglo-Saxon Alton Buckle

Opening Times: Tue to Sat 10:00-17:00.
Admission: Free. Location: Town centre.   Map Ref: 3

Jane Austen's House

Chawton, Alton GU34 1SD   Tel: 01420 83262

17th century house where Jane Austen lived between 1809-17. She wrote and revised her novels here. Memorabilia of Jane Austen and her family. Donkey carriage and pretty garden.

Opening Times: Mar to Nov daily 11:00-16:30,   Admission: Adult £4.00, Child 50p,
Concession/Group £3.00.   Location: One and a half miles south west of Alton.   Map Ref: 3

ANDOVER

Andover Museum

 Hampshire County Council

6 Church Close, Andover SP10 1DP   Tel: 01264 366283   Fax: 01264 339152   Email: musmda@hants.gov.uk
Web: www.hants.gov.uk/museum/andoverm

Flints, fossils, freshwater fish and natural habitats introduce the Andover area - detailed archaeology displays depict the rich story of human activity from the Stone Age to Saxon times. Local history episodes involve the reading of the Riot Act and an infamous Work House Scandal. The gallery has regularly changing exhibitions and the museum hosts numerous clubs and societies with a busy calendar.

Opening Times: Tue to Sat 10:00-17:00. Apr to Sep Sun and BH 14:00-17:00. Admission: Free. Location: Near St Mary's Church, three minutes walk from town centre.
Exhibitions & Events 2003 : 18 Jan to 22 Feb: Recycled Textiles by Deirdre Wood, 8 Mar to 22 Apr: 54:

Children's workshop in action

Photography by David Allen, Curator of Andover Museum, 10 May to 5 Jul: Exploring Space: Interactive exhibition for families in partnership with Stevenage Museum.   Map Ref: 4

Hampshire & Isle of Wight

Museum of the Iron Age

6 Church Close, Andover SP10 1DP Tel: 01264 366283 Fax: 01264 339152
Email: musmda@hants.gov.uk Web: www.hants.gov.uk/museum/ironagem

Discover a way of life destroyed by the Romans. Life-sized models of weaver and warrior, reconstructed rampart and roundhouse, miniature street scene, recently excavated objects, replicas of tools, a plough, grave pits and more.

Opening Times: Tue to Sat 10:00-17:00, Apr to Sep Sun and BH 14:00-17:00.
Admission: Free. Location: Near St Mary's Church, three minutes walk from town centre.
Map Ref: 4

BASINGSTOKE

Basing House

Redbridge Lane, Basing, Basingstoke RG24 7HB Tel: 01256 467294
Fax: 01256 326283 Email: musmat@hants.gov.uk
Web: www.hants.gov.uk/museum/basingho

Hampshire County Council

Hampshire's most exciting historic ruin was once England's largest private palace, home of the Marquess of Winchester, Treasurer of Elizabeth I. His immense building covered eight acres and replaced a great Norman Castle. Civil war brought disaster to Basing which fell to the forces of Cromwell after a two year siege. Today the site, with its dovecote towers, secret tunnel, restored garden, museum and spectacular barn make an attraction of beauty and great historic interest.

Exploring the ruins of the Old House

Opening Times: Apr to Sep Wed to Sun and BH 14:00-16:00. Admission: Adult £2.00, Child £1.00, Concessions £1.00. Location: Entrance in centre of Old Basing, short drive from Basingstoke Town Centre and junction 6 of the M3. Map Ref: 5

Milestones - Hampshire's Living History Museum

Leisure Park, Churchill Way, Basingstoke RG21 6YR Tel: 01256 477766
Fax: 01256 477784 Email: gary.wragg@hants.gov.uk
Web: www.milestones-museum.com

Winner of the Social and Industrial History Award under the National Heritage Museum of the Year scheme. Atmospheric street scenes with shops from the late Victorian period to early 1940s bring Hampshire's recent history to life. An amazing 20,000 objects, including the Tasker and Thornycroft historic vehicles, are supported by easily accessible information and free audio-guide tours. Adults can enjoy a pint of Milestone Ale in The Baverstock Arms, a traditional Edwardian pub, and children can let off steam in the play store, a range of giant objects from the 1930s.

Opening Times: Tue to Fri 10:00-17:00, Sat & Sun 11:00-17:00.
Admission: Adult £6.50, Child £3.50, Concession £5.25, Family £16.00, Group Discounts. Map Ref: 5

Jubilee Street, Milestones Museum

The Vyne

Sherborne St John, Basingstoke RG24 9HL Tel: 01256 881337 Fax: 01256 881720
Email: thevyne@ntrust.org.uk Web: www.nationaltrust.org.uk/thevyne

At the forefront of country house architecture, interior design and taste for over 400 years, this fascinating country house is set within attractive gardens with lakeside and woodland walks.

Opening Times: House & Gardens: Mar to 2 Nov Mon to Wed 13:00-17:00, Sat & Sun 11:00-17:00 (prebooked tours 11:00-13:00). Garden only: Feb & Mar 11:00-16:00. Admission: House & Garden: Adult £6.50, Child £3.25, Family £16.25. Garden only: Adult £3.50, Child £1.75, National Trust Members Free. Map Ref: 6

Willis Museum

Old Town Hall, Market Place, Basingstoke RG21 7QD   Tel: 01256 465902
Fax: 01256 471455   Email: musmst@hants.gov.uk
Web: www.hants.gov.uk/museum/willis

Hampshire
County
Council

Discover Basingstoke's past from the rich archaeological heritage beneath our feet to a tour through the last 200 years. Meet Pickaxe, a 19th century scavenger scraping a living from the streets, and revisit the days of twin-tubs and teddy boys in the 1960s sitting room. There is always something new to see with a regularly changing programme of Special Exhibitions, children's quizzes, cafe and gifts.

Opening Times: Mon to Fri 10:00-17:00, Sat 10:00-16:00.
Admission: Free.   Location: Top of town, ten minutes walk from bus/train station. Follow signs for tourist information centre.
Exhibitions & Events 2003 : 11 Jan to 22 Feb: Heart and Matter: the illustrations of Graham Greene and Raymond Chandler by Geoff Grandfield, 8 Mar to 19 Apr: Exploring Space: interactive exhibition for families, 3 May to 21 Jun: Basingstoke Art Club.

The 1960s kitchen   Map Ref: 5

BEAULIEU

Beaulieu Abbey & Display of Monastic Life

John Montage Building, Beaulieu SO42 7ZN   Tel: 01590 612345
Fax: 01590 612624   Email: info@beaulieu.co.uk
Web: www.beaulieu.co.uk

Beaulieu

Palace House, once the Great Gatehouse of Beaulieu Abbey. The family home of Lord Montagu of Beaulieu, the house contains splendid rooms full of fine portraits, picture, furniture, family memorabilia and photographs. The surviving monastic buildings house an absorbing exhibition about its history and the life of worship lived there by the monks; the former refectory is now the pretty parish church.

Opening Times: May to Sep 10:00-18:00, Oct to Apr 10:00-17:00. Closed Xmas.   Admission: Please phone for latest prices.   Location: Beaulieu is in the heart of the New Forest.

Beaulieu Abbey   Map Ref: 7

Bucklers Hard Village

Maritime Museum, Bucklers Hard, Beaulieu SO42 7XB   Tel: 01590 616203   Fax: 01590 616283   Email: info@bucklershard.co.uk   Web: www.bucklershard.co.uk

The historic and picturesque shipbuilding village of Bucklers Hard. After setting a course for its Maritime Museum and Historic Cottages savour the sight and sounds of the countryside on a ramble along the Riverside Walk.

Opening Times: Easter to Sep 10:30-17:00, Oct to Easter 11:00-16;00. Closed Xmas.
Admission: Please phone for latest prices.   Location: Five minutes from the world famous National Motor Museum at Beaulieu.   Map Ref: 8

National Motor Museum

John Montagu Building, Beaulieu SO42 7ZN   Tel: 01590 612345
Fax: 01590 612624   Email: info@beaulieu.co.uk   Web: www.beaulieu.co.uk

Beaulieu

The collection features 250 vehicles as well as memorabilia and displays. From some of the earliest examples of motoring in the 1890s to legendary World Record Breakers, 'film star' cars to family cars from the 30s, 40s and 50s. There is also a stunning James Bond Boats Exhibition and a sensational Motorsport Gallery.

Opening Times: May to Sep 10:00-18:00, Oct to Apr 10:00-17:00. Closed Xmas.   Admission: Please phone for latest prices.   Location: Beaulieu is in the heart of the New Forest.   Map Ref: 7

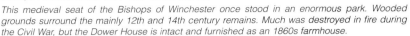

BISHOP'S WALTHAM

Bishop's Waltham Palace

Bishops Waltham SO32 1DH   Tel: 01489 892460

This medieval seat of the Bishops of Winchester once stood in an enormous park. Wooded grounds surround the mainly 12th and 14th century remains. Much was destroyed in fire during the Civil War, but the Dower House is intact and furnished as an 1860s farmhouse.

Opening Times: Apr to Sep daily 10:00-18:00, Oct daily 10:00-17:00.   Admission: Adult £2.50, Child £1.30, Concession £1.90.   Location: Five miles from junction 8 of M27.   Map Ref: 9

EASTLEIGH

Eastleigh Museum

The Citadel, 25 High Street, Eastleigh SO50 5LF   Tel: 023 8064 3026
Fax: 023 8065 3582 Email: musmaj@hants.gov.uk
Web: www.hants.gov.uk/museum/eastlmus

Hampshire County Council

Take a tour through Eastleigh's past and discover what life was like during the 1930s. Meet Mr & Mrs Brown, a local engine driver and his wife. Visit our recreation of their home, a Victorian terraced house for which Eastleigh is well known. The museum has also recreated part of the Southern Railway Locomotive Works, and a steam engine footplate. Special exhibitions, Local Studies Area, Whistle Stop Café and Gift Shop.

Local historians undertake research for the Museum

Opening Times: Tue to Fri 10:00-17:00, Sat 10:00-16:00. Admission: Free. Location: Town centre location, five minutes walk from bus and train station.   Exhibitions & Events 2003 : To 8 Mar: Behind the Time Clock: A collection of fascinating objects used or made by the Pirelli factory in Eastleigh, 15 Mar to 26 Apr: Discover Gamelan: Indonesian orchestra with community workshops, 10 May to 14 Jun: Open Art Competition.   Map Ref: 10

FAREHAM

Royal Armouries at Fort Nelson

Fort Nelson, Down End Road, Fareham PO17 6AN   Tel: 01329 233734
Fax: 01329 822092 Email: fnenquiries@armouries.org.uk
Web: www.armouries.org.uk

ROYAL ARMOURIES
FORT NELSON

Wonderfully restored Victorian fortress overlooking Portsmouth Harbour. Houses the National Collection of Artillery from the famous 'Gladiator' Catapult to the infamous Iraqi Supergun. Live gun firings everyday. Regular special events throughout the year, including band concert and military tattoo.

Opening Times: Apr to Oct daily 10:00-17:00, Nov to Mar 10:30-16:00. Closed 25-26 Dec. Last admission one hour before closing. Admission: Free. Location: Junction 11 of M27, follow brown tourist signs for Royal Armouries.

Portisdown Artillery volunteers with 16pr field gun   Map Ref: 11

Westbury Manor Museum

84 West Street, Fareham PO16 0JJ
Tel: 01329 824895 Fax: 01329 825917
Email: musmjb@hants.gov.uk
Web: www.hants.gov.uk/museum/westbury

Hampshire County Council

Westbury Manor Museum is housed in an impressive 18th century building in the heart of town. It unravels the history of the ancient borough of Fareham with displays on the natural, social and industrial history of the area. Highlights include The Strawberry Story, The Poor Law and the local brick industry. Exhibitions are shown in the temporary exhibitions gallery with topics ranging from contemporary art to photography and local history..

The Strawberry Story   *(continued over page)*

FAREHAM *(continued)*

Opening Times: Mon to Fri 10:00-17:00, Sat 10:00-16:00. Admission: Free. Location: Town centre, opposite Fareham Shopping Centre. Exhibitions & Events 2003 : 20 Jan to 28 Feb: The Titchfield Tapestries, 15 Mar to 26 Apr: The Chosen Letter: created and creative shapes, 5 to 19 May: Locks Heath and Sarisbury Camera Club, 26 May to 28 Jun: The Meon Valley Railway: Centenary Exhibition. Map Ref: 11

FORDINGBRIDGE

Rockbourne Roman Villa

Rockbourne, Fordingbridge SP6 3PG   Tel: 01725 518541   Email: musmjh@hants.gov.uk
Web: www.hants.gov.uk/museum/rockbourne

The remains of the largest known Roman villa in the area. Mosaics, remains of underfloor heating system and outline of 40 rooms in original positions. Museum, special events and facilities for schools.

Opening Times: Apr to Sep daily 10:30-18:00. Admission: Adult £1.95, Concession £1.10, Family £5.00. Location: Three miles west of Fordingbridge off the B3079. Map Ref: 12

GOSPORT

Gosport Museum and Gosport Gallery

Walpole Road, Gosport PO12 1NS   Tel: 023 9258 8035   Fax: 023 9250 1951   Email: musmop@hants.gov.uk
Web: www.hants.gov.uk/museum/gosport

Hampshire County Council

The Local History Gallery tells the story of the Borough from the earliest times, with fascinating objects, old photographs, archive film and life-sized costume figures. Discover more about the ground beneath your feet in the Geology Gallery, containing rare fossils and even a dinosaur footprint. The Gosport Gallery, housed in a separate building, hosts a regular programme of exhibitions from costume and textiles to photography and contemporary art.

A 200 million year old ammonite in the Geology Gallery

Opening Times: Tue to Sat 10:00-17:00. Admission: Free. Location: In town centre, a few minutes walk from ferry and bus station. Exhibitions & Events 2003 : 18 Jan to 1 Mar: Discover Gamelan: Indonesian orchestra with community workshops, 15 Mar to 3 May: Trilogy: Stitched textiles by three local artists, 17 May to 30 Aug: Marvellous Meals: A potted history of food. Map Ref: 13

Royal Navy Submarine Museum

Haslar Jetty Road, Gosport PO12 2AS
Tel: 023 92 529217/510354   Fax: 023 92 511349
Email: rnsubs@rnsubmus.co.uk Web: www.rnsubmus.co.uk

SUBMARINE MUSEUM

Celebrate a hundred years of submarines at The Royal Navy Submarine Museum, Gosport's Premier Waterfront Tourist Attraction on Portsmouth Harbour. Step on board for a guided tour of the UK's only walk on submarine HMS Alliance. This unique attraction offers you the chance to discover stories of undersea adventure and vividly brings the heroic story of the Royal Navy's Submarine Service to life.

Opening Times: Apr to Oct 10:00-17:30, Nov to Mar 10:00-16:30. Closed Xmas & New Year. Admission: Adult £4.00, Child £2.75, OAP £2.75, Family (2 adults and 2 children) £11.00.

Royal Navy Submarine Museum

Location: From junction 11 on M27 follow A32. Pass the Gosport Ferry and turn left at Haslar Road. Over Haslar Bridge, the Museum is second left. Map Ref: 13

Guided or Private Tours	Disabled Access	Gift Shop or Sales Point	Café or Refreshments	Restaurant	Car Parking

Hampshire & Isle of Wight

GOSPORT (continued)

SEARCH   ♿

50 Clarence Road, Gosport PO12 1BU   Tel: 023 9250 1957   Fax: 023 9250 1921
Email: musmjw@hants.gov.uk   Web: www.hants.gov.uk/museum/search

Hampshire Museums' hands-on education centre using real museum collections for lifelong learning. Superb facilities for schools and other groups. Open days and summer holiday workshops for families.

Opening Times: Pre-booked groups only, apart from special open days. Enquiries Mon to Fri 09:00-17:30. Admission: Special open days free, small charge for family workshops, school groups and other groups. Please telephone. Location: In town centre, a few minutes walk from ferry and bus station.   Map Ref: 13

HAVANT

Havant Museum   ♿ 🖨 🚽   Hampshire County Council

56 East Street, Havant PO9 1BS   Tel: 023 9245 1155   Fax: 023 9249 8707
Email: musmop@hants.gov.uk   Web: www.hants.gov.uk/museum/havant

The contents of an old chemist's shop

The museum houses local history displays including Scalextric, Bronze Age and Roman hoards and local transport. It is the home of the nationally important Vokes Collection of Firearms. The Local Studies Collection contains an impressive range of resources and the special exhibition gallery hosts a wide range of shows from contemporary art and craft to photography and natural history.

Opening Times: Tue to Sat 10:00-17:00.
Admission: Free. Location: Short walk from town centre, next to Arts Centre. Exhibitions & Events 2003 : 11 Jan to 19 Apr: Invaders: Solve the Ancient Mystery in this interactive exhibition, 3 May to 21 Jun: Why did I buy that? A Graphicus Touring exhibition.   Map Ref: 14

HIGHCLERE

Bronze fiigure of Harpocrates from the Egyptian Centre.

Highclere Castle   🔍 ♿ 🎲 🖨 🌐 🚽 🏛

Highclere, near Newbury RG20 9RN   Tel: 01635 253210
Fax: 01635 255315
Email: theoffice@highclerecastle.co.uk
Web: www.highclerecastle.co.uk

Some of the old cellars in the Castle now house the impressive private museum of ancient Egyptian finds amassed from excavations in Thebes by the 5th Earl of Carnarvon and Howard Carter between 1907 and 1913. An additional gallery of photographs recalls their discovery, in 1922, of the tomb of Tutankhamun, probably the greatest archaeological story ever.

Opening Times: 1 Jul to 31 Aug, 19-21 Apr, BH 3-5 May, 24-26 May & 25 Aug Tue to Sun & Sun to Fri 11:00-17:00, Sat 11:00-15:30. Admission: Adult £7.00, Child £3.50, Concession £5.50, Family £17.00. Ground & Garden only - Adult £4.00, Child £1.50.   Map Ref: 15

ISLE OF WIGHT

Bembridge Maritime Museum & Shipwreck Centre   ♿ 🎲 🌐 🚽

Providence House, Sherbourne Street, Bembridge, Isle of Wight PO35 5SB   Tel: 01983 872223
Web: www.isle-of-wight.uk.com/shipwrecks

Local history and story of Bembridge Lifeboats - past and present. Countless artefacts recovered from local shipwrecks, unique collection of ship models and much more.

Opening Times: Apr to Oct daily 10:00-17:00. Admission: Please phone for details.
Location: Centre of Bembridge village.   Map Ref: 16

Brading Roman Villa

Morton Old Road, Brading, Isle of Wight PO36 0EN   Tel / Fax: 01983 406223

Large Romano British courtyard style villa, with fine mosaic floors and artefacts of Roman occupation - museum in covered west wing with large number of site finds.

Opening Times: 20 Mar to 2 Nov daily 09:30-17:00. Admission: Adult £2.95, Child/Student £1.50, Family £7.50, Group £1.50.   Map Ref: 17

400-year-old Chamber Organ, present to Princess Beatrice

Carisbrooke Castle Museum

Newport, Isle of Wight PO30 1XY Tel: 01983 523112   Fax: 01983 536126   Email: carismus@lineone.net
Web: www.carisbrookecastlemuseum.org.uk

Accommodated inside the Castle's Great Hall, this independent museum exhibits material relating to the Castle and the history of the Isle of Wight. The Castle exhibition includes items connected with the imprisonment of King Charles I. Local history displays are changed regularly, and may feature Island places and people, and aspects of social history.

Opening Times: Apr to Sep daily 10:00-18:00, Oct 10:00-17:00, Nov to Mar daily 10:00-16:00. Closed Xmas & New Year.
Admission: Adult £5.00, Child £2.50, Concession £3.80, Family £12.50. Location: One mile south west of Newport.   Map Ref: 18

Cowes Maritime Museum

Branch Library & Maritime Museum, Beckford Road, Cowes, Isle of Wight PO31 7SG
Tel: 01983 823433   Fax: 01983 823841   Email: rachel.silverson@iow.gov.uk

Ship models, photographs and real boats reflect Cowes' yachting and shipbuilding heritage. The museum holds photographs and archives from Samuel White Shipyard.

Opening Times: Mon to Wed, Fri 09:30-18:00, Sat 09:30-16:00. Admission: Free.
Location: Just off High Street, five minutes from bus and ferry terminal.   Map Ref: 19

Dinosaur Isle

Culver Parade, Sandown, Isle of Wight PO36 8QA   Tel: 01983 404344   Fax: 01983 407502
Web: www.dinosaur-isle.uk.com

Resurrects dinosaurs which lived 125 million years ago, along with their ancient habitat. Unlocks the rocky tombs of fossils and brings them together in the first ever, purpose built dinosaur attraction in Britain.

Opening Times: Apr to Oct daily 10:00-18:00, Nov to Mar daily 10:00-16:00. Admission: Adult £4.60, Child £2.60, Family £12.00. Location: Situated on the B3395 coast road at Culver Parade.   Map Ref: 20

Isle of Wight Steam Railway

The Railway Station, Havenstreet, Isle of Wight PO33 4DS   Tel: 01983 882204   Fax: 01983 884515   Email: hugh@iwsteamrailway.co.uk   Web: www.iwsteamrailway.co.uk

A working museum of the island's railway history. A ten mile round trip in Victorian and Edwardian carriages, often hauled by a Victorian locomotive. Museum artefacts on display.

Opening Times: Apr & May Thu & Sun 10:00-16:00, Jun to Sep daily 10:00-16:00, Oct Thu, Sat & Sun 10:00-16:00 (times are for 2002). Admission: Admission & Train: Adult £7.50, Child £4.00, OAP £6.50 (prices are for 2002). Location: Havenstreet Village Station, rail served on open days.   Map Ref: 21

Lilliput Antique Doll and Toy Museum

High Street, Brading, Isle of Wight PO36 0DJ   Tel: 01983 407231
Email: lilliput.museum@btconnect.com   Web: www.lilliputmuseum.com

One of Britain's finest and most comprehensive collections of antique dolls and toys with over 2000 exhibits dating from c2000 BC to c1945. All are genuine, there are no modern reproductions.

Opening Times: Daily 10:00-17:00. Closed Xmas. Admission: Adult £1.95, Child/Concession £1.00. Location: In Brading Town Centre.   Map Ref: 17

Hampshire & Isle of Wight

Museum of Island History

The Guildhall, High Street, Newport, Isle of Wight PO30 1TY   Tel: 01983 823366   Fax: 01983 833841   Email: rachel.silverson@iow.gov.uk

Discover the history of the Isle of Wight from the dinosaurs to the present day, through the latest hands-on exhibits, computers and interactives. The museum also houses the Island's central Tourist Information Centre.

Opening Times: Mon to Sat 10:00-17:00 and Sun 11:00-15:30.   Admission: Adult £1.80, Child/OAP £1.00, Families £4.00.   Location: In the Guildhall, town centre of Newport. Two minute walk from bus station.   Map Ref: 18

National Wireless Museum

Puckpool Park, Seaview, Isle of Wight PO34 5AR   Tel: 01983 567665   Fax: 01983 563730

A collection of radio, television and sound reproduction, for educational, historical and cultural purposes.

Opening Times: 14:00-17:00.   Admission: Free.   Map Ref: 22

Newport Roman Villa

Cypress Road, Newport, Isle of Wight PO30 1HE   Tel: 01983 529720   Fax: 01983 823841   Email: rachel.silverson@iow.gov.uk

Discover the luxuries of third century Roman British life. The Villa has a wonderfully preserved bath suite and reconstructed living room, kitchen and charming herb garden. Hands on activities.

Opening Times: Apr to Oct Mon to Sat 10:00-16:30, also Sun in Jul & Aug 12:00-16:00. Open for group bookings only Nov to Mar.   Admission: Adult £2.00 Child/OAP/Concession £1.20 Families £5. Group bookings (01983) 823847.   Location: The villa is ten minute walk from central bus station.   Map Ref: 18

Nunwell House (Aylmer Military Collection)

Brading, Isle of Wight PO36 0JQ   Tel: 01983 407240

A historic and beautifully furnished house - a family home since 1522. Special collection of one family's militaria.

Opening Times: 25-26 May, 30 Jun to 3 Sep Mon to Wed 13:00-17:00. Tours at 13:30, 14:30 & 15:30.   Admission: Adult £4.00, Child (under 10) £1.00, OAP £3.50.   Location: Signed on A3055. Short walk from Brading Station or bus stop.   Map Ref: 17

Osborne House

East Cowes, Isle of Wight PO32 6JY   Tel: 01983 200022

Osborne House was built for Queen Victoria and Prince Albert as a private home. The house was built by Thomas Cubitt in Italianate style and is set among terraced gardens and filled with treasured mementoes.

Opening Times: Apr to Sep daily 10:00-18:00, Oct daily 10:00-17:00. Please phone to check winter opening/pre-booked guided tours of house only.   Admission: House & Grounds: Adult £8.00, Child £4.00, Concession £6.00, Family £20.00. Grounds only: Adult £4.50, Child £2.30, Concession £3.40. Tour rates available.   Location: One mile south east of East Cowes.   Map Ref: 23

St Barbe Museum & Art Gallery

New Street, Lymington SO41 9BH   Tel: 01590 676969   Fax: 01590 679997   Email: office@stbarbe-museum.org.uk   Web: www.stbarbe-museum.org.uk

The Museum tells the story of the New Forest coastal area, with chronological and themed displays which include boat building, smuggling and the Barton Fossils. The Art Galleries feature changing art exhibitions.

Opening Times: Mon to Sat 10:00-16:00.   Admission: Adult £3.00, Concession £2.00. Group rates available.   Location: In town centre, only one minute walk from High Street.   Map Ref: 24

NEW MILTON

Sammy Miller Museum

Bashley Manor, Bashley Cross Road, New Milton BH25 5SZ   Tel: 01425 620777   Fax: 01425 619696   Web: www.sammymiller.co.uk

Sammy Miller is a legend in his own lifetime, winning competitions for 46 years. The museum houses the finest collection of fully restored motorcyles in Europe, including factory racers and exotic prototypes.

Opening Times: Daily 10:00-16:30. Closed Xmas.   Admission: Adult £3.50, Child £1.50.
Location: New Milton Hampshire off A35 at Hinton Church.   Map Ref: 25

PETERSFIELD

Bear Museum

38 Dragon Street, Petersfield GU31 4JJ   Tel: 01730 265108   Web: www.bearmuseum.co.uk

Established in 1984 the world's first museum of teddy bears. Housing displays of most manufacturers over the years. Also, main agent for Steiff new teddy bears. 2002 was the centenary of the Teddy Bear.

Opening Times: Tue to Sat 10:00-16:30. Closed Sun, Mon and BH.   Admission: Free.
Location: 100 yards south from bottom of High Street, with Tesco car park opposite.
Map Ref: 26

Flora Twort Gallery

Church Path, Petersfield GU32 1HS   Tel: 01730 260756
Web: www.hants.gov.uk/museum/floratwo

Hampshire County Council

A charming gallery, once the home and studio of local artist Flora Twort. It is now devoted to the display of her delightful paintings and drawings, which form a very personal record of Petersfield between the wars. The ground floor of the building has been transformed into a restaurant serving coffee, lunch and afternoon teas. It is also open for dinner on two evenings each week.

Opening Times: Tue to Sat 09:45-17:00.
Admission: Free.   Location: Town centre location.

The Flora Twort Gallery   Map Ref: 26

PORTCHESTER

Portchester Castle

Castle Street, Portchester PO16 9QW   Tel: 023 9237 8291

A residence for kings, this castle has a history stretching back nearly 2000 years. Built by the Romans as a defence against barbarian attacks, Porchester became a royal castle in the medieval period. The collection includes extensive excavation material.

Opening Times: Apr to Sep daily 10:00-18:00, Oct daily 10:00-17:00, Nov to Mar daily 10:00-16:00. Closed Xmas & New Year.   Admission: Adult £3.50, Child £1.80, Concession £2.60.
Location: On south side of Portchester off A27, junction 11 on M27.   Map Ref: 27

PORTSMOUTH

Charles Dickens Birthplace Museum

393 Old Commercial Road, Portsmouth PO1 4QL   Tel: 023 9282 7261

Born in this modest house in 1812. Beautifully restored room settings recreate Regency life. With memorabilia, illustrations from Charles Dickens' published works, portraits of the Dickens family and the couch on which he died.

Opening Times: Apr to Sep daily 10:00-17:30, Oct daily 10:00-17:00.   Admission: Adult £2.50, Child £1.50, OAP £1.80, Family £6.50.   Location: Ten minute walk from town centre/Portsmouth & Southsea Railway Station.   Map Ref: 28

Hampshire & Isle of Wight

City Museum & Records Office

Museum Road, Old Portsmouth, Portsmouth PO1 2LJ   Tel: 023 9282 7261

Dedicated to local history and fine and decorative art. 'The Story of Portsmouth' displays room settings showing life in Portsmouth from the 17th century to the 1950s using modern audio-visual techniques. Experience the different life-styles of the Victorian working poor in the 'Dockyard Workers Cottage' and the affluent 'Victorian Parlour'. A 1930s kitchen with everything including the kitchen sink! A 1930s 'Art Deco' dining room and a 1950s front-room complete with flying ducks on the wall and early television showing 'Listen With Mother'. The 'Portsmouth at Play' exhibition looks at all aspects of leisure pursuits from the Victorian period to the 1970s. The museum has a fine and decorative art gallery and temporary exhibition gallery with regular changing exhibitions. The Record Office contains the official records of the City of Portsmouth from the 14th century and private and commercial records. Collections and Exhibits of consequence: 17th Century Furniture; Art Deco Furniture - Frank Dobson Sculptures (Terracottage & Bronze), Ceri Richards Relief Work 'Le Piano', Ronald Ossory Dunlop Painting 'Still Life with Black Bottle'; JMW Turner RA watercolour 'Gosport, the Entrance to Portsmouth Harbour' c.1829. Local History: Sir Alec Rose (Round the World Yachtsman - artefacts), Verrecahias Ice Cream Parlour and artefacts.

Opening Times: Apr to Sep daily 10:00-17:30, Oct to Mar daily 10:00-17:00. Closed 24-26 Dec. Admission: Free. Location: Ten minute walk from the town centre/Portsmouth and Southsea Railway Station. Seven minute walk from Harbour Railway/Bus Station   Exhibitions & Events 2003 : For Exhibition and Events please telephone for details.   Map Ref: 28

D-Day Museum and Overlord Embroidery

Clarence Esplanade, Portsmouth PO5 3NT   Tel: 023 9282 7261

D-Day Museum Overlord Embroidery

The D-Day Museum was created to specifically commemorate the Normandy Landings on 6 June 1944 and to house the magnificent and colourful 'Overlord Embroidery' inspired by the Bayeux Tapestry. The 83 metre long embroidery depicts the moving story of 'the longest day ...' and Soundguides are available in four languages. An archive film show (in five languages) includes original footage and brings this period of the Second World War alive to the visitor. The exciting displays and exhibits recreate what it must have been like to live through this period and the events of that day. The equipment, the men who took part... it's all here at the D-Day Museum. Experience life in the Anderson Shelter and the period front room of the ARP Warden. 'Listen While You Work' in the factory scene, keep vigil with the troops camped in the forest waiting their time to embark. Eavesdrop on communications in 'The Map Room', Southwick House. Board a 'Dakota' and be the first to land in a field in France and hear the story behind the crashed Horsa Glider, pass through the German pill-box and see the armada approaching the beaches and, finally, board an original landing craft of the period.

Opening Times: Apr to Sep daily 10:00-17:30, Oct to Mar daily 10:00-17:00. Closed 24-26 Dec. Admission: Adult £5.00, Child £3.00, OAP £3.75, Family £13.00. Group rates: Adult £4.25, Child £2.50, OAP £3.20, Student £2.30.   Exhibitions & Events 2003 : For Exhibitions and Events please telephone for details.   Map Ref: 28

Natural History Museum & Butterfly House

Cumberland House, Eastern Parade, Southsea, Portsmouth PO4 9RF   Tel: 023 9282 7261

Wildlife dioramas and geology of the Portsmouth area, it has a full size reconstruction of Dinosaur 'Iguanodon' and other fossil remains. During the summer months, British and European butterflies flying free.

Opening Times: Apr to Sep daily 10:00-17:30, Oct to Mar daily 10:00-17:00. Closed 24-26 Dec. Admission: Apr to Oct: Adult £2.50, Child £1.50, OAP £1.80, Family £6.50. Nov to Mar: Adult £2.00, Child £1.20, OAP £1.50, Family £5.20.   Location: Situated Canoe Lake area, nearest bus stop - Festing Road.   Map Ref: 28

Portsmouth Historic Dockyard

Building 1/7 College Road, Portsmouth   Tel: 023 9286 1533
Fax: 023 9229 5252   Email: mail@historicdockyard.co.uk
Web: www.historicdockyard.co.uk

HMS Victory

No visit to Southern England is complete without a trip to Portsmouth Historic Dockyard. The Historic Dockyard is the leading attraction on the South Coast and is home to the world famous historic ships, Mary Rose, HMS Victory, HMS Warrior 1860 and the stunning new interactive attraction, Action Stations. Together with the Dockyard Apprentice Exhibition and Harbour Tours around the modern fleet, it is without doubt one of the most exciting, entertaining and educational days out for all the family in the country.

HMS Warrior

Action Stations is the Historic Dockyard latest major attraction. It is a showcase for the modern day Navy and simulates what it is like to go to sea on a Type 23 Frigate. Mary Rose is the only recovered 16th century warship on display in the world and was a favourite of Henry VIII. She sank in the Solent in 1545, watched by the horrified king. In 1805, HMS Victory gained her immortality at the Battle of Trafalgar along with Nelson, Britain's greatest naval hero. The world's oldest commissioned warship, her gun-decks vividly depict the harsh conditions in which ordinary sailors lived, worked and fought. Opposite HMS Victory is the award-winning Royal Naval Museum and its four exciting galleries. One of them is devoted to The History of HMS Victory exhibition, focussing on the admirals, crews and craftsmen who have worked on board her. Just 55 years separate Trafalgar and the launch of the mighty HMS Warrior 1860, pride of Queen Victoria's Black Battlefleet. Explore her four huge decks and discover why she was the ultimate deterrent being the first warship powered by steam and sail, the largest and fastest of her day.

Opening Times: Nov to Feb 10:00-17:00, Mar to Oct 10:00-17:30. Admission: Adult £13.75, Child/OAP £11.00, Family £44.00. Location: Portsmouth. Exhibitions & Events 2003 : 27 Nov to 30 Nov: A Festival of Christmas 2003.   Map Ref: 28

Royal Marines Museum

Eastney Esplanade, Southsea, Portsmouth PO4 9PX   Tel: 023 9281 9385   Fax: 023 9283 8420
Email: info@royalmarinesmuseum.co.uk   Web: www.royalmarinesmuseum.co.uk

An award winning museum that helps you discover the exciting 330 year story of the Royal Marines through dramatic and interactive displays. Visit the Museum at what was one of the most stately Officers' Messes in England and tour its world famous medal collection.

Opening Times: Jun to Aug daily 10:00-17:00, Sep to May daily 10:00-16:30.
Admission: Adult £4.00, Child £2.25, OAP £3.00, Family £12.00. Location: On the seafront, about one mile east of South Parade Pier.   Map Ref: 28

Southsea Castle

Clarence Esplanade, Southsea, Portsmouth PO5 3PA   Tel: 023 9282 7261

Built by Henry VIII in 1544 to protect Portsmouth Harbour. Military history from Tudor times to the Victorians. 'Time Tunnel Experience' showing 'Life in the Castle', underground passages and audio-visual presentation.

Opening Times: Apr to Sep daily 10:00-17:30, Oct daily 10:00-17:00. Admission: Adult £2.50, Child £1.50, OAP £1.80, Family £6.50. Location: Situated on Southsea Seafront. Nearest bus stop - Palmerston Road.   Map Ref: 28

			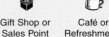		
Guided or Private Tours	Disabled Access	Gift Shop or Sales Point	Café or Refreshments	Restaurant	Car Parking

Hampshire & Isle of Wight

Treadgold Industrial Heritage Museum

1 Bishop Street, Portsea, Portsmouth PO1 3DA   Tel: 023 9282 4745
Fax: 023 9283 7310   Email: lawton@treadgoldm33.freeserve.co.uk
Web: www.hants.gov.uk/museum/treadgold

     Hampshire
County
Council

The forge workshop

This 'Victorian time capsule' comprises an ironmonger's shop and storerooms, offices, stable, workshop with forges and a reconstructed tenement c1810. A rare industrial archaeological site, it houses an entire collection of tools, machinery, office paperwork and shop stock at its original location. The listed collection of buildings dates to 1706.

Opening Times: Apr to Sep Wed to Thu 10:00-16:00. Schools and other groups, by appointment, weekdays throughout the year. Admission: Free. Location: Near Portsmouth historic dockyard, three minute walk from rail and bus station. Map Ref: 28

SOUTHAMPTON

Bursledon Windmill

Windmill Lane, Bursledon, Southampton SO31 8BG   Tel: 023 8040 4999
Email: musmgb@hants.gov.uk   Web: www.hants.gov.uk/museum/windmill

Hampshire's only working windmill, built in 1813 and lovingly restored. Wooden machinery, traditional timber-framed barn and granary. Stoneground flour made and sold to visitors. Nature trail and special events. Teachers pack.

Opening Times: May to Sep Sat & Sun 10:00-16:00, Oct to Apr Sun 10:00-16:00. Admission: Adult £1.50, Concession 75p, Family £3.75. Location: Short drive from junction 8 of the M27. Map Ref: 29

John Hansard Gallery

University of Southampton, Highfield, Southampton SO17 1BJ   Tel: 023 8059 2158   Fax: 023 8059 4192   Email: hansard@soton.ac.uk

Around six contemporary visual art exhibitions per year lasting approximately seven weeks each. University collection. Sculpture trail.

Opening Times: Tue to Fri 11:00-17:00, Sat 11:00-16:00. Please contact Gallery for Easter & Xmas closures. Admission: Free. Location: On the west side of the University of Southampton, next to the Turner Sims Concert Hall and Student Health Centre. Map Ref: 29

Museum of Archaeology

Gods House Tower, Winkle Street, Southampton SO14 2NY   Tel: 023 8063 5904
Fax: 023 8033 9601   Email: k.wardley@southampton.gov.uk
Web: www.southampton.gov.uk/leisure/museums

Gods House Tower Museum, main hall

One of the top designated archaeology collections in the country. The displays use finds from excavations within the city. Highlights include colourful imported pottery and glass from the medieval port, evidence of international trade and local industry from Saxon Hamwic and objects from everyday life in Roman Clausentum. Activities for children include 'try on a toga', mosaic making and interactive CD-Rom.

Opening Times: Tue to Fri 10:00-12:00 & 13:00-17:00, Sat 10:00-12:00 & 13:00-16:00, Sun 14:00-17:00. Admission: Free. Location: In old town area, near Isle of Wight ferry terminal, five minutes walk from West Quay Shopping Centre. Exhibitions & Events 2003 : Oct to Dec 02: Bones - An absolutely 'fibulous' exhibition for all the fami, Jan to Jul 03: Out of Egypt - Discover mummies and scarabs. Write your own hieroglyphics, Jul 03 to Jan 04: St Michael's Church - An interactive exhibition showing the results of a year long project by the Young Archaeologists Club. Map Ref: 29

Hampshire & Isle of Wight

Southampton City Art Gallery

Civic Centre, Southampton SO14 7LP   Tel: 023 8083 2277   Fax: 023 8083 2153
Email: art.gallery@southampton.gov.uk   Web: www.southampton.gov.uk/leisure/arts

The most outstanding gallery in the south of England, internationally renowned for its collection of contemporary works by British artists. The collection numbers over 3500 works and spans six centuries of European art history. The gallery presents four major temporary exhibitions a year, which range from historic to contemporary art.

Opening Times: Tue to Sat 10:00-17:00, Sun 13:00-16:00. Closed Mon. Admission: Free. Location: City centre, five minute walk from railway station, opposite Watts Park, in Commercial Road.   Map Ref: 29

Galley 3, Southampton City Art Gallery

Southampton Maritime Museum

Wool House, Bugle Street, Southampton SO14 2AR
Tel: 023 8022 3941   Fax: 023 8033 9601
Email: historic.sites@southampton.gov.uk
Web: www.southampton.gov.uk/leisure/museums

The Wool House was built as a Warehouse for the medieval wool trade. It is now a museum telling the story of the port of Southampton and the great liners that sailed from here to all parts of the world. Highlights include Titanic Voices Exhibition, telling the real story of the Titanic through original artefacts and the voices of local people whose lives were affected by the tragedy.

Opening Times: Tue to Fri 10:00-13:00 & 14:00-17:00, Sat 10:00-13:00 & 14:00-16:00, Sun 14:00-17:00. Admission: Free.

Enjoy a memorable day at the Southampton Maritime Museum

Location: Corner of Bugle Street and Town Quay Road, five minutes walk from West Quay Shopping Centre.   Exhibitions & Events 2003 : Titanic - The 90th Anniversary - see new artefacts never before on public display, Sep 02 to Feb 03: Royal Mail Line, Mar 03 to Feb 03: America & Hamburg Line, Oct 03 to Jul 04: Dockers Choice - see items from the museums collections personally chosen by Southampton's dock workers.   Map Ref: 29

Tudor House Museum & Garden

Bugle Street, Southampton SO14 2AD   Tel: 023 8063 5904   Fax: 023 8033 9601
Email: historic.sites@southampton.gov.uk   Web: www.southampton.gov.uk/leisure/museums

Tudor House is closed while a full building survey and photographic record are made, prior to restoration. Group visits are available to see this work in progress.

Opening Times: Closed for refurbishment. Admission: Free. Location: Bugle Street, five minutes walk from West Quay Shopping Centre.   Map Ref: 29

Museum of Army Flying

Middle Wallop, Stockbridge SO20 8DY   Tel: 01980 674421   Fax: 01264 781694
Email: enquiries@flying-museum.org.uk   Web: www.flying-museum.org.uk

This award winning museum celebrates over 100 years of Army Aviation and is home to one of the country's finest historical collections of military kites, gliders, aeroplanes and helicopters. Imaginative tableaux trace the developments of Army flying from pre World War I to today's modern Army Air Corps. The museum includes a children's Science and Education centre.

Opening Times: Daily 10:00-16:30. Admission: Adult £5.00, Child £3.50, Concession £4.00. Group rates available. Location: On the A343 between Andover and Salisbury.   Map Ref: 30

Sopwith Pup 1916 with World War I military cycle

Hampshire & Isle of Wight

WATERLOOVILLE

Goss & Crested China Centre

62 Murray Road, Horndean, Waterlooville PO8 9JL   Tel: 023 925 97440   Fax: 023 925 91975
Email: info@gosschinaclub.demon.co.uk   Web: www.gosscrestedchina.co.uk

A vast display of Victorian and Edwardian crested china souvenir ware made in the Staffordshire Potteries between 1860 and 1939. These include World War I, animals, miniatures, cottages, Parian busts of royalty, politicians etc.

Opening Times: Mon to Sat 09:00-17:00. Closed Sun & BH.   Admission: Free.   Location: Nine miles from Portsmouth, nine miles from Petersfield.   Map Ref: 31

WHITCHURCH

Whitchurch Silk Mill

28 Winchester Street, Whitchurch RG28 7AL   Tel: 01256 892065   Fax: 01256 893882   Email: silkmill@btinternet.com   Web: www.whitchurchsilkmill.org.uk

This delightful Grade II watermill built on the river Test in 1800 has produced silk continuously since the 1820s. Now a working museum it keeps alive the art of making silk on machinery installed between 1890 and 1950. It used to produce silk for lining Burberry raincoats and for legal and academic gowns and weaves short runs for theatrical costume and historic houses.

Opening Times: Tue to Sun 10:30-17:00, also BH Mon. Last admission 16:15. Closed 24 Dec to 2 Jan.
Admission: Adult £3.50, Child £1.75, OAP/Student £3.00, Family (2 adults and 3 children) £8.75.   Location: Near town centre, 15 minute walk from rail station. Map Ref: 32

Traditional Silk Making at Whitchurch Silk Mill

WINCHESTER

City of Winchester Museum

The Square, Winchester   Tel: 01962 848269
Email: museums@winchester.gov.uk   Web: www.winchester.gov.uk/heritage

Tells Winchester's nationally important story, as a major Roman centre and afterwards as the principal city of Alfred and later Anglo-Saxon and Norman kings. The story continues through the centuries with Winchester's revival as a fashionable county town in the 18th century and displays include reconstructed Victorian & Edwardian shops. Lift to all floors.

Opening Times: Apr to Oct Mon to Sat 10:00-17:00, Sun 12:00-17:00. Nov to Mar Tue to Sat 10:00-16:00, Sun 12:00-16:00.
Admission: Free.   Location: The Square, between High Street and the Cathedral.   Map Ref: 33

Guildhall Gallery

Broadway, Winchester SO23 9LJ   Tel: 01962 848289   Email: museums@winchester.gov.uk
Web: www.winchester.gov.uk/heritage

Frequently changing programme of exciting exhibitions of paintings, craft, photography, ceramics and sculpture.

Opening Times: During exhibitions: Apr to Oct Mon to Sat 10:00-17:00, Sun 14:00-17:00. Nov to Mar Tue to Sat 10:00-16:00, Sun 14:00-16:00.   Admission: Free.   Location: The Broadway, situated in the Victorian Guildhall above the Tourist Information Centre.   Map Ref: 33

Guided or Private Tours	Disabled Access	Gift Shop or Sales Point	Café or Refreshments	Restaurant	Car Parking

The Gurkha Museum

Peninsula Barracks, Romsey Road, Winchester
SO23 8TS   Tel: 01962 842832/843657
Fax: 01962 877597   Email: curator@thegurkhamuseum.co.uk
Web: www.the gurkhamuseum.co.uk

A unique commemoration of Gurkha service to the British Crown and people spanning 190 years, two world wars and numerous smaller campaigns. There is much about Nepal, its people, culture, arts and customs.

Opening Times: Mon to Sat 10:00-17:00, Sun 12:00-16:00. Closed Xmas & New Year. Admission: Adult £1.50, Child/OAP 75p. Group 50p per person. Location: Town centre, near Great Hall.

Map Ref: 33

The King's Royal Hussars Museum in Winchester

Peninsula Barracks, Romsey Road, Winchester SO23 8TS   Tel: 01962 828541/828539
Fax: 01962 828538   Email: beresford@krhmuseum.freeserve.co.uk   Web: www.krh.org.uk

Story of famous cavalry regiments; 10th Royal Hussars (Prince of Wales' Own) and 11th Hussars (Prince Albert's Own) 'The Cherry Pickers' raised in 1715. The Royal Hussars 1969-1992 and today's regiment, The King's Royal Hussars from 1992. See the Charge of the Light Brigade, experience World War I trench, and see the cupboard in which Private Fowler was hidden in a French farm for three years during World War I.

The diary of The Charge of The Light Brigade by RSM Loy Smith

Opening Times: Tue to Fri 10:00-12:45 & 13:15-16:00
Sat, Sun, BH and half term Mon 12:00-16:00.

Admission: Free. Location: Beside Great Hall/Law Courts.

Map Ref: 33

Light Infantry Museum

Peninsula Barracks, Romsey Road, Winchester SO23 8TS   Tel: 01962 828550   Fax: 01962 828534

A collection which depicts the Light Infantry Regiment, its origins, soldiers and operations. Particular displays are the Berlin Wall, Northern Ireland, Gulf War and Sir John Moore.

Opening Times: Tue to Sat and holiday Mon 10:00-16:00 (closed for lunch). Sun 12:00-16:00.
Admission: Free, but donations welcome. Location: Top of town, behind the Great Hall and five minutes from railway station.

Map Ref: 33

Royal Hampshire Regiment Museum & Memorial Garden

Serle's House, Southgate Street, Winchester SO23 9EG
Tel: 01962 863658   Fax: 01962 888302

History of the regiment 1702 to 1992. Medals, uniforms, colours, weapons and many personal artefacts. Covers regulars, Volunteers, Territorials and Militia.

Opening Times: Mon to Fri 11:00-15:30. Closed 2 weeks Xmas & New Year. Weekends & BH Apr to Oct only 12:00-16:00. Admission: Free. Location: Near town centre, two minute walk from high street.

Map Ref: 33

Westgate

High Street, Winchester   Tel: 01962 848269   Email: museums@winchester.gov.uk
Web: www.winchester.gov.uk/heritage

Medieval gateway. Former debtors' prison. Contains: prisoners' graffiti, unique collection of weights & measures, armour, Tudor ceiling from Winchester College. Brass rubbing. Rooftop city views.

Opening Times: Apr to Oct Mon to Sat 10:00-17:00, Sun 12:00-17:00. Feb to Mar Tue to Sat 10:00-16:00, Sun 12:00-16:00. Closed Nov to Jan. Admission: Free. Location: High Street, close to Great Hall.

Map Ref: 33

The region boasts some singularly handsome towns including Hereford, once the capital of the powerful Anglo-Saxon kingdom of Mercia and now home to the magnificent twelfth century cathedral which towers over the banks of the River Wye. Worcester too has its proud history, being an important centre during the Civil War. The Cotswolds in the east offer magnificent views and inspired much of the music of Sir Edward Edgar.

There are a number of excellent museums and galleries dealing with this rich region.

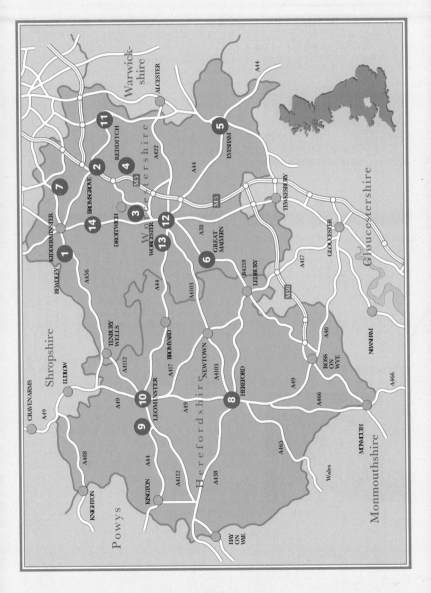

The Red Map References should be used to locate Museums etc on the pages that follow

BEWDLEY *Worcs*

Bewdley Museum

The Shambles, Load Street, Bewdley DY12 2AE   Tel: 01299 403573   Fax: 01299 404740
Email: museum-wfd@online.rednet.co.uk

Housed in the town's old Butchers Shambles, the museum provides a fascinating insight into the growth and trades of the town. Displays feature the work of basket and besom makers, charcoal burners, pewterers and brass founders. Daily craft demonstrations.

Opening Times: Apr to Sep daily 11:00-17:00, Oct daily 11:00-16:00.   Admission: Adult £2.00, Child Free, OAP/Concession £1.00.   Location: Bewdley - off the A456 Leominster Road, on the B4190.
Map Ref: 1

Severn Valley Railway

The Railway Station, Bewdley DY12 1BG   Tel: 01299 403816   Fax: 01299 400839   Web: www.svr.co.uk

Loco 3442 crossing River Severn
on Victoria Bridge

A standard-gauge steam railway running between Kidderminster and Bridgnorth, 16 miles. The journey provides fine views of the River Severn and visitors can alight at any of the four intermediate stations. Refreshments at main stations and on most trains. Special events throughout the year. The railway is home to one of the largest collections of pre-nationalisation locomotives, coaches and wagons.

Opening Times: Every Sat & Sun. 4 May to 29 Sep daily, Feb, Apr, Oct local school holidays.   Admission: Adult £10.50, Child £5.30, OAP £8.40, Family £28.00.
Location: On A448 Comberton Hill. Signposted from all major roads.
Map Ref: 1

BROMSGROVE *Worcs*

Avoncroft Museum of Historic Buildings

Stoke Heath, Bromsgrove B60 4JR   Tel: 01527 831363   Fax: 01527 876934
Email: avoncrofteducation@compuserve.com   Web: www.avoncroft.org.uk

Collection of over 25 historic buildings, including windmill, prefab and church. Includes the National Telephone Kiosk collection.

Opening Times: Mar & Nov Tue to Thu, Sat & Sun 10:30-16:00. Apr to Jun, Sep to Oct Tue to Fri 10:30-16:30. Jul & Aug Mon to Fri 10:30-17:00, Sat & Sun 10:30-17:30.   Admission: Adult £5.50, Child £2.75, Concession £4.50, Family £14.50. Party rates available.   Location: Three miles north of junction 5, M5, three miles south of junction 1, M42. Off A38, south of Bromsgrove.
Map Ref: 2

Bromsgrove Museum

26 Birmingham Road, Bromsgrove B61 0DD   Tel / Fax: 01527 831809

An old workshop at the Museum

Bromsgrove Museum gives an insight into local history with displays of past craft and industries such as nail, glass, lead, button and salt making. Also incorporated into the Museum is a street of Victorian and Edwardian shops, including a chemists, stationers and cobblers. There are also displays on The Bromsgrove Guild and AE Housman.

Opening Times: Mon to Sat 10:30-12:30 13:00-16:30.
Admission: Free.   Location: Near town centre, on Birmingham Road.
Map Ref: 2

Guided or Private Tours	Disabled Access	Gift Shop or Sales Point	Café or Refreshments	Restaurant	Car Parking

DROITWICH SPA *Worcs*

Droitwich Heritage Centre

St Richard's House, Victoria Square, Droitwich Spa WR9 8DS   Tel: 01905 774312   Fax: 01905 794226

See the fascinating history of Droitwich from prehistoric Salt Town to luxury Spa. BBC Radio room with hands-on display. Brass rubbing, Tourist Information Centre and souvenirs.

Opening Times: Mon to Sat 10:00-16:00. Close Sun and BH.   Admission: Free.
Location: Town centre location, ten minute walk from rail station.   Map Ref: 3

Hanbury Hall & Gardens

School Road, Hanbury, Droitwich Spa WR9 7EA   Tel: 01527 821214   Fax: 01527 821251
Email: hanbury@smtp.ntrust.org.uk   Web: www.ntrustsevern.org.uk

Beautiful English country house with tranquil reconstructed 18th century gardens and parkland. Many unusual features including outstanding staircase murals, working mushroom house and orangery, Watney Collection of fine porcelain and Dutch flower paintings.

Opening Times: 22 Mar to 29 Oct, Sat to Wed - gardens, tearoom, shop 12:00-17:30, hall 13:00-17:30. Sat - Gardens, tearoom, shop 11:00-16:00, House 11:30-15:30.
Admission: House & Garden: Adult £5.00, Child £2.50, Family £12.00. Garden only: Adult £3.00, Child £1.60.   Location: Junction 5 of M5, four and a half miles east of Droitwich off B4090.   Map Ref: 4

EVESHAM *Worcs*

The Almonry Heritage Centre

Abbey Gate, Evesham WR11 4BG   Tel: 01386 446944   Fax: 01386 442348
Email: tic@almonry.ndo.co.uk   Web: www.evesham.uk.com

Exhibits relating to Evesham Abbey 709-1540, Battle of Evesham 1265. Agricultural and social history - Anglo Saxon treasure, archaeology, children's activities.

Opening Times: Mon to Sat 10:00-17:00, Sun 14:00-17:00. Closed Sun Nov, Dec & Jan.
Admission: Adult £2.00, Child Free, OAP/Concession £1.00.   Map Ref: 5

GREAT MALVERN *Worcs*

Malvern Museum

Priory Gatehouse, Abbey Road, Great Malvern WR14 3ES   Tel: 01684 567811

The museum is located in the ancient Priory Gatehouse. It takes visitors from the earliest Iron Age settlements, through to the medieval community, the arrival of the Water Cure, Victorian enterprise and the scientific advances made by radar research.

Opening Times: Easter to Oct daily 10:30-17:00. Closed Wed in term time.   Admission: Adult £1.00, Under 7s Free, Concession 20p.   Location: In town centre, close to Tourist Office and main Post Office.   Map Ref: 6

HAGLEY *Worcs*

Hagley Hall

Hagley DY9 9LG   Tel: 01562 882408   Fax: 01562 882632

Grade I Georgian House set in Grade I Park. Containing a fine collection of 18th century portraits and furniture. Hagley Hall is the home of Viscount and Viscountess Cobham.

Opening Times: 3 to 27 Jan, 4 to 24 Feb, 1 to 8 Mar, 1 to 9 Apr, 25 to 29 Aug 14:00-17:00.
Closed all Sat.   Admission: Adult £3.50, Child £1.50, Concession £2.50.   Location: One mile from Hagley Station.   Map Ref: 7

Museums • Galleries • Historic Houses

Please let us know of any collections that are not listed in this guide that you feel
should be listed. E-mail us on *editor@tomorrows.co.uk*
or return the Report Form on page 448

Herefordshire & Worcestershire

Hereford Museum & Art Gallery
Broad Street, Hereford HR4 9AU   Tel: 01432 260692
Fax: 01432 342492
Web: www.museumsherefordshire.gov.uk

Hereford Museum displays 'A Sense of Place', a permanent exhibition which gives an insight to the county of Herefordshire. Included are objects from collections on agriculture, landscape, folklore, schooldays and cooking. Included are community cases with changing displays, an observation beehive and hands-on displays for children. The Art Gallery houses a varied programme of temporary exhibitions on art, craft, photography and other themes.

Opening Times: Tue to Sat 10:00-17:00, Sun (Apr to Sep) 10:00-16:00, BH Mon 10:00-16:00. Closed Mon, Xmas & New Year and Good Friday. Admission: Free. Location: In the town centre, opposite Hereford Cathedral.
Map Ref: 8

Hereford Museum & Art Gallery

Mappa Mundi & Chained Library
5 College Cloisters, Cathedral Close, Hereford HR1 2NG   Tel: 01432 374202   Fax: 01432 374220

The Mappa Mundi and Chained Library Exhibition is open all year round and is famous for housing both the spectacular medieval map of the world and the cathedral's unique Chained Library. Here the stories of these national treasures are told through models, original artefacts and the latest interactive computer technology.

Opening Times: Summer: Mon to Sat 10:00-16:15, Sun 11:00-15:15. Winter: Mon to Sat 11:00-15:15, closed Sun. Admission: Adult £4.00, Under 5s Free, Concession £3.50, Family £10.00. Location: Town centre.
Map Ref: 8

Old House
High Town, Hereford HR1 2AA   Tel: 01432 260694   Fax: 01432 342492
Web: www.museums.herefordshire.gov.uk

Built in 1621, one of Hereford's finest timber-framed buildings, the last remaining from Butcher's Row. Furnished in 17th century style on three floors, the house includes a kitchen, hall and bedrooms.

Opening Times: Tue to Sat 10:00-17:00, Sun (Apr to Sep) 10:00-16:00, BH Mon 10:00-14:00. Closed Mon, Xmas & New Year and Good Friday. Admission: Free. Location: In the pedestrian area of the High Town at the heart of the city.
Map Ref: 8

Burton Court
Eardisland, Leominster HR6 9DN   Tel: 01544 388231   Email: helenjsimpson@hotmail.com
Web: www.burtoncourt.co.uk

14th century Great Hall, European and Oriental costumes, ship models, natural history specimens, working model fairground. Archaeology dig.

Opening Times: Spring BH to end Sep Wed, Thu, Sat, Sun & BH 14:30-18:00.
Admission: Adult £3.50, Child £2.00, Groups £3.00. Location: Near Leominster, five miles on A44.
Map Ref: 9

Leominster Folk Museum
Etnam Street, Leominster HR6 8AL   Tel: 01568 615186   Email: sallywhitfield@lineone.net

The purpose of Leominster Folk Museum is to collect, display and preserve local material for the education and enjoyment of the public.

Opening Times: Easter to Oct Mon to Fri 10:30-16:00, Sat 10:30-13:00. Open BH.
Admission: Free. Location: Near town centre.
Map Ref: 10

Herefordshire & Worcestershire

Forge Mill Museum & Bordesley Abbey

Needle Mill Lane, Riverside, Redditch B98 8HY   Tel: 01527 62509
Email: museum@redditchbc.gov.uk   Web: www.redditchbc.gov.uk

Industrial museum with unique displays and collections telling the fascinating story of how needles are made. Also archaeological site museum with children's activities showing finds from the adjacent Cistercian Abbey of Bordesley.

Opening Times: Easter to Sep Mon to Fri 11:00-16:30, Sat & Sun 14:00-17:00. Feb to Easter & Oct to Nov Mon to Thu 11:00-16:00, Sun 14:00-17:00. Admission: Adult £3.50, Child 75p, OAP £2.50. Pre-booked Group rates available.   Location: Off A441 Birmingham to Evesham road; junction 2 on M42. Located just north of Redditch Town Centre.   Map Ref: 11

Commandery

Sidbury, Worcester WR1 2HU   Tel: 01905 361821   Fax: 01905 361822
Email: thecommandery@cityofworcester.gov.uk
Web: www.worcestercitymuseums.org.uk

The commandery is the most important secular building in Worcester dating back nearly 1000 years. As well as period rooms such as the Great Hall and Painted Chamber there are exhibitions on the building's past and the English Civil War, when the building served as the Royalist Headquarters at the Battle of Worcester in 1651.

Opening Times: Mon to Sat 10:00-17:00, Sun 13:30-17:00. Admission: Charges apply. Location: Two minute walk from Worcester Cathedral.   Map Ref: 12

King Charles II at the Commandery's Oak Apple Day

The Elgar Birthplace Museum

Crown East Lane, Lower Broadheath, Worcester WR2 6RH   Tel: 01905 333224   Fax: 01905 333426   Email: birthplace@elgar.org   Web: www.elgar.org

A fascinating insight into the life and music, family and friends, inspirations and musical development of one of Britain's greatest composers, Sir Edward Elgar. Historic birthplace cottage in pretty garden. New exhibition and special events in the Elgar Centre, opened in 2000.

Opening Times: Daily 11:00-17:00. Closed Xmas to end Jan. Admission: Adult £3.50, Child £1.75, Concession £3.00, Family £8.75. Reduction for pre-booked groups. Location: Three miles west of Worcester, signposted off Worcester/Leominster road.   Map Ref: 13

Museum of Local Life

Friar Street, Worcester WR1 2NA   Tel: 01905 722349   Email: nburnett@cityofworcester.gov.uk

Small community museum depicting everyday lives of Worcester people in the past. Victorian kitchen, school room.

Opening Times: Mon to Wed, Fri & Sat 10:30-17:00. Admission: Free. Location: Five minutes from Cathedral.   Map Ref: 12

Museum of Worcester Porcelain

Severn Street, Worcester WR1 2NE   Tel: 01905 746000   Fax: 01905 617807
Email: museum@royal-worcester.co.uk   Web: www.royal-worcester.co.uk

Travel on a design journey through time and see rare porcelain sumptuously displayed in period room settings and dining scenes in the Georgian, Victorian and 20th Century galleries.

Opening Times: Mon to Sat 09:00-17:30, Sun 11:00-17:00. Admission: Adult £3.00, Concession £2.25. Location: Two minute walk from Worcester Cathedral and town centre.
            Map Ref: 12

WORCESTER *(continued)*

Worcester City Museum & Art Gallery

♿ ⚫ ▢ **WORCESTER MUSEUMS**

Foregate Street, Worcester WR1 1DT   Tel: 01905 25371   Fax: 01905 616979   Email: artgalleryandmuseum@cityofworcester.gov.uk
Web: www.worcestercitymuseums.org.uk

Housed in a beautiful Victorian building, the City Museum & Art Gallery runs a lively programme of exhibitions, activities and events for all the family. Explore the fascinating historic displays or drop in and see one of our contemporary art exhibitions. Visit our award winning café, gallery shop, children's activity area and museums of the Worcestershire Regiment and Yeomanry.

Opening Times: Mon to Fri 09:30-17:30, Sat 09:30-17:00. Closed Sun. Admission: Free. Location: Town centre, 150 yards from Foregate Street Railway Station.   Map Ref: 12

The beautiful Victorian building that houses the collections

Worcestershire County Museum

✎ ♿ ⚫ ▢ ♿ **WORCESTERSHIRE COUNTY MUSEUM HARTLEBURY · CASTLE**

Hartlebury Castle, Hartlebury, Worcester DY11 7XZ   Tel: 01299 250416
Fax: 01299 251890   Email: museum@worcestershire.gov.uk

Housed in the sandstone home of the Bishops of Worcester for over a thousand years, the County Museum illustrates local life from the Roman period until the 20th century. Particular exhibits include reconstructed cider mill, horse-drawn transport, female costume and social history from the Victorian and Edwardian eras.

Opening Times: Feb to Nov Mon to Thu 10:00-17:00, Fri & Sun 14:00-17:00. Closed Sat & Good Friday. Other BH in season 11:00-17:00. Admission: Adult £2.50, Child/Concession £1.20, Family £6.50. Location: Four miles south of Kidderminster, signed from A449 Worcester Road.   Map Ref: 14

Hartlebury Castle, home of the WCM and Bishops of Worcester

Kent

Kent, the closest county to the continent, through which a host of armies poured including the Roman armies of Julius Caesar, the Saxon hordes of Horsa and Hengist and on a quieter note, missionaries from Rome on their way to Canterbury, the spiritual capital of England. Long known as the 'Garden of England', this pleasant region has always attracted the powerful and wealthy to build their manors and mansions here.

Splendid and varied museums together with historic houses cover Roman occupation, naval history through to the Second World War, and encompass Charles Darwin to Charles Dickens

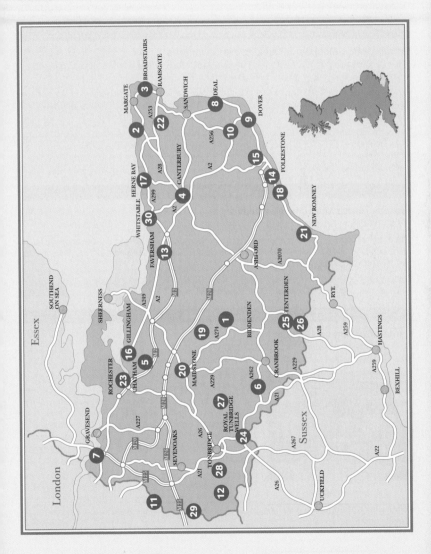

The Red Map References should be used to locate Museums etc on the pages that follow

Kent

Lashenden Air Warfare Museum

Headcorn Aerodrome, Headcorn, Ashford TN27 9HX Tel: 01622 890226/206783 Fax: 01622 206783 Email: lashairwar@aol.com

The museum preserves the aviation heritage of Kent, with particular emphasis on World War II. There is a separate building housing a First World War display, including various uniforms, tunics etc.

Opening Times: Easter Sun to end Oct 10:30-18:00. Nov to Easter 10:30-15:30. Closed Xmas & New Year. Admission: Free. Location: Nine miles south of Maidstone on A274, one mile from Headcorn.
Map Ref: 1

BIRCHINGTON

Powell-Cotton Museum & Quex House & Gardens

Quex Park, Birchington CT7 0BH Tel: 01843 842168 Fax: 01843 846661 Email: powell-cotton.museum@virgin.net Web: www.powell-cottonmuseum.co.uk

An extraordinary collection, within a museum, stately home and garden setting, of African and Asian animal displays, tribal artefacts, weapons, cannons, archeology, chinese porcelain and much more.

Opening Times: Apr to Oct Tue to Thu, Sun & BH 11:00-17:00, Nov & Mar Sun 11:00-16:00. Quex House: 14:00-17:00, closed Dec, Jan and Feb. Admission: Adult £4.00, Child/OAP £3.00, Student £2.50, Family £12.00. Location: Coastal location, near town centre, 20 minute walk from railway station.
Map Ref: 2

BROADSTAIRS

Dickens House Museum, Broadstairs

2 Victoria Parade, Broadstairs CT10 1QS Tel / Fax: 01843 863453 Email: aleeault@aol.com

This lovely old house, once the home of Miss Mary Pearson Strong on whom Dickens based much of the character of Miss Betsey Trotwood ('David Copperfield'), is now a museum to commemorate the novelist's association with Broadstairs.

Opening Times: Easter to Oct daily 11;30-17:00. Admission: Adult £2.00, Child £1.00, Student £1.00, Family discount. Location: On the main seafront.
Map Ref: 3

CANTERBURY

Canterbury Roman Museum

Butchery Lane, Canterbury Tel: 01227 785575 Fax: 01227 455047
Email: museums@canterbury.gov.uk Web: www.canterbury-museum.co.uk

Acclaimed Hands-On area

Step below today's Canterbury to discover an exciting part of the Roman town including the real remains of a house with fine mosaics. Experience everyday life in the reconstructed market place and see exquisite silver and glass. Try your skill on the touch-screen computer, and in the hands-on area with actual finds. Use the computer animation of Roman Canterbury to join the search for the lost temple.

Opening Times: Mon to Sat 10:00-17:00 plus Jun to end Oct on Sun 13:30-17:00. Closed Good Friday and Xmas. Last admission 16:00 Admission: Adult £2.60, Concession £1.65, Family £6.80 (until 31.3.2003). Location: Town centre, part of the Long Market, near the Cathedral.
Map Ref: 4

Guided or Private Tours	Disabled Access	Gift Shop or Sales Point	Café or Refreshments	Restaurant		Car Parking

Kent

Canterbury Royal Museum & Art Gallery with Buffs Regimental Museum

18 High Street, Canterbury CT1 2RA   Tel: 01227 452747   Fax: 01227 455047
Email: museum@canterbury.gov.uk   Web: www.canterbury-artgallery.co.uk

A splendid Victorian building, houses decorative arts and the city's picture collections - including a gallery for TS Cooper, England's finest cattle painter. The art gallery is the major space in the area for the visual arts with a varied exhibitions programme. Here too is the Buffs Museum, which tells the story of one of England's oldest infantry regiments and its worldwide service.

Opening Times: Mon to Sat 10:00-17:00. Closed Good Friday and Xmas. Admission: Free. Location: Situated on the first floor of the Beaney Institute in the High Street, almost opposite the Post Office. Exhibitions & Events

The Art Gallery

2003 : 11 Jan: Fossil Roadshow - Ice Age Man & Mammoth: A focus on the last Ice Age in Kent, flint tools, activities and demonstrations, 18 Jan to 1 Mar: Whistler: Haden and the rise of the painter - etcher, 9 Mar to 26 Apr: Landscape and Light: Paintings by John Titchell, Norman Adams, Fred Cuming and Colin Hayes.   Map Ref: 4

Canterbury West Gate Towers

St Peters Street, Canterbury   Tel: 01227 452747   Fax: 01227 455047   Email: museums@canterbury.gov.uk   Web: www.canterbury-museum.co.uk

Medieval West Gate is one of England's finest city gates. Built in about 1380, it has a guard chamber with its 'murder holes' and battlement cells on view. On display are arms and armours from the Civil War to the Second World War. Displays also tell the story of the city defenders. There are fine panoramic views over the city from the battlements.

Opening Times: Mon to Sat 11:00-12:30 13:30-15;30. Closed Good Friday & Xmas. Admission: Adult £1.00, Concession 65p, Family £2.50 (until 31.3.2003). Location: The museum stands at the end of the main street beside the river.   Map Ref: 4

View from the Battlements

Museum of Canterbury

Poor Priests Hospital, Stour Street, Canterbury   Tel: 01227 452747   Fax: 01227 455047   Email: museum@canterbury.gov.uk   Web: www.canterbury-museum.co.uk

21st century interactive museum, whose theme is the city itself and its turbulent story. Housed in the medieval Poor Priests' Hospital, the newly refurbished and extended museum has a range of exhibits from pre-Roman times to the end of the 20th century including the Anglo-Saxon Canterbury Cross. New is the medieval discovery gallery, Joseph Conrad Gallery and Rupert Bear Museum.

Opening Times: Mon to Sat 10:30-17:00 (last admission 16:00). Closed Xmas & Good Friday. Admission: Adult £2.60, Concession £1.65, Family £6.80 (until 31.3.2003). Location: In town centre, situated in the Medieval Poor Priests Hospital, just off St Margarets Street or High Street and within easy walking distance of Cathedral.

The Magnificent Oak Beams of the Great Hall

Exhibitions & Events 2003 : Mar: Science Week - Special events for the national celebration of science, with activities for all the family.   Map Ref: 4

St Augustines Abbey

Longport, Canterbury CT1 1TF   Tel: 01227 767345

This great shrine, founded by St Augustine in 597, the year he arrived in England from Rome, marks the birthplace of Christianity in this country. St Augustine himself is buried here.

Opening Times: Apr to Sep daily 10:00-18:00, Oct daily 10:00-17:00, Nov to Mar daily 10:00-16:00. Closed Xmas & New Year. Admission: Adult £3.00, Child £1.50, Concession £2.30. Location: In Longport, quarter of a mile east of Cathedral Close.   Map Ref: 4

Kent

The Historic Dockyard Chatham

The Historic Dockyard, Chatham ME4 4TZ   Tel: 01634 823800   Fax: 01634 823801   Email: info@chdt.org.uk
Web: www.chdt.org.uk

Maritime and naval heritage site covering 80 acres. Displays include Britain's last operational WWII destroyer and submarine Ocelot. Wooden Walls is an 18th century dockyard adventure and in Lifeboat! 16 of the RNLI's most historic craft are displayed. The Ropewalk is the last ropewalk from the age of sail and the Museum of The Royal Dockyard details Chatham's naval history.

Opening Times: 15 Feb to 2 Nov daily 10:00-18:00 (or dusk if earlier). Nov Sat & Sun (weekdays for special openings and pre-booked groups). Closed Dec & Jan. Admission: Adult £9.50, Child £6.00, Concession £7.00. Location: Regular buses to Main Gate from Chatham Rail Station. Exhibitions & Events 2003 : 19 to 21 Apr: Easter Steam and Transport Festival, 24 to 26 May: Historic Dockyard, 23 to 25 Aug: International Petanque and French Festival, Date TBA: Christmas Festival.   Map Ref: 5

Kent Police Museum

The Historic Dockyard, Dock Road, Chatham ME4 4TZ   Tel / Fax: 01634 403260
Email: kentpolmus@aol.com   Web: www.kent-police-museum.co.uk

Museum showing the history of the Kent County Constabulary from 1857 to current day. The collection consists of Police artefacts of uniform, equipment, vehicles and photographs.

Opening Times: Please phone for opening times. Admission: No entry fee to Police Museum.
Location: Within the Historic Dockyard, Chatham next to Rochester north of M2.   Map Ref: 5

The Royal National Lifeboat Collection

The Historic Dockyard, Chatham ME4 4TZ   Tel: 01634 823800   Web: www.lifeboats.org.uk

'Lifeboat!, The Royal National Lifeboat Collection'. The gallery has been created around a collection of 15 historic lifeboats.

Opening Times: Apr to Oct daily 10:00-16:00. Nov, Feb & Mar Wed, Sat & Sun 10:00-16:00.
                                                                                                                             Map Ref: 5

Finchcocks Living Museum of Music

Goudhurst, Cranbrook TN17 1HH   Tel: 01580 211702   Fax: 01580 211007
Email: katrina@finchcocks.co.uk   Web: www.finchcocks.co.uk

Celebrated collection of 100 period keyboard instruments; 40 in concert condition. Housed in fine Georgian manor in beautiful gardens. Pictures and prints on musical themes. Recitals/Demonstrations for all visitors. Festive and many special events.

Opening Times: Open Days: Easter to Sep Sun & BH Mon, also Aug Wed & Thu 14:00-18:00.
By appointment Mar to Dec most days. Admission: Open Days: Adult £7.50, Child £4.00.
Group rates available. Location: One mile off A262.   Map Ref: 6

Dartford Borough Museum

Market Street, Dartford DA1 1EU   Tel: 01322 224739   Fax: 01322 343209

The museum presents the history and archaeology of the Borough of Dartford through permanent displays together with temporary exhibitions which draw upon the extensive reserve collections.

Opening Times: Mon to Fri 12:30-17:30, Sat 09:00-13:00 & 14:00-17:00. Closed Wed & Sun.
Admission: Free. Location: In town centre, adjacent to library and central park.   Map Ref: 7

Kent

Walmer Castle

Kingsdown Road, Walmer, Deal CT14 7LJ   Tel: 01304 364288

Walmer Castle was one of a chain of coastal artillery forts built by Henry VIII to protect the Downs. Walmer was transformed when it became the official residence of the Lords Warden of the Cinque Ports.

Opening Times: Apr to Sep daily 10:00-18:00, Oct daily 10:00-17:00, Nov to Dec & Mar Wed to Sun 10:00-16:00, Jan to Feb Sat & Sun 10:00-16:00. Closed Xmas & New Year.
Admission: Adult £5.50, Child £2.80, Concession £4.10, Family £13.80.   Location: On coast south of Walmer on A258. Junction 13 off M20 or from M2 to Deal.   Map Ref: 8

DOVER

View of the Anti-aircraft Control Room. © English Heritage

Dover Castle

Dover CT16 1HN   Tel: 01304 201628/211067

For over 2000 years, the site of Dover Castle has protected the stretch of English coast closest to Europe. From the Iron Age to the Atomic Age, the castle's defences have grown to meet the changing demands of warfare. Hidden inside the White Cliffs of Dover is a fascinating and secret world: below, deep underground, are miles of tunnels. The keeps, built in the 1180s, contain displays devoted to the siege of 1216 and the arrival of the Court of Henry VIII in 1539.

Opening Times: Apr to Sep daily 10:00-18:00, Oct daily 10:00-17:00, Nov to Mar daily 10:00-16:00. Closed Xmas & New Year.
Admission: Adult £8.00, Child £4.00, Concession £6.00, Family £20.00.   Location: On east side of Dover.   Map Ref: 9

Discovering archaeology, the interactive lab at Dover Museum

Dover Museum & The Bronze Age Boat Gallery

Market Square, Dover CT16 1PB   Tel: 01304 201066

Dover Museum tells the story of the town and port since prehistoric times, a town that for centuries has been the Gateway to England. Displays include Dover's history as a Roman port and Saxon town, Cinque Ports, Napoleonic Wars, Victorian Dover, and the two World Wars. Also on display is the world's oldest sea-going boat. Found in Dover in 1992, it is 3,550 years old, older than Tutankhamun and from the same age as Stonehenge.

Opening Times: Open Oct to Apr daily, 10:00-17:30, May to Sep daily 10:00-18:00. Closed Xmas & New Year. Admission: Adults £1.75, Child/OAP 95p, Group discount 10%.   Location: In Town Centre, three minutes from main Bus Station, 10 minutes from Dover Priory Railway Station.   Map Ref: 9

Dover Transport Museum

White Cliffs Business Park, Honeywood Road, Whitfield, near Dover CT16 2HJ   Tel: 01304 822409 Fax: 01303 241245 Email: Dave@classicomnibus.co.uk
Web: www.dovertransportmuseum.co.uk

Bicycles to buses, model railways and tramway, Leonardo Da Vinci to the Channel Tunnel. Road, sea, air, transport, hundreds of models, replica shops, bygones.

Opening Times: Apr to Oct Wed to Sat 13:30-17:30, Sun & BH 10:30-17:00. Groups at any time by prior arrangement. Admission: Adult £2.00, Child £1.00, OAP £1.50, Family £5.00.
Location: Just off A2 Whitfield (MacDonalds) roundabout, three miles outside Dover.
            Map Ref: 10

Guided or Private Tours	Disabled Access	Gift Shop or Sales Point	Café or Refreshments	Restaurant	Car Parking

Kent

Down House

Luxted Road, Downe BR6 7JT   Tel: 01689 859119

From his study at Down House, Charles Darwin worked on the scientific theories that first scandalised and then revolutionised the Victorian world, culminating in the publication of 'On the Origin of Species by means of Natural Selection'. 3,500 objects relating to Darwin's work remain including portraits, photographs, family furniture, memorabilia from the Beagle voyage and manuscripts, including his Beagle Journal.

Opening Times: Please telephone to check times and pre-book for the month of Aug. Groups over 11 must pre-book at all times.
Admission: Adult £6.00, Child £3.00, Concession £4.50.
Location: In Luxted Road, Downe, off A21 near Biggin Hill.

The Old Study © English Heritage

Map Ref: 11

Kent & Sharpshooters Yeomanry Museum

Hever Castle, Edenbridge TN8 7NG   Tel: 01732 865224   Email: ksymuseum@aol.com
Web: www.ksymuseum.org.uk

Includes pictures, uniforms, badges, medals, flags, weapons of the East Kent Yeomanry, West Kent Yeomanry, 3rd/4th County of London Yeomanry (Sharpshooters).

Opening Times: Mar to Nov 12:00-18:00, during winter time (GMT) 12:00-16:00.
Admission: Adult £8.00, Child £4.40, OAP £6.80, Family £20.40.   Location: Three miles south east of Edenbridge off the B2026.

Map Ref: 12

Chart Gunpowder Mills

Choat Close, Faversham ME13 7SE   Tel: 01795 534542   Fax: 01795 533261
Email: faversham@btinternet.com   Web: www.faversham.org

The world's oldest gunpowder mills, which made powder for Nelson at Trafalgar and Wellington at Waterloo. Display explains how powder is made. Restored and managed by voluntary effort.

Opening Times: Easter to Oct Sat, Sun & BH 14:00-17:00.   Admission: Free.   Location: Ten minute walk from town centre and mainline railway station.

Map Ref: 13

Fleur de Lis Heritage Centre

13 Preston Street, Faversham ME13 8NS   Tel: 01795 534542   Fax: 01795 533261
Email: faversham@btinternet.com   Web: www.faversham.org

Recently expanded and updated, and housed in 16th century premises, the centre's colourful displays tell the story of 2,000 years of life in one of Britain's most historic ports.

Opening Times: Mon to Sat 10:00-16:00, Sun 10:00-13:00.   Admission: Adult £2.00, Child/OAP/Disabled £1.00.   Location: In town centre, four minute walk from mainline station.
Map Ref: 13

Maison Dieu

Ospringe Street, Ospringe, Faversham ME13 8TW   Tel: 01795 534542   Fax: 01795 533261
Email: faversham@btinternet.com   Web: www.faversham.org

Finds from a nearby Roman cemetry, and displays tracing the history of Ospringe, are housed in the 13th century building which was once part of a Royal Lodge and pilgrims' hostel.

Opening Times: Easter to Oct Sat, Sun & BH 14:00-17:00.   Admission: Adult £1.00, Child/OAP 50p.   Location: On main A2, 20 minute walk town centre and mainline railway station.

Map Ref: 13

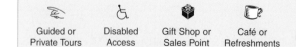

Guided or Private Tours	Disabled Access	Gift Shop or Sales Point	Café or Refreshments	Restaurant	Car Parking

Kent

FOLKESTONE

Folkestone Museum & Gallery

Grace Hill, Folkestone CT20 1HD   Tel / Fax: 01303 256710
Email: folkestonelibrary@kent.gov.uk

Story of Folkestone, important Victorian seaside resort and Channel Port. Audio and film, hands-on activities. Programme of events for Museum and Gallery. New Craft Gallery, research facilities.

Opening Times: Mon, Tues & Thu 09:30-18:00, Fri 09:30-19:00, Wed & Sat 09:30-17:00, Sun 10:00-16:00. Closed BH.   Admission: Free.   Location: Two minutes walk from bus station and pay car parks.   Map Ref: 14

Kent Battle of Britain Museum

Aerodrome Road, Hawkinge, Folkestone CT18 7AG   Tel: 01303 893140
Email: kentbattleofbritainmuseum@btinternet.com   Web: www.kbobm.org.uk or www.kentbattleofbritainmuseum.org.uk

Most important collection of Battle of Britain artefacts on show in the country - aircraft, vehicles, weapons, flying equipment, prints, relics from over 600 crashed Battle of Britain aircraft.

Opening Times: Good Friday to 30 Sep Tue to Sun 10:00-17:00. Closed Mon except BH. Closed Oct to Easter.   Admission: Adult £3.50, Child £2.00, OAP £3.00. Group discounts available.   Location: Three miles north of Folkestone. Off Aerodrome Road, Hawkinge.
                                                                              Map Ref: 15

GILLINGHAM

Royal Engineers Museum

Prince Arthur Road, Gillingham ME4 4UG   Tel: 01634 406397   Fax: 01634 822371
Email: remuseum.rhqre@gnet.gov.uk   Web: www.royalengineers.org.uk

Displays of engineering equipment, working models, superb medal galleries with 25 VCs and the regalia of four Field Marshalls including Kitchener. Costumes and curios from around the world.

Opening Times: Mon to Thu 10:00-17:00, Sat, Sun & BH 11:30-17:00. Friday by appointment only. Closed Xmas & New Year.   Admission: Adult £3.50, Child/OAP £2.00, Family £9.00. Guided Tours £5.00 per person.   Location: Prince Arthur Road, Gillingham, 20 minute walk from Gillingham Station.   Map Ref: 16

HERNE BAY

Herne Bay Museum & Gallery

12 William Street, Herne Bay CT6 5EJ   Tel: 01227 367368   Email: museum@canterbury.gov.uk
Web: www.hernebay-museum.co.uk

The museum highlights the history of the Victorian seaside resort of Herne Bay. Find out about the town's famous pier. See exciting finds from the nearby Roman fort and Saxon church of Reculver, as well as fossils including mammoth tusks and fossilised sharks teeth. Also on display is a famous 'bouncing bomb' from World War II. The art gallery has regularly changing temporary exhibitions.

Opening Times: Mon to Sat 10:00-16:00 plus Jul & Aug on Sun 13:00-16:00. Closed Good Friday & Xmas. Admission: Free.   Location: Town centre, 12 William

Victorian seaside publicity poster

Street, near the seafront at the Clock Tower end, in the same building as the Visitor Information Centre.   Exhibitions & Events 2003 : 22 Mar to 26 Apr: W T M Hawksworth: A Centenary Celebration - Watercolours and drawings of coastal scenes and Canterbury by this well known local artist.   Map Ref: 17

HYTHE

Hythe Local History Room

Oaklands, 1 Stade Street, Hythe CT21 6BG   Tel: 01303 266152   Fax: 01303 262912
Email: admin@hythe-kent.com   Web: www.hythe-kent.com

Three rooms depicting history of the town and cinque port of Hythe - social and military history.

Opening Times: Mon 09:30-18:00, Tue to Thu 09:30-17:00, Fri 09:30-19:00, Sat 09:30-16:00. Admission: Free.   Location: Hythe, in Oaklands Park, entrance to via Public Library.
                                                                              Map Ref: 18

Kent

Dog Collar Museum

🦜 ♿ ⬢ 📷 ◑ 🚒

Leeds Castle, Maidstone ME17 1PL   Tel: 01622 765400   Fax: 01622 735616
Email: enquiries@leeds-castle.co.uk   Web: www.leeds-castle.com

The Dog Collar Museum at Leeds Castle is home to the world's finest collection of historic dog collars with some of the exhibits dating back over 500 years.

Opening Times: Mar to Oct 10:00-17:00, Nov to Feb 10:00-15:00. Closed Xmas, 28 Jun & 5 July.   Admission: Mar to Jun, Sep & Oct: Adult £11.00, Child £7.50, OAP/Student £9.50. Jul & Aug: Adult £12.00, Child £8.50, OAP/Student £10.50, Nov to Feb Adult £9.50, Child £6.00, OAP/Student £8.00.   Location: Seven miles east of Maidstone at junction 8 of M20.

Map Ref: 19

Maidstone Museum & Bentlif Art Gallery

⬢ 📷

St Faiths Street, Maidstone ME14 1LH   Tel: 01622 754497

One of the finest general collections in the south east. Galleries include Japanese art, costume and natural history. A wide selection of temporary exhibitions.

Opening Times: Mon to Sat 10:00-17:15, Sun 10:00-16:00. Closed Xmas Day.
Admission: Free.   Location: Nr town centre, five minutes walk from Maidstone East Railway Station.

Map Ref: 20

Museum of Kent Life

♿ ⬢ 📷 🚒

Lock Lane, Sandling, Maidstone ME14 3AU   Tel: 01622 763936
Fax: 01622 662024   Email: enquiries@museum-kentlife.co.uk
Web: www.museum-kentlife.co.uk

Kent's award-winning open air museum is home to an outstanding collection of historical buildings which house exhibitions on life in Kent over the last 150 years. An early 20th century village hall and reconstruction of cottages from the 17th & 20th centuries are more recent buildings to be viewed.

Opening Times: Feb to Nov daily 10:00-17:30.   Admission: Adult £5.50, Child/Student £3.50, OAP £4.00.   Location: Five minutes from Maidstone.   Exhibitions & Events 2003 : 18 to 21 Apr: Easter Chicken Hunt, 2 & 3 Aug: Hand-made in Kent, 6 & 7 Sep: Beer & Hop Festival, 1 Nov: Bonfire Night Family Party.

The Old Study © English Heritage

Map Ref: 20

Tyrwhitt-Drake Museum of Carriages

⬢

Archbishops Stables, Mill Street, Maidstone ME15 6YE   Tel: 01622 754497

Major collection of carriages, items include private and state vehicles, some items belonging to Queen Victoria. Housed in historic medieval stables.

Opening Times: Daily 10:00-15:45.   Admission: Adult £2.00, Child £1.05, Under 5s Free, Family £4.00.   Location: Town centre, two minutes walk from High Street.

Map Ref: 20

Romney Hythe & Dymchurch Railway

♿ ⬢ 📷 ◑ 🚒

New Romney TN28 8PL   Tel: 01797 362353   Fax: 01797 363591
Email: rhdr@romneyrail.fsnet.co.uk   Web: www.rhdr.demon.co.uk

Most complete collection of one-third full size steam engines in the world (11 in all). Also toy and model museum on site.

Opening Times: Feb half term, Easter to end Sep and Oct half term daily, also in Mar & Oct Sat & Sun 09:00-18:00.   Admission: Please phone for details.
Location: Most stations within five minutes of A259. Hythe Station is three miles from junction 11 of M20.

Map Ref: 21

Kent

Spitfire & Hurricane Memorial Building

The Airfield, Manston Road, Ramsgate CT12 5DF   Tel / Fax: 01843 821940
Email: pete@spitfire752.freeserve.co.uk   Web: www.spitfire-museum.com

The Memorial Building houses wartime Spitfire & Hurricane fighter aircraft together with an ever expanding display of original and emotive memorabilia from the 1939-1945 war periods. Battle of Britain Tapestry. 'Dambusters' and 'Channel Dash' displays. The Merlin Cafeteria has superb views across London (Manston) Airport. Study/research room and Allied Air Forces Memorial Garden.

Opening Times: Apr to Sep 10:00-17:00, Oct to Mar 10:00-16:00. Closed Xmas & New Year.
Admission: Free. Location: On B2050 road, adjacent to London (Manston) Airport. Follow brown tourism signs.
Map Ref: 22

Spitfire MK XVI - TB752 on display

Guildhall Museum

High Street, Rochester ME1 1PY   Tel: 01634 848717   Fax: 01634 832919   Email: guildhall.museum@medway.gov.uk
Web: www.medway.gov.uk

A museum for all the family. Colourful and attractive displays in two historic buildings feature the archaeology, local and social history of the Medway towns. The 'Hulks Experience' highlights the cramped, insanitary and harsh conditions forced upon Napoleonic prisoners-of-war and convicts incarcerated on the Medway Hulks. The museum also features everyday life in Victorian and Edwardian times.

Opening Times: Daily 10:00-16:30. Closed Xmas & New Year.
Admission: Free. Location: In Rochester High Street, 15 minutes walk from Rochester Railway Station.

Reconstruction of 17th Century Militia
Map Ref: 23

Tunbridge Wells Museum and Art Gallery

Civic Centre, Mount Pleasant, Royal Tunbridge Wells TN1 1JN   Tel: 01892 554171
Web: www.tunbridgewells.gov.uk/museum

From Tunbridge ware caskets to Pantiles paintings and Minnie the LuLu terrier to an 18th century polonaise, there are displays to fascinate everyone at Tunbridge Wells Museum. The Art Gallery has varied and frequently changing art and craft exhibitions. Educational workshops and other events for all ages are held linked to the exhibit collections and Tunbridge Wells history.

Opening Times: Mon to Sat 09:30-17:00. Closed Sun & BH.
Admission: Free. Location: In the Library and Museum building, next to the Town Hall, just off the A264.
Map Ref: 24

The Art Gallery

Kent

Colonel Stephens Railway Museum

Tenterden Town Station, Station Road, Tenterden TN30 6HE   Tel: 01580 765350   Fax: 01580 765654   Email: kesroffice@aol.com   Web: www.hfstephens-museum.org.uk

Displays depicting the career of light railway promoter and engineer Lt Colonel Holman F Stephens, his pre-Raphaelite childhood, military career and involvement in 17 railways are covered with pictures, models, tableaux and relics.

Opening Times: Apr to Oct when trains run on Kent & East Sussex Railway 12:30-16:30 (hours extended for special events). Train times: tel. 01580 765155   Admission: Adult £1.00, Child 50p, Under 8s Free. Special rates for pre-booked groups of 10 or more.   Location: Adjacent to Tenterden Town Station, Station Road. 300 yards from High Street.   Map Ref: 25

Ellen Terry Memorial Museum

Smallhythe Place, Tenterden TN30 7NG   Tel: 01580 762334   Fax: 01580 761960   Email: smallhytheplace@ntrust.org.uk   Web: www.nationaltrust.org.uk

Early 16th century timber-framed house, once the home of celebrated Victorian actress Ellen Terry. Many personal and theatrical mementoes. Beautiful stage costumes from her partnership with Sir Henry Irving at Lyceum Theatre.

Opening Times: Apr to Oct Sat to Wed 11:00-17:00.   Admission: Adult £3.40, Child £1.70, Family £8.50. National Trust Members Free.   Location: Two and a half miles from Tenterden, eight miles from Rye, bus service from both towns.   Map Ref: 26

Kent & East Sussex Railway

Tenterden Town Station, Station Road, Tenterden TN30 6HE   Tel: 01580 765155   Fax: 01580 765654   Email: enquiries@kesr.org.uk   Web: www.kesr.org.uk

You can experience the nostalgia of the days of steam and travel in the sedate pace of yesteryear over ten and a half miles of beautiful countryside.

Opening Times: Please telephone for opening times.   Admission: Adult £9.00, Child £4.50, OAP £8.00.   Location: Tenterden Town Centre.   Map Ref: 26

The Hop Farm Country Park

Beltring, Paddock Wood, Tonbridge TN12 6PY   Tel: 01622 872068   Fax: 01622 872630   Email: info@thehopfarm.co.uk   Web: www.thehopfarm.co.uk

Set in the heart of Kent amongst the largest collection of Victorian Oast Houses in the World. There are a number of exhibitions and museums within the Oast Houses, including the Hop Story Museum, an award winning museum featuring the Story of Hop Picking and Kent Rural Heritage. The Decades Experience is an interactive walk through the 20th century, scenes including a Victorian Street, Wartime Britain and Pop Larkin's Kitchen.

Opening Times: Daily 10:00-17:00.   Admission: Adult £6.50, Child/OAP £5.50, Family (2 adults and 2 Children) £18.00.   Map Ref: 27

Penshurst Place & Gardens

Penshurst, Tonbridge TN11 8DG   Tel: 01892 870307   Fax: 01892 870866   Email: enquiries@penshurstplace.com   Web: www.penshurstplace.com

Penshurst Place is one of Kent's loveliest historic houses with 10 acres of walled Tudor gardens, set in a peaceful rural setting in the medieval village of Penshurst. The oldest part of the house is the Barons Hall, built in 1342 it is regarded as one of the best preserved examples of medieval domestic architecture in England. A series of Staterooms contain a wonderful collection of portraits, tapestries, furniture, porcelain and armour from the past five centuries. The gardens, largely unaltered since Tudor times, have been developed by generations of the Sidney

Kent

Baron's Hall

family who first came to Penshurst in 1552. The walled garden is divided by yew hedging into a series of small garden 'rooms', each with its own colour and season. Today Penshurst Place remains the ancestral home of Viscount De L'Isle and his family, descendant of the famous Elizabethan poet and courtier, Sir Philip Sidney. Modern facilities include a Toy Museum, a Garden Tea Room, Gift Shop, Plant Centre, Venture Playground, and a Woodland Trail with plenty of free parking for cars and coaches. Special events at Penshurst Place include an exciting variety of shows in Home Park, drama, falconry, music, historic entertainment and storytelling in the house and grounds.

Opening Times: Sat & Sun from 1 Mar, daily from 29 Mar to 2 Nov. House: 12:00-17:00, Grounds: 10:30-18:00. Admission: Adult £6.50, Child £4.50, Concession £6.00. Location: Six miles from Tunbridge Wells and Tonbridge. Exhibitions & Events 2003 : 1 Mar to 2 Nov: A Family Home for 450 years. Map Ref: 28

WESTERHAM

Chartwell

THE NATIONAL TRUST

Westerham TN16 1PS Tel: 01732 868381 Fax: 01732 868193
Email: kchxxx@smtp.ntrust.org.uk Web: www.nationaltrust.org.uk

Dining Room

The family home where Britain's wartime prime minister lived for more than 40 years. The rooms, which are kept as they were in Sir Winston Churchill's lifetime, offer an insight into both his domestic and political life. Photographs, books and personal possessions, including his famous cigars, evoke his career, personality and family. Museum and exhibition rooms contain displays, sound recordings and collections of memorabilia including many gifts from other world leaders, uniforms and correspondence. The house contains several of Sir Winston's own paintings and more are on view in his studio, together with his easel and paint box. Many features created by Sir Winston survive in the garden including the walls he built himself, the swimming pool and lake and ponds stocked with the golden orfe he loved to feed.

Opening Times: 22 Mar to 2 Nov Wed to Sun 11:00-17:00. In addition Tue in Jul & Aug & BH Mon.
Admission: National Trust Members Free. Adult £6.50, Child £3.25, Family £16.25, Garden & Studio £3.25.
Location: Two miles south of Westerham (A25) on B2026, M25 junction 5 & 6, Metrobus 246 from Bromley Station to gate. Sevenoaks six and a half miles. Exhibitions & Events 2003 : Please telephone for details

The Studio

Map Ref: 29

Squerryes Court

Westerham TN16 1SJ Tel: 01959 562345/563118 Fax: 01959 565949
Email: squerryes.court@squerryes.co.uk Web: www.squerryes.co.uk

17th century manor house. Paintings collected by the Warde family 1747-1774, including 17th and 18th century Italian, Dutch and English schools. 18th century Soho tapestries. Items connected with General Wolfe. Pre-booked guided tours.

Opening Times: Apr to Sep Wed, Sat, Sun and BH House: 13:30-17:30, Garden: 12:00-17:30. Admission: Adult £4.80, Child £2.60, OAP £4.20, Family £12.20. Group rates available. Garden only: Adult £3.20, Child £1.60, OAP £2.70, Family £7.20. Location: Half a mile west of Westerham, just off A25. Map Ref: 29

Kent

Oyster dredge used to scrape the seabed for oysters

Whitstable Museum & Gallery ♿ ●

Oxford Street, Whitstable CT5 1DB   Tel: 01227 276998
Fax: 01227 772379   Email: museums@canterbury.gov.uk
Web: www.whitstable-museum.co.uk

The museum explores Whitstable's unique coastal community and its seafaring traditions with special features on oyster fishery, diving and shipping for which the town was famous. Ship portraits, archaeology and an early piece of silent film showing the oyster fishers dredging for oysters can be seen as well as an original horse drawn fire engine. The art gallery has a range of changing exhibitions.

Opening Times: Mon to Sat 10:00-16:00 plus Jul & Aug Sun 13:00-14:00. Closed Good Friday and Xmas.   Admission: Free.
Location: Town centre, in Oxford Street, close to the theatre, library and St Marys Hall. Easy walking distance of car parks and railway station.   Exhibitions & Events 2003 : 25 Jan to 1 Mar: B G Wildlife photographer of the year 2002: Prize winning images showcasing the very best of the international photography of natural subjects from the prestigious competition organised by BBC Wildlife Magazine and the Natural History Museum, London.   Map Ref: 30

Key to Classifications

see Classifications Index on page 413

Anthropology	Jewellery	Railway
Archaeological	Literature & Libraries	Religion
Art Galleries	Maritime	Roman
Arts, Crafts & Textiles	Military & Defence	Science - Earth
China, Glass & Ceramics	Mills - Water & Wind	& Planetary
Communications	Multicultural	Sculpture
Egyptian	Music & Theatre	Sporting History
Fashion	Natural History	Stately Homes
Geology	Oriental	Toy & Childhood
Health & Medicine	Palaces	Transport
Horticultural	Police, Prisons & Dungeons	Victoriana

Lancashire

The cities and towns of the county reflect in their buildings the prosperity brought to the area by the Industrial Revolution. The seaside resorts still retain their well-deserved popularity. Blackpool, with its spectacular illuminations, piers and golden beaches, remains arguably Britain's most popular.

The cities of Lancashire, proud of their industrial heritage, present through their museums and galleries a quite remarkably comprehensive history of the Industrial Revolution and Lancashire's rich cultural, historical and natural heritage.

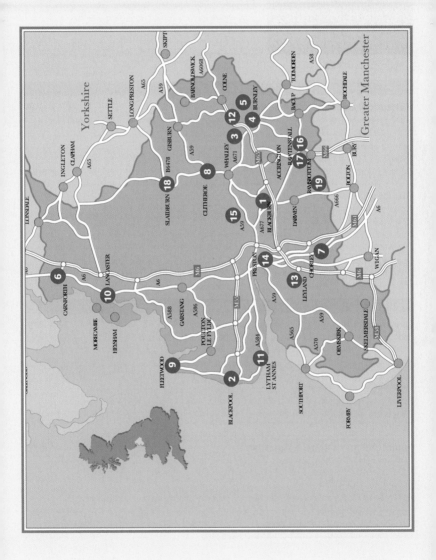

The Red Map References should be used to locate Museums etc on the pages that follow

Lancashire

Blackburn Museum & Art Gallery

Museum Street, Blackburn BB1 7AJ   Tel: 01254 667130   Fax: 01254 695370
Email: stephen.whittle@blackburn.gov.uk   Web: www.blackburn.gov.uk/museum

Collections of medieval manuscripts and early printed books, large collections of coins, Japanese prints, Greek and Russian icons. Extensive collections of local social history and textile history in the adjoining Lewis Textile Museum (admission by appointment). Other attractions include Victorian paintings and sculpture, ceramics, Egyptology and contemporary art exhibitions.

Opening Times: Tue to Sat 10:00-16:45. Closed Sun, Mon & BH. Admission: Free. Location: Town centre, five minute walk from railway and central bus station.

HoKusai Lightning over Mount Fuji

Map Ref: 1

BLACKPOOL

Blackpool Lifeboat Station & Visitor Centre

The Promenade, Adjacent New Bonney Street, Blackpool FY1 5YA   Tel: 01253 290816
Web: www.lifeboats.org.uk

Viewing gallery above lifeboats with displays, exhibits and videos portraying the RNLI in Blackpool.

Opening Times: All year.   Admission: Free.   Map Ref: 2

Grundy Art Gallery

Queen Street, Blackpool FY1 1PX   Tel: 01253 478170   Fax: 01253 478172
Email: grundyartgallery@blackpool.gov.uk

A historic and modern collection always on show. Lively temporary exhibitions. Small display of Blackpool's history, specialising in craft jewellery, some for sale at shop. Relaxing atmosphere.

Opening Times: Mon to Sat 10:00-17:00, closed Sun and BH.   Admission: Free.   Location: In the town centre near Talbot Road Bus Station and Blackpool North Railway Station and North Pier tramstops.   Map Ref: 2

BURNLEY

Gawthorpe Hall

Padiham, Burnley BB12 8UA   Tel: 01282 771004   Fax: 01282 770178
Email: gawthorpehall@museumoflancs.org.uk   Web: www.bringinghistoryalive.co.uk

A magnificent Jacobean house set in formal gardens, with many rooms remodelled in the Victorian period by Sir Charles Barry. The hall also houses the internationally important Rachel Kay-Shuttleworth textile collection.

Opening Times: Apr to Oct Tue to Thu & Sat to Sun, 13:00-17:00.   Admission: Adult £3.00, Child Free, Concession £1.50, Family & Friends Season Ticket £8.00.   Location: Outskirts of Padiham, frequent bus service from Burnley.   Map Ref: 3

Natural History Centre & Aquarium

Towneley Hall Art Gallery/Museums, Townley Park, off Todmorden Road, Burnley BB11 3RQ
Tel: 01282 424213   Fax: 01282 436138   Email: towneleyhall@burnley.org.uk
Web: www.towneleyhall.org.uk

Collection of local, national and international natural history specimens, fossils and geology.

Opening Times: Mon to Fri 10:00-17:00, Easter to Oct also Sun 12:00-17:00.   Admission: Free.   Location: One and a half miles south east of town centre, one mile from Park entrance on Todmorden Road (A671). Left from front of main hall.   Map Ref: 4

Guided or Private Tours	Disabled Access	Gift Shop or Sales Point	Café or Refreshments	Restaurant	Car Parking

Lancashire

Queen Street Mill Museum

Queen Street, Harle Syke, Burnley BB10 2HX   Tel: 01282 412555   Fax: 01282 430220
Email: queenstreet.mill@mus.lancscc.gov.uk   Web: www.bringinghistoryalive.co.uk

The last commercial steam powered textile mill in Europe, today it offers a unique experience with the sight, sound and smell of working Lancashire looms driven by the steam engine, 'Peace'.

Opening Times: Mar to Nov and BH during the season.   Admission: Adult £2.50, Child Free, Concession £1.25, Family & Friends Season Ticket £8.00.   Location: 15 minute drive from Burnley Town Centre, bus journey from Burnley approximately half an hour.   Map Ref: 5

Towneley Hall Art Gallery & Museum

Towneley Holmes Road, off Todmorden Road, Burnley BB11 3RQ   Tel: 01282 424213
Fax: 01282 436138   Email: townhall@burnley.gov.uk   Web: www.towneleyhall.org.uk

18th and 19th century oil and watercolour paintings; studio pottery; Royal Lancastrian Pilkington Pottery; 17th and 18th century oak furniture; 18th century glass; 18th and 19th century clocks and watches.

Opening Times: Mon to Fri 10:00-17:00, Sun 12:00-17:00. Closed Sat.   Admission: Free. Charge for tours.   Location: One and a half miles south east of town centre, one mile from Park entrance on Todmarden Road (A671).

Towneley Hall   Map Ref: 4

Leighton Hall

Carnforth LA5 9ST   Tel: 01524 734474   Fax: 01524 720357   Email: info@leightonhall.co.uk
Web: www.leightonhall.co.uk

Set in beautiful parkland against a backdrop of the Lakeland Fells, award winning neo Gothic Leighton Hall is the lived-in home of the Gillow furniture-making family

Opening Times: May to Sep Tue to Fri & Sun 14:00-17:00 (open 12:30 in Aug).
Admission: Adult £5.00, Child £3.50, OAP £4.00.   Map Ref: 6

Astley Hall Museum & Art Gallery

Astley Park, Chorley PR7 1NP   Tel: 01257 515555   Fax: 01257 515556
Email: astleyhall@lineone.net   Web: www.astleyhall.co.uk

A furnished house dating back to the 1580s, including fine oak furniture of the 16th and 17th centuries. Also, a collection of 18th century creamware and fine art from 17th century portraits to contemporary art.

Opening Times: Apr to Oct Tue to Sun 12:00-17:00 and BH. Nov to Mar Sat & Sun 12:00-16:00.
Admission: Adult £2.95, Concession £1.95. Group rates available.   Location: One mile west of Chorley, off A581 Southport Road.   Map Ref: 7

Clitheroe Castle Museum

Castle Hill, Clitheroe BB7 1BA   Tel / Fax: 01200 424568
Email: hannah.chalk@mus.lancscc.gov.uk   Web: tourism@ribblevalley.gov.uk

We hold and display a range of local history and geology collections, which focus on Clitheroe and surrounding areas. Witchcraft Exhibition until August 2003. Please ring for details of events.

Opening Times: 24 Feb to 28 Feb daily, 1 Mar to 13 Apr Sat to Wed, 14 Apr to 26 Oct daily, 27 Oct to 14 Dec Sat & Sun 11:00-16:30.   Admission: Adult £1.60, Child £0.25, OAP £0.75, Family £3.40.   Location: Near town centre, ten minute walk from bus and railway stations.   Map Ref: 8

Lancashire

Fleetwood Museum

Queens Terrace, Fleetwood FY7 6BT   Tel: 01253 876621   Fax: 01253 878088
Email: fleetwoodmuseum@museumoflancs.org.uk   Web: www.nettingthebay.org.uk

Situated in the Decimus Burton designed Custom House building, the museum covers the history of Fleetwood and the fishing and maritime collections of Morecambe Bay. The museum also includes a full size dolls' boarding house and an interactive gallery.

Opening Times: Apr to early Nov & BH throughout the season.   Admission: Adult £2.00, Child/Concessions £1.00, Family £5.00.   Location: On Queens Terrace, opposite P&O Ferry Booth - between the market and Knott End Ferry. Within easy walking distance of buses and trams.   Map Ref: 9

Cottage Museum

15 Castle Hill, Lancaster   Tel: 01524 64637   Fax: 01524 841692
Email: awhite@lancaster.gov.uk   Web: www.lancaster.gov.uk/council/museums

A cottage of 1739, refitted and divided c.1820, and furnished in the style of that date.

Opening Times: Easter to Sep daily 14:00-17:00.   Admission: Adult 75p, Concession 25p.
Location: Near city centre, close to Castle.   Map Ref: 10

Judges Lodgings Museum

Church Street, Lancaster LA1 1YS   Tel: 01524 32808
Email: judgeslodgings.lcc@btinternet.com   Web: www.bringinghistoryalive.co.uk

Lancaster's oldest town house, The Judges' Lodgings, displays an impressive collection of Gillow furniture in period rooms. Also includes porcelain, silver and paintings and a Museum of Childhood with dolls, toys and games.

Opening Times: Good Friday to end of Oct.   Admission: Adult £2.00, Child/Concessions £1.00, Family £5.00.   Location: Town centre, five minutes from bus station and ten minutes from railway station.   Map Ref: 10

Lancaster City Museum

Market Square, Lancaster LA1 1HT   Tel: 01524 64637   Fax: 01524 841692
Email: awhite@lancaster.gov.uk   Web: www.lancaster.gov.uk/council/museums

Collections illustrate history and archaeology of Lancaster and North Lancashire. Paintings, decorative arts and a series of changing exhibitions.

Opening Times: Mon to Sat 10:00-17:00. Closed Xmas.   Admission: Free.   Location: City centre, five minutes from main rail and bus stations.   Map Ref: 10

Medieval Fish Stall

Lancaster Maritime Museum

Custom House, St Georges Quay, Lancaster LA1 1RB   Tel: 01524 382264   Fax: 01524 841692   Email: awhite@lancaster.gov.uk   Web: www.lancaster.gov.uk/council/museums

Collections illustrate the history of the Port of Lancaster, fishing in Morecombe Bay, slaving and the West Indies trade. Changing exhibitions.

Opening Times: Easter to Oct daily 11:00-17:00, Nov to Easter daily 12:30-16:00.
Admission: Adult £2.00, Concession £1.00.   Location: On St George's Quay, five minutes from city centre.   Map Ref: 10

Museums • Galleries • Historic Houses

Please let us know of any collections that are not listed in this guide that you feel should be listed. E-mail us on *editor@tomorrows.co.uk*
or return the Report Form on page 448

Lancashire

Museum of The Kings Own Royal Regiment (Lancaster)

City Museum, Market Square, Lancaster LA1 1HT
Tel: 01524 64637 Fax: 01524 841692
Email: kingsownmuseum@iname.com
Web: www.lancaster.gov.uk/council/museums

Collections illustrate the history and actions of the King's Own Royal Regiment (Lancaster) (4th of Foot) from its raising in 1680 to the present day. Uniforms, medals, archives and photographs.

Opening Times: Mon to Sat 10:00-17:00. Closed Xmas.
Admission: Free. Location: City centre, five minutes from main rail and bus station.   Map Ref: 10

King's Own Gallery with uniform c1760

Peter Scott Gallery   PETER SCOTT GALLERY

Lancaster University, Lancaster LA1 4YW Tel: 01524 593057 Fax: 01524 592603
Email: m.p.gavagan@lancaster.ac.uk Web: www.peterscottgallery.com

The gallery presents temporary exhibitions and associated talks and houses the University's Art Collection. The Collection includes works by significant European artists Joan Miró, Pablo Picasso, Victor Vasarely and Max Ernst, and British artists Barbara Hepworth, Sir Terry Frost and Andy Goldsworthy. The University's stunning collection of Royal Lancastrian Pottery is on permanent display in the John Chambers Ceramics Room.

Scottie Wilson, Flowering Thoughts
©Peter Scott Gallery, Lancaster University

Opening Times: Mon to Fri 11:00-16:00 & late Thu 18:00-20:30, during exhibitions. Please telephone for details. Group bookings welcome. Admission: Free.
Location: On Lancaster University Campus. Accessible by road, leave junction 33 on M6; A6 to Lancaster. Public transport Lancaster Railway Station, Bus to university from city centre. Exhibitions & Events 2003 : 20 Jan to 21 Mar: Albert Irvin (Main Gallery), 20 Jan to 21 Mar: A E Seguy: Illustrations and Designs (Manton Room), 5 to 30 May: 'Enter the Conjuror's Cabinet' David Tinker: A Retrospective Exhibition (Main Gallery), 5 to 30 May: Tom Wood (Manton Room), Mid Jun: Student Degree Show, Sep: Student MA Show.
                                                                         Map Ref: 10

Roman Bath House

Castle Hill, Vicarage Field, Lancaster Tel: 01524 64637

Conserved ruin forming bath wing of important Roman house just outside the fort walls. Demolished c.340 AD to build new walls and ditch, but preserved in upcast.

Opening Times: Open all daylight hours. Admission: Free. Location: Near Castle and Priory Church, two minutes from rail station.   Map Ref: 10

Ruskin Library

Lancaster University, Lancaster LA1 4YH Tel: 01524 593587 Fax: 01524 593580
Email: ruskin.library@lancaster.ac.uk Web: www.lancs.ac.uk/users/ruslinlib/

Largest collection of books, manuscripts and drawings by and relating to the writer and artist John Ruskin (1819-1900), in an award-winning new building. Public gallery with at least three exhibitions a year.

Opening Times: Mon to Sat 11:00-16:00, Sun 13:00-16:00. Admission: Free. Location: South of Lancaster, on A6 just off junction 33 of M6.   Map Ref: 10

Guided or Private Tours	Disabled Access	Gift Shop or Sales Point	Café or Refreshments	Restaurant	Car Parking

Lancashire

Lytham Heritage Centre

2 Henry Street, Lytham FY8 5LE   Tel / Fax: 01253 730767
Email: thecentre@lythamheritage.fsnet.co.uk   Web: www.lythamheritage.fsnet.co.uk

A Grade II Listed building built in 1899, formerly the Manchester and County Bank. Acquired by Lytham Heritage Group in 1996 and converted into an exhibition centre and gallery in a Victorian style. A variety of exhibitions include Lytham Heritage and local community arts and crafts.

Opening Times: Tue to Sun & BH 10:00-16:00.
Admission: Free.   Location: In Lytham Town Centre, at the corner of the Piazza.   Map Ref: 11

'Lytham Heritage Centre' from a Watercolour by Tom Eccles

Lytham Windmill Museum

East Beach, Lytham FY8 4HZ   Tel / Fax: 01253 730767
Email: thecentre@lythamheritage.fsnet.co.uk   Web: www.lythamheritage.fsnet.co.uk

Built in 1805 and worked as a corn mill until 1919, the Windmill Museum, housed in a restored Grade II listed building, is now a permanent heritage exhibition. Displays record the 200 years history of the mill and explain its machinery, with models and memorabilia. The basement includes many tableaux of Victorian life in Lytham. The museum was awarded National Museum status in 2001 and won an Award from Northwest Tourist Board as a Visitor Attraction.

Lytham Windmill Museum on Lytham Green

Opening Times: May to Sep Tue to Thu, Sat & Sun 10:30-13:00 & 14:00-16:30. Admission: Free. Location: Near town centre on Lytham Green overlooking River Ribble.   Map Ref: 11

Pendle Heritage Centre

Barrowford, Nelson BB9 6JQ   Tel: 01282 661701/2   Fax: 01282 611718

Exhibitions on the development of the building and the history of this part of Lancashire, including the story of the Pendle Witches. The Pendle Arts Gallery holds regular exhibitions by professional artists. There is a well stocked shop and a garden tea-room serving home-cooked food, as well as a Tourist Information Centre.

Opening Times: Daily 10:00-17:00. Closed Xmas.
Location: Five minutes from junction 13 of the M65.
Pendle Heritage Centre, rebuilt frontage   Map Ref: 12

British Commercial Vehicle Museum

King Street, Leyland, Preston PR25 2LE   Tel: 01772 451011   Fax: 01772 623404

Britain's premier collection of fully restored commercial and passenger vehicles tracing the history of road transport over the last 100 years.

Opening Times: Apr to Sep Sun, Tue & Wed 10:00-16:30. Oct Sun 10:00-16:30. Open BH.
Admission: Adult £4.00, Child/OAP £2.00, Family £10.00.   Location: Exit M6 at junction 28, one mile from exit.   Map Ref: 13

Guided or Private Tours	Disabled Access	Gift Shop or Sales Point	Café or Refreshments	Restaurant	Car Parking

Lancashire

Harris Museum & Art Gallery

Market Square, Preston PR1 2PP   Tel: 01722 258248   Fax: 01772 886764
Email: harris.museum@preston.gov.uk   Web: www.visitpreston.com/harris

The Harris offers the best of Preston's heritage in a beautiful Grade I listed building, with its collections of paintings, sculpture, textiles, costume, glass and ceramics, as well as The Story of Preston Gallery. The museum shows an exciting programme of exhibitions and has a national reputation for contemporary art shows. The programme also includes local history, fine and decorative art and contemporary craft.

Opening Times: Mon to Sat 10:00-17:00. Closed BH. Admission: Free. Location: Market Square, Preston, one minute from bus station, five minutes from railway station.   Map Ref: 14

Harris Museum and Art Gallery, Preston

Museum of Lancashire

Stanley Street, Preston PR1 4YP   Tel: 01772 264075   Fax: 01772 264079
Web: www.bringinghistoryalive.co.uk

Housed in Preston's Old Sessions House, the museum features aspects of Lancashire's rich cultural, historical and natural heritage.

Opening Times: Daily 10:30-17:00, closed Thursdays, Sundays and BH. Admission: Adult £2.00, Concession £1.00, Child Free. Location: Town centre, five minutes walk from bus station.   Map Ref: 14

The National Football Museum

Sir Tom Finney Way, Deepdale, Preston PR1 6RU   Tel: 01772 908442   Fax: 01772 908433
Email: enquiries@nationalfootballmuseum.com   Web: www.nationalfootballmuseum.com

The world's largest collection of football memorabilia including the FIFA, FA, Football League and Wembley Collections. Inter-active gallery and children's education trail.

Opening Times: Tue to Sat 10:00-17:00, Sun 11:00-17:00, Midweek Match Day 10:00-19:30. Closed Mon except BH.   Admission: Adult £6.95, Child £4.95. Full range of concessions. Location: One mile from town centre.   Map Ref: 14

Queens Lancashire Regiment

Fulwood Barracks, Preston PR2 8AA   Tel: 01772 260362   Fax: 01772 260583

Extensive museum, archive and library, containing material relating to 30th, 40th, 47th, 59th, 81st and 82nd Regiments of Foot, The East Lancashire, South Lancashire, Loyal (North Lancashire), Lancashire and Queen's Lancashire Regiment.

Opening Times: Tue to Thu 10:00-16:00 or by appointment. Admission: Free. Guided groups £2.00 per person. Location: Two miles north of town centre.   Map Ref: 14

Ribchester Roman Museum

Riverside, Ribchester, Preston PR3 3XS   Tel: 01254 878261
Email: ribchestermuseum@btconnect.com   Web: www.ribchestermuseum.org

This museum contains displays of military life at Roman Ribchester. New exhibitions include many exciting finds from the site.

Opening Times: Mon to Fri 09:00-17:00, Sat to Sun 11:00-17:30. Admission: Adult £2.00, Child £1.00. Location: On B6245 off A59. Bus routes from Blackburn and Preston.
                                                                    Map Ref: 15

Helmshore Textile Museum

Helmshore Road, Helmshore, Rossendale BB4 4NP   Tel: 01706 226459   Fax: 01706 218554
Email: helmshore.museum@mus.lancscc.gov.uk   Web: www.bringinghistoryalive.co.uk

Two of Lancashire's original textile mills. View international treasures including an Arkwright Water

Lancashire

Frame and an improved Spinning Jenny. Enjoy live demonstrations of traditional textile techniques, plus new Revolution Gallery.

Opening Times: Apr to Oct. Admission: Adult £3.00, Child Free, Concession £1.50, Family & Friends Season Ticket £8.00. Location: Rural location, approximately 15 minutes from junction 5 on M65. Map Ref: 16

Rossendale Museum
Whitaker Park, Rawtenstall, Rossendale BB4 6RE   Tel: 01706 244682   Fax: 01706 250037

19th century mill owner's residence set in a park, now a museum with varied collections, including local history, fine decorative arts, natural history. Features - William Bullock's tiger and python, small collection of late Victorian wallpapers.

Opening Times: Please telephone for times. Admission: Free. Location: Quarter of a mile from Rawtenstall centre; off A681; on main Accrington to Rochdale bus route. Map Ref: 17

SLAIDBURN

Slaidburn Heritage Centre
25 Church Street, Slaidburn BB7 3ER   Tel / Fax: 01200 446161

Audio-visual presentation and artefacts relating to heritage of Slaidburn, including the unique 'Angel Stone Viking Carving'. Slaidburn is a conservation area in the heart of the Forest of Bowland an area of outstanding beauty. Centre offers tourist information, morning coffee, light lunches and afternoon tea.

Opening Times: Apr to Oct Tue to Sun 11:00-17:00, Nov to Mar Thu to Sun 11:00-16:00. Admission: Free. Location: On the B6478 between Settle and Citheroe, near St Andrews Church. Car park in village. Map Ref: 18

TURTON

Turton Tower
Chapletown Road, Turton BL7 0HG   Tel: 01204 852203   Fax: 01204 853759
Email: turtontower.lcc@btinternet.com   Web: www.bringinghistoryalive.co.uk

A distinctive English country house with period rooms displaying a magnificent collection of decorative woodwork, paintings and furniture, including items loaned from the Victoria and Albert Museum.

Opening Times: Feb to Nov. Admission: Adult £3.00, Concessions £1.50, Child Free. Location: Suburban location, nearest railway station one and a half miles - Bromley Cross. Buses stop outside. Map Ref: 19

Leicestershire & Nottinghamshire

Leicestershire is the home of the famous Quorn, Belvoir and Cottesmore hunts. However to the west of the county many of the towns belong to the industrial east Midlands. Nottinghamshire, lying in the low ground of the Trent basin, is the county of Robin Hood and Sherwood Forest.

The social history of these counties is preserved in some of the most comprehensive and attractive Museums in the land, catering for all interests and tastes.

The Red Map References should be used to locate Museums etc on the pages that follow

Leicestershire & Nottinghamshire

The Manor House

Manor Road, Donnington-le-Heath, Coalville LE67 2FW   Tel / Fax: 01530 831259
Email: museums@leics.gov.uk   Web: www.leics.gov.uk

Medieval manor house dating back to 1280, with a fascinating history. The surrounding grounds have scented herb gardens, and the adjoining stone barn is home to a tempting restaurant.

Opening Times: Apr to Sep daily 11:00-17:00. Oct to Mar daily 11:00-15:00.   Admission: Free.
Location: Southern outskirts of Coalville.   Map Ref: 1

Snibston Discovery Park

Ashby Road, Coalville LE67 3LN   Tel: 01530 278444   Fax: 01530 813301
Email: snibston@leics.gov.uk   Web: www.leics.gov.uk

One of the largest and most dynamic museums in the Midlands, Snibston is Leicestershire's all-weather science and industry museum. Visitors can get their hands-on loads of fun in the popular 'Science Alive!' Gallery or explore the county's rich heritage in the Transport, Extractives, Engineering, Textiles and Fashion Galleries. Other attractions include guided colliery tours, outdoor science and water playgrounds, sculptures and nature reserve.

An interactive exhibit in the
Science Alive! Gallery

Opening Times: Daily 10:00-17:00.   Admission: Adult £5.25, Child £3.25, Concession £3.50. Group rates available.   Map Ref: 1

The Queens Royal Lancers

Belvoir Castle, Belvoir, Grantham NG31 7TJ   Tel: 01159 573295   Fax: 01559 573195
Email: mickholtby@deathglorylancers.co.uk   Web: www.deathorglory.com

The museum traces the military and social history of the 16th/5th lancers, the 17th/21st lancers and The Queens Royal Lancers from their formation to present day. Weapons, uniforms, paintings, silver and personal artefacts form part of this fine collection.

Opening Times: 28 Mar to 1 Apr (Easter), 4-7, 14, 21 & 28 Apr, May to Sep Wed to Sun, BH and Oct Sun only, all 11:00-17:00.   Admission: Adult £7.00, Child £3.50, OAP £5.50, Family (2 adults and 2 Children) £17.00.   Location: Six miles from the A1 at Grantham and 12 miles from Melton Mowbray. Nottingham and Stamford are within half an hours drive. Follow brown heritage signs.   Map Ref: 2

Abbey Pumping Station Museum

Corporation Road, Off Abbey Lane, Leicester LE4 5PX   Tel: 0116 299 5111   Fax: 0116 299 5125   Web: www.leicestermuseums.ac.uk

Home to Gimson beam engines, exhibits include cinema equipment, vehicles, an interactive loo and public health and sanitation displays. The museum is also home to an impressive historic vehicle collection, including a coal-fired fish and chip van!

Opening Times: Please contact the site for seasonal opening hours.   Admission: Free (except for certain special events).   Map Ref: 3

Belgrave Hall and Gardens

Church Road, off Thurcaston Road, Belgrave, Leicester LE4 5PE   Tel: 0116 266 6590
Web: www.leicestermuseums.ac.uk

Belgrave Hall is an 18th century Queen Anne house furnished in both Edwardian and Victorian room settings. There are several separate gardens and a glasshouse containing permanent collections of tropical, sub-tropical and alpine plants.

Opening Times: Please contact the site for seasonal opening hours.   Admission: Free.
Map Ref: 3

Leicestershire & Nottinghamshire

Guildhall

Guildhall Lane, Leicester LE1 5FQ   Tel: 0116 253 2569   Web: www.leicestermuseums.ac.uk

The Guildhall is one of Leicester's most famous buildings, dating back to the 14th century. Visitors can step back in time and see the Victorian police cells and maybe even a few ghosts!

Opening Times: Please contact the site for seasonal opening hours. Admission: Free.

Map Ref: 3

Jewry Wall Museum

St Nicholas Circle, Leicester LE1 4LB   Tel: 0116 225 4971
Web: www.leicestermuseums.ac.uk

Local pre-historic, Roman and medieval artefacts. The museum houses several exhibitions including a series of illustrations showing street scenes from Iron Age, Roman, Saxon, Medieval and 18th century Leicester.

Opening Times: Please contact the site for seasonal opening hours. Admission: Free.

Map Ref: 3

Leicestershire CCC Museum

County Ground, Grace Road, Leicester LE2 8AD   Tel: 0116 2832128

Collections of cricket memorabilia; bats, trophies, photographs. Themed showcases eg Ball-making, many archives from 1870 onwards, caps, blazers, medals etc.

Opening Times: Mon to Fri 09:30-15:30, winter by appointment. Admission: Free.
Location: Two miles from town centre, access from M1/M69.

Map Ref: 3

New Walk Museum & Art Gallery

53 New Walk, Leicester LE1 7EA   Tel: 0116 225 4900   Web: www.leicestermuseums.ac.uk

Visitors of all ages will be fascinated by the Ancient Egypt gallery with its mummies, coffins and other treasures, and by the dinosaurs, rock and fossils collection in the Natural History section. The museum is a major regional Art Gallery with a notable collection of German Expressionist and European art dating from the 15th century to the present day. Wild Space, the interactive natural sciences exhibition, is a must-see for anyone interested in the natural world.

The Dinosaurs at New Walk Museum

Opening Times: Please contact us for seasonal opening hours. Admission: Free. Location: Situated in the historic New Walk area of the city of Leicester.

Map Ref: 3

Newarke Houses Museum

The Newarke, Leicester LE2 7BY   Tel: 0116 225 4980   Web: www.leicestermuseums.ac.uk

Newarke Houses Museum is composed of two historic houses, Wygston's Chantry House and Skeffington House. The Museum houses many fine collections including clocks, toys, greeting cards and coins.

Opening Times: Please contact us for seasonal opening hours. Admission: Free.   Map Ref: 3

Bellfoundry Museum

Freehold Street, Loughborough LE11 1AR   Tel: 01509 233414   Fax: 01509 263305
Email: museum@taylorbells.co.uk   Web: www.taylorbells.co.uk

Exhibits showing how bells are made and tuned. Material relating to history of Taylor Family and Company. Examples of bells, many of which can be rung by visitors. Only Bell Museum in the UK.

Opening Times: Tue to Fri & summer Sat 10:00-12:30 & 13:30-16:30. Winter Sat - please call for dates & times. Sun - tour on first Sun in month at 14:00. Admission: Adult £1.50, Child 75p.
Tour of Works (inc Museum): Adult £3.80, Child £1.90. Location: 15 minute walk from town centre, ten minute walk from railway station.

Map Ref: 4

LOUGHBOROUGH *(continued)*

Charnwood Museum
Queen's Hall, Granby Street, Loughborough LE11 3DU   Tel: 01509 233754   Fax: 01509 268140   Email: museums@leics.gov.uk   Web: www.leics.gov.uk

Charnwood Museum features a wide range of exhibits, which reflect local history and industries. Permanent exhibitions are in four areas: 'Coming to Charnwood', 'The Natural World of Charnwood', 'Living off the Land' and 'Earning a Living'.

Opening Times: Mon to Fri 10:00-16:30, Sun 14:00-17:00.   Admission: Free.   Location: Within town centre.   Map Ref: 4

Great Central Railway Museum

Great Central Road, Loughborough LE11 1RW   Tel: 01509 230726
Fax: 01509 239791   Email: booking-office@gcrailway.co.uk   Web: www.gcrailway.co.uk

Main Line Steam trains - every weekend throughout the year. Recreating the experience of famous expresses of the steam age. Passenger trains also on weekdays, June to September. See one of our classic demonstration freight or parcel trains. Relax in the comfort of our classic corridor trains - steam heated in winter. Just like British Railways in the great years of steam.

Opening Times: Jun to Sep Sat & Sun, also weekdays.
Admission: Free - donations welcome.
Location: Located south east of Loughborough Town Centre. 15 minute walk from Loughborough Railway Stn.

'Green Arrow' on Great Central Railway

Map Ref: 4

MANSFIELD *Notts*

Mansfield Museum & Art Gallery
Leeming Street, Mansfield NG18 1NG   Tel: 01623 463088   Fax: 01623 412922
Email: mansfield_museum@hotmail.com

Permanent display galleries showing local, natural and social history of Mansfield and district, along with fine and decorative arts from days gone by. Always something new to see due to the varied programme of temporary exhibitions.

Opening Times: Mon to Sat 10:00-17:00.   Admission: Free.   Location: In the town centre.
Map Ref: 5

MARKET BOSWORTH *Leics*

Bosworth Battlefield Visitor Centre & Country Park
Sutton Cheney, Market Bosworth CV13 0AD   Tel: 01455 290429   Fax: 01455 292841
Email: bosworth@leics.gov.uk   Web: www.leics.gov.uk

Site of the Battle of Bosworth 1485, the decisive battle of the War of the Roses where Richard III lost his life and his crown to the future Henry VII. Visitor centre with exhibitions and film theatre telling the story of this fateful battle. Battle trail (open all year), take a stroll around the trail with information boards explaining the course of the battle. Living history events throughout summer. Medieval spectacular including battle re-enactment August.

Opening Times: 1 Apr to 31 Oct Daily 11:00-17:00. Nov & Dec Sun 11:00-Dusk. Mar Sat & Sun 11:00-17:00.
Admission: Adult £3.00, Concession £2.00, Family £8.50.

Subject to review   Location: Site is bounded by A5, A444 and B585 and is clearly signposted from all these roads in the vicinity of Market Bosworth.   Map Ref: 6

Guided or Private Tours	Disabled Access	Gift Shop or Sales Point	Café or Refreshments	Restaurant	Car Parking

Leicestershire & Nottinghamshire

Foxton Canal Museum

Middle Lock, Foxton, Market Harborough LE16 7RA Tel: 0116 279 2657
Email: mike@foxcm.freeserve.co.uk   Web: www.foxcanal.fsnet.co.uk

The story of canals, locks and boat lifts with models, interactive displays and artefacts. There is a play boat and working lock model for younger visitors. High tech touch-screen display, and lots of artefacts.

Opening Times: Easter to Oct daily 10:00-17:00, Oct to Easter Sat to Wed 11:00-16:00.
Admission: Adult £2.50, Child Free (up to three children free with each full paying adult),
Concession £2.00.   Location: Five miles from Market Harborough at Foxton Locks. Follow
brown signs.   Map Ref: 7

Harborough Museum

Adam & Eve Street, Market Harborough LE16 7AG   Tel: 01858 821085   Fax: 01858 821086
Email: museums@leics.gov.uk   Web: www.leics.gov.uk

Displays include the Symington Collection of Corsetry and reconstruction of a local shoemaker's workshop.

Opening Times: Mon to Fri 10:00-16:30, Sun 14:00-17:00. Admission: Free. Location: Within
town centre.   Map Ref: 8

Melton Carnegie Museum

Thorpe End, Melton Mowbray LE13 1RB   Tel: 01664 569946   Fax: 01664 564060
Email: museums@leics.gov.uk   Web: www.leics.gov.uk

Permanent displays feature local and natural history of the area and include work by British sporting artist John Ferneley as well as collections featuring foxhunting, the Stilton cheese and pork pie industries and the famous two-headed calf.

Opening Times: Daily 10:00-16:30. Admission: Free.   Map Ref: 9

British Horological Institute

Upton Hall, Upton, Newark-on-Trent NG23 5TE   Tel: 01636 813795   Fax: 01636 812258

A fascinating collection of clocks, watches and tools in a fine country house with beautiful grounds. Includes some beautiful grandfather clocks and the original Speaking Clock.

Opening Times: Apr to Oct Tue to Sat 11:00-17:00, Sun 14:00-17:00. Nov to Mar Tue to Fri
13:30-16:30. Admission: Adult £3.50, Child £2.00, OAP £3.00. Location: In the centre of
Upton village, ten minutes drive from Newark.   Map Ref: 10

Gilstrap Heritage Centre

Castlegate, Newark-on-Trent NG24 1BG

Castle Story Exhibition featuring 1000 years of Newark Castle.

Opening Times: Oct to Mar 09:00-17:00, Apr to Sep 09:00-18:00. Admission: Free.
Location: Situated in the grounds of Newark Castle in the town centre.   Map Ref: 11

Millgate Museum

48 Millgate, Newark-on-Trent NG24 4TS   Tel: 01636 655730   Fax: 01636 655735
Email: museums@nsdc.info

Re-created streets, shops and rooms showing the commercial, social and domestic life of Newark. New 20th Century Gallery. Also Mezzanine Gallery displaying work of local artists.

Opening Times: Mon to Fri 10:00-17:00 Sat, Sun & BH 13:00-17:00. Admission: Free.
Location: On the riverside walk, five minutes from Newark Town Centre.   Map Ref: 11

Newark Air Museum

Winthorpe Showground, Newark-on-Trent NG24 2NY   Tel / Fax: 01636 707170
Email: newarkair@lineone.net   Web: www.newarkairmuseum.co.uk

UK's largest volunteer managed aviation museum displaying 60 aircraft and cockpit sections from across the history of aviation. Large under cover display areas, artefact displays, souvenir shop and cafe.

Opening Times: Mar to Oct daily 10:00-17:00. Nov to Feb daily 10:00-16:00. Admission: Adult £4.25, Child £2.50, OAP £3.50. Location: Easy access from A1, A17, A46 and A1133, follow brown/white signs. Map Ref: 12

Newark Museum

Appletongate, Newark-on-Trent NG24 1JY Tel: 01636 655740 Fax: 01636 655745
Email: museums@nsdc.info

Ever wondered about Newark's early history? Find out more from the fine archaeology collections. Also look out for Newark's Civil War Heritage. Free fun trails link all the displays.

Opening Times: Mon to Sat 10:00-13:00, 14:00-17:00, closed Thu. Apr to Sep also open Sun 14:00-17:00, BH 13:00-17:00. Admission: Free. Location: Town centre, close to parish church. Map Ref: 11

Newark Town Treasures & Art Gallery

Market Place, Newark-on-Trent NG24 1DU Tel: 01636 680333 Fax: 01636 680350
Email: post@newark.gov.uk Web: www.newark.gov.uk

Museum housed in Grade I listed Georgian Town Hall designed by John Carr in 1776. Collection consists of sumptuous civic gifts and paintings from 17th and 18th centuries. Temporary exhibitions in the Spotlight Gallery.

Opening Times: Mon to Fri 11:00-16:00, Sat 12:00-15:00 all year. Closed Sun & BH.
Admission: Free. Location: Town centre. Map Ref: 11

Vina Cooke Museum of Dolls & Bygone Childhood

The Old Rectory, Cromwell, Newark-on-Trent NG23 6JE Tel: 01636 821364

A corner of the Toy Room - 'Nanny' on duty

Large collection of dolls, toys, prams, dolls houses, books, games and costumes. Handmade dolls by Vina Cooke depicting royalty, stage, screen and historical characters. Also various christening robes, children's clothing and accessories. Attractively displayed in late 17th century Dower House and former rectory. An Easter Monday Extravaganza takes place every year, with Morris dancers and fascinating craft displays.

Opening Times: Daily except Fri 10:30-12:00, 14:00-17:00. Fri, evenings and other hours by appointment. Admission: Adult £2.95, Child £1.50, OAP £2.50.

Location: Five miles north of Newark, easy access from A1. Next to church in village of Cromwell. Map Ref: 10

Angel Row Gallery

Central Library Building, 3 Angel Row, Nottingham NG1 6HP Tel: 0115 915 2869 Fax: 0115 915 2860 Email: deborah.dean@nottinghamcity.gov.uk

A varied and constantly changing programme of exhibitions covering the whole range of contemporary art.

Opening Times: Mon to Sat 10:00-17:00. Admission: Free. Location: City centre, one minute walk from market square. Map Ref: 13

Brewhouse Yard Museum

Castle Boulevard, Nottingham NG7 1FB Tel: 0115 915 3600 Fax: 0115 915 3601
Email: alisonb@ncmg.demon.co.uk

A realistic glimpse of life in Nottingham over the past 300 years.

Opening Times: Daily 10:00-17:00. Admission: Adult £1.50, Child/Concession 80p, Family £3.80. Location: Ten minutes walk from city centre. Map Ref: 13

Leicestershire & Nottinghamshire

Castle Museum & Art Gallery

Nottingham NG1 6EL   Tel: 0115 915 3700   Fax: 0115 915 3653
Email: marketing@ncmg.demon.co.uk   Web: www.nottinghamcity.gov.uk

Nottingham Castle is a 17th century mansion building, on the site of a medieval castle built by William the Conqueror. Nottingham Castle houses a range of historic and contemporary art, ceramics and silverware.

Opening Times: Daily 10:00-17:00.   Admission: Free Mon to Fri. Sat, Sun & BH - Adult £2.00, Child/Concession £1.00, Family (2 adult and 4 children) £5.00.   Location: Five minutes walk from Nottingham City Centre, easy access from train and bus station.   Map Ref: 13

Djanogly Art Gallery

Lakeside Arts Centre, University Park, Nottingham NG7 2RD   Tel: 0115 846 7777
Email: neil.walker@nottingham.ac.uk   Web: www.lakesidearts.org.uk

Temporary exhibition galleries offering a year-round programme of contemporary and historic fine art exhibitions with education activities and events targeted at general public and schools/colleges.

Opening Times: Mon to Sat 11:00-17:00, Sun & BH 14:00-17:00.   Admission: Free.
Location: One and a half miles outside city centre, on major bus route. Easy access by car from motorway.   Map Ref: 13

Galleries of Justice

GALLERIES *of* **JUSTICE**

Shire Hall, High Pavement, Nottingham NG1 1HN
Tel: 0115 952 0555   Fax: 0115 993 9828
Email: info@galleriesofjustice.org.uk
Web: www.galleriesofjustice.org.uk

Journey with us through 300 years of Crime and Punishment on this historic site, where your senses are bombarded with the sounds, sights and smells of justice and injustice, the guilty and the innocent. Witness a real trial in the authentic Victorian courtroom before being sentenced and 'sent down' to the original cells and medieval caves.

Opening Times: Tue to Sun & BH 10:00-17:00. Closed Xmas & New Year.   Admission: Adult £6.95, Child £5.25, Concession £5.95, Family £19.95.   Location: Midland Railway Station and Victoria Bus Station ten minute walk.   Map Ref: 13

Green's Mill & Science Centre

Windmill Lane, Sneinton, Nottingham NG2 4QB   Tel: 0115 915 6878   Fax: 0115 915 6875
Email: enquiries@greensmill.org.uk   Web: www.greensmill.org.uk

A unique working windmill built at the beginning of the 19th century, once home to the mathematical genius and miller George Green. The outhouses also house a science centre.

Opening Times: Wed to Sun & BH 10:00-16:00.   Admission: Free.   Location: One mile outside Nottingham City Centre.   Map Ref: 13

Industrial Museum

Courtyard Buildings, Wollaton Park, Nottingham NG8 2AE   Tel: 0115 915 3910
Email: carolb@ncmg.demon.co.uk

The Museum is housed in the 18th century stable block for Wollaton Hall. It tells the story of the industries of Nottingham and its environs, from heavy industries such as coal mining and engineering to its famous lace.

Opening Times: Apr to Sep daily 11:00-17:00. Oct to Apr daily 11:00-16:00.
Admission: Weekdays Free. Weekends and BH Adult £1.50, Child/Concession 80p, Family £3.80.   Location: Four miles from Nottingham City Centre off the A6514.   Map Ref: 14

Long Eaton Town Hall

Derby Road, Long Eaton, Nottingham   Tel: 0115 907 1141   Fax: 0115 932 9264
Email: museum@erewash.gov.uk   Web: www.erewash.gov.uk

Temporary exhibitions of art, local and social history. Plus Howitt bequest of paintings.

Opening Times: Mon to Fri 10:00-16:00.   Admission: Free.   Location: Near town centre.
                                                          Map Ref: 15

Leicestershire & Nottinghamshire

Museum of Costume & Textiles
51 Castle Gate, Nottingham NG1 6AF   Tel: 0115 915 3500
Email: jeremyf@ncmg.demon.co.uk

200 years of costume displayed in a series of period room sets. A fine collection of machine made and hand made lace dating from the 16th century. A collection of tapestries dating from the 17th century.

Opening Times: Wed to Sun & BH 11:00-17:00.   Admission: Free.   Location: One minute walk from the market square in the city centre. Map Ref: 13

Natural History Museum, Wollaton Park
Wollaton Park, Nottingham NG8 2AE   Tel: 0115 915 3900   Fax: 0115 915 3932
Email: carolb@ncmg.demon.co.uk

Nottingham's natural history collection housed in an Elizabethan mansion, set in 500 acres of natural parkland.

Opening Times: Apr to Sep daily 11:00-17:00. Oct to Mar daily 11:00-16:00.   Admission: Free, except Sat, Sun & BH Adults £1.50, Child/Concession 80p, Family £3.80.   Location: Three miles from Nottingham City Centre. Follow signs off the A52. Map Ref: 14

Oakham Castle
Market Place, Oakham   Tel: 01572 758440   Fax: 01572 758445
Email: museum@rutland.gov.uk   Web: www.rutnet.co.uk/rcc/rutlandmuseums

Oakham Castle, in the town centre, was a fortified manor house. With its medieval musician sculptures and fine architecture, its Great Hall is one of the most important monuments of Norman England. Over 200 unique presentation horseshoes, forfeited by peers and royalty to the lord of the manor, hang inside. The Great Hall is a popular venue for civil marriages.

Opening Times: Late Mar to late Oct Mon to Sat 10:00-13:00 & 13:30-17:00, Sun 13:00-17:00. Late Oct to late Mar closes 16:00 daily. Closed Good Friday & Xmas.   Admission: Free.   Location: Off Market Place.

The 12th century Great Hall of Oakham Castle

Map Ref: 16

Rutland County Museum
Catmose Street, Oakham LE15 6HW   Tel: 01572 758440   Fax: 01572 758445
Email: museum@rutland.gov.uk   Web: www.rutnet.co.uk/rcc/rutlandmuseums

In a splendid late 18th century indoor riding school near Oakham town centre, the Rutland County Museum has extensive rural life collections. On show are rural tradesmen's tools and farming equipment of all kinds, with domestic collections, local archaeology, and a special gallery on the Volunteer Soldier in Leicestershire and Rutland. Temporary exhibitions and a Coffee Corner are additional attractions.

Opening Times: Mon to Sat 10:00-17:00, Sun 14:00-17:00. Late Oct to late Mar 14:00-16:00. Closed Good Friday & Xmas.   Admission: Free.   Location: On A6003 just south of town centre.

The Rutland County Museum's 1794 riding school building

Map Ref: 16

Newstead Abbey
Newstead Abbey Park, Ravenshead NG15 8GE   Tel: 01623 455900   Fax: 01623 455904
Email: enquiries@newsteadabbey.org.uk   Web: www.newsteadabbey.org.uk

A beautiful historic house set in glorious landscape of gardens and parkland. Founded as a monastic house in the late 12th century, Newstead Abbey became the Byron family seat in 1540.

Opening Times: Apr to Sep daily 12:00-17:00.   Admission: Adult £4.00, Child £1.50,

Leicestershire & Nottinghamshire

RAVENSHEAD *Notts (continued)*

Concession £2.00, Family £6.00.   Location: 12 miles north of Nottingham on the A60, close to junction 27 of the M1.   Map Ref: 17

Papplewick Pumping Station

off Longdale Lane, Ravenshead NG15 9AJ   Tel: 0115 963 2938   Fax: 0115 955 7172
Email: secretary@papplewickpumpingstation.co.uk
Web: www.papplewickpumpingstation.co.uk

Late Victorian working waterworks in landscaped grounds. One of Europe's great industrial monuments. Original engines/boilers in magnificent Temple of Steam.

Opening Times: BH and other weekends operational.   Admission: Adult £3.00, Child £1.50, Concession/Group £2.50.   Location: Signposted off A60/A614 seven miles north of Nottingham.
Map Ref: 17

RETFORD *Notts*

Bassetlaw Museum & Percy Laws Memorial Gallery

Amcott House, Grove Street, Retford DN22 6JU   Tel / Fax: 01777 713749

Collections relating to the history and archaeology of North Nottinghamshire. Continuous programme of short-term exhibitions. Permanent display of the Retford civic plate. In restored Georgian town house setting.

Opening Times: Mon to Sat 10:00-17:00. Closed Sun & BH.   Admission: Free.   Location: 200 metres from town centre (Market Square), three minutes from bus station.   Map Ref: 18

WORKSOP *Notts*

Creswell Crags Museum and Education Centre

Crags Road, Welbeck, Worksop S80 3LH   Tel: 01909 720378   Fax: 01909 724726
Email: info@creswell.crags.org.uk   Web: www.creswell-crags.org.uk

Limestone gorge with caves and lake. One of Britain's most important archaeology sites, home to Ice Age hunters 40,000 years ago. Museum displays, education centre, 'Virtually The Ice Age' website.

Opening Times: Feb to Oct daily 10:30-16:30, Nov to Jan Sun only 10:30-16:30.
Admission: Free.   Location: Half mile east of Creswell village on B6042 (off A616), 20 minutes walk from Creswell Railway Station.   Map Ref: 19

Harley Gallery

Welbeck, Worksop S80 3LW   Tel: 01909 501700   Fax: 01909 488747   Email: ssherrit@harley-welbeck.co.uk   Web: www.harleygallery.co.uk

A changing display of contemporary arts and crafts exhibitions. Craft shop selling work from emminent British artists, a museum showing fine/decorative arts from The Portland Collection and a range of events/workshops exploring the arts.

Opening Times: Feb to Dec Tue to Sun 10:00-17:00.   Admission: Free.   Location: Situated on the A60 Mansfield Road, five miles south of Worksop.   Map Ref: 19

Mr Straw's House

7 Blyth Road, Worksop S81 0JG   Tel: 01909 482380   Web: www.nationaltrust.org

A semi-detached house offering a tantalising glimpse into the past. Letters, photos, furniture, household objects - all shown in their rightful places where the family left them.

Opening Times: Apr to Oct Tue to Sat 11:00-16:30. Due to the domestic scale of the property pre-booking is essential for all visitors.   Admission: Adult £4.20, Child £2.10, Family £10.50, National Trust Members Free.   Location: Follow signs to Bassetlaw Hospital, Blyth Grove is signposed on B6045.   Map Ref: 20

Worksop Museum

Worksop Public Library, Memorial Avenue, Worksop S80 2BP   Tel / Fax: 01777 713749

Permanent introductory exhibition to the Pilgrim Father's Story. Programme of art exhibitions. Display of the Arundel Marble statue from the frieze of the Great Altar of Pergamon in Asia Minor.

Opening Times: Mon to Wed & Fri 09:30-17:00, Thu & Sat 09:30-13:00. Closed Sun & BH.
Admission: Free.   Location: Within Public Library in setting of Memorial Gardens, five minutes walk from main street.   Map Ref: 20

Lincolnshire

The county town Lincoln dominates the old county of Lincolnshire, standing on the central chalk ridge, the Lincolnshire Edge. The impressive triple towered cathedral overlooks the ancient historic city with its beautiful stained glass windows and the famous Lincoln Imp. Skegness, Lincolnshire's seaside resort, was developed during the nineteenth century and flourished with the coming of the railway in 1873. The Holland region of drained Fen is the commercial bulb-growing centre, ablaze with colour during the Spring months leading to Spalding's spectacular Tulip Parade in May.

A fine selection of museums and historic houses encapsulate the local and social history of Lincolnshire.

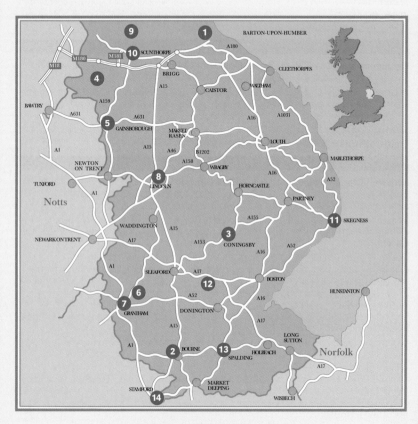

The Red Map References should be used to locate Museums etc on the pages that follow

Lincolnshire

BARTON-UPON-HUMBER *N Lincs*

Baysgarth House Museum
Baysgarth Leisure Park, Caistor Road, Barton-upon-Humber DN18 6AH   Tel: 01652 632318

An 18th century mansion house with fine period rooms, a collection of 18th and 19th century English and Oriental pottery and an industrial museum in the stable block.

Opening Times: Tue to Sun & BH 10:00-16:00. Closed Mon and Xmas & New Year.
Admission: Free.   Location: Near town centre, three minutes walk from Market Place.

Map Ref: 1

BOURNE *Lincs*

Grimsthorpe Castle

Bourne PE10 0LY   Tel: 01778 591205   Fax: 01778 591259   Email: ray@grimsthorpe.co.uk
Web: www.grimsthorpe.co.uk

Dating from 13th century. Stunning treasure house with beautiful contents including paintings, furniture, tapestries. Surrounded by parkland, lakes, gardens, deer herd and woodland walks.

Opening Times: Apr to Sep Thu & Sun, Aug Thu to Sun 11:00-18:00 (castle open 13:00).
Admission: Adult £6.50, Child £3.50, Concession £5.50.   Location: On the A151, ten minutes drive from the A1.

Map Ref: 2

CONINGSBY *Lincs*

Battle of Britain Memorial Flight Visitor Centre

RAF Coningsby, Coningsby LN4 4SY   Tel: 01526 344041   Fax: 01526 342330
Email: bbmf@lincolnshire.gov.uk   Web: www.lincolnshire.gov.uk/bbmf

Unique opportunity to view the historic aircraft of BBMF at their home base at RAF Coningsby. Visitors are shown around the hangar by knowledgeable volunteers. Aircraft absent mid June to October 2003.

Opening Times: Mon to Fri 10:00-17:00. Closed Sat, Sun, BH and two weeks at Xmas.
Admission: Adult £3.50, Child £1.50, OAP £2.00, Groups £2.00.   Location: Half mile from Coningsby Village.

Map Ref: 3

EPWORTH *N Lincs*

Epworth Old Rectory

1 Rectory Street, Epworth DN9 1HX   Tel: 01427 872268
Email: epworth@oldrectory63.freeserve.co.uk   Web: www.epworthrectory.freeserve.co.uk

1709 Queen Anne House, boyhood home of John and Charles Wesley. Set in large grounds, with portraits, period furniture, prints, memorabilia.

Opening Times: Mar to Oct daily. Mar, Apr & Oct 10:00-12:00 & 14:00-16:00. May, Jun, Jul, Aug & Sep Mon to Sat 10:00-16:30, Sun 14:00-16:30. Admission: Adult £3.00, Child £1.00, OAP £2.50, Family £7.00.   Location: 200 yards from Epworth Town Centre.

Map Ref: 4

GAINSBOROUGH *Lincs*

Gainsborough Old Hall

Parnell Street, Gainsbrorough DN21 2NB   Tel: 01427 612669   Fax: 01427 612779
Email: gainsboroughholdhall@lincolnshire.gov.uk   Web: www.lincolnshire.gov.uk

Gainsborough's own medieval manor house. Principally a timber-framed building with a brick tower, magnificent Great Hall and one of the best preserved medieval kitchens in the country.

Opening Times: Mon to Sat 10:00-17:00, Sun 14:00-17:30. Closed Sun from end of Oct to Easter, Xmas & New Year.   Admission: Adult £2.50 Child £1.00 OAP £1.50.   Location: In the centre of Gainsborough.

Map Ref: 5

Lincolnshire

Belton House

Belton, Grantham NG32 2LS   Tel: 01476 566116   Fax: 01476 579071   THE NATIONAL TRUST
Email: belton@smtp.ntrust.org.uk   Web: www.nationaltrust.org.uk

The stunning interiors of this restored country house contain exceptionally fine plasterwork and wood carving, as well as important collections of paintings, furniture, tapestries and silverware.

Opening Times: 23 Mar to 3 Nov Wed to Sun & BH Mon, Good Friday & Tue 4 Jun. Admission: Adult £5.60, Child £2.80, Family £14.00. Group rates available if pre-booked. Location: Three miles north east of Grantham on A607 Grantham to Lincoln Road.   Map Ref: 6

Grantham Museum

St Peters Hill, Grantham NG31 6PY   Tel: 01476 568783   Fax: 01476 592457
Email: grantham.museum@lincolnshire.gov.uk

Grantham Museum is the interpretation centre of the town with displays from its earliest archaeological remains, to displays on Isaac Newton, the Dambusters and Margaret Thatcher. Regular temporary exhibitions and events. Please contact the Museum for further details.

Opening Times: Mon to Sat 10:00-17:00, also BH & Good Friday. Closed Xmas & New Year.
Admission: Free. Location: Situated in the centre of Grantham next to the Guildhall.Map Ref: 7

Doddington Hall

Lincoln LN6 4RU   Tel: 01522 694308   Fax: 01522 685259
Email: fionawatson@doddingtonhall.free-online.co.uk   Web: www.doddingtonhall.free-online.co.uk

The Hall stands today exactly as it was built in 1600. The elegant Georgian interior contains a fascinating collection of pictures, textiles, porcelain and furniture that reflect four centuries of unbroken occupation.

Opening Times: House & Gardens: May to Sep Sun, Wed & BH. Gardens only: Feb to May Sun, Wed & BH. Admission: House & Gardens: Adult £4.60, Child £2.30, Family £12.75. Gardens: Adult £3.10, Child £1.55. Location: Clearly signposted off the A46 Lincoln by-pass on the B1190.   Map Ref: 8

Greyfriars

Broadgate, Lincoln LN2 1HQ   Tel: 01522 530401   Fax: 01522 530724
Email: hollandk@lincolnshire.gov.uk

Greyfriars is a beautiful 13th century building located in the lower part of Lincoln. Greyfriars is used to display annual themed exhibitions drawn from the collections of the City and County Museum, which range from pre-history to 1750. A lively programme of events throughout the year.

Opening Times: Tue to Sat 10:00-13:00 & 14:00-16:00. Closed 25-26 Dec and New Years Day.
Admission: Free. Location: Located in the lower part of Lincoln between St Swithin's Church and central library.   Map Ref: 8

Lincoln Castle

Castle Hill, Lincoln LN1 3AA   Tel: 01522 511068   Fax: 01522 512150

The castle was built by William the Conqueror in 1068 on a site occupied since Roman times. It is one of only two castles in Britain with two mottes.

Opening Times: Apr to Oct Mon to Sat 09:30-17:30, Sun 11:00-17:30. Nov to Mar Mon to Sat 09:30-16:30, Sun 11:00-16:30. Closed Xmas & New Year. Admission: Admission charge.
Location: In Lincoln, 16 miles north-east of Newark-on-Trent.   Map Ref: 8

Museum of Lincolnshire Life

The Old Barracks, Burton Road, Lincoln LN1 3LY   Tel: 01522 528448   Fax: 01522 521264
Email: lincolnshire.museum@lincolnshire.gov.uk

The largest community museum in Lincolnshire boasting a nationally renowned agricultural

Lincolnshire

collection; richly represented industrial and social history displays, and incorporating the newly refurbished Royal Lincolnshire Regimental Museum and an 18th century working windmill nearby.

Opening Times: May to Oct 10:00-17:30. Nov to Apr Mon to Sat 10:00-17:30, Sun 14:00-17:30. Closed Xmas & New Year.   Admission: Adult £2.00, Child 60p, Family £4.50, Groups of 10 or over £1.60 per adult.   Location: Within five minutes walk of Lincoln Cathedral and Castle sites.

Map Ref: 8

Royal Lincolnshire Regiment Museum

Museum of Lincolnshire Life, Burton Road, Lincoln LN1 3LY   Tel: 01522 528448

The newly refurbished Regimental Galleries display over 300 years of the regiment's history from its inception to its amalgamation with the Royal Anglian Regiment. It uses objects and text to portray life as a soldier from 1685 to 1960.

Opening Times: May to Oct 10:00-17:00. Nov to Apr Mon to Sat 10:00-17:30, Sun 14:00-17:30. Admission: Adult £2.00, Child 60p, Family £4.50, Group of 10 or more £1.60 per adult. Location: Within five minutes walk of Lincoln Cathedral and Castle sites.

Map Ref: 8

Usher Gallery

Lindum Road, Lincoln LN2 1NN   Tel: 01522 527980   Fax: 01522 560165
Email: usher.gallery@lincolnshire.gov-uk

Major Lincolnshire venue for fine and decorative arts including the Peter de Wint Collection. A lively programme of temporary exhibitions throughout the year.

Opening Times: Tue to Sat 10:00-17:30, Sun 14:30-17:00. Closed 24-31 Dec, Mon except BH. Admission: Adult £2.00, Child/Concession 50p. Free day Fri.   Location: Situated on the slope below the Cathedral, five minutes from the town centre.

Map Ref: 8

Normanby Hall

Normanby Hall Country Park, Normanby, Scunthorpe DN15 9HU   Tel: 01724 720588
Fax: 01724 721248

Normanby Hall is a Regency country house designed by Sir Robert Smirke and furnished in period style. It also contains a costume gallery in which annually changing exhibitions are held.

Opening Times: 31 Mar to 28 Sep daily 13:00-17:00. Other times by appointment. Admission: Adult £3.50, Concession £2.50, Family £9.50 (2002 prices). Special Rates for North Lincolnshire residents & Groups.   Location: Four miles north of Scunthorpe off the B1430.

Map Ref: 9

Normanby Park Farming Museum

Normanby Hall Country Park, Normanby, Scunthorpe DN15 9HU   Tel: 01724 720588
Fax: 01724 721248

The Normanby Park Farming Museum shows the history of farming and rural crafts in the late 19th and early 20th centuries. Holding regular activities for children.

Opening Times: 31 Mar to 28 Sep daily 13:00-17:00. Other times by appointment. Admission: Adult £3.50, Concession £2.50, Family £9.50 (2002 prices). Special Rates for North Lincolnshire residents & Groups.   Location: Four miles north of Scunthorpe off the B1430. Map Ref: 9

North Lincolnshire Museum

Oswald Road, Scunthorpe DN15 7BD   Tel: 01724 843533

The museum housed in a Victorian vicarage, depicts North Lincolnshire's early and later history, through displays of geology, archaeology and social history.

Opening Times: Tue to Sat & BH 10:00-16:00, Sun 13:00-16:00. Closed Mon and Xmas & New Year.   Admission: Free.   Location: Near town centre, two minute walk from railway station, bus stop outside.

Map Ref: 10

Church Farm Museum

Church Road South, Skegness PE25 2HF   Tel: 01754 766658   Fax: 01754 898243
Email: walkerr@lincolnshire.gov.uk

Agricultural and country life museum 19th to 20th century. Set in original farm house and farm

Lincolnshire

buildings. Lincolnshire thatched mud and stud cottage, barns and waggon hovel re-built on site.

Opening Times: Apr to Oct 10:30-17:30. Admission: Adult £1.00, Child 50p. Location: 15 minutes walk from railway station. Map Ref: 11

SLEAFORD *Lincs*

Heckington Windmill

Hale Road, Heckington, Sleaford NG34 9JJ   Tel: 01529 461919

Working 19th century windmill (major repairs expected 2002). Only eight sailed mill in Western Europe. Technical displays on history, mills and milling. Sales of stoneground flour etc.

Opening Times: Please contact. Admission: Adult £1.50, Child 75p, Under 5s Free. Location: Heckington is a village in Lincolnshire between Sleaford and Boston by-passed by A17. The mill is adjacent to Heckington Railway Station. Map Ref: 12

SPALDING *Lincs*

Ayscoughfee Hall Museum & Gardens

Churchgate, Spalding PE11 2RA   Tel: 01775 725468   Fax: 01775 762715
Email: kwardman@sholland.gov.uk   Web: www.sholland.gov.uk

Ayscoughfee Hall is a late medieval (1429) wool merchant's house set in five acres of walled gardens. The formal gardens were set out in 1720 and show an important 'footprint' of an early Georgian urban garden. It is home to the Museum of South Holland Life and Spalding Tourist Information Centre. Tennis, putting and bowling facilities are available in the garden and children's play area and activities.

Opening Times: Mon to Fri 9:00-17:00, Mar to Oct Sat 10:00-17:00, Sun & BH 11:00-17:00. Admission: Free. Location: Five minutes walk from town centre, ten minutes from railway station. On east bank of River Welland. Exhibitions & Events 2003 : Please telephone for Gallery information. Map Ref: 13

STAMFORD *Lincs*

Burghley House

Stamford PE9 3JY   Tel: 01780 752451   Fax: 01780 480125
Email: burghley@burghley.co.uk   Web: www.burghley.co.uk

Burghley House

18 state rooms including one of the most important private collections of 17th century Italian paintings, the earliest inventoried collection of Japanese ceramics in the west and wood carving by Grinling Gibbons and his followers. There are also four magnificent state beds, fine examples of English and continental furniture and important tapestries and textiles.

Opening Times: Good Friday 29 Mar to 27 Oct 11:00-17:00. Admission: Adult £7.10, Child £3.50, OAP £6.50. Location: One mile east of Stamford on B1443, close to A1 clearly signposted. Map Ref: 14

Burghley House

Stamford Museum

Broad Street, Stamford PE9 1PJ   Tel: 01780 766317   Fax: 01780 480363
Email: stamford_museum@lincolnshire.gov.uk   Web: www.lincolnshire.gov.uk/stamfordmuseum

Displays illustrate the history of this fine stone town and include Stamford Ware pottery, the visit of Daniel Lambert and the town's more recent industrial past. Temporary exhibitions and holiday activities.

Opening Times: Apr to Sep Mon to Sat 10:00-17:00, Sun 14:00-17:00. Oct to Mar Mon to Sat 10:00-17:00. Closed 24-26 Dec & New Years Eve & Day. Admission: Free. Location: Town centre. Map Ref: 14

Central London

In a sense London is one enormous museum: from the first century AD when the Romans settled here through the early medieval period of the building of the first St Paul's Cathedral, the Norman period of the construction of the White Tower, the prosperous years of the Livery Companies, through plague, fire and pestilence and the gracious years of Wren's building, to the London of today, this city has drawn to itself the nation's talent and expertise. This great city of history and pageantry has become the treasure house of Britain's skills where everything is recorded in a vast selection of the finest, and certainly the most fascinating, museums and galleries of the world.

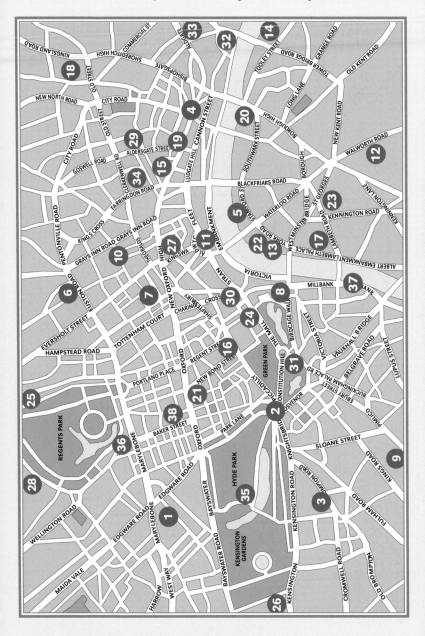

The Red Map References should be used to locate Museums etc on the pages that follow

London Underground System

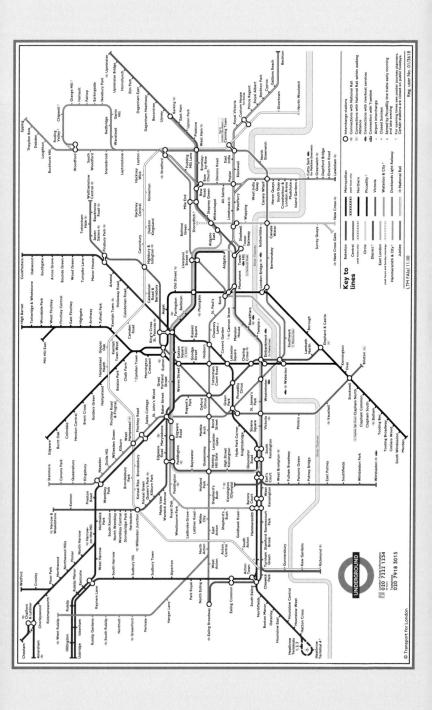

Alexander Fleming Laboratory Museum

St Marys Hospital, Praed Street, London W2 1NY   Tel: 020 7886 6528   Fax: 020 7886 6739
Email: kevin.brown@st-marys.nhs.uk

In situ reconstruction of Fleming's laboratory as it was in 1928 when he discovered penicillin there, with video and exhibition telling the story of the man, the mould and its impact on mankind.

Opening Times: Mon to Thu 10:00-13:00 (other times by appointment). Admission: Adult £2.00, Concession £1.00. Location: A two minute walk from Paddington Station.   Map Ref: 1

Apsley House

Hyde Park Corner, London W1J 7NT   Tel: 020 7499 5676   Fax: 020 7493 6576

Apsley House, famously known as No. 1 London, is one of the capital's finest residences. Ancestral home of the Dukes of Wellington since 1815, its sumptuous interiors house the first Duke's outstanding collection of paintings, silver, porcelain and sculpture. London Tourist Board Small Visitor Attraction of the Year 2001.

Opening Times: Tue to Sun 11:00-17:00. Admission: Adult £4.50, Under 18s/OAP Free, Concession £3.00, Group £2.50. Price includes free sound guide. Location: Hyde Park Corner.

Apsley House, The Waterloo Gallery   Map Ref: 2

Baden Powell House

Suite 210, 28 Old Brompton Road, South Kensington, London SW7 3SS   Tel: 020 7584 7031
Fax: 020 7590 6902   Email: conferences.bphhostel@scout.org.uk   Web: www.scouts.org.uk

Welcomed by the only granite statue in London - Lord Robert Baden-Powell (founder of the Scouting Movement) welcomes you to a memorial to his life-time achievements. It hosts a display, which depicts his life story and boasts memorabilia given to him by world delegations. As an artist Baden-Powell produced some magnificent paintings and sketches, which are also on display.

Opening Times: 4 Jan to 21 Dec daily 07:00-23:00.
Admission: Free. Location: Central London, South Kensington - five minute walk from Gloucester Road and South Kensington tube stations.   Map Ref: 3

The Granite Statue welcoming you to Baden Powell House

Bank of England Museum

Bank of England, Threadneedle Street, London EC2R 8AH   Tel: 020 7601 5491
Fax: 020 7601 5808   Email: june.greenhalf@bankofengland.co.uk
Web: www.bankofengland.co.uk

The Museum is housed within the Bank of England itself, right at the heart of the City of London. It traces the history of the Bank from its foundation by Royal Charter in 1694 to its role today as the nation's central bank. There are gold bars dating from ancient times to the modern market bar, coins and a unique collection of bank notes.

Opening Times: Mon to Fri 10:00-17:00, also day of Lord Mayor's Show. Closed Sat & Sun & BH.
Admission: Free. Location: One minute walk from Bank underground, ten minutes from Liverpool Street, Fenchurch Street and Cannon Street.   Map Ref: 4

Visitors are invited to try to lift a London Good Delivery Bar

---

Bankside Gallery

48 Hopton Street, London SE1 9JH   Tel: 020 7928 7521   Fax: 020 7928 2820
Email: info@banksidegallery.com   Web: www.banksidegallery.com

Bankside Gallery is home to the Royal Watercolour Society and the Royal Society of Painter-Printmakers, and stages an annual programme of exhibitions of members' work.

Opening Times: Tue 10:00-20:00, Wed to Fri 10:00-17:00, Sat, Sun & BH Mon 11:00-17:00.
Admission: Adult £3.50, Concession £2.00. Group rates available. Some exhibitions free.
Location: Situated on riverside, near Blackfriars Bridge and adjacent to Tate Modern. Map Ref: 5

Central London

The British Library

96 Euston Road, London NW1 2DB   Tel: 020 7412 7332
Email: visitor-services@bl.uk Web: www.bl.uk

The Lindisfarne Gospels:
Opening page of St Luke's Gospel

On display are hundreds of items from the world's greatest collection of books, manuscripts, music, stamps, sound recordings and maps. The Library's collections span over three millennia and contain items from all continents of the world. The John Ritblat Gallery is home to a permanent exhibition of over 200 of the Library's Treasures. It includes documents which made and recorded history, sacred texts from the world's religions, masterpieces of illumination, landmarks of printing, great works of literature and music and major advances in science and mapmaking. Items on display include Codex Sinaiticus (c350), Magna Carta (1215), the Gutenberg Bible (1455), Shakespeare's First Folio (1623), as well as works in the handwriting of Leonardo da Vinci, Lord Nelson, Lewis Carroll, Handel, Sir Paul McCartney and many others. It also features the Library's award winning Turning the Pages computer interactive, which allows you to turn pages or unroll a scroll simply by touching a screen. The Pearson Gallery is home to special thematic exhibitions. The Workshop of Words, Sounds and Images traces the story of book production and offers regular free demonstrations. There is also an extensive display of philatelic material, which is probably the best permanent display of stamps in the world, and National Sound Archive Jukeboxes offering a changing selection of sounds from their extensive collection of recordings. Visitors can also see the Kings Library, housed in a 17 metre glass-walled tower at the heart of the building, plus a number of other major works of art.

Early copy of The Canterbury Tales
at the British Library

Opening Times: Galleries: Mon 09:30-18:00, Tue 09:30-20:00, Wed to Fri 09:30-18:00, Sat 09:30-17:00, Sun & BH 11:00-17:00. Closed 1 Jan, 18-20 Sep, 24-26 Dec 30-31 Dec early closing at 17:00. The Reading Room times differ.   Admission: Free.   Location: Next door to St Pancreas mainline station, five minutes from both Euston and Kings Cross.   Exhibitions & Events 2003 : To 31 Mar: Magic Pencil: children's book illustration today, 15 May to 30 Sep: The Painted Labyrinth; the world of the Lindisfarne Gospel, From Nov: Patent Pending (dates to be confirmed).   Map Ref: 6

British Museum   THE BRITISH MUSEUM

Great Russell Street, London WC1B 3DG   Tel: 020 7323 8000
Email: information@thebritishmuseum.ac.uk
Web: www.thebritishmuseum.ac.uk

Permanent display and special exhibitions of the works of man from prehistory to the present day. Permanent displays of antiquities from Egypt, the ancient Near East, Greece and Rome as well as Prehistory, Roman Britain, Medieval, Renaissance, Modern and Oriental collection. Also the national collection of prints and drawings, coins and banknotes. The Great Court houses the Clore Education Centre, galleries and exhibition space and improved visitor facilities.

The South Facade of the British Museum, London

Opening Times: Sat to Wed 10:00-17:30, Thu & Fri 10:00-20:30.   Admission: Free.   Location: Nearest underground stations: Tottenham Court Road, Holborn, Russell Square.   Map Ref: 7

Cabinet War Rooms

Clive Steps, King Charles Street, London SW1A 2AQ   Tel: 020 7930 6961   Fax: 020 7839 5897   Email: cwr@iwm.org.uk   Web: www.iwm.org.uk

The secret headquarters of Winston Churchill and his Cabinet. Step back in time and view the original complex just as it was left at the end of six years of war, when the lights were finally extinguished.

Opening Times: Apr to Sep daily 09:30-18:00, Oct to Mar daily 10:00-18:00. Last admission 17:15. Closed 24-26 Dec.   Admission: From 1 Apr 2002: Adult £5.80, Child Free, OAP/Student £4.20. Group rates available.   Location: Two minutes from Westminster Underground Station.
                                                                                    Map Ref: 8

Carlyle's House

National Trust, 24 Cheyne Row, London SW3 5HL   Tel: 020 7352 7087
Fax: 020 7352 5108   Web: www.nationaltrust.org.uk/thameschilterns

THE NATIONAL TRUST

The Drawing Room - where Thomas Carlyle
wrote The French Revolution

This Chelsea Queen Anne house was the home of historian, social writer, ethical thinker and powerful public speaker Thomas Carlyle for some 47 years until his death in 1881. The skilful Scottish home making of his wife Jane is much in evidence and the Victorian period decor is still in place. Their academic and domestic lives can be experienced today.

Opening Times: 23 Mar to 3 Nov Wed to Fri 14:00-17:00, Sat, Sun and BH Mon & Tue 4 Jun 11:00-17:00.
Admission: Adult £3.60, Child £1.80, National Trust Members Free.   Location: Off Chelsea Embankment between Albert & Battersea bridges, or via Kings Road and Oakley Street.   Map Ref: 9

The Charles Dickens Museum

48 Doughty Street, London WC1N 2LX   Tel: 020 7405 2127   Fax: 020 7831 5175
Email: dhmuseum@rmplc.co.uk   Web: www.dickensmuseum.com

The only surviving London home of Charles Dickens. Here, between 1837 and 1839 he completed Pickwick Papers, Oliver Twist, Nicholas Nickleby and Barnaby Rudge.

Opening Times: Mon to Sat 10:00-17:00, Sun 11:00-17:00.   Admission: Adult £4.00, Child £2.00, Concession £3.00, Family £9.00.   Location: Central London, near Russell Square.
Map Ref: 10

Chelsea Physic Garden

66 Royal Hospital Road, London SW3 4HS   Tel: 020 7352 5646   Fax: 020 7376 3910
Email: maureen@cpgarden.demon.co.uk   Web: www.chelseaphysicgarden.co.uk

Walled garden of 3.5 acres dating from 1674 and containing collections of medicinal plants, rare and tender species and plants linked to plant hunters. Glasshouses. 1773 rock garden and botanical order beds. Plant sale. Snowdrop opening 3-10 Feb 2002.

Opening Times: 7 Apr to 27 Oct Wed 12:00-17:00 & Sun 14:00-18:00. Special opening for Chelsea Flower Show 20 to 24 May and Chelsea Festival 17 to 21 Jun 12:00-17:00.
Admission: Adult £4.00, Child £2.00, Concession £2.00, OAP £4.00.   Location: Twelve minute walk from Sloane Square tube station, on 239 bus route.   Map Ref: 9

Vincent Van Gogh, Self-Portrait with
Bandaged Ear 1889

Courtauld Institute Gallery

Somerset House, Strand, London WC2R 0RN   Tel: 020 7848 2526
Fax: 020 7848 2589   Email: galleryinfo@courtauld.ac.uk
Web: www.courtauld.ac.uk

The Gallery has one of the most important and best-loved small collections in the country, including world-famous Impressionist and post-Impressionist paintings. It is an integral part of the Courtauld Institute of Art, the oldest centre for the teaching of history of art in England and is housed at Somerset House, one of the finest 18th century buildings in London.

Opening Times: Daily 10:00-18:00.   Admission: Adult £5.00, Concessions £4.00.   Location: Central London. Nearest Undergrounds: Temple, Charing Cross, Holborn and Covent Garden.   Map Ref: 11

Cuming Museum

155/157 Walworth Road, London SE17 1RS   Tel: 020 7701 1342
Fax: 020 7703 7415   Email: cuming.museum@southwark.gov.uk

Home of the rich and unusual Cuming Collection and museum of Southwark's history. Between 1780 and 1900 the Cuming family collected objects from all over the world. In 1900 the unique collection of everyday and extraordinary objects was left to the people of Southwark and the gallery was opened in 1906. The museum has an active programme of events and activities, a changing temporary exhibition space and hands-on family area.

Opening Times: Tue ot Sat 10:00-17:00.   Admission: Free.
Location: Near Elephant & Castle Shopping Centre, five minutes walk on the Walworth Road.   Map Ref: 12

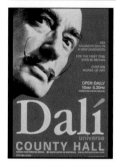

Dali Universe

Riverside Building, County Hall, London SE1 7PB
Tel: 020 7620 2720   Fax: 020 7620 3120
Email: info@daliuniverse.com   Web: www.daliuniverse.com

The Dali Universe is a conceptual art space housing Europe's most important collection by the master Surrealist, Salvador Dali. Arranged thematically to cover the major influences of Dali's life and work, the Dali Universe features more than 500 original works of art, from sculpture to rare etchings, furniture to gold jewellery. Among the highlights are the Mae West Lips sofa, the Lobster Telephone and

The Divine Comedy. The Dali Universe boasts three themed areas - Sensuality and Feminity; includes the world-renowned Mae West Lips sofa and the famous sculpture Buste de Femme Retrospectif, which remains one of the defining classics of Surrealism from the 1930s. Graphics illustrating the major themes of literature are also featured, including ten rare lithographs from the Romeo and Juliet series and twelve erotic Casanova images. Religion and Mythology; reflects Salvador Dali's tempestuous and ambiguous relationship with the church. Two of Dali's most famous masterpieces - the epic illustrations of the Bible and Dante's Divine Comedy number well over 100 graphics in this area. In Dreams and Fantasy; Dali's enduring fascination with the subconscious as the true canvas for expression of personality comes

Space Venus ©

into vivid focus via his sculptural works such as the Persistence of Memory and the Profile of Time. Other works that refer to a life lived through dreams and distorted visions of reality include the enchanting Alice in Wonderland and Don Quichotte. Since opening its doors two years ago in June 2000, the Dali Universe has proved to be a phenomenal success for domestic visitors and overseas ones alike. With more than 500,000 entrances to date, Dalimania has decidedly swept over London.

Opening Times: Daily 10:00-17:30.   Admission: Adult £8.50, Child (10-16 yrs) £4.95, Under 10s £1.00, OAP/Student £7.50.   Location: Next to the London Eye.   Map Ref: 13

Design Museum   **Desigmuseum**

28 Shad Thames, London SE1 2YD   Tel: 020 7403 6933
Fax: 020 7378 6540   Web: www.designmuseum.org

The Design Museum is the world's first museum of industrial design, fashion and architecture. Concerned as much with the future as the past, a changing exhibition programme captures the excitement and ingenuity of design's evolution through the 20th and 21st centuries.

Opening Times: Daily 10:00-17:45 (last entry 17:15).
Admission: Adult £6.00, Concession £4.00, Family (2 adults and 2 children) £16.00.   Location: London, ten minutes from Tower Hill and London Bridge Tubes.

Design Museum, London, © Jefferson Smith   Map Ref: 14

Dr Johnsons House

17 Gough Square, London EC4A 3DE   Tel / Fax: 020 7353 3745
Email: curator@drjh.dircon.co.uk   Web: www.drjh.dircon.co.uk

This House can be described as a shrine to the English language, for it was here that Dr Samuel Johnson worked for many years to compile the first comprehensive English Dictionary which was published in 1755.

Opening Times: May to Sep Mon to Sat 11:00-17:30, Oct to Apr Mon to Sat 11:00-17:00. Closed BH.   Admission: Adult £4.00, Child £1.00, Under 10s Free, Concession £3.00. Group rate £3.00.   Location: Near two underground lines (Blackfriars, Chancery Lane) and many bus routes.   Map Ref: 15

Dunhill Museum & Archive

48 Jermyn Street, London SW1Y 6DL   Tel: 020 7838 8233

A cross-section of the company's history, its products and famous customers, from motoring accessories in the 1890s, to pipes in 1910, lighters and other related products from the 1920s up to the 1950s.

Opening Times: Mon to Fri 09:30-18:00, Sat 10:00-18:00.   Admission: Free.   Location: Just below Piccadilly, a minutes walk from the Royal Academy.   Map Ref: 16

Florence Nightingale Museum

Gassiot House, 2 Lambeth Palace Road, London SE1 7EW   Tel: 020 7620 0374

Large collection of Florence Nightingale personal items including childhood souvenirs, her dress, furniture from her houses and Harley Street Hospital and honours awarded to Nightingale in old age. There is a small military history collection of souvenirs from the Crimean War, including military medals and military nursing uniforms from Scutari Hospital. There is also a small nursing history collection.

Opening Times: Mon to Fri 10:00-17:00. Sat, Sun & BH 11:30-16:30. Closed Good Friday and Xmas.

Lifesize reconstruction of a Crimean wardscene

Admission: Adult £4.80, Child/OAP/Student £3.80, Family (2 adults and 2 children) £12.00.   Location: Car park level of St Thomas' Hospital, opposite Houses of Parliament. Nearest tube station - Westminster, Waterloo and London North.

Map Ref: 17

Geffrye Museum

Kingsland Road, London E2 8EA
Tel: 020 7739 9893   Fax: 020 7729 5647   Email: info@geffrye-museum.org.uk   Web: www.geffrye-museum.org.uk

The Geffrye Museum presents the changing style of the English domestic interior through a series of period rooms from 1600 to the present day. Fine collections of furniture, paintings and decorative arts. Attractive gardens including an award-winning walled herb garden and a series of period gardens.

Opening Times: Tue to Sat 10:00-17:00, Sun 12:00-17:00. Closed Mon (except BH), Good Friday and Xmas & New Year.
Admission: Free.   Location: Liverpool Street Tube, then bus 149 or 242. Old Street Tube exit 2, then bus 243.   Exhibitions & Events

Regency Room, 1800-1830

2003 : Feb to May: Gutted: A Photographic Exhibition of Holly Street Interiors, Sep to Jan: Homes & Gardens, Dec to Jan: Christmas Past - 400 years of Seasonal Traditions in English homes.   Map Ref: 18

Museums • Galleries • Historic Houses

Please let us know of any collections that are not listed in this guide that you feel should be listed. E-mail us on *editor@tomorrows.co.uk* or return the Report Form on page 448

Gilbert Collection

Gilbert Collection

Somerset House, Strand, London WC2R 1LA Tel: 020 7420 9400 Fax: 020 7420 9440 Email: info@gilbert-collection.org.uk Web: www.gilbert-collection.org.uk

The Silver Gallery

The Gilbert Collection is London's newest museum of decorative arts. The collection was formed over four decades by Sir Arthur Gilbert, a Londoner who moved to California in 1949 and made this extraordinary gift to the nation in 1996, 'I felt it should return to the country of my birth.' Thanks to Sir Arthur and the Heritage Lottery Fund, today this pre-eminent collection is beautifully housed in the vaulted spaces of the Embankment Building of the newly restored Somerset House, overlooking the Thames. The sequences of 17 galleries creates an impressive setting for treasure of English and Continental gold and silver, precious snuffboxes, miniature portraits in enamel and Italian cabinets and tables.

Frederick the Great Snuffbox

Opening Times: Daily 10:00-18:00. Closed 24-26 Dec. Admission: Adult £5.00, Child/Student Free, Concession £4.00. Location: Located in the Embankment Building at Somerset House, between Covent Garden and the South Bank. Exhibitions & Events 2003 : For up to date details of special exhibitions, tours, talks, workshops and seminars call the Gilbert Collection or visit the website. Map Ref: 11

Guildhall Art Gallery

Guildhall Yard, London EC2P 2EJ Tel: 020 7606 3030

Pleading 1876,
Sir Lawrence Alma-Tadema oil on panel

The Corporation of London's renowned collection of works of art is now on view in a new gallery opened in 1999. The display includes Victorian art, including famous Pre-Raphaelite works, London subjects from the 17th century to the present, portraits from the 16th century onwards and one of Britain's largest oil paintings. There is also a programme of temporary exhibitions.

Opening Times: Mon to Sat 10:00-17:00, Sun 12:00-16:00. Admission: Adult £2.50, Child Free, Concession £1.00. Location: Follow street signs in the City of London for Guildhall Art Gallery and Guildhall.

Map Ref: 19

HMS Belfast launch 17 March 1938

HMS Belfast

HMS BELFAST

Morgan's Lane, Tooley Street, London SE1 2JH Tel: 020 7940 6300 Fax: 020 7403 0719 Email: jwilson@iwm.org.uk Web: www.iwm.org.uk

HMS Belfast is a cruiser that was launched in 1938 and served throughout the Second World War, playing a leading role. After the war, she supported United Nations forces in Korea and remained in service with the Royal Navy until 1965. In 1971 she was saved for the nation as a unique and historic reminder of Britain's naval heritage in the first half of the 20th century.

Opening Times: 1 Mar to 31 Oct 10:00-18:00. 1 Nov to 28 Feb 10:00-17:00. Closed 24-26 Dec. Admission: Adult £5.80, Child Free, OAP/Student/Concession £4.40, Groups (10+): Adult £4.60, OAP/Student/Concession £3.80. Location: The ship is three minutes walk from London Bridge Station. Map Ref: 20

Guided or Private Tours	Disabled Access	Gift Shop or Sales Point	Café or Refreshments	Restaurant	Car Parking

Central London

Handel House Museum

25 Brook Street, London W1K 4HB   Tel: 020 7495 1685   Fax: 020 7495 1759
Email: mail@handelhouse.org   Web: www.handelhouse.org

Located in the house where G F Handel lived from 1723 until his death in 1759. Portraits, furniture, manuscripts, live music, family events, study days, all in beautiful 18th century interiors.

Opening Times: Tue to Sat 10:00-18:00 (Thu until 20:00), Sun 12:00-18:00.   Admission: Adult £4.50, Child £2.00, Concession £3.50.   Location: Mayfair, London.   Map Ref: 21

Hayward Gallery

South Bank Centre, Belvedere Road, London SE1 8XZ   Tel: 020 7928 3144   Fax: 020 7401 2664   Email: visual_arts@hayward.org.uk   Web: www.haywardgallery.org.uk

The Hayward Gallery acts as a fulcrum in visual culture, a bridge between the experimental and the established. It provides a prominent platform for emerging art and artists and new perspectives on internationally acclaimed artists. Challenging received opinions and crossing boundaries, the Hayward provokes critical debate and extends ideas about what art can be. With the freedom to present work from any era and in any medium, in depth and with authority, the Hayward offers the chance to experience and enjoy the constantly changing world of art. The Hayward administers the Arts Council Collection and National Touring Exhibitions on behalf of the Arts Council of England

Opening Times: Daily 10:00-18:00, Tue & Wed until 20:00.   Location: South Bank, one minute walk from Waterloo Station.
Exhibitions & Events 2003 : For Exhibitions and Events please telephone for details. Map Ref: 22

Imperial War Museum

Lambeth Road, London SE1 6HZ   Tel: 020 7416 5320

The Imperial War Museum traces the history of 20th century conflict from 1914, covering both World Wars and conflicts involving Britain and the Commonwealth post 1945. The museum has permanent exhibitions illustrating military, social, scientific and artistic aspects of war. Also a permanent exhibition dedicated to the Holocaust, art galleries, interactive displays and a changing programme of temporary exhibitions, including the 1940s House and 'Women in Uniform' opening in 2003.

Opening Times: Daily 10:00-18:00. Closed 24-26 Dec.
Admission: Free   Location: Central London, 15 minute walk from Waterloo Station, five minutes from Lambeth North.   Map Ref: 23

The Large Exhibits Gallery

Institute of Contemporary Arts

The Mall, London SW1Y 5AH   Tel: 020 7930 0493   Fax: 020 7930 9851
Email: info@ica.org.uk   Web: www.ica.org.uk

See art from contemporary artists like Damien Hirst, Steve McQueen and Tracey Emin. Watch fascinating arthouse cinema from directors like Wong Kar Wai, Jan Svankmajer and Jane Campion. Listen to talks by philosopher Anthony Grayling, Professor Stuart Hall and journalist Rosie Millard and attend dance, music and theatrical performances. The ICA houses art galleries, two cinemas, a bar and café, a new media centre, a theatre and a bookshop.

Opening Times: Mon 12:00-23:00, Tue to Sat 12:00-01:00, Sun 12:00-22:30.   Admission: ICA Members Free. Annual Membership Adult £30.00, Concession £20.00.
Day Membership Weekdays £1.50, Weekends £2.50.   Location: Five minute walk from Trafalgar Square. Nearest tubes - Charing Cross and Piccadilly Circus.   Map Ref: 24

Gold Birth Amulet,
English, mid 19th century

Jewish Museum - Camden Town, London's Museum of Jewish Life

Raymond Burton House, 129/131 Albert Street,Camden Town, London NW1 7NB   Tel: 020 7284 1977   Fax: 020 7267 9008   Email: admin@jmus.org.uk
Web: www.jewishmuseum.org.uk

Visit the Jewish Museum with its world's finest collection of Jewish ceremonial art - awarded designated status in recognition of its outstanding national importance. Housed in the lively area of Camden Town, the Museum features a History Gallery tracing Jewish immigration and settlement in Britain and a Ceremonial Art Gallery illustrating Jewish religious life with object of rarity and beauty. Special exhibition, family activities and events are held throughout the year.

Opening Times: Mon to Thu 10:00-16:00, Sun 10:00-17:00. Closed Fri, Sat, Jewish Festivals and Public Holidays.   Admission: Adult £3.50, Child £1.50, OAP £2.50, Family £8.00.   Location: Three minute walk from Camden Town Underground Station.
Exhibitions & Events 2003 : 20 Nov to 6 Apr: By the Rivers of Babylon - A major new exhibition exploring the roots and heritage of the Iraqi Jews, May to Aug: A Time to be Born - Jewish Traditions of Childbirth.   Map Ref: 25

Kensington Palace, State Apartments & Royal Ceremonial Dress Collection

London W8 4PX   Tel: 0870 751 5170/751 5176   Web: www.kensington-palace.org.uk

A Court Occasion at Kensington Palace

Featuring dresses from the Royal Ceremonial Dress Collection, HM Queen Elizabeth I and Diana, Princess of Wales, this elegant palace truly is the home of royal fashion. Birthplace of Queen Victoria and designed by Sir Christopher Wren, the magnificent State Apartments provide a tranquil setting for the impressive display of paintings from the Royal Collection.

Opening Times: Mar to Oct daily 10:00-17:00. Nov to Feb 10:00-16:00. Closed 24-26 Dec and 1 Jan.
Admission: Adult £10.00, Child £6.50, OAP/Student £7.50, Family £30.00. Subject to change April 2003.
Location: Five minutes from High Street Kensington Underground.   Map Ref: 26

Leighton House Museum

12 Holland Park Road, London W14 8LZ   Tel: 020 7602 3316 ext 302   Fax: 020 7371 2467
Email: leightonhousemuseum@rbkc.gov.uk   Web: www.rbkc.gov.uk/leightonhousemuseum

Leighton House was the home of Frederic, Lord Leighton (1830-1896), the great classical painter and President of The Royal Academy. The house was built between 1864-79 to designs by George Aitchison and is the expression of Leighton's vision of a private palace devoted to art.

Opening Times: 11:00-17:30 daily. Closed Tue.   Admission: Free - donations welcome.
Location: Ten minutes from High Street Kensington Underground.   Map Ref: 26

The Library & Museum of Freemasonry

Freemasons Hall, 60 Great Queen Street, London WC2B 5AZ   Tel: 020 7395 9250   Fax: 020 7404 7418

18th Century Masonic Aprons

One of the finest collections of Masonic material in the world: pottery and porcelain, glassware, silver, furniture and clocks, Masonic jewels and regalia, portraits, prints, photographs and social history items.

Opening Times: Mon to Fri 10:00-17:00.
Admission: Free. Location: Close to Covent Garden/Holborn Tube Station.   Map Ref: 27

Central London

London's Transport Museum

Covent Garden, London WC2E 7BB
Tel: 020 7379 6344   Fax: 020 7565 7253

London's Transport Museum Covent Garden Piazza

'Knifeboard' horse bus circa 1875

Located in the heart of London's Covent Garden, the Museum is housed in the original Victorian Flower Market. The Museum is bright and airy with upper levels and a glass walkway, offering visitors a unique perspective of the historic buses, trams and trains. Complementing the display of vehicles are galleries housing originals of the famous Underground map and vibrant posters from the Museum's extensive collection. Designed to appeal to Londoners and tourists alike, the Museum invites visitors to take a journey through time, telling the story of interaction between transport, the capital and its people from 1800 to the present day. Hands-on exhibits, special Kidzones, working models and the latest technology, including videos and touch-screen displays in several languages, contribute to the story. For visitors wanting to delve further into transport history, one innovative feature of the Museum is its new Learning Centre. This drop-in information space contains a wealth of resources including books, journals, on-line databases and the Museum's website. Facilities include a shop, café, baby changing and disabled toilets. A lift and ramps provide wheelchair and pushchair access throughout the Museum.

West Ham Electric Tram 1910, LCC Tramways Class E1 1907/8, Metropolitan 1931

Opening Times: Sat to Thu 10:00-18:00, Fri 11:00-18:00.
Closed 24-26 Dec.   Admission: Adult £5.95, Child Free, Concession £4.50. Group rates available.   Location: Nearest Underground: Covent Garden, Holborn, Leicester Square.
Exhibitions & Events 2003 : Underground Summer: Exhibition for Families.   Map Ref: 27

Lord's Tour & MCC Museum

Lord's Ground, London NW8 8QN   Tel: 020 7432 1033   Fax: 020 7266 3825
Email: tours@mcc.org.uk   Web: www.lords.org

A fully guided tour of 'The Home of Cricket' including the Pavilion, MCC Museum and many other places of interest. The collection includes fine art, portraits, memorabilia and other items such as the world renowned Ashes urn.

Opening Times: Guided Tours Apr to Sep 10:00, 12:00 & 14:00, Oct to Mar 12:00 & 14:00. No tours on major Match Days/restrictions other Match Days. Check for Xmas opening
Admission: Adult £6.50, Child £4.50, Concession £5.00, Family £19.00. Group rates available.
Location: Located in St John's Wood in central London, 15 minute walk from St John's Wood tube station.   Map Ref: 28

Museum of Garden History

Lambeth Palace Road, London SE1 7LB   Tel: 020 7401 8865   Fax: 020 7401 8869
Email: info@museumgardenhistory.org   Web: www.museumgardenhistory.org

Fine collection of historic garden tools and information about the history of gardening in Britain. Replica 17th century knot garden and art exhibitions. Housed in an historic church building.

Opening Times: Feb to mid Dec daily 10:30-17:00.   Admission: Voluntary admission charge £2.50, Concession £2.00.   Location: Next to Lambeth Palace, at the end of Lambeth Bridge. A ten minute walk Vauxhall, Lambeth North. 15 minutes Waterloo.   Map Ref: 17

Museums • Galleries • Historic Houses

Please let us know of any collections that are not listed in this guide that you feel should be listed. E-mail us on *editor@tomorrows.co.uk* or return the Report Form on page 448

Museum of London

150 London Wall, London EC2Y 5HN Tel: 020 7600 3699 Fax: 020 7600 1058
Email: info@museumoflondon.org.uk Web: www.museumoflondon.org.uk

The Museum of London is the world's largest urban history museum. With a collection of more than a million objects, the museum aims to inspire a passion for London in all visitors. The collections cover every aspect of social life from pre-historic times to the present through material ranging from archaeological finds to contemporary photographs and the magnificent Lord Mayor's coach.

Lord Mayor's Coach

Opening Times: Mon to Sat 10:00-17:50, Sun 12:00-17:50. Closed 24-26 Dec, 1 Jan. Admission: Free.
Location: Near St Paul's tube station. Map Ref: 29

Museum of The Royal Hospital Chelsea

Royal Hospital Road, Chelsea, London SW3 4SR Tel: 020 7881 5203 Fax: 020 7881 5463
Email: eventsao@chelsea-pensioners.org.uk Web: www.chelsea-pensioners.org.uk

Illustrated panels covering the history of the Royal Hospital, a large diorama of the Hospital estate c. 1742, documents, uniforms, cap badges and a replica of a modern Pensioners cubicle. A recent addition is the Sovereign's Mace presented to the Royal Hospital in 2002 by HM The Queen together with the Parade Chair which was the Royal Hospital's gift to Her Majesty.

Opening Times: Mon to Sat 10:00-12:00 & 14:00-16:00, Sun 14:00-16:00 (only Apr to Sep). Closed BH.
Admission: Free. Location: Five minutes from Sloane Square Underground. Map Ref: 9

View of The Royal Hospital from the north

Museums of The Royal College of Surgeons of England

35/43 Lincoln's Inn Fields, London WC2A 3PE Tel: 020 7869 6560 Fax: 020 7869 6564
Email: museums@rcseng.ac.uk Web: www.rcseng.ac.uk/museums/default.asp

From John Hunter's specimen collection and Joseph Lister's pioneering antiseptic spray, to Charles Babbage's brain and George Stubbs's painting of The Rhinoceros, the Museums of the Royal College of Surgeons of England hold a fascinating and richly diverse range of material collected over the last three centuries.

Opening Times: Mon to Fri 10:00-17:00. Closed Sat, Sun & BH. Admission: Free. Charges apply for guided tours. Donations welcome. Location: Central London, ten minutes walk from Holborn Tube Station. Map Ref: 27

National Army Museum

Royal Hospital Road, Chelsea, London SW3 4HT Tel: 020 7730 0717 Fax: 020 7823 6573
Email: info@national-army-museum.ac.uk Web: www.national-army-museum.ac.uk

Discover the colourful story of the British Army and how the men and women who have served in it have lived and fought, from the middle ages, through two world wars, to the present day. Find out the facts behind some of the most remarkable episodes in Britain's history and the experiences of the people involved. Interactive displays enable visitors to try on helmets and kit from different eras, feel the weight of a

Rifleman of the 95th Regiment, c1809

Tudor cannonball, survey the opposing forces on a huge model of the Battle of Waterloo, explore a reproduction First World War trench and even test modern 'military' skills in exciting computer challenges. There's so much to see, from portraits by Reynolds and Gainsborough, to a lamp used by Florence Nightingale, the frostbitten fingers of Everest Conqueror Major Michael 'Bronco' Lane,

'Tommy' goes to War c1914

and even the skeleton of Napoleon's horse. Life-like models range from an Agincourt archer to an SAS trooper, and together with videos, photos, amazing anecdotes and a host of unusual personal relics, the ordinary soldier's story is brought vividly to life. Affording your trip won't be a battle - admission is free! New this year - newly refurbished Art Gallery features paintings not previously displayed at the Museum.

Opening Times: Daily 10:00-17:30. Closed 24-26 Dec, 1 Jan, Good Friday, early May BH. Admission: Free. Location: Ten minutes from Sloane Square Tube (Circle/District lines); 20 minutes from Victoria Station. Exhibitions & Events 2003 : 23 Mar: Zulu War Day, 2 to 5 Apr: Holiday Activities for Families, 18 Apr: Researching a WW1 Military Ancestor Genealogy Half-Day, 13 Jun: Researching a Victorian Military Ancestor Genealogy Half-Day, 20 to 21 Jul: Battlefield Archaeology International Conference. Regular special events weekends on the first weekend of every month. Map Ref: 9

National Gallery

Trafalgar Square, London WC2N 5DN   Tel: 020 7747 2885   Fax: 020 7747 2423
Email: information@ng-london.org.uk   Web: www.nationalgallery.org.uk

The National Gallery, London

The National Gallery possesses one of the greatest collections of European paintings in the world, housed in a building that is an internationally recognised landmark. Its permanent collection spans the period from about 1250 to 1900 and consists of over 2,300 works by many of the world's most famous artists. Admission to the permanent collection is free. The National Gallery also organises and hosts major temporary loan exhibitions, often in close collaboration with other national and international museums and galleries.

Titian: Bacchus and Ariadne

Admission may be charged for some of these exhibitions. The gallery also offers a wide variety of free talks, guided tours and lectures. There are also courses, practical workshops and family days on the second Saturday and Sunday of each month. The National Gallery also has shops selling products inspired by the collection, Crivelli's Garden restaurant in the Sainsbury Wing and a café for light snacks and refreshments.

Opening Times: Daily 10:00-18:00, Wed until 21:00. Closed 24-26 Dec & 1 Jan. Admission: Free. Location: North side of Trafalgar Square. Exhibitions & Events 2003 : 31 Jan to 27 Apr: Holbein: Portraits of Sir Henry and Lady Guildford, 19 Feb to 18 May: Titian, 19 Mar to 22 Jun: Ron Mueck: Making Sculpture at the National Gallery, 14 May to 3 Aug: Pissarro in London, 25 Jun to 14 Sep: A Private Passion: 19th century paintings and drawings from the Grenville L Winthrop Collection, Harvard University, 10 Jul to 28 Sep: Paradise, 22 Oct to 4 Jan: Bill Viola, 19 Nov to 15 Feb: Thomas Jones in Italy. Map Ref: 30

National Portrait Gallery

NATIONAL PORTRAIT GALLERY

St Martin's Place, London WC2H 0HE
Tel: 020 7306 0055   Fax: 020 7306 0056
Web: www.npg.org.uk

Early 20th Century Galleries -
© Andrew Putler

The National Portrait Gallery is home to the largest collection of portraiture in the world featuring famous British men and women who have created history from the middle ages until the present day. Over one thousand portraits are on display across three floors with sitters from Shakespeare to the Rolling Stones. The Ondaatje Wing, including new Tudor Galleries and Twentieth Century Galleries, also has a roof-top restaurant with spectacular views across London and a state-of-the-art lecture theatre. The Portrait Cafe serves a selection of refreshments and the gift/book shop offers a wide range of goods based on the Gallery's collection.

National Portrait Gallery

Central London

Opening Times: Mon to Wed, Sat & Sun 10:00-18:00. Thu & Fri 10:00-21:00. Admission: Free, although a fee is charged for some exhibitions - Adult £6.00, Concession £4.00.
Location: Nearest tube station - Leicester Square, Charing Cross. Mainline service - Charing Cross. Buses to Trafalgar Square. Exhibitions & Events 2003 : To
12 Jan: Americans, To 16 Feb: Mad, Bad and Dangerous (The Cult of Byron), 6 Feb to 27 May: Julia Margaret Cameron, 12 Jun to 21 Sep: BP Portrait Award, 25 Jun to 12 Oct: Tessa Traegaer - Woman Gardeners, Oct to Feb 04: Below Stairs, Nov to Feb 04: Contemporary Photography Prize.
Map Ref: 30

The World's most lifelike robotic T-rex

Natural History Museum

Cromwell Road, London SW7 5BD Tel: 020 7942 5000
Fax: 020 7942 5075

Arguably the finest museum of nature in the world. Highlights include 'Dinosaurs' featuring a huge, roaring, breathing T-rex, 'The Power Within' offering an 'earthquake experience' and the beautiful 'Earths Treasury' displaying a unique collection of gems and minerals. September marks the opening of phase one of the Darwin Centre, a major new life sciences complex providing unprecedented access to the Museum's amazing specimen collections.

Opening Times: Mon to Sat 10:00-17:50, Sun 11:00-17:50.
Admission: Free. Location: Five minutes walk from South Kensington Tube Station.
Map Ref: 3

Old Operating Theatre, Museum & Herb Garret

9A St Thomas Street, Southwark, London SE1 9RY Tel: 020 7955 4791 Fax: 020 7378 8383
Email: curator@thegarret.org.uk Web: www.thegarret.org.uk

The museum houses a Victorian operating theatre. It has displays on surgery and herbal medicine. A secret, atmospheric space situated in the roof of a 300 year old church. Spiral staircase access.

Opening Times: Daily 10:30-17:00. Closed 15 Dec to 5 Jan. Admission: Adult £4.00, Child £2.50, Concession £3.00, Family £10.00. Group Visit Service (pre-booked) also available.
Location: Five minute walk from London Bridge station.
Map Ref: 20

Percival David Foundation of Chinese Art

53 Gordon Square, London WC1H 0PD Tel: 020 7387 3909 Fax: 020 7383 5163
Email: ej4@soas.ac.uk Web: www.pdfmuseum.org.uk

The Percival David Foundation houses the finest collection of Chinese ceramics outside China. There are approximately 1700 items in the collection dating mainly to the period 10th-18th century. Guided Tours by prior arrangement only.

Opening Times: Mon to Fri 10:30-17:00. Closed Sat, Sun & BH. Admission: Free, donations welcome. Location: Ten minute walk Russell Square, Euston Square, Euston and Goodge St Underground Stations.
Map Ref: 6

Pollocks Toy Museum

1 Scala Street, London W1T 2HL Tel: 020 7636 3452 Email: info@pollocksmuseum.co.uk
Web: www.pollocksmuseum.co.uk

A delightful museum occupying adjoining Georgian and Victorian houses. Exhibits include optical toys, teddies, dolls houses, toy theatres, tin toys and dolls. Toy theatre performances are given during school holidays.

Opening Times: Mon to Sat, 10:00-17:00. Closed Sun and BH. Admission: Adult £3.00, Child/Student £1.50. Location: Two minutes from Goodge Street Underground Station.
Map Ref: 6

Guided or Private Tours	Disabled Access	Gift Shop or Sales Point	Café or Refreshments	Restaurant	Car Parking

The Queen's Gallery

Buckingham Palace, London SW1A 1AA   Tel: 020 7321 2233   Fax: 020 7930 9625
Email: information@royalcollection.org.uk   Web: www.royal.gov.uk

The current exhibition of Royal Treasures - a Golden Jubilee Celebration is a celebration of the individual tastes of monarchs and other members of the royal family with a selection of 450 outstanding works from one of the world's greatest collections of art. Future exhibitions include: Leonardo da Vinci: The Divine and the Grotesque and Fabergé.

Opening Times: Daily 10:00-17:30 (last admission 16:30).
Admission: Adult £6.50, Child £3.00, OAP £5.00, Under 5s Free, Family (2 adults and 2 children) £16.00.
Location: Buckingham Palace Road, next to Buckingham Palace. Five minute walk from Victoria Station.Map Ref: 31

The Diamond Diadem, 1820.
The Royal Collection © 2002

Royal Academy of Arts

Burlington House, Piccadilly, London W1J 0BD   Tel: 020 7300 8000   Fax: 020 7300 8001   Email: webmaster@royalacademy.org.uk   Web: www.royalacademy.org.uk

The Royal Academy of Arts is world famous for its programme of outstanding exhibitions all year round. Highlights of 2003 include Aztecs, a ground breaking exhibition of work from this fascinating civilsation, the ever popular Summer Exhibition and Kirchner, a major show of the German Expressionist's work.

Opening Times: Daily 10:00-18:00, Fri until 22:00.
Admission: Prices vary for each exhibition, concessions available.   Location: In the centre of the West End of London. Two minutes walk from Green Park and Piccadilly Circus Underground Stations.   Map Ref: 16

Spectacular new courtyard, opened in 2002 by the Queen, houses modern sculpture

Royal Fusiliers Museum

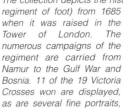

HM Tower of London, London EC3N 4AB
Tel: 020 7488 5610/5612   Fax: 020 7481 1093
Email: royalfusiliers@freeserve.co.uk

The collection depicts the history of the Royal Fusiliers (the seventh regiment of foot) from 1685 when it was raised in the Tower of London. The numerous campaigns of the regiment are carried from Namur to the Gulf War and Bosnia. 11 of the 19 Victoria Crosses won are displayed, as are several fine portraits, and many items of memorabilia.

Early 20th Century Galleries -
© Andrew Putler

20th Battalion, Flanders 1916

Opening Times: Mar to Oct daily 09:30-18:00, Oct to Mar daily 09:30-17:00. Admission: Adults 50p, Child Free.
Location: Within HM Tower of London.   Map Ref: 32

Royal Institution's Michael Faraday Museum

The Royal Institution, 21 Albemarle Street, London W1S 4BS   Tel: 020 7409 2992   Fax: 020 7629 3569   Email: ri@ri.ac.uk   Web: www.ri.ac.uk

The museum contains a reconstruction of Faraday's laboratory as it was in the 1850s with original apparatus and furniture. Also on display is the first electric transformer and electric generator both made by Faraday in 1831.

Opening Times: Mon-Fri 10:00-17:00, closed BH. Admission: Adult £1.00, Concession 50p.
Location: Close to Green Park Underground Station.   Map Ref: 16

Royal London Hospital Archives & Museum

Royal London Hospital, Whitechapel, London E1 1BB   Tel: 020 7377 7608
Email: jonathan.evans@bartsandthelondon.nhs.uk   Web: www.brlcf.org.uk

The London (founded 1740) became Britain's largest voluntary hospital. Its story is told in the crypt of the former hospital church. Exhibits feature surgery, nursing, children and health, x-rays, dentistry, nursing, uniforms and videos. The lives and works of individuals like Dr Barnardo, Edith Cavell, Joseph Merrick and Lord Knutsford also feature.

Opening Times: Mon to Fri 10:00-16:30. Closed Sat, Sun & BH. Admission: Free. Location: Three minute walk from Whitechapel Underground Station.   Map Ref: 33

The London Hospital Children's Party (detail), 1897 by Lucien Davis

The Saatchi Gallery

The Riverside Gallery, County Hall, London SE1 7PB   Tel: 020 7823 2332   Fax: 020 7823 2334
Email: philippa@saatchi-gallery.co.uk

The Saatchi Gallery opened in March 1985. Max Gordon, a leading British architect, was commissioned by Charles Saatchi to convert 30,000 square feet of warehousing into a contemporary art museum. Its aim is to introduce new art, or art largely unseen in the UK to a wider audience. The Gallery draws from a collection of over 2000 paintings, sculptures and installations.

The Physical Impossibility of Death in the Mind of Someone Living, by D Hirst

Opening Times: Daily 10:00-22:00. Gallery re-opens Spring 2003 Admission: Adult £5.00, Concession £3.00. (2002)   Map Ref: 13

St Bartholomew's Hospital Museum

St Bartholomew's Hospital, West Smithfield, London EC1A 7BE   Tel: 020 7601 8152
Email: marion.rea@bartsandthelondon.nhs.uk   Web: www.brlcf.org.uk

The Museum of St Bartholomew's Hospital tells the story of this renowned institution. On display are original archives dating back to the 12th century and works of art, surgical instruments and medical equipment.

Opening Times: Tue to Fri 10:00-16:00. Closed BH. Admission: Free. Location: St Bartholomew's Hospital is near Smithfield Market, a few minutes walk from St Paul's Cathedral and the Museum of London.   Map Ref: 34

St John's Gate

Museum of the Order of St John, St Johns Lane, Clerkenwell, London EC1M 4DA   Tel: 020 7253 6644   Fax: 020 7336 0587

St John's Gate, Museum of the Order of St John, St John Ambulance. The Priory of Clerkenwell was built by the Knights Hospitaller in the 1140s and it is their remarkable story that lies behind the modern work of today's St John Ambulance. The Knights' surprising tale is revealed through collections including furniture, paintings, silver, armour, stained glass and other items, housed in this early 16th century gatehouse. It contains one of the country's few remaining

wooden Tudor spiral staircases. Also given to Mary Tudor as her palace after the Dissolution. Royalty, authors and artists, Shakespeare, Hogarth, Edward Cave, Dr Johnson, Dickens and David Garrick were just a few of its notable visitors. Guided tours at 11:00 and 14:30 on Tuesday, Fridays and Saturdays, take visitors through upstairs rooms inside the Gate and over to the Priory Church and 12th century Crypt. The four ground floor exhibition rooms are open daily 10:00-17:00, 10:00-16:00 on Saturday (closed Sunday and bank holiday weekends). Two reference libraries are housed in

Central London

the Gate, open by appointment only, one with specialist collections relating to the Knights of St John, the Knights Templar, the Crusades and related subjects; the other, the St John Ambulance reference collection.

Opening Times: Mon to Fri 10:00-17:00, Sat 10:00-16:00. Closed Sun & BH weekend. Tours: Tue, Fri & Sat 11:00 & 14:30. Admission: Free, donations requested for tours: Adult £5.00, Concession £3.50. Location: Four minute walk from Farringdon Station. Exhibitions & Events 2003 : For Exhibitions and Events please telephone for details.   Map Ref: 34

Science Museum

Exhibition Road, London SW7 2DD   Tel: 0870 870 4868   Web: www.sciencemuseum.org.uk

See, touch and experience the major scientific advances of the last 300 years at the largest museum of its kind in the world with a state of the art IMAX cinema and virtual reality simulator is really something to entertain and inspire all.

Opening Times: Daily 10:00-18:00. Closed Xmas. Admission: Free. Location: Five minute walk from South Kensington Tube Station.   Map Ref: 3

The Science Museum's Welcome Wing

Serpentine Gallery

Serpentine Gallery

Kensington Gardens, London W2 3XA   Tel: 020 7402 6075
Fax: 020 7402 4103   Email: press@serpentinegallery.org
Web: www.serpentinegallery.org

The Serpentine Gallery, situated in the heart of Kensington Gardens in a 1934 tea pavilion, was founded in 1970 by the Arts Council of Great Britain. Attracting over 400,000 visitors a year it is one of London's most loved galleries for modern and contemporary arts.

Opening Times: Daily 10:00-18:00. Admission: Free. Location: Underground: Knightsbridge, South Kensington or Lancaster Gate. Buses: 9, 10, 12, 24, 52.

Serpentine Gallery, ó Peter Durant/ arcblue.com   Map Ref: 35

Shakespeare's Globe Exhibition

21 New Globe Walk, Bankside, London SE1 9DT   Tel: 020 7902 1500   Fax: 020 7902 1515   Web: www.shakespeares-globe.org

Shakespeare's Globe Exhibition is the most exciting place in which to explore Shakespeare's theatre and the London in which he lived and worked. A visit to the Exhibition includes a tour into today's working theatre. Let one of our storytellers introduce you to the Globe. During the matinees, in the theatre season, exhibition storytellers will take visitors on a virtual tour of the Globe.

Opening Times: Oct to Apr 10:00-17:00, May to Sep 09:00-16:00. Closed Xmas. Admission: Adult £8.00, Child £5.00, OAP £6.00, Group £7.50. Location: On Bankside next to Tate Modern and opposite St Paul's Cathedral.   Map Ref: 5

Shakespeare's Globe, © Richard Kalina

Central London

Sherlock Holmes Museum

221b Baker Street, London NW1 6XE
Tel: 020 7935 8866
Web: www.sherlock-holmes.co.uk

The Sherlock Homes Museum

The Museum has already had over 2 million visitors since opening 12 years ago. It is unique. It is in a Georgian building dating from 1815. It is totally unspoiled (by which is meant unmodernised!) and is identical to the lodging house described in the stories. The rooms in Mr Holmes's apartment on the first floor are maintained just as he would have left them nearly 100 years ago! The Museum has entertainment, cultural and educational value. Sherlock Holmes is very much a part of England's literary heritage and visitors flock to Baker Street to see how we are perpetuating this great legend. There is a large and attractive souvenir shop on the ground floor of the Museum, containing the world's largest and most varied range of Sherlockian memorabilia, which is of tremendous interest to the collector.

The Sitting Room at The Sherlock Holmes Museum

Opening Times: Daily 09:30-18:00. Closed Xmas Day. Admission: Adult £6.00, Child £4.00. Groups of Under 16s one free for every 8, 10% Group Discount for over 16s. Location: One minute walk from Baker Street Underground Station. Map Ref: 36

Sir John Soane's Museum

13 Lincolns Inn Fields, London WC2A 3BP Tel: 020 7405 2107
Fax: 020 7831 3957 Email: wpalin@soane.org.uk
Web: www.soane.org

Collection of antique fragments, sculpture, painting, models, books and drawings amassed by the architect Sir John Soane (1753-1837) in three linked houses built by him between 1793 and 1824. The interiors and collection were preserved by an Act of Parliament on his death in 1837.

The Dome Area.
Photo: Martin Charles

Opening Times: Tue to Sat 10:00-17:00, open late on first Tue of each month 18:00-21:00. Admission: Free. Location: Central London, two minutes from Holborn Tube Station. Exhibitions & Events 2003 : 14 Feb to 19 Apr: John Soane and the Wooden Bridges of Switzerland, 25 Apr to 14 Jun: John Flaxman: Drawings and Sketches, 27 Jun to 27 Sep: Bob the Roman: The Architechure of Robert Adam. Map Ref: 27

Tate Britain

Millbank, London SW1P 4RG Tel: 020 7887 8008 Fax: 020 7887 8729 Web: www.tate.org.uk

The national gallery of British art from 1500 to the present day, from the Tudors to the Turner Prize. Tate holds the greatest collection of British art in the world, including works by Blake, Constable, Epstein, Gainsborough, Hockney, Moore, Stubbs and Turner. The gallery is the world centre for the understanding and enjoyment of British art and it runs an excellent programme of special exhibitions and events throughout the year.

Giovanna Baccelli, Oil on canvas
by Thomas Gainsborough 1782

Opening Times: Daily 10:00-17:50. Admission: Free, but charges apply for special exhibitions. Location: On the North bank of the Thames by Vauxhall Bridge, five minutes walk from Pimlico Tube Station. Map Ref: 37

Guided or Private Tours	Disabled Access	Gift Shop or Sales Point	Café or Refreshments	Restaurant	Car Parking

Central London

Tate Modern

Bankside, London SE1 9TG   Tel: 020 7887 8000   Fax: 020 7887 8729   Web: www.tate.org.uk

Tate Modern displays the Tate collection of international modern art from 1900 to present day, including major works by artists such as Bacon, Dali, Duchamp, Giacometti, Matisse, Picasso, Rothko and Warhol.

Opening Times: Sun to Thu 10:00-18:00, Fri & Sat 10:00-22:00.   Admission: Free.   Location: Situated opposite St Paul's Cathedral on banks of River Thames, close to both Southwark and Blackfriars Tube.   Map Ref: 5

Art of Commitment, Tate Modern, Photocredit Marcus Leith

Theatre Museum: National Museum of the Performing Arts

Russell Street, Covent Garden, London WC2E 7PR   Tel: 020 7943 4700
Fax: 020 7943 4777   Web: www.theatremuseum.org

Make-up demonstrations daily
at Theatre Museum

The Theatre Museum, situated in the heart of London's Theatreland, celebrates performance in Britain through imaginative exhibitions, workshops and events based on the world's most exciting performing arts collections. The galleries, charting the British stage from today back to Shakespeare's time, are brought to life by tour guides who explore the work of star performers, practitioners and their audiences using videos, photographs, costumes, designs and other memorabilia. Hands-on demonstrations reveal the secrets and skills of stage make-up and costume. Booking essential 020 7943 4806.

Opening Times: Daily 10:00-18:00. Closed Mon & BH.   Admission: Free.   Location: One minute walk from Covent Garden Underground.   Map Ref: 7

Tower Bridge Experience

Tower Bridge Experience

Tower Bridge, London SE1 2UP
Tel: 020 7403 3761   Fax: 020 7357 7935
Email: enquiries@towerbridge.org.uk
Web: www.towerbridge.org.uk

See inside London's most famous landmark, with a new exhibition which opened in 2002. Discover the history of Tower Bridge and find out how it works. Experience the breathtaking views and be amazed by the unique architecture.

Opening Times: Daily 09:30-18:00.   Admission: Adult £4.50, Child £3.00, OAP £3.00.   Location: Rail stations: London Bridge and Fenchurch Street. Underground Stations: Tower Hill and London Bridge.   Map Ref: 32

H M Tower of London

Tower Hill, London EC3N 4AB   Tel: 0870 756 6060/751 5177   Web: www.tower-of-london.org.uk

The Imperial State Crown

Founded by William the Conqueror, this fortress and royal palace now displays armour including items worn by Henry VIII and Charles I, and houses an impressive collection of 17th century weapons. Marvel at the breathtaking Crown Jewels and enjoy the tales of over 900 years of history and intrigue as your attention is captured on a Yeoman Warder 'Beefeater' tour.

Opening Times: Mar to Oct Mon to Sat 09:00-17:00, Sun 10:00-17:00. Nov to Feb Tue to Sat 09:00-16:00, Sun to Mon 10:00-16:00. Closed 24-26 Dec & 1 Jan.
Admission: Adult £11.50, Child £7.50, OAP/Student £8.75, Family £34.00. Prices subject to change April 2003.   Map Ref: 32

Victoria and Albert Museum

Cromwell Road, South Kensington, London SW7 2RL   Tel: 020 7942 2000
Web: www.vam.ac.uk

The V&A Dome

The V&A is the world's greatest museum of art and design. More than seven miles of galleries are filled with outstanding collections of objects dating from 3000BC to the present day, including glass, textiles, ceramics, photography, jewellery and fashion. Highlights include the breathtaking Cast Courts, paintings by Constable and the largest collection of Italian Renaissance sculpture outside Italy. In addition, there is an exciting programme of exhibitions, displays, activities and contemporary events. The British Galleries tell the story of British design from 1500-1900. From Chippendale to Morris and Adam to Mackintosh, all of the top British designers of the times feature in the beautiful sequence of 15 galleries. The wealth of exhibits is enhanced by computer interactives, objects to handle, video screens and audio programmes, offering an entirely new visitor experience in a stunning and innovative setting. A must see for your visit to London.

The breathtaking V&A Cast Courts

Opening Times: Daily 10:00-17:45, on Wed & last Fri of month 10:00-22:00.   Admission: Free. A separate charge may apply to some special exhibitions and events.   Location: Close to South Kensington Underground. A short walk from Harrods.   Exhibitions & Events 2003 : Until 2 Feb: Rewind: 40 years of Design and Advertising from the DRAD Awards, 27 Mar to 20 Jul: Art Deco: 1910-1939, 17 Apr to 17 Aug: Guy Bourdin, 9 Oct to 18 Jan: Gothic: Art for England 1400 to 1547.   Map Ref: 3

Wallace Collection

Hertford House, Manchester Square, London W1U 3BN   Tel: 020 7563 9500

Room 3, Dining Room. © The Wallace Collection

The Wallace Collection is both a national museum and the finest private art collection ever assembled by one family. The collection was acquired principally in the 19th century by the third and fourth Marquesses of Hertford and Sir Richard Wallace, the illegitimate son of the 4th Marquess. It was bequeathed to the nation by Sir Richard's widow in 1897 and is displayed on three floors of Hertford House, the family's main London residence. The 26 rooms present unsurpassed collections of French 18th century painting, furniture and porcelain together with Old Master paintings by, among others, Titian, Canaletto,

Gallery 5, The Front State Room.
© The Wallace Collection

Rembrandt, Hals, Rubens, Velázquex and Gainsborough. Our magnificent collection of princely arms and armour is shown in four galleries and there are further important displays of gold boxes, miniatures, French and Italian sculpture and fine medieval and Renaissance works of art, including maiolica, glass, Limoges enamels, silver and jewellery. By the terms of Lady Wallace's bequest nothing must be added or loaned to the Collection. This provision has preserved the remarkable character of one of the greatest collections ever made by an English family.

Opening Times: Mon to Sat 10:00-17:00, Sun 12:00-17:00.   Admission: Free.   Location: On a garden square just off Oxford Street, behind Selfridges department store.   Map Ref: 38

Guided or Private Tours	Disabled Access	Gift Shop or Sales Point	Café or Refreshments	Restaurant	Car Parking

Wesleys Chapel, Museum of Methodism & John Wesleys House

49 City Road, London EC1Y 1AU   Tel: 020 7253 2262   Fax: 020 7608 3825

John Wesley's House, Library and personal belongings. Collections relating to the history of Methodism including paintings, ceramics and manuscript letters. An 18th century Georgian House furnished with Wesley's personal belongings.

Opening Times: Mon to Sat 10:00-16:00. Sun 12:00-14:00. Admission: Adult £4.00, Concession £2.00. Location: One minute walk from Old Street Underground Station. Exit No.4.   Map Ref: 34

Whitechapel Art Gallery

Whitechapel Art Gallery

80/82 Whitechapel High Street, London E1 7QX   Tel: 020 7522 7888   Fax: 020 7622 7887   Email: info@whitechapel.org   Web: www.whitechapel.org

Situated in London's East End, the Whitechapel has always aimed to bring the best visual arts to the widest possible public. The Gallery has no permanent collection, but mounts a diverse programme of international modern and contemporary art.

Opening Times: Tue to Sun 11:00-18:00 (Wed until 20:00). Admission: Free, (one paying exhibition per year). Location: Aldgate East Underground.   Exhibitions & Events 2003 : 10 Dec to 2 Mar 03: Mies van der Rohe: 1905-1938, 18 Mar to 18 May: Christina Iglesias, 27 May to 7 Jun: A Short History of Performance: Part II, 17 Jun to 24 Aug: Janet Cardiff (Lower Gallery) Philip Lorca di Corcia (Upper Galleries).   Map Ref: 33

Key to Classifications
see Classifications Index on page 413

Anthropology	Jewellery	Railway
Archaeological	Literature & Libraries	Religion
Art Galleries	Maritime	Roman
Arts, Crafts & Textiles	Military & Defence	Science - Earth
China, Glass & Ceramics	Mills - Water & Wind	& Planetary
Communications	Multicultural	Sculpture
Egyptian	Music & Theatre	Sporting History
Fashion	Natural History	Stately Homes
Geology	Oriental	Toy & Childhood
Health & Medicine	Palaces	Transport
Horticultural	Police, Prisons & Dungeons	Victoriana

Within a bus ride or a short underground journey from Central London, there are many exceptional museums, galleries and historic houses covering subjects as diverse as Rugby, Lawn Tennis, Botany, Artillery, Keats, Palaces, Clipper Ships and also housing important collections of paintings and furniture.

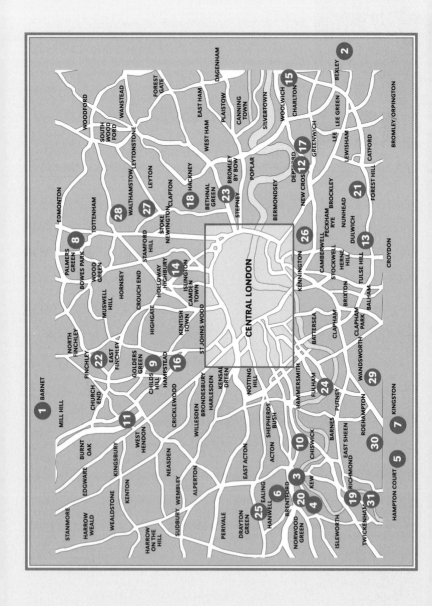

The Red Map References should be used to locate Museums etc on the pages that follow

Outer London

Museum of Domestic Design & Architecture (MoDA)

Middlesex University, Cat Hill, Barnet EN4 8HT   Tel: 020 8362 5244   Fax: 020 8411 6639   Email: moda@mdx.ac.uk   Web: www.moda.ac.uk

The Museum of Domestic Design & Architecture (MoDA) houses one of the most important and comprehensive collections of late 19th and 20th century decorative design for the home, including the world-renowned Silver Studio Collection. Located in north London, MoDA offers a wide-ranging exhibition and events programme throughout the year alongside its permanent exhibition, 'Exploring Interiors: Decoration of the Home 1900-1960'.

The Practical Householder, Cover Oct 1957

Opening Times: Tue to Sat 10:00-17:00, Sun 14:00-17:00. Closed Mon, Easter, BH & Xmas. Admission: Free. Location: Tube: Piccadilly line to Oakwood or Cockfosters. Car: from junction 24 of M25 follow A111 signposed Cockfosters to MoDA.   Map Ref: 1

BEXLEY

Hall Place

Hall Place, Bourne Road, Bexley DA5 1PQ   Tel: 01322 526574   Fax: 01322 522921   Email: museum@bexleyheritagetrust.freeserve.co.uk

Grade I listed Tudor/Stewart country house with panelled Great Hall and Ministrels' Gallery. Set in award winning gardens. Numerous historical and artistic exhibitions throughout the year. Rooms available for hire.

Opening Times: 1 Nov to end Feb Tue to Sat 10:00-17:00. Closed Sun & Mon. Mar to Oct Mon to Sat 10:00-17:00, Sun 11:00-17:00. Admission: Free. Location: Between Bexley and Bexley Heath, nearest railway station Bexley.   Map Ref: 2

BRENTFORD

Kew Bridge Steam Museum

Green Dragon Lane, Brentford TW8 0EN   Tel: 020 8568 4757   Fax: 020 8569 9978   Email: info@kbsm.org   Web: www.kbsm.org

Magnificent 19th century steam powered pumping station used to supply London's water. Also Water For Life Gallery exploring social use of water. Engines work every weekend.

Opening Times: Daily 11:00-17:00. Closed Good Friday and week prior to Xmas.
Admission: Adult £4.60, Child £2.50, OAP £3.70, Family £11.95. Location: Junction 2 of M4, A205 to Kew Bridge, museum on north side of river. Two minutes from Kew Bridge Station.
Map Ref: 3

Syon Park

Brentford TW8 8JF   Tel: 020 8560 0882   Fax: 020 8568 0936   Email: info@syonpark.co.uk   Web: www.syonpark.co.uk

Syon House is the London home of the Duke of Northumberland. The House is Tudor in origin and was transformed by Robert Adam into one of his earliest and finest interiors. Many of the furnishings are from the Adam period or were brought to Syon from Northumberland House after its demolition in 1874. The collection contains the spectacular Sevres vase and interesting portraits by Van Dyck and Lely.

Opening Times: 26 Mar to 2 Nov Wed, Thu, Sun & BH 11:00-17:00.
Admission: Adult £6.95, Child £5.95, Concession £6.50, Family £15.00.

Long Gallery   Map Ref: 4

Outer London

Kings Staircase,
Hampton Court Palace

Hampton Court Palace

East Molesey KT8 9AU   Tel: 0870 752 7777/751 5175
Web: www.hampton-court-palace.org.uk

Over 500 years of royal history is brought together to create Britain's greatest palace. Immaculately restored gardens, stunnning architecture and one of the finest collections of Renaissance paintings in Europe are complemented by costumed performances and the world famous maze. Enjoy one of our guided or audio tours and come face to face with the life of a royal court.

Opening Times: Daily mid Mar to mid Oct Mon 10:00-17:15, Tue to Sun 09:30-17:15. Mid Oct to mid Mar Mon 10:15-17:45, Tue to Sun 09:30-17:45. Closed 24-26 Dec.   Admission: Adult £11.00, Child £7.25 OAP/Student £8.25, Family £33.00. Subject to change April 2003.   Location: Two minute walk from Hampton Court Station.
Map Ref: 5

Osterley Park House

Jersey Road, Isleworth TW7 4RB   Tel: 020 8232 5050   Fax: 020 8232 5080
Email: tosgen@smtp.ntrust.org.uk   Web: www.nationaltrust.org.uk

Robert Adam Villa, spectacular interiors contain one of Britain's most complete examples of Adam's work. Ground floor houses the Jersey Galleries which host exhibitions of contemporary art while the house is open.

Opening Times: 2 to 24 Mar, Sat & Sun, 27 Mar to 3 Nov Wed to Sun & BH. Closed Good Friday. House & Jersey Galleries 13:00-16:30, Shop 13:00-17:30, Tearoom 11:30-17:00. Admission: Adult £4.40, Child £2.20, Family £11.00, Group £3.80.   Location: Junction of Thornbury and Jersey Road off the A4. Eight miles from Central London, five miles from Heathrow, 20 minute walk from Osterley Piccadilly line underground Station.   Map Ref: 6

Kingston Museum

Wheatfield Way, Kingston upon Thames KT1 2PS   Tel: 020 8546 5386   Fax: 020 8547 6747
Email: king.mus@rbk.kingston.gov.uk

The Museum has two permanent galleries telling the story of Kingston, ancient origins and Town of Kings. The Eadweard Muybridge Gallery describes the life and work of this internationally renowned pioneer photographer.

Opening Times: 10:00-17:00, closed Wed & Sun.   Map Ref: 7

Bruce Castle Museum
(Haringey Libraries, Archives & Museum Service)

Lordship Lane, London N17 8NU   Tel: 020 8808 8772   Fax: 020 8808 4118
Email: museum.services@haringey.gov.uk   Web: www.haringey.gov.uk

16th century manor house set in parkland. Once owned by Sir Rowland Hill, the postal reformer, it houses Haringey's local history and art exhibitions, collections and archives.

Opening Times: Wed to Sun 13:00-17:00.   Admission: Free.   Location: Underground to Seven Sisters or Wood Green, then 123 or 243 Bus. Overland rail to Bruce Grove then 10 minute walk.   Map Ref: 8

Camden Arts Centre

Arkwright Road, London NW3 6DG   Tel: 020 7435 2643/ 5224   Fax: 020 7794 3371
Email: info@camdenartscentre.org   Web: www.camdenartscentre.org

The centre is a venue for contemporary visual art and education. A changing programme of exhibitions, artists' residencies, offsite projects and artist-led activities offers you an opportunity to look, to make and to discuss.

Opening Times: Tue to Thu 11:00-19:00, Fri to Sun 11:00-17:30. Closed Mon and BH.
Admission: Free.   Location: On Finchley Road/Arkwright Road, ten minutes walk from Finchley Road Tube.   Map Ref: 9

Chiswick House

Burlington Lane, London W4 2RP   Tel: 020 8995 0508

Surrounded by beautiful gardens, close to the centre of London lies one of England's finest Palladian villas, designed by the third Earl of Burlington. Collections include 19 paintings from Lord Burlington's original collection.

Opening Times: Apr to Sep Wed to Sun & BH 10:00-17:30, Oct Wed to Sun 10:00-17:00, every Sat 10:00-14:00. Closed Nov to Mar.   Admission: Adult £3.50, Child £1.80, Concession £2.70. Location: Burlington Lane, Chiswick Railway station half a mile, Turnham Green Tube three quarters of a mile.   Map Ref: 10

Church Farmhouse Museum

Greyhound Hill, Hendon, London NW4 4JR   Tel: 020 8203 0130   Fax: 020 8359 2885
Web: www.barnet.gov.uk/cultural_services

17th century farmhouse with reconstructed Victorian period dining room, kitchen and laundry room. Four temporary exhibitions on local and social history and the decorative arts each year. Small public garden.

Opening Times: Mon to Thu 10:00-12:30 13:30-17:00, Sat 10:00-13:00 & 14:00-17:30, Sun 14:00-17:30. Closed Fri.   Admission: Free.   Location: Next to St Mary's Church, Hendon. One minute walk from bus stop.   Map Ref: 11

Cutty Sark Clipper Ship

King William Walk, Greenwich, London SE10 9HT
Tel: 020 8858 3445   Fax: 020 8853 3589
Email: info@cuttysark.org.uk   Web: www.cuttysark.org.uk

Cutty Sark the world's sole surviving tea clipper

Cutty Sark was built in 1869 to be the fastest clipper in the annual race to bring the first of the season's crop of tea home to Britain. She is the world's sole surviving tea clipper, and since being opened to the public in 1957, has welcomed over 15 million visitors across her gangplank. Visitors 'come aboard' via an entrance to the 'Tween Deck', so called because it is between the Main Deck and the Lower Hold. This is the main museum display area telling Cutty Sark's history and details of merchant trade, together with displays of original artefacts and models. The new children's interpretive panels give the same information but in a fun and colourful way. The souvenir shop is also on deck. The Main Deck houses the crew and officers' accommodation, restored to 1870s condition - a real insight to life on board a Victorian tea clipper. The Gallery, Carpenter's workshop and the masts can also be seen, complete with their 11 miles of rigging. The Lower Hold houses one of the world's largest collections of colourful merchant ships' figureheads, as well as our new children's 'hands-on' activities.

'Masters Saloon', Cutty Sark

Opening Times: Daily 10:00-17:00. Closed Xmas.   Admission: Adult £3.90, Child/Student £2.90, OAP £2.90, Family £9.70.   Location: Greenwich Town Centre, seven minutes from railway station, one minute from tube and ferry links.   Map Ref: 12

Dulwich Picture Gallery

Gallery Road, London SE21 7AD   Tel: 020 8693 5254   Fax: 020 8299
8700   Email: i.evans@dulwichpicturegallery.org.uk   Web: www.dulwichpicturegallery.org.uk

Dulwich Picture Gallery is the greatest find in London; a magnificent collection of masterpieces by Rembrandt, Poussin, Watteau, Rubens, Canaletto, Gainsborough and many more. The critically-acclaimed international loan exhibitions and its setting in the beautiful 18th century village of Dulwich, make the Gallery a must for all art lovers. The building has been described as the most perfect small art gallery in the world.

Opening Times: Tue to Fri 10:00-17:00, Sat, Sun & BH 11:00-17:00.
Admission: Adult £4.00, OAP £3.00, Concession Free.
Location: Dulwich is in south east London, 12 minutes by train from Victoria to West Dulwich.

The enfilade of galleries designed in 1811 by Sir John Soane   Map Ref: 13

Estorick Collection of Modern Italian Art

39A Canonbury Square, Islington, London N1 2AN   Tel: 020 7704 9522   Fax: 020 7704 9531
Email: curator@estorickcollection.com   Web: www.estorickcollection.com

The permanent collection has at its core powerful images by early 20th century Futurists housed in the intimate setting of a large Georgian villa. Also on display are works by figurative artists.

Opening Times: Wed to Sat 11:00-18:00, Sun 12:00-17:00. Closed Mon, Tue, Xmas & New Year.
Admission: Adult £3.50, Concession £2.50.   Location: A five minute walk from Highbury and
Islington Underground Stations.   Map Ref: 14

The Fan Museum

12 Crooms Hill, Greenwich, London SE10 8ER   Tel: 0208 3051441   Fax: 0208 2931889
Email: admin@fan-museum.org   Web: www.fan-museum.org

The only museum in the world entirely dedicated to the history of fans and to the art and craft of fan-making. Situated within Maritime Greenwich, a World Heritage site.

Opening Times: Tue to Sat 11:00-17:00, Sun 12:00-17:00.   Admission: Adult £3.50,
Concession £2.50, Under 7s Free. OAP Free on Tue after 14:00 (except for Groups).
Location: Greenwich Town Centre, five minute walk from Greenwich BR and Cutty Sark DLR
Station.   Map Ref: 12

Fenton House

Windmill Hill, Hampstead, London NW3 6RT   Tel / Fax: 0207 435 3471
Email: tfehse@smtp.ntrust.org.uk

Charming William and Mary Merchants' House with fine collections of Georgian furniture, porcelain and needlework and the Benton Fletcher Collection of early keyboard instruments. Walled gardens include a kitchen garden and apple orchard.

Opening Times: 2 to 17 Mar Sat & Sun 14:00-17:00. 23 Mar to 3 Nov Sat, Sun & BH 11:00-
17:00, Wed, Thu & Fri 14:00-17:00.   Admission: Adult £4.40, Child £2.20, Family £11.00.
Garden only: Adult £1.00, Child Free. National Trust Members Free.   Location: Hampstead
Tube 300m.   Map Ref: 9

Firepower - The Royal Artillery Museum

Royal Arsenal, Woolwich, London SE18 6ST   Tel: 020 8855 7755   Fax: 020 **FIREPOWER**
8855 7100   Email: info@firepower.org.uk   Web: www.firepower.org.uk

In the historically secret Royal Arsenal at Woolwich, artillery from slingshot to shell. Alongside the huge guns see gunners' uniforms, artwork and medals. The dramatic Field of Fire presentation

using big screens and surround sound tells the story of 20th century gunners in their own words, from Burma to Bosnia.

Opening Times: Nov to Mar Fri to Sun 11:00-17:00, Apr to Oct Wed to Sun 11:00-17:30 & BH. Booked groups Thu 11:00-17:00 Admission: Adult £6.50, Child £4.50, OAP £5.50, Concession £5.50, Family £18.00, Group discount available. Location: Royal Arsenal, Woolwich. Five minutes from Woolwich Arsenal Railway Station.

Visit the Monster Bits Gallery   Map Ref: 15

Freud Museum

20 Maresfield Gardens, Hampstead, London NW3 5SX   Tel: 020 7435 2002/5167   Fax: 020 7431 5452   Email: freud@gn.apc.org   Web: www.freud.org.uk

Home of Sigmund Freud and his family when they came to London as refugees from Nazi persecution, the family recreated their Vienna home in London. Displays include his extensive library and collection of 2000 antiquities.

Opening Times: Wed to Fri 12:00-17:00. Admission: Adult £5.00, Concession £2.00.

Map Ref: 16

Greenwich Borough Museum

232 Plumstead High Street, London SE18 1JT   Tel: 020 8855 3240   Fax: 020 8316 5754   Email: beverley.burford@greenwich.gov.uk

Permanent displays of local history including social history, archaeology and natural history. A temporary exhibition programme, an education service for schools, a children's Saturday Club and an adult lecture and workshop programme.

Opening Times: Mon 14:00-19:00, Tue, Thu, Fri & Sat 10:00-13:00 & 14:00-17:00. Closed Wed, Sun & BH. Admission: Free. Location: First floor Plumstead Library in High Street. Ten minutes walk or five minutes by bus from Plumstead Railway Station.   Map Ref: 17

Gunnersbury Park Museum

Gunnersbury Park, London W3 8LQ   Tel: 020 8992 1612   Fax: 020 8752 0686   Email: gp-museum@cip.org.uk

A beautiful 19th century mansion, Gunnersbury Park Museum was formerly home to the Rothschild family. It is now the community museum for Ealing and Hounslow. In contrast to the grand house, see where the servants lived and worked, in our original 19th century kitchens. View the horse drawn vehicles of Gunnersbury, including the Rothschilds' State and travelling carriages.

Opening Times: Apr to Oct daily 13:00-17:00. Nov to Mar daily 13:00-16:00. Victorian Kitchens: Apr to Oct Sat, Sun & BH 13:00-17:00. Admission: Free. Location: In park, on bus route (E3), near tube station (Acton Town).

Map Ref: 3

Hackney Museum

Parkside Library, Victoria Park Road, London E8 1EA   Tel: 020 8986 6914   Fax: 020 8985 7600

Discover why people have come to Hackney from all over the world for the past 1000 years, through room sets, interactives, personal stories and museum objects.

Opening Times: Mon, Tue & Thu 09:30-20:00, Fri 10:00-20:00, Sat 09:00-18:00. Closed Wed & Sun. Admission: Free. Location: In the heart of Central Hackney, two minute walk from Hackney Central Railway Station.   Map Ref: 18

Ham House

Ham Street, Ham, Richmond, London TW10 7RS   Tel: 020 8940 1950   Fax: 020 8332 6903   Email: hamhouse@ntrust.org.uk   Web: www.nationaltrust.org.uk/southern

Outstanding Stuart house famous for its lavish interiors and spectacular collections of fine

Outer London

furniture, textiles and paintings. Also includes 17th century formal garden and an 18th century dairy.

Opening Times: Apr to Oct House: Sat to Wed 13:00-17:00, Garden: Sat to Wed 11:00-18:00, closed Xmas & New Year. Admission: House & Garden: Adult £6.00, Child £3.00, Family £15.00. Garden only: Adult £2.00, Child £1.00, Family £5.00 (prices subject to increase in 2003). Location: South Bank of Thames, West of A307, at Petersham, readily accessible from M3 and M25. Bus route 65 from Kingston and 371 from Richmond Station.　　　　Map Ref: 19

Hampstead Museum　　　　　　　　　　　　　　　　　　🕭 ❂ ◪

Burgh House, New End Square, London NW3 1LT　Tel: 020 7431 0144　Fax: 020 7435 8817
Email: hampsteadmuseum@talk21.com

Queen Anne House containing a collection tracing the history of Hampstead from pre-historic times to the present day. Notable is the Helen Allingham collection and 'Isokon' furniture.

Opening Times: Wed to Sun 12:00-17:00, Sat by appointment. BH 14:00-17:00. Closed Good Friday, Easter Monday, Xmas & New Year. Admission: Free. Location: Near central Hampstead, a five minute walk from Hampstead Tube Station.　　　　Map Ref: 16

Hogarth's House　　　　　　　　　　　　　　　　　　　　❂

Hogarth Lane, Great West Road, London W4 2QN　Tel: 020 8994 6757

Early 18th century house which was the country home of William Hogarth (1697-1764) during the last 15 years of his life. Displays of his prints, information on the life of this 'Father of English Painting', and a secluded garden containing Hogarth's mulberry tree.

Opening Times: Apr to Oct Tue to Fri 13:00-17:00, Sat, Sun & BH 13:00-18:00. Nov to Mar Tue to Fri 13:00-16:00, Sat, Sun & BH 13:00-17:00. Closed Mon except BH, Good Friday, 25-26 Dec and Jan. Admission: Free. Location: On A4 (Great West Road) near Hogarth Roundabout, Chiswick. Nearest tube station - Turnham Green (15 minutes walk).　　　　Map Ref: 20

Sri Lankan Mask,
photo H Scheebeli

Horniman Museum & Gardens　　　　　　　♿ ❂ ◪

100 London Road, Forest Hill, London SE23 3PQ　Tel: 020 8699 1872　Fax: 020 8291 5506
Email: enquiry@horniman.demon.co.uk
Web: www.horniman.ac.uk

Set in 16 acres of gardens, this fascinating, free museum has unique exhibitions, events and activities to delight adults and children alike. Housed in Townsend's stunning Arts and Crafts building, the museum has outstanding collections which illustrate the natural and cultural world. Discover the African Worlds gallery featuring the largest African mask, experience the Natural History Gallery with many original specimens from the Victorian age and explore marine ecology in the Living Waters Aquarium with tropical fish and seahorses. A new £13.4m development opened to the

Horniman Clock Tower, photo M Harding

public in 2002 which has dramatically transformed the museum for the future. Four new galleries are accompanied by a host of new facilities, a new entrance to link the Museum with the Gardens and greatly improved access provision. Treasures - stunning artefacts from every continent in a new gallery celebrating world cultures, Hands-On Base - masses of exhibits to touch and explore in a fun interactive space, Monster Creepy Crawlies - monstrously large bugs to seize the imagination of children of all ages, New shop and café - overlooking the Gardens. Music - a dynamic new environment for our internationally renowned collection of musical instruments incorporating sound and vision.

Opening Times: Mon to Sat 10:30-17:30, Sun 14:00-17:30. Closed 24-26 Dec.
Admission: Free. Location: South Circular Road (A205), free parking opposite. Forest Hill BR, 13 mins from London Bridge. Exhibitions & Events 2003 : For Exhibitions and Events please telephone for details.　　　　Map Ref: 21

Jewish Museum - Finchley, London's Museum of Jewish Life

The Sternberg Centre, 80 East End Road, Finchley, London N3 2SY   Tel: 020 8349 1143
Fax: 020 8343 2162   Email: jml.finchley@lineone.net   Web: www.jewishmuseum.org.uk

Lively social history displays tracing Jewish immigration and settlement in London with reconstructions of tailoring and furniture workshops and hands-on activities for children. Moving exhibition on British born Holocaust survivor Leon Greenman OBE. Group visits and education programmes by arrangement.

Opening Times: Mon to Thu 10:30-17:00, Sun 10:30-16:30. Closed Fri, Sat, Jewish Festivals and Public Holidays. Also closed Sun in month of Aug and BH weekends. Admission: Adult £2.00, Child Free, OAP £1.00. Location: Nearest underground station Finchley Central (via Station Road and Manor View). Located on A504.   Map Ref: 22

Keats House

Keats Grove, Hampstead, London NW3 2RR   Tel: 020 7435 2062
Email: keatshouse@corpotlondon.gov.uk   Web: www.cityoflondon.gov.uk
www.keatshouse.org.uk

The Keats House Collection contains original letters from John Keats to his family and friends, manuscripts by Keats and his circle, personal possessions and a reference collection about Keats and the romantic movement.

Opening Times: Nov to Mar Tue to Sun 12:00-16:00, from April open until 17:00. Closed Xmas, New Year and Good Friday. Admission: Adult £3.00, Child Free, Concession £1.50. Tickets are valid for one year. Location: On the edge of Hampstead Heath close to mainline and underground stations and bus routes.   Map Ref: 16

Kenwood House

Hampstead Lane, London NW3 7JR
Tel: 020 8348 1286

Kenwood houses one of the most important collections of paintings, given to the nation by Lord Iveagh - including works by Rembrandt, Gainsborough, Turner, Van Dyck to name but a few. The house was remodelled by Robert Adam for the great judge, Lord Mansfield, and the richly decorated library is one of his masterpieces.

Opening Times: Apr to Sep daily 10:00-17:30, Oct daily 10:00-17:00, Nov to Mar daily 10:00-16:00. Closed Xmas & New Year. Admission: Free, donations welcome. Location: Hampstead Lane.
Mirrored recess in the Library © English Heritage   Map Ref: 16

Museum of Childhood at Bethnal Green

Cambridge Heath Road, London E2 9PA   Tel: 020 8983 5200   Fax: 020 8983 5225
Email: bgmc@vam.ac.uk   Web: www.museumofchildhood.org.uk

One of the best collection of toys and games in the world, dating from the 16th century to the present day.

Opening Times: Mon to Thu, Sat & Sun 10:00-17:50. Closed Fri, Xmas & New Year.
Admission: Free. Location: One minute walk from Bethnal Green Tube Station.   Map Ref: 23

Museum of Fulham Palace

Fulham Palace, Bishops Avenue, London SW6 6EA   Tel / Fax: 020 7736 3233

The museum within Fulham Palace tells the story of this nationally important site, home of the Bishops of London until 1973. Displays include archaeology, paintings and garden history.

Opening Times: Nov to Feb Thu to Sun 13:00-16:00, Mar to Oct Wed to Sun 14:00-17:00. Open BH Mon, Closed Xmas and Good Friday. Admission: Adult £1.00, Concession 50p, accompanied Child Free. Location: Off Bishops Avenue. Tube Putney Bridge, District Line, ten minute walk.   Map Ref: 24

Outer London

National Maritime Museum

🦢 ♿ 🎁 ☕ 🍴

Romney Road, Greenwich, London SE10 9NF   Tel: 020 8858 4422
Web: www.nmm.ac.uk

20 modern public galleries at Greenwich display a fraction of the huge collections of this museum: 4,520 oil paintings; 100,000 books; 1,000 flags; 100,000 maps and charts; 70,000 prints and drawings; etc. Properties include Queen's House (Inigo Jones 1635) and the Royal Observatory Greenwich (Wren 1675). Major reference library. Web research service (www.nmm.ac.uk), maritime gateway: www.port.nmm.ac.uk and new www.portcities.org.uk. Also www.ukmcs.org.uk.

National Maritime Museum, Stanhope entrance

Opening Times: Sep to Jun daily 10:00-17:00, Jul & Aug daily 10:00-18:00. Closed Xmas. Admission: Free, charge for special exhibitions. Location: Near town centre, adjoining Greenwich Park.

Map Ref: 17

Pitzhanger Manor House

🦢 ♿ 🎁 ☕

Walpole Park, Mattock Lane, Ealing, London W5 5EQ   Tel: 020 8567 1227   Fax: 020 8567 0595   Email: pitshanger@ealing.gov.uk   Web: www.ealing.gov.uk/pitshanger

A collection of Martinware pottery, made between 1873 and 1923 and known for its naturalistic, humorous and sometimes grotesque decoration, is displayed in the Victorian wing of this Georgian villa.

Opening Times: Tue to Sat 11:00-17:00. May to Sep Sun 13:00-17:00. Admission: Free.
Location: Eight minute walk from Ealing Broadway Station, near town centre.   Map Ref: 25

Ragged School Museum

🦢 ♿ 🎁 ☕

46/50 Copperfield Road, Bow, London E3 4RR   Tel: 020 8980 6405   Fax: 020 8983 3481
Email: enquiries@raggedschoolmuseum.org.uk   Web: www.raggedschoolmuseum.org.uk

Displays on Tower Hamlets and its people, recreated Victorian classroom and activities for children during holiday periods.

Opening Times: Wed & Thu 10:00-17:00 and first Sun in month 14:00-17:00. Admission: Free.
Location: A ten minute walk from tube and DLR stations.   Map Ref: 23

Royal Air Force Museum

🦢 ♿ 🎁 ☕ 🍴 🚗   Royal Air Force Museum

Grahame Park Way, Hendon, London NW9 5LL   Tel: 020 8358 4849
Fax: 020 8358 4981   Email: groupbusiness@rafmuseum.com   Web: www.rafmuseum.com

Take off to the Royal Air Force Museum and flypast the history of aviation right up to the latest Eurofighter. With over 80 aircraft exhibits, a simulator ride, hands on section, film shows, art gallery, uniforms and medals section, interactive sound and light show, gift shop, picnic area, and licensed restaurant, this is a fun, free and fantastic day out for everyone.

Opening Times: Daily 10:00-18:00. Closed Xmas & New Year. Admission: Free. Location: Colindale Tube Station, Northern line, ten minute walk from station. Thames Link, Mill Hill Broadway, Bus 303. Exhibitions &

RAF11-Lancaster

Events 2003 : In 2003 the museum celebrates 100 years of aviation with the development of the Milestones of Flight exhibition and the relocation of the historic 1917 Grahame-White Aircraft Factory. The popular hands on section for children - fun'n'flight - is also set to expand and will include numerous interactives which are both fun and educational.   Map Ref: 11

🦢	♿	🎁	☕	🍴	🚗
Guided or Private Tours	Disabled Access	Gift Shop or Sales Point	Café or Refreshments	Restaurant	Car Parking

South London Gallery

65 Peckham Road, London SE5 8UH
Tel: 020 7703 6120   Fax: 020 7252 4730
Email: mail@southlondongallery.org.uk
Web: www.southlondongallery.org.uk

Described by The Independent as 'a mecca for the art pilgrim', the SLG has a reputation for having its finger on the pulse of contemporary art. Since 1993, the Gallery has staged ground-breaking solo exhibitions including Gilbert & George, Tracey Emin and Barbara Kruger. Located in the heart of a thriving artistic community in Camberwell, the Gallery is held in great affection by the general public and artists alike.

Opening Times: Tue to Fri 11:00-18:00, Thu 11:00-19:00, Sat & Sun 14:00-18:00. Closed Mon. Admission: Free.

Location: Peckham/Camberwell border, 15 minute walk from Peckham Rye or Demark Hill railway stations.   Map Ref: 26

Sutton House

2 & 4 Homerton High Street, Hackney, London E9 6JQ   Tel: 020 8986 2264   Fax: 020 8525 9051   Email: suttonhouse@smtp.ntrust.org.uk   Web: www.nationaltrust.org.uk

Enjoy the unexpected in the oldest surviving brick house in East London. Built in 1535 Sutton House is fascinating for its visible layers of change. See the original Tudor linenfold panelling, 17th century painted staircase, Georgian parlour, Victorian study and 1980s squatter's mural.

Opening Times: 6 to 24 Feb, Wed and Sun 11:30-17:30. 1 Mar to 22 Dec, Fri and Sat 13:00-17:30. Phone for more details.   Admission: Adult £2.10, Child 50p, Family £4.70. National Trust Members Free.   Location: At the corner of Isabella Road and Homerton High Street. Frequent local buses. Quarter mile Hackney Central Station, half mile Hackney Downs Station. Map Ref: 27

Vestry House Museum

Vestry Road, Walthamstow, London E17 9NH   Tel: 0208 509 1917
Email: vestry.house@al.lbwf.gov.uk

Vestry House Museum is housed in Walthamstow's original workhouse, built in 1730. The museum now serves as a centre for the collection, preservation and interpretation of the past and present story of Waltham Forest.

Opening Times: Mon to Fri 10:00-17:30, Sat 10:00-17:00. Closed Sun & BH.   Admission: Free.
Location: One minute walk from Walthamstow Tube/Bus Station.   Map Ref: 28

Wandsworth Museum

The Courthouse, 11 Garratt Lane, London SW18 4AQ   Tel: 020 8871 7074/7075   Fax: 020 8871 4602   Email: wandsworthmuseum@wandsworth.gov.uk
Web: www.wandsworth.gov.uk/museum

Follow the story of Wandsworth from pre-historic times to the present. Discover how Battersea, Balham, Tooting, Putney, Roehampton, Earlsfield, Wandsworth and Southfields grew from country villages to London's biggest suburb. Interactive displays, changing exhibitions and special events.

Opening Times: Tue to Sat 10:00-17:00, Sun 14:00-17:00. Closed Mon and BH.
Admission: Free. Location: Opposite Wandsworth Shopping Centre. Ten minute walk from Wandsworth Town Station and 15 minutes walk from East Putney Tube.   Map Ref: 29

The Wernher Collection at Ranger's House

Chesterfield Walk, Blackheath, London SE10 8QX   Tel: 020 8853 0035

Rangers House is home to the magnificent Suffolk collection of paintings, given to the nation by the Hon Greville and Mrs Howard, including Old Masters and the famous series of portraits by William Larkin.

Opening Times: Apr to Sep Wed to Sun & BH 10:00-18:00, Oct Wed to Sun 10:00-17:00. Nov to Mar Wed to Sun 10:00-16:00. Closed 22 Dec to 2 Mar 2004.   Admission: Call 020 8853 0035 for details   Location: Chesterfield Walk, train Blackheath or Greenwich.   Map Ref: 17

Outer London

William Morris Gallery

Lloyd Park, Forest Road, London E17 4PP   Tel: 020 8527 3782   Fax: 020 8527 7070
Web: www.lbwf.gov.uk/wmg

Permanent displays of work by William Morris (1834-1896) designer, craftsman, writer and socialist, housed in his boyhood home. Work by other Arts and Crafts movement designers. Pre-Raphaelite paintings.

Opening Times: Tue to Sat & first Sun of each month 10:00-13:00 14:00-17:00.
Admission: Free.   Location: 15 minute walk from Walthamstow Central Tube Station (Victoria line)
Map Ref: 28

Wimbledon Lawn Tennis Museum

Centre Court, AELTC, Church Road, Wimbledon, London SW19 5AE
Tel: 020 8946 6131   Fax: 020 8944 6497   Email: museum@aeltc.com
Web: www.wimbledon.org/museum

The Museum, located within Centre Court, tells the story of lawn tennis and explains many of the quintessentially English traditions associated with the game. Its exhibits encapsulate the prestige, the glamour and the glory associated with The Championship. The Museum features views of the world-famous Centre Court, the original Championship trophies, and film and video footage of great players in action.

The Home of Tennis

Opening Times: Daily 10:30-17:00. Closed Xmas & New Year. Only open to tournament visitors during Championships. Closed middle Sun of the Championships and Mon after.   Admission: Adult £5.50, Child £3.50, Concessions £4.50, please call for Group rates.   Location: From London take A3 to Portsmouth, turn left into A219 towards Wimbledon. 20 minute walk from Wimbledon Station, 15 minute walk from Southfields Underground
Map Ref: 30

Woodlands Art Gallery

90 Mycenae Road, Blackheath, London SE3 7SE   Tel / Fax: 020 8858 5847
Web: www.wag.co.uk

The new exhibitions each month have a variety of sources from local art groups to local school, community groups, individually grouped artists from England and abroad.

Opening Times: Mon to Thu 11:00-17:30, Sat 11:00-17:00, Sun 14:00-17:00. Closed Wed, Fri and set up weeks, please phone to check.   Admission: Free.   Location: Near Blackheath Standard. Bus route, Westcombe Park. Tube, North Greenwich. Bus 108, 422 from tube. 53 from central London, 286, 202, 54.
Map Ref: 17

2 Willow Road

London NW3 1TH   Tel / Fax: 020 7435 8166

The National Trust's only modern movement house completed in 1939. Contains 20th century works of art collected by its architect Erno Goldfinger.

Opening Times: Thu to Sat 12:00-17:00.   Admission: Adult £4.40, Child £2.20.
Location: Hampstead, north London, ten minutes walk from underground.
Map Ref: 16

Museums • Galleries • Historic Houses

Please let us know of any collections that are not listed in this guide that you feel should be listed. E-mail us on *editor@tomorrows.co.uk*
or return the Report Form on page 448

RICHMOND

Museum No 1 (Economic Botany)

Plants & People, Royal Botanic Gardens, Kew, Richmond TW9 3AE
Tel: 020 8332 5706

This fascinating and highly accessible exhibition gives visitors a glimpse into Kew's collections and emphasises their importance. It serves as a timely reminder of the close relationship between plants and people in every aspect of their lives. In the gardens explore the world from rainforest to desert in vast magnificent glasshouses. Discover exotic plants in tropical surroundings or just relax in the beauty of the world's most famous garden. Every season is a new experience at Kew and there is so much to enjoy:

The Palm House

30,000 types of plants; museum with interactive; exhibition; unique art galleries; places to eat and shop. Visit at any time of the year, in any weather.

Opening Times: Daily 09:30, closing times vary. Admission: Adult £6.50, Child Free, Concession £4.50 (Prices subject to change from January 2003). Location: Ten minute walk from Kew Bridge and Kew Gardens Station. Exhibitions & Events 2003 : 9 Feb to 10 Mar: Orchids at the Edge: Beauty in Danger, 23 Mar to 12 May: Spring to Life, 1 Jun to 30 Sep: Colour Sensation, 12 Oct to 3 Nov: Autumn Festival, 28 Nov to 6 Jan: Christmas Festival. Map Ref: 3

The Pagoda

Museum of Richmond

Old Town Hall, Whittaker Avenue, Richmond TW9 1TP Tel: 020 8332 1141 Fax: 020 8948 7570 Email: musrich@globalnet.co.uk Web: www.museumofrichmond.com

The museum celebrates the unique history of Richmond with colourful displays spanning prehistoric times to the present day. Special exhibits feature Richmond Palace, the magnificent Tudor creation which gave the town its name.

Opening Times: All year Tue to Sat 11:00-17:00, May to Sep Sun 13:00-16:00. Closed Mon. Admission: Free. Location: In the town centre, one minute from River Thames, five minutes from station. Map Ref: 19

Public Record Office Museum

Ruskin Avenue, Kew, Richmond TW9 4DU Tel: 020 8392 5202 Fax: 020 8392 5345 Email: events@pro.gov.uk Web: pro.gov.uk

Official documents from the Domesday Book to military reports of D-Day Landings. The National Archive of the United Kingdom holds Government papers from 11th century to recent releases.

Opening Times: Mon & Wed, Fri & Sat 09:30-17:00, Tue & Thu 10:00-19:00. Closed BH. Admission: Free. Location: Ten minutes from tube/railway station. Map Ref: 3

TWICKENHAM

Marble Hill House

Richmond Road, Twickenham TW1 2NL Tel: 020 8892 5115

Marble Hill House contains an important collection of early Georgian furniture and paintings. Set in 66 acres of parkland, this magnificent Thames-side Palladian villa was built for Henrietta Howard, Countess of Suffolk and mistress of King George II.

Opening Times: Apr to Sep Wed to Sun & BH 10:00-18:00, Oct Wed to Sun 10:00-17:00. Closed Nov to Mar. Admission: Adult £3.50, Child £1.80, Concession £2.70. Location: Richmond Road, frequent bus service, St Margarets Station quarter of a mile, Richmond Tube - one mile. Map Ref: 31

Museum of Rugby

Rugby Road, Twickenham TW1 1DZ   Tel: 020 8892 8877   Fax: 020 8892 2817
Email: museum@rfu.com   Web: www.rfu.com

Few would dispute that sport has an appeal that crosses gender, age and racial barriers. But few people would connect the thrills and spills of the top level competition with the standard museum environment. How can a museum compete with drama, excitement and appeal of live sport? The answer is simple: today's sports museums with their hands-on exhibits and interactive screens and sounds are more than just testaments to facts and figures, but living breathing ways of connecting with the unrivalled excitement that

Children 'in action' on the Scrum Machine

only sport can provide. You can find out all about rugby, its history and its star players by visiting The Museum of Rugby, Twickenham. The world's finest collection of rugby memorabilia is housed at the Museum of Rugby, which takes visitors through the history of the sport from 1823 to the present day. The Museum also offers fans a tour of Britain's most famous Rugby Stadium.

The Twickenham Experience

Opening Times: Tue to Sat 10:00-17:00, Sun 11:00-17:00,
BH 10:00-17:00. Closed Match Day, post Match Day Sun, Mon, Good Friday and Xmas.
Admission: Museum & Tour: Adult £6.00, Concession £4.00. Museum or Tour Adult £4.00,
Concession £3.00. Family £19.00.   Location: Situated inside RFU Twickenham Stadium.
Exhibitions & Events 2003 : For Exhibitions and Events please telephone for details. Map Ref: 31

Orleans House Gallery

Riverside, Twickenham TW1 3DJ   Tel: 020 8892 0221   Fax: 020 8744 0501
Email: galleryinfo@richmond.gov.uk   Web: www.richmond.gov.uk/orleanhouse

Borough art gallery comprising 18th century Octagon Room designed by James Gibbs, historical and contemporary exhibitions throughout the year situated in tranquil park by the River Thames.

Opening Times: Tue to Sat 13:00-17:30, Sun & BH 14:00-17:30.
Oct to Mar Closes 16:30. Admission: Free. Location: Ten minute walk from station.   Map Ref: 31

Norfolk

The jewel of the county is undoubtedly Norwich, the county town with its superb cathedral built in Caen stone and its impressive Norman Castle. To the east of Norwich are the Norfolk Broads, an area of glorious reedy lakes and meandering waterways. Norfolk, a highly efficient farming county was largely bypassed by the Industrial Revolution and its consequent urban development.

A quarter of Norfolk's museums lie within the surrounds of Norwich and as one would expect in a county with such a pastoral background there are many excellent rural life museums.

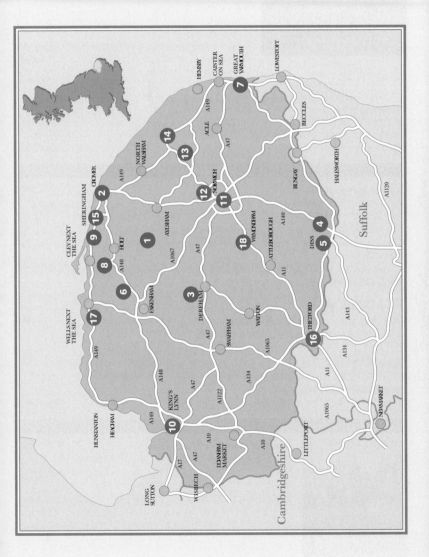

The Red Map References should be used to locate Museums etc on the pages that follow

Norfolk

Blickling Hall

THE NATIONAL TRUST

Blickling, Aylsham NR11 6NF   Tel: 01263 738030   Fax: 01263 731660
Web: www.nationaltrust.org.uk

South Front of Blickling Hall,
built by Sir Henry Hobart

Blickling Hall is one of the most spectacular country houses in East Anglia. The 17th century red brick house is flanked by two immense yew hedges and has an extensive colourful garden surrounded by historic park and woodland. The house contains fine furniture, pictures and tapestries set in magnificent State Rooms. The Peter the Great Room dominated by its massive tapestry of Peter the Great at the Battle of Poltawa. Close to the Hall you will find a delightful secret garden, an 18th century orangery and a dry moat with a wide range of colourful plants. To the south of the house are the great yew hedges planted in the 17th century.

Opening Times: House: 23 Mar to 3 Nov Wed to Sun & BH 13:00-17:00. Garden, Shop & Restaurant: 23 Mar to 3 Nov Wed to Sun & BH 10:15-17:15.   Admission: House & Garden: Adult £6.70, Child £3.35. Garden only: Adult £3.80, Child £1.90.   Location: One and half miles northwest Aylsham, Norfolk.   Exhibitions & Events 2003 : For Exhibitions and Events please telephone for details.   Map Ref: 1

Cromer Museum

East Cottages, Tucker Street, Cromer NR27 9HB   Tel: 01263 513543   Fax: 01263 511651
Email: cromer.museum@norfolk.gov.uk   Web: www.norfolk.gov.uk/tourism/museums

Enter the Victorian fisherman's cottage illuminated by gaslight and imagine what it was like to live in Cromer at the end of the 19th century. Find out about Henry Blogg's famous lifeboat rescues and much more.

Opening Times: Mon to Sat 10:00-17:00, Sun 14:00-17:00.   Admission: Adult £1.80, Child 90p, Concession £1.40.   Location: In Tucker Street, opposite the East end of Cromer Parish Church.
Map Ref: 2

RNLI Henry Blogg Lifeboat Museum

No 2 Boathouse, The Promenade, Cromer NR27 9HE   Tel: 01263 511294
Web: www.lifeboats.org.uk

Display on the life of Coxwain Henry Blogg, winner of three RNLI Gold Medals for bravery. Also displays relating to Cromer Lifeboats and the Royal National Lifeboat Institution.

Opening Times: May to Sep daily 10:00-16:00. By appointment in winter.   Admission: Free.
Location: Near town centre.   Map Ref: 2

Playing the Game of Life in the
Workhouse Experience

Roots of Norfolk at Gressenhall

Gressenhall, Dereham NR20 4DR   Tel: 01362 860563
Fax: 01362 860385   Email: gressenhall.museum@norfolk.gov.uk
Web: www.norfolk.gov.uk/tourism/museums

A museum of rural life housed in a former workhouse, with displays on village and rural life and a farm worked with horses and stocked with rare breeds, all in an idyllic rural setting with farm woodland and riverside trails, gardens, a children's play area and the Mardlers Rest Café. A perfect day out for all the family, whatever the weather.

Opening Times: Mar to Dec daily 10:00-17:00.   Admission: Adult £4.70, Child £3.30, Concession £4.00, Family £13.00.
Location: On B1146, three miles north west of Dereham. Follow brown signs from A47 and Dereham Town Centre.   Map Ref: 3

Norfolk

DISS

100th Bomb Group Memorial Museum

Common Road, Dickleburgh, Diss IP21 4PH   Tel: 01379 740708

A fine collection of USAAF uniforms, decorations, combat records, equipment, memorabilia and wartime photographs.

Opening Times: Sat, Sun & BH 10:00-17:00, May to Sep also open Wed. Also by appointment. Closed Nov, Dec & Jan.   Admission: Free.   Location: Turn off the A140 at Dickleburgh by pass (to Thorpe Abbotts), 17 miles south of Norwich, 26 miles north of Ipswich.   Map Ref: 4

Diss Museum

11 Market Hill, Diss IP22 3JZ   Tel: 01379 650618   Email: dissmuseum@lineone.net

Registered award-winning museum of local history. Well researched, changing displays about Diss and district, with something for everyone.

Opening Times: 12 Mar to 30 Nov Wed to Thu 14:00-16:00, Fri to Sat 10:30-16:30. May to Aug Sun 14:00-16:00.   Admission: Free.   Location: Middle of the Market Square.   Map Ref: 5

FAKENHAM

Thursford Collection

Thursford, Fakenham NR21 0AS   Tel: 01328 878477   Fax: 01328 878415
Email: admin@thursfordcollection.co.uk

A glittering Aladdin's cave of majestic old road engines and mechanical organs of magical variety all gleaming with colour. Robert Wolfe stars live in the mighty Wurlitzer show, and there's a programme of music too from Thursford's nine very different mechanical pipe organs. Old farm buildings have been transformed into a small village with a touch of Charles Dickens' England.

Opening Times: Good Friday to last Sun in Sep daily 12:00-17:00. Closed Sat   Admission: Adult £5.00, Child £2.50, Under 4s Free, OAP £4.70, Student £4.25. Group rates available.   Location: One mile off A148 between Fakenham and Holt.   Map Ref: 6

Savages Venetian Gondola Ride

GREAT YARMOUTH

Elizabethan House

4 South Street, Great Yarmouth NR30 2QH   Tel: 01493 855746   Fax: 01493 745526
Web: www.norfolk.gov.uk/tourism/museums

A Tudor merchant's house hidden behind a Georgian street front, with furnished rooms and displays of home life through the ages. Visit the panelled parlour where the death of King Charles I was decided.

Opening Times: 1 Apr to 31 Oct Mon to Fri 10:00-17:00, Sat & Sun 13:15-17:00.
Admission: Adult £2.60, Child £1.30, Concession £2.00, Family £6.00.   Map Ref: 7

Old Merchants House & Row 111 Houses

South Quay, Great Yarmouth NR30 2RQ   Tel: 01493 857900

These two 17th century houses are a type of building unique to Great Yarmouth. They are two of the earliest surviving merchants' houses in England, and contain original fixtures and displays of local architectural fittings.   Map Ref: 7

The Tolhouse Museum

Tolhouse Street, Great Yarmouth NR30 2SH   Tel: 01493 745526   Fax: 01493 745459
Web: www.norfolk.gov.uk/tourism/museums

The Tolhouse was once the town courtroom and gaol. It is one of the oldest civic buildings in the country. A visit to the dungeons is a chilling experience, with their original cells and lifelike models of Victorian prisoners.

Opening Times: 1 Apr to 31 Oct Mon to Sat 10:00-17:00, Sun 13:15-17:00.   Admission: Adult £2.60, Child £1.30, Concession £2.00.   Location: In Tolhouse Street next to Great Yarmouth's Central Library.   Map Ref: 7

Norfolk

Glandford Shell Museum
Glandford, Holt NR25 7JR   Tel: 01263 740081

Sir Alfred Jodrell built this charming Victorian museum for his unique collection of sea shells and artefacts. Little has changed here for almost a hundred years...some call it a time capsule. Also see the evocative John Craske tapestry.

Opening Times: Easter Sat to 31 Oct Tue to Sat 10:00-12:30 & 14:00-16:30. Admission: Adult £1.50, Child 50p, OAP £1.00. Location: Situated midway between Letheringsett and Blakeney on the north Norfolk coast.   Map Ref: 8

Muckleburgh Collection
Weybourne, Holt NR25 7EG   Tel: 01263 588210/608

The Museum is housed in the former Ack-Ack NAAFI. Since the Museum's inception 13 years ago it has carefully restored tanks and other military vehicles; to date there are 16 working tanks and other guns and vehicles.

Opening Times: Feb to Good Friday Sun 10:00-17:00, Good Friday to 2 Nov daily 10:00-17:00, Feb Half Term 10:00-17:00 Admission: Adult £4.95, Child £2.50, OAP £3.50. Location: Four miles west of Sheringham.   Map Ref: 9

Houghton Hall
Kings Lynn PE31 6UE   Tel: 01485 528569   Fax: 01485 528167
Email: enquiries@houghtonhall.com   Web: www.houghtonhall.com

18th century Palladian Mansion built by Britain's first Prime Minister, Sir Robert Walpole. Model soldier collection with over 20,000 model soldiers and militaria. Newly restored walled garden.

Opening Times: 20 Apr to 28 Sep Wed, Thu, Sun & BH. Admission: Adult £6.50, Child £3.00. Excluding House Adult £4.00, Child £2.00. Location: Just off the A148 King's Lynn to Cromer road.   Map Ref: 10

Lynn Museum
Market Street, King's Lynn PE30 1NL   Tel: 01553 775001   Email: lynn.museum@norfolk.gov.uk
Web: www.norfolk.gov.uk/tourism/museums

Tells the story of the people and places of King's Lynn and West Norfolk. Travel back through history and explore the changing local landscape from the earliest farmers, through Roman, Saxon and medieval times.

Opening Times: Tue to Sat. Closed BH, Xmas & New Year. Please ring for times.
Admission: Adult £1.00, Child 60p, Concession 80p. Location: Entrance off King's Lynn Bus Station, adjacent to the shopping precinct.   Map Ref: 10

Tales of the Old Gaol House
Saturday Market Place, King's Lynn PE30 5DQ   Tel: 01553 774297   Fax: 01553 772361
Email: gaolhouse@west-norfolk.gov.uk   Web: www.west-norfolk.gov.uk

Set in the town's old cells, visitors have the chance to hear the stories and experience the sights (and smells) of Lynn's criminal past. Also housed there are some of Britain's finest civic treasures, including the priceless King John Cup.

Opening Times: Easter to end Oct daily 10:00-17:00, Nov to Easter closed Wed & Thu. Last admission 16:15 daily. Admission: Adult £2.40, Concession £1.75. Location: Town centre, ten minutes walk from bus station, in the heart of the medieval part of King's Lynn.   Map Ref: 10

Town House Museum of Lynn Life
46 Queen Street, King's Lynn PE30 5DQ   Tel: 01553 773450
Email: townhouse.museum@norfolk.gov.uk   Web: www.norfolk.gov.uk/tourism/museums

Housed in a 19th century town house and former inn. Displays focus on the everyday life of Lynn people through the ages and take you through a series of carefully reconstructed rooms.

Opening Times: Please ring for times. Closed BH, Xmas & New Year. Admission: Adult £1.80, Child 90p, Concession £1.40. Location: Queen Street in the heart of historic 'Old Lynn' and close to the medieval Guildhall and St Margaret's Church.   Map Ref: 10

Bridewell Museum

Bridewell Alley, Norwich NR2 1AQ   Tel: 01603 667228   Email: museums@norfolk.gov.uk
Web: www.norfolk.gov.uk/tourism/museums

This former merchant's house, part of which dates from 1325, became an 'open' prison for vagrants, children and women (a Bridewell), before becoming a museum focusing on Norwich life and industry.

Opening Times: Feb to 31 Oct Mon to Sat 10:00-17:00.   Admission: Adult £2.00, Child £1.00, Concession £1.50, Family £5.00.   Location: In city centre.   Map Ref: 11

City of Norwich Aviation Museum

Old Norwich Road, Horsham St Faith, Norwich NR10 3JF   Tel: 01603 893080
Web: www.cnam.co.uk

Aircraft on display include a massive Vulcan Bomber and Civil and Military aeroplanes which have flown from Norfolk over the past 40 years. Inside displays feature the achievement and sacrifces of the heroes and pioneers who have formed the aviation history of Norfolk.

Opening Times: Apr to Oct Tue to Sat 10:00-17:00, Sun & BH 12:00-17:00. Nov to Mar Wed & Sat 10:00-16:00 Sun 12:00-16:00. Closed Xmas & New Year.   Admission: Adult £2.50, Child/Concession £1.50, OAP £2.00, Family £7.00.   Location: One mile from A140 Norwich to Cromer road, follow brown tourist signs.   Map Ref: 12

Inspire Hands on Science Centre

St Michaels Church, Coslany Street, Norwich NR3 3DT   Tel: 01603 612612   Fax: 01603 616721   Email: inspire@science-project.org   Web: www.science-project.org

Hands-on exhibits, shows and special events. Science shop and light refreshments, perfect for families, parties and schools.

Opening Times: Daily 10:00-17:30 (last admission 16:30).   Admission: Adult £4.20, Child £3.60, Under 3s Free, Saver (2 adults and 2 children) £12.00.   Location: Norwich City Centre, five minutes walk from market.   Map Ref: 11

Norwich Castle Museum & Art Gallery

Shirehall, Market Avenue, Norwich NR1 3TQ   Tel: 01603 493625   Fax: 01603 493623
Email: museum@norfolk.gov.uk   Web: www.norfolk.gov.uk/tourism/museum

Norwich Castle has outstanding archaeology, natural history and fine art collections and is placed with treasures as diverse as ancient gold jewellery, silver, delicate porcelain and Roman pottery. See the best collections anywhere of the Norwich School of Artists, Norwich Silver, Lowestoft Porcelain, ceramic teapots and regular exhibitions from Tate.

Opening Times: Mon to Sat 10:30-17:00, Sun 14:00-17:00. Closed Xmas & New Year.   Admission: Please call for details.   Location: In city centre.   Map Ref: 11

Norwich Castle Museum & Art Gallery

Royal Air Force Air Defence Radar Museum

RAF Neatishead, Norwich NR12 8YB   Tel: 01692 633309   Fax: 01692 633214
Web: www.neatishead.raf.mod.uk

History of radar and air defence from 1935 to date. Housed in original 1942 building. Features Battle of Britain, 1942 operations, Cold War Operations Room and Space Defence. Radar convoy vehicles.

Opening Times: Apr to Sep second Sat each month, BH Mon, Tue & Thu 10:00-17:00. Oct to Mar second Sat each month.   Admission: Adult £3.00, Child over 12 £1.00, Under 12s Free.   Location: Near Horning, Norfolk.   Map Ref: 13

Royal Norfolk Regimental Museum

Shirehall, Market Avenue, Norwich NR1 3JQ   Tel: 01603 493649   Fax: 01603 630214
Email: museum@norfolk.gov.uk   Web: www.norfolk.gov.uk/tourism/museums

Situated in the Shirehall, which dates from the early 1830s. The displays are themed and set out

Norfolk

chronologically with excellent interpretative panels, designed for those with no military knowledge as well as the military historian.

Opening Times: Mon to Sat 10:00-17:00, Sun 14:00-17:00. Admission: Adult £1.80, Child 90p, Concession £1.40. Location: In the Shirehall buildings at the base of Norwich Castle opposite Anglia TV. Map Ref: 11

Free-standing male figure,
New Zealand

Sainsbury Centre for Visual Arts

University of East Anglia, Norwich NR4 7TJ
Tel: 01603 593199/592467 Fax: 01603 259401
Email: scva@uea.ac.uk Web: www.uea.ac.uk/scva

The Robert and Lisa Sainsbury Collection is housed in two distinctive buildings by Lord Foster. Combining modern Western art with fine and applied arts from Africa, the Pacific, the Americas, Asia, Egypt, medieval Europe and the ancient Mediterranean, the collection contains some 1200 objects reflecting over 5000 years of creativity. It is particularly well known for works by Francis Bacon, John Davies, Alberto Giacometti and Henry Moore.

Opening Times: Tue to Sun 11:00-17:00. Wed until 20:00 during special exhibitions Admission: Adult £2.00, Concessions £1.00.
Map Ref: 11

Strangers Hall Museum

Charing Cross, Norwich NR2 4AL Tel: 01603 667229 Email: museums@norfolk.gov.uk
Web: www.norfolk.gov.uk/tourism/museums

One of the oldest and most fascinating buildings in Norwich. It is typical of houses occupied by the well-to-do city merchants when Norwich was in its heyday.

Opening Times: Tours Wed and Sat, please ring for times. Admission: Adult £2.50, Child £1.50, Concession £2.00.
Map Ref: 11

Sutton Windmill & Broads Museum

Sutton, Stalham, Norwich NR12 9RZ Tel: 01692 581195 Fax: 01692 583214 Email: broadsmuseum@btinternet.com

Windmill with nine floors. Museum has seven buildings, 1880s pharmacy, Tobacco Museum, kitchen items, animal traps, veterinary, TVs, radios, large engines, razors, banknotes, farm and trade tools, leathertrades, camera, soaps, polish, trade tricycles and coopers display.

Opening Times: Apr to Sep daily 10:00-17:30.
Admission: Child £1.50, OAP £3.50. Location: One mile off A149, nr Stalham. Brown tourism signs on A149.

Milk Hand Cart c1910
Map Ref: 14

North Norfolk (M & GN) Railway Museum

The Station, Station Approach, Sheringham NR26 8RA Tel: 01263 822045 Fax: 01263 820801 Email: enquiries@mandgn.co.uk Web: www.mandgn.co.uk

The Midland & Great Northern joint railway society is the support charity behind the North Norfolk Railway. The society is dedicated to preserving our railway heritage in East Anglia, especially that of the M & GN Railway. Displays of smaller artefacts are currently on view in the Sheringham Museum Coach and the model railway facilities at Weybourne and Holt. The society's collection of locomotives and rolling stock is also based on the railway.

Opening Times: Feb to Oct & Dec each day of timetable railway service. Admission: Free. Location: Museum coach is on platform three at the North Norfolk Railway's

Sheringham Station.
Map Ref: 15

Norfolk

Sheringham Museum

Station Road, Sheringham NR26 8RE   Tel: 01263 821871   Fax: 01263 825741
Email: lattaway@globalnet.co.uk

Boat building, fishing industry, lifeboats, Roman kiln, beach finds, war years, 'The Weybourne Elephant' - one and a half million years old, photographic displays, gallery.

Opening Times: Easter week to end of Oct, two weekends immediately prior to Xmas.
Admission: Adult £1.00, Child/Concession 50p, Groups of 10+ 35p.   Location: Station Road - in town centre; four minutes walk from main car park.   Map Ref: 15

THETFORD

Ancient House Museum

White Hart Street, Thetford IP24 1AA   Tel: 01842 752599
Email: ancient.house.museum@norfolk.gov.uk   Web: www.norfolk.gov.uk/tourism/museums

This magnificent timber-framed Tudor merchant's house was built about 1490, with an extension added about 1590. The house is jetted and timber-framed, using oak with wattle and daub in-fill with fine carved ceiling and fireplace timbers.

Opening: Mon to Sat 10:00-12:30, 13:00-17:00. Also open 1 Jun to 31 Aug Sun 14:00-17:00.
Admission: Sep to Jun free, Adult £1.00, Child 60p, OAP/Student/Concession 80p. Map Ref: 16

WELLS-NEXT-THE-SEA

The Bygones Museum at Holkham

Holkham Park, Wells-next-the-Sea NR23 1AB   Tel: 01328 711383   Fax: 01328 711707
Email: s.harvey@holkham.co.uk   Web: www.holkham.co.uk

Over 5000 items of domestic and agricultural memorabilia, carriages, vintage cars, working steam engines, kitchen, dairy, laundry. Music and money boxes. Typewriters and sewing machines.

Opening Times: 19, 20, 21 Apr, 3 May to 27 Oct daily 10:00-17:30. Closed Wed. Admission:
Holkham Hall & Bygones Museum: Adult £10.00, Child £5.00, Family £25.00. Museum: Adult £5.00, Child £2.50.   Location: 2 miles west of Wells-next-the-Sea, off A149 coast rd. Map Ref: 17

Thomas Coke-First Earl of Leicester

Holkham Hall

Wells-next-the-Sea NR23 1AB   Tel: 01328 710227
Fax: 01328 711693 Email: p.minchin@holkham.co.uk
Web: www.holkham.co.uk

This classic Palladian mansion was built in the mid 1700s by Thomas Coke, the first Earl of Leicester and is home to his descendants. It has a magnificent alabaster entrance hall and the sumptuous state rooms house Greek and Roman Statues, fine furniture and paintings by Rubens, Van Dyck, Gainsborough and many others. The Bygones Museum, housed in the Hall's original stable block, has more than 5,000 items of domestic and agricultural memorabilia on display from gramophones to fire engines.

Opening Times: May to end Sep Thu to Mon 13:00-17:00 (last admission 16:30). Plus following BHs - 19, 20 & 21 Apr, 3, 4 & 5 May, 24, 25 & 26 May, 23, 24 & 25 Aug 11:30-17:00. Admission: Holkham Hall: Adult £6.50, Child £3.25. Bygones Museum: Adult £5.00, Child £2.50. Combined ticket (Hall & Bygones): Adult £10.00, Child £5.00, Family £25.00. Location: Holkham is two miles west of Wells-next-the-Sea on the main A149, within easy reach of Norwich on the A1067, Kings Lynn on the A148 and London and Cambridge from the M11 and the A10.   Map Ref: 17

WYMONDHAM

Wymondham Heritage Museum

10 The Bridewell, Norwich Road, Wymondham NR18 0NS   Tel: 01953 600205
Web: www.wymondham-norfork.co.uk

Award-winning museum in 18th century model prison built 1785, later serving as a police station and courthouse. Dungeon and original cell. Displays about history of the building and town including Kett's rebellion, agriculture and brushmaking.

Opening Times: Mar to Nov Mon to Sat 10:00-16:00, Sun 14:00-16:00.   Admission: Adult £2.00, Child 50p, Concession £1.50. Groups by prior arrangement.   Location: Near town centre, two minutes walk from Market Cross and central car park.   Map Ref: 18

Never was such an area blessed with so many museums, exhibitions, shows, galleries and festivals. It is not surprising considering that this northern region (comprising Northumberland, Cleveland, County Durham and Tyne & Wear) is simply steeped in history, social, industrial and military and all minutely recorded in some of the finest museums in Britain. Added to this there are four hundred square miles of National Park telling its own story of the majestic beauty of the extreme north from Hadrian's Wall to the Cheviots and the Scottish Border. Hadrian's Wall, of course, boasts a string of museums telling their story of the Roman occupation of these lands, and most cities and towns of the region have their own museums.

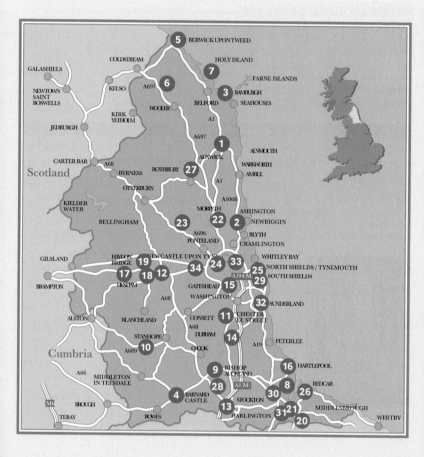

The Red Map References should be used to locate Museums etc on the pages that follow

Northumberland, Tyne & Wear, Durham

Alnwick Castle

Alnwick NE66 1NQ   Tel: 01665 510777/511100   Fax: 01665 510876
Email: enquires@alnwickcastle.com   Web: www.alnwickcastle.com

Set in magnificent Capability Brown landscape, Alnwick Castle is the home of the Duke of Northumberland. Owned by his family, the Percies, since 1309, the castle was a major stronghold during the Scottish wars. Restorations by the First and Fourth Dukes have transformed the massive fortress into a comfortable family home. The Italian Renaissance style State Rooms are filled with fine furniture, porcelain and paintings by Canaletto, Van Dyck and Titian.

Within the grounds are the recently refurbished museums of the Northumberland Fusiliers (1674 to present day), Northumberland Archaeology and the Percy Tenantry Volunteers (1798-1814). Quizzes and a location for the Harry Potter film make it a magical place for the whole family. Events include: birds of prey demonstrations, live music, open-air theatre and Wellington's Redcoat camp.

Opening Times: 1 Apr to 31 Oct daily 11:00-17:00 (last admission at 16:15). Admission: Adult £7.50, Child (under 16) Free, Concession £6.50.   Exhibitions & Events 2003 : For details of events visit the website or telephone 01665 510777.
Map Ref: 1

Bondgate Gallery

22 Narrowgate, Alnwick NE66 1JG Tel: 01665 576450

Eight exhibitions per year, also craft work including wood and glass.

Opening Times: Mon to Sat 10:30-16:00. Admission: Free. Location: 22 Narrowgate.
Map Ref: 1

Woodhorn Colliery Museum

Queen Elizabeth II Country Park, Ashington NE63 9YF Tel: 01670 856968 Fax: 01670 810958

Mining and social history displays within original late 19th century pit buildings. Highlights include paintings by the Ashington Group, miners' banners and a varied programme of temporary exhibitions. Families welcome.

Opening Times: Wed to Sun & BH 10:00-16:00 (17:00 May to Aug). Admission: Free.
Location: Ten minute walk from Ashington Bus Station.
Map Ref: 2

The RNLI Grace Darling Museum

2 Radcliffe Road, Bamburgh NE69 7AE Tel: 01668 214465 Web: www.lifeboats.org.uk

Items relating to the life of Grace Darling, including the original coble used for rescue.

Opening Times: Easter to Oct Mon to Sat 10:00-17:00, Sun 12:00-17:00. Admission: Free.
Map Ref: 3

Northumberland, Tyne & Wear, Durham

The Bowes Museum

Newgate, Barnard Castle DL12 8NP   Tel: 01833 690606   Fax: 01833 637163
Email: info@bowesmuseum.org.uk   Web: www.bowesmuseum.org.uk

A world-class visitor attraction. Don't miss this unique fine art gallery, housed in a magnificent French chateau in the picturesque market town of Barnard Castle in Teesdale. Learn the romantic story of the founders, John and Josephine Bowes. See the famous silver swan musical automaton. See paintings by Boudin, Canaletto and Goya. Join in the busy programme of exhibition and events.

Opening Times: Jan to Dec daily 11:00-17:00. Closed 25 to 26 Dec & 1 Jan. Admission: Adult £5.00, OAP/Concession £4.00, Under 16s Free. Group rates available. Location: Barnard Castle. Exhibitions & Events 2003 : To 26 Jan: Shipshape - Paintings by James Dodds, To 30 Mar: The Road to Impressionism - 19th century French paintings, including Monet, Boudin and Sisley loans, 5 Feb to 23 Mar: Reaching Beneath the Surface - Ceramic installation by Philomena Prestsell, 5 Apr to 1 Jun: Meridiano de Greenwich - Contemporary Spanish & English paintings, 14 Jun to tbc: Guild of Glass Engravers - Survey exhibition, 10 Nov to 2 Dec: Images 27 - Association of illustrators.   Map Ref: 4

The Bowes Museum has 30 public galleries. Set in formal gardens and parkland

Berwick-upon-Tweed Borough Museum & Art Gallery

The Clock Block, Berwick Barracks, Ravensdowne, Berwick-upon-Tweed TD15 1DQ
Tel: 01289 330044   Fax: 01289 330540

Berwick Museum, housed within Ravensdowne Barracks, explores local social history in 'Window on Berwick'. Also on display are many of the paintings and artefacts given to the town by Sir William Burrell.

Opening Times: 1 Nov to 29 Mar Wed to Sun 10:00-16:00, 30 Mar to 31 Oct daily 10:00-18:00.
Admission: Adult £2.80, Child £1.90, Concession £2.10. Location: Near town centre. Map Ref: 5

The King's Own Scottish Borderers Regimental Museum

The Barracks, Berwick-upon-Tweed TD15 1DG   Tel: 01289 307426
Fax: 01289 331928 Email: kosbmus@milnet.uk.net
Web: www.kosb.co.uk

The history of the Regiment from 1689 to the present day is traced through displays of uniforms, badges, medals, weapons, paintings and relics from the various campaigns in which it has been involved. Tableaux and dioramas dramatically bring to life the Regiment's battles and aspects of the soldier's profession.

Opening Times: Mon to Sat 09:30-16:30. Closed certain public holidays, Xmas & New Year. Admission: Adult £2.70, Child £1.40, Under 5s Free, Concession £2.00. Members of English Heritage Free. Members of Historic Scotland and CADW Free or half price. Location: Within Berwick Barracks, beside the town of Ramparts, two minutes walk from the town centre.   Map Ref: 5

Regimental Cap Badge

Lady Waterford Gallery

Ford Village, Berwick-upon-Tweed TD15 2QA   Tel: 01890 820524

A Victorian Hall, formerly Ford village school, houses the Waterford Murals created by Louisa Marchioness of Waterford from 1862 to 1883. The murals depict well known stories from the Bible, using children from the school and other local people as the subjects.

Opening Times: 23 Mar to 3 Nov, daily 10:30-12:30 & 13:30-17:30 Admission: Adult £1.50, Child over 12s £0.50, OAP/Concession £1.00. Location: Approx 12 miles south west from Berwick-upon-Tweed, Signposted from the A1 and A697.   Map Ref: 6

Northumberland, Tyne & Wear, Durham

Lindisfarne Priory

Holy Island, Berwick-upon-Tweed TD15 2RX   Tel: 01289 389200

One of the holiest sites of Anglo-Saxon England, Lindisfarne was renowned as the original burial place of St Cuthbert. Founded in 635 by St Aidan who came from Iona, it was the centre of Christianity in Scotland. Lindisfarne was a treasure house of jewels and manuscripts, including incomparable illuminated Gospels (now in British Library), and is still a holy site and place of pilgrimage today. In the award winning museum one of the most important collections of Anglo-Saxon stonework is on display.

Lindisfarne Priory © English Heritage

Opening Times: Apr to Sep daily 10:00-18:00, Oct daily 10:00-17:00, Nov to Mar daily 10:00-16:00. Closed Xmas & New Year.   Admission: Adult £2.90, Child £1.50, Concession £2.20.   Location: On Holy Island, only reached at low tide across causeway. For details of tides telephone Berwick Tourist Information 01289 330733.   Map Ref: 7

Billingham Art Gallery

Queensway, Billingham TS23 2LN   Tel: 01642 397590   Fax: 01642 397594

Offers an exciting selection of art to suit all tastes, providing a lively forum for local artists to exhibit their work.

Opening Times: Mon to Sat 09:00-17:00. Closed Sun & BH.   Admission: Free.
Location: Town centre.   Map Ref: 8

Binchester Roman Fort

Bishop Auckland   Tel: 01388 663089   Web: www.durham.gov.uk/bincester

Once the largest Roman Fort in County Durham. Now carefully excavated and displayed for you to enjoy to the full.

Opening Times: 18 to 21 Apr and 28 Apr to 28 Sept.   Admission: Adult £1.60,
Child/Concession 80p.   Map Ref: 9

Killhope, the North of England Lead Mining Museum

near Cowshill, Upper Weardale, Bishop Auckland DL13 1AR   Tel: 01388 537505   Fax: 01388 537617   Email: killhope@durham.gov.uk   Web: www.durham.gov.uk/killhope

Explores the life of North Pennine lead mining families. Visitors walk down the original mine tunnel and discover the working conditions of Victorian miners. See how miners lived and worked. Woodland walk & picnic site.

Opening Times: Apr to Sep 10:30-17:00, Oct Sat & Sun 10:30-17:00.   Admission: Without Mine: Adult £3.40 Child £1.70 Family £8.50. With Mine: Adult £5.00, Child £2.50, Family £12.50.
Location: On A689, 20 minutes from Stanhope and ten minutes from Alston.   Map Ref: 10

Key to Classifications
see Classifications Index on page 413

Anthropology	Jewellery	Railway
Archaeological	Literature & Libraries	Religion
Art Galleries	Maritime	Roman
Arts, Crafts & Textiles	Military & Defence	Science - Earth
China, Glass & Ceramics	Mills - Water & Wind	& Planetary
Communications	Multicultural	Sculpture
Egyptian	Music & Theatre	Sporting History
Fashion	Natural History	Stately Homes
Geology	Oriental	Toy & Childhood
Health & Medicine	Palaces	Transport
Horticultural	Police, Prisons & Dungeons	Victoriana

Northumberland, Tyne & Wear, Durham

Beamish, The North of England Open Air Museum
Beamish, Chester-le-Street DH9 0RG   Tel: 0191 370 4000
Fax: 0191 370 4001   Email: museum@beamish.org.uk   Web: www.beamish.org.uk

Experience the past at England's favourite open air museum - it's no ordinary museum but a vast, living and working experience of life as it was in the Great North. Buildings have been rebuilt and furnished to create a Colliery Village, Town Street, Railway Station and working Farm of 1913 and an 1825 Railway and Manor House. Photo archive and library. Designated museum.

Opening Times: Apr to Oct daily 10:00-17:00. Nov to Mar Tue to Thu, Sat & Sun 10:00-16:00. Closed Mon & Fri, Xmas & New Year.   Admission: Apr to Oct 02, Adult £12.00, Child £6.00, OAP £9.00 (2002 prices). Group

Recreation of The 1825 Railway at Beamish

rates available. Winter months reduced operation, everyone pays £4.00.   Location: North west of Durham (12 miles), signposted from junction 63 of A1M, Chester-le-Street.   Map Ref: 11

Corbridge Roman Site Museum
Corbridge NE45 5NT   Tel: 01434 632349

Originally the site of a fort on the former patrol road, Corbridge evolved into a principal town of the Roman era, flourishing until the fifth century. The large granaries are among its most impressive remains. The museum contains a vast selection of finds from the area, illustrating the history of Hadrian's Wall.

Opening Times: Apr to Sep daily 10:00-18:00, Oct daily 10:00-17:00, Nov to Mar Wed to Sun 10:00-13:00 & 14:00-16:00. Closed Xmas & New Year.   Admission: Adult £3.10, Child £1.60, Concession £2.30.   Location: Half a mile north west of Corbridge - signed Corbridge Roman Site.   Map Ref: 12

Darlington Railway Centre & Museum
North Road Station, Darlington DL3 6ST   Tel: 01325 460532   Fax: 01325 287746
Email: museum@darlington.gov.uk   Web: www.drcm.org.uk

Experience the atmosphere of the steam railway in the historic North Road Station of 1842. See Stephenson's 'Locomotion' and explore the railway heritage of the North East through a collection of engines, carriages/wagons and railway ephemera.

Opening Times: Daily 10:00-17:00. Closed Xmas & New Year.   Admission: Adult £2.10, Child £1.05, Concession £1.50.   Location: 15 minute walk from town centre, frequent bus service.   Map Ref: 13

DLI - Durham Light Infantry Museum & Durham Art Gallery
Aykley Heads, Durham DH1 5TU   Tel: 0191 384 2214   Fax: 0191 386 1770
Web: www.durham.gov.uk/dli

Interactive museum for all ages, telling the story of DLI soldiers and life on the 'home front'. Art Gallery - Exhibitions and events all year. Beautiful grounds with new nature walk.

Opening Times: Apr to Oct 10:00-17:00. Nov to Mar 10:00-16:00. Closed Xmas Day.   Admission: Adult £2.50, Concession £1.25, Family £6.25.   Location: Ten minute walk from city centre.   Map Ref: 14

Guided or Private Tours	Disabled Access	Gift Shop or Sales Point	Café or Refreshments	Restaurant	Car Parking

DURHAM *(continued)*

Durham Art Gallery

Aykley Heads, Durham DH1 5TU   Tel: 0191 384 2214   Web: www.durham.gov.uk/dli

Featuring a changing programme of artistic exhibitions and events. Details available in our Events Brochure and on our website.

Opening Times: 1 Apr to 31 Oct 10:00-17:00, 1 Nov to 31 Mar 10:00-16:00. Admission: Charges, family ticket available.   Map Ref: 14

Durham City Young Embroiderers Workshop

Durham University Oriental Museum

Elvet Hill, Durham DH1 3TH   Tel / Fax: 0191 374 7911   Email: oriental.museum@durham.ac.uk
Web: www.dur.ac.uk/oriental.museum

The Oriental Museum is the only museum in the North East devoted solely to Oriental art and archaeology. Here you can explore cultures that range from Ancient Egypt to Imperial China and modern Japan.

Opening Times: Mon to Fri 10:00-17:00, Sat to Sun 12:00-17:00. Closed Xmas & New Year.
Admission: Adult £1.50, Concessions 75p, Family £3.50.   Location: Five minute from bus stop.
15 minute walk from town centre.   Map Ref: 14

The Monks Dormitory, Durham Cathedral

The College, Durham DH1 3EH   Tel: 0191 386 4266   Fax: 0191 386 4267
Email: enquiries@durhamcathedral.co.uk   Web: www.durhamcathedral.co.uk

Magnificent beamed roof and collection of pre-conquest stones. During August facsimile of Lindisfarne Gospels.

Opening Times: 7 Apr to 28 Sep Mon to Sat 10:00-15:30, Sun 12:30-15:15.   Admission: Adult 80p, Child 20p, Family £1.50.   Location: In cloisters of Durham Cathedral.   Map Ref: 14

Museum of Archaeology, University of Durham

The Old Fulling Mill, The Banks, Durham DH1 3EB   Tel: 0191 3743623   Fax: 0191 374 7911
Web: www.dur.ac.uk/archaeology

The Old Fulling Mill is a 16th century mill originally part of the Cathedral estates. It houses an archaeology museum tracing the history of Durham City from prehistoric to post-medieval times.

Opening Times: Apr to Oct daily 11:00-16:00. Nov to Mar Fri to Mon 11:30-15:30.
Admission: Adult £1.00, Concession 50p, Family £2.50.   Location: Five minutes from city centre on riverbank below Cathedral.   Map Ref: 14

Treasures of St Cuthbert Exhibition

The Chapter Office, The College, Durham DH1 3EH   Tel: 0191 386 4266   Fax: 0191 386 4267
Email: enquiries@durhamcathedral.co.uk   Web: www.durhamcathedral.co.uk

St Cuthbert's Coffin and Pectoral Cross, Anglo Saxon embroideries, silverware, seals, manuscripts. 'Turning the pages' electronic version of Lindisfarne Gospels.

Opening Times: Mon to Sat 10:00-16:00, Sun 14:00-16:30 (Dec & Jan 16.15). Closed Xmas & Good Friday.   Admission: Adult £2.00, Child 50p, Concession £1.50, Family £5.00.
Location: In cloisters of Durham Cathedral.   Map Ref: 14

GATESHEAD *Tyne & Wear*

Bowes Railway Centre

Springwell Village, Gateshead NE9 7QJ   Tel: 0191 416 1847

Rope haulage, on set days steam locomotives, Victorian workshops, colliery railway artefacts, two display exhibition areas.

Opening Times: Mon to Fri 09:00-16:00 - Static only. Set operating days. Admission: Static: Free. Operating days: Adult £2.00, Child/Concession £1.00.   Location: Just outside Springwell village, five minutes walk from Wrekenton.   Map Ref: 15

Shipley Art Gallery

Prince Consort Road, Gateshead NE8 4JB   Tel: 0191 477 1495
Fax: 0191 478 7917   Web: www.twmuseums.org.uk

*The Shipley Art Gallery combines a dazzling display of the latest
glass, jewellery, ceramics, textiles and furniture alongside stunning
historical artworks. The Craft Gallery features over 700 breathtaking
pieces by the county's leading makers and paintings including Dutch
and Flemish Old Masters. The fascinating history of the town is told
in 'Made in Gateshead' and the Gallery stages superb temporary
exhibitions.*

Opening Times: Mon to Sat 10:00-17:00, Sun 14:00-17:00.
Admission: Free.   Location: Ten minute walk from town centre and
metro station.   Map Ref: 15

HARTLEPOOL *Cleveland*

HMS Trincomalee Trust

Jackson Dock, Hartlepool TS24 0SQ   Tel: 01429
223193

*HMS Trincomalee was built in 1817 and is the oldest ship afloat in
Britain. This classic British frigate has been fully and sensitively
restored and interpreted in an award-winning scheme. There are
disabled lifts between three decks. The ship provides a unique
opportunity to experience life aboard a British warship two centuries
ago. There are audio guides with guided tours available for groups.*

Opening Times: Apr to Oct 10:30-17:00, Nov to Mar 11:00-17:00.
Closed Xmas & New Year.   Admission: Adult £4.00, Concession
£3.00, Family (2 adults and 3 children) £11.00. Education Groups
£1.70.   Location: Located at Hartlepool Historic Quay. Follow the
brown tourist signs for the Quay and look for the masts! Map Ref: 16

HMS Trincomalee

Hartlepool Art Gallery

Church Square, Hartlepool TS24 8EQ   Tel: 01429 869706   Fax: 01429 523408
Email: arts-museums@hartlepool.gov.uk   Web: www.destinationhartlepool.com

*Programme of changing exhibitions feature the best of
contemporary art and craft and a varied and innovative
selection from Hartlepool's collection, including
'Centrestage' theatre, schools exhibition Apr to Jun. Also
views from tower of Hartlepool (small charge).*

Opening Times: Tue to Sat 10:00-17:30, Sun 14:00-17:00.
Closed Mon, Xmas & New Year.   Admission: Free.
Location: In magnificent converted Victorian Church, one
minute walk from Hartlepool Railway Station.   Map Ref: 16

Museum of Hartlepool

Jackson Dock, Hartlepool   Tel: 01429 860006
Fax: 01429 867332
Email: historic.quay@hartlepool.gov.uk
Web: www.destinationhartlepool.com

*The museum of Hartlepool tells the story of Hartlepool from
prehistoric times to the present day using many original artefacts,
photographs, models, hands-on and interactive displays.
Fascinating archaeological finds from the stone age and the time of
the Saxons give way to the engineering and shipbuilding
achievements of the Victorians. The constant presence of the sea
has influenced the development of the town throughout its history
and this is reflected in many of the objects on display. Toys and
games, sport and education provide a picture of social conditions.
The paddle steamer 'Wingfield Castle' is moored alongside the museum quay and has a café on
board.*

Northumberland, Tyne & Wear, Durham

HARTLEPOOL *(continued)*

Opening Times: Daily 10:00-17:00. Closed 25-26 Dec & New Year's Day. Admission: Free.
Location: At Hartlepool Marina, ten minutes walk from Hartlepool Railway Station.
Exhibitions & Events 2003 : 1 Jun to 9 Jun: Museum Week - Family fun activities to keep the children occupied during half term. This year the theme is Cultural Fun; join the fun, children's workshops, and enjoy the other activities arranged for the week, 26 May to 30 May 2003.
Map Ref: 16

HAYDON BRIDGE *Northumberland*

Housesteads Roman Fort & Museum
Haydon Bridge NE47 6NN Tel: 01434 344363

Housesteads is the most complete example of a Roman fort in Britain and is one of the twelve permanent forts built by Emperor Hadrian in around 124 AD. The museum houses a range of objects found at the site, including flat-bottomed pottery and larger cooking pots which are Friesian in origin. Some of the Wall has been partially reconstructed to give one of the most vivid pictures of the Romans and their works in Britain.

Housesteads Fort © English Heritage

Opening Times: Apr to Sep daily 10:00-18:00, Oct daily 10:00-17:00, Nov to Mar daily 10:00-16:00. Closed Xmas & New Year. Admission: Adult £3.10, Child £1.60, Concession £2.30. National Trust Members Free. Location: Nearly three miles north east of Bardon Mill on B6318.
Map Ref: 17

HEXHAM *Northumberland*

Chesterholm Museum - Vindolanda
Bardon Mill, Hexham NE47 7JN Tel: 01434 344 277 Fax: 01434 344 060 Email: info@vindolanda.com
Web: www.vindolanda.com

Vindolanda is a Roman Frontier military and civilian site, with archaeologists on site April to August, Sunday to Thursday, weather permitting. Vindolanda also offers an Open Air Museum featuring a Roman Temple, Shop and House, and an extensive museum housing finds from the site such as Roman boots, shoes, jewellery, textiles and special photographs of the rare ink on wood tablets written nearly 2000 years ago.

Aerial View of Roman Vindolanda

Opening Times: Nov to Feb daily 10:00-16:00, Mar & Oct daily 10:00-17:00, Apr & Sep daily 10:00-17:30, May & Jun daily 10:00-18:00, Jul & Aug daily 10:00-18:30. Admission: Adult £3.90, Child £2.80, OAP/Concession £3.30. Discounted joint saver tickets available with the Roman Army Museum. Location: One mile north of the A69, near Bardon Mill, Northumberland. Map Ref: 18

HEXHAM-ON-TYNE *Northumberland*

Chesters Fort & Museum
Chollerford, Humshaugh, Hexham-on-Tyne NE46 4EP Tel: 01434 681379

Chesters is one of the best-preserved examples of a cavalry fort. Many parts are still visible, including the barracks and a finely preserved bath house. The museum houses the important Clayton Collection of altars and sculptures.

Opening Times: Apr to Sep daily 09:30-18:00, Oct daily 10:00-17:00, Nov to Mar daily 10:00-16:00. Closed Xmas & New Year. Admission: Adult £3.10, Child £1.60, Concession £2.30.
Location: Quarter mile west of Chollerford on B6318.
Map Ref: 19

MIDDLESBROUGH *Cleveland*

Captain Cook Birthplace Museum

Stewart Park, Marton, Middlesbrough TS7 6AS   Tel: 01642 311211   Fax: 01642 317419

The Museum marks the site of Cook's birthplace in Marton on the outskirts of Middlesbrough. Recently transformed, it uses computers, films, special effects and interactives to give a unique insight into Cook's early life and his seafaring career in Whitby and the Royal Navy. Life aboard ship for the officers and crew, the fascinating discoveries made by

Exploring the wonders of life in the 18th century, when Cook was a lad

the ship's scientists and the legacy of Cook's visits are explored in detail. There are temporary exhibitions on related subjects and a varied programme of education and events. Collections - ethnography from countries visited by Cook plus maritime material, especially 18th century.

Opening Times: Mar to Oct Tue to Sun 10:00-17:30, Nov to Jan Tue to Sun 09:00-15:30, Feb Tue to Sun 09:00-16:00.
Admission: Adult £2.40, Child £1.20, OAP £1.20, Family £6.00.
Location: Within Stewart Park, Marton. Five minutes from Marton Railway Station.   Exhibitions & Events 2003 : For Exhibitions and Events please telephone for details.   Map Ref: 20

Sailing into uncharted waters with Cook

Cleveland Crafts Centre

Gilkes Street, Middlesbrough TS1 5EL   Tel: 01642 808090

Programme of craft based temporary exhibitions. Collection of studio pottery - Haile, Slee Leach etc on permanent display. A major collection of international contemporary jewellery occasionally on display.

Opening Times: Tues to Sat 10:00-17:30. Admission: Free. Location: In the town centre, at the rear of the bus station   Map Ref: 21

Middlesbrough Art Gallery

320 Linthorpe Road, Middlesbrough TS1 3QY   Tel: 01642 358139

Mainly 20th century British art which is now considered one of the finest collections in the north of England. Artists in the collection include David Bomberct, Jacob Epstein, Frank Auerbach, Stanley Spencer, Dame Elizabeth Frink and Paula Rego.

Opening Times: Tues to Sat 10:00-17:30. Admission: Free. Location: Near the town centre, on main road and bus routes.   Map Ref: 21

MORPETH *Northumberland*

Morpeth Chantry Bagpipe Museum

Bridge Street, Morpeth NE61 1PJ   Tel: 01670 519466   Fax: 01670 511326
Email: amoore@castlemorpeth.gov.uk

A unique museum, specialising in the Northumbrian small pipes, which are set in the context of bagpipes from around the world, from India to Inverness.

Opening Times: Jan to Dec Mon to Sat 10:00-17:00. Admission: Adult £1.50, Child/OAP 80p, Family £3.50. Location: Town centre, one minute from bus station, five minutes from railway station.   Map Ref: 22

Wallington

THE NATIONAL TRUST

Cambo, Morpeth NE61 4AR   Tel: 01670 773600   Fax: 01670 774420
Email: nwaplr@smtp.ntrust.org.uk   Web: www.nationaltrust.org.uk

Magnificent plaster work and notable ceramic collection. Large collection of dolls' houses and toys. Museum of Curiosities. Famous collection of Pre-Raphaelite depictions of Northumbrian history.

Opening Times: 23 Mar to 30 Sep daily except Tue 13:00-17:00. Admission: Adult £5.70, Group £5.20. Location: 20 minutes from Newcastle Airport.

The Central Hall at Wallington

Map Ref: 23

Castle Keep Museum

The Castle Keep, Castle Garth, Newcastle upon Tyne NE1 1RQ   Tel: 0191 2327938
Web: thekeep-newcastle.org.uk

Built in 1168-1178 one of the finest surviving examples of a Norman keep. Panoramic views of the city, the Tyne and its bridges (overlooks central railway station and main rail lines) from its roof. Small museum with artefacts relevant to site.

Opening Times: Apr to Sep daily 09:30-17:30, Oct to Mar daily 09:30-16:30. Closed Good Friday, 25-26 Dec & New Year. Admission: Adult £1.50, Child/OAP 50p. Special rates for parties of 12 or more. Location: Near town centre, three minutes walk from central railway station.

Map Ref: 24

Hancock Museum

Barras Bridge, Newcastle upon Tyne NE2 4PT   Tel: 0191 222 6765   Fax: 0191 222 6753
Web: www.twmuseums.org.uk

The North of England's premier Natural History Museum unravels the secrets of the natural world through sensational galleries. For more than one hundred years visitors have gained an insight into the animal kingdom and the powerful and sometimes destructive forces of Nature. From the Dinosaurs to live animals, the Hancock is home to creatures past and present and even the odd Egyptian mummy or two.

Opening Times: Mon to Sat 10:00-17:00, Sun 14:00-17:00. Admission: Adult £3.95, Child/Concession £2.95, Under 4s Free, Family £12.50. Location: Five minutes walk from city centre.

Map Ref: 24

Hatton Gallery

The Quadrangle, University of Newcastle, Newcastle upon Tyne NE1 7RU   Tel / Fax: 0191 222 6059   Email: hatton-gallery@ncl.ac.uk   Web: www.ncl.ac.uk/hatton

Permanent collections on display - African art and the Kurt Schwitters Merzbarn. In addition the gallery presents a series of prestigious and stimulating temporary exhibitions.

Opening Times: Mon to Fri 10:00-17:30, Sat 10:00-16:30. Closed Sun, BH and Xmas & New Year. Admission: Free. Location: City centre, two minutes walk from Haymarket Metro Station and Haymarket Bus Station.

Map Ref: 24

Laing Art Gallery

New Bridge Street, Newcastle upon Tyne NE1 8AG   Tel: 0191 232 7734 Fax: 0191 222 0952 Web: www.twmuseums.org.uk

The North of England's premier art gallery displays a stunning array of watercolours, costume, silver, glass, pottery and sculpture alongside a striking programme of historical and contemporary exhibitions. Major works by leading Pre-Raphaelite artists including Willian Holman Hunt and Edward Burne-Jones by L S Lowry. Younger visitors can let their artistic skills run riot in the P & G Children's Gallery which includes soft play, puzzles and books. Art on Tyneside

looks about the rich history of art and craft on Tyneside, including paintings, silver, ceramic, glass and textiles. Using sound, interactive games and open exhibits, the exhibitions also features a re-creation of an 18th century coffee shop, a Victorian art gallery and Tyne Bridge. The hugely popular and high profile temporary exhibition programme of both historical and contemporary art has made the Laing Art Gallery one of the most popular art galleries in the UK. The gallery also offers a café and new craft shop that sells everything from art history books to the latest contemporary craft.

Opening Times: Mon to Sat 10:00-17:00, Sun 14:00-17:00.
Admission: Free. Location: One minute walk from city centre.
Exhibitions & Events 2003 : For Exhibitions and Events please
telephone for details.   Map Ref: 24

Military Vehicle Museum

Exhibition Park Pavillion, Newcastle upon Tyne NE2 4PZ   Tel: 0191 281 7222
Email: miltmuseum@aol.com   Web: www.military.museum.org.uk

Over 50 vehicles, 60 cabinets depicting a soliders life from 1900 to date. World War I trench, Anderson Shelter and Home Front display.

Opening Times: Mar to Nov daily 10:00-16:00, closed Aug BH. Nov to Mar Sat, Sun and school holidays 10:00-16:00. Closed 25-26 Dec & New Years Day.   Admission: Adult £2.00, Child/Concession £1.00, Under 5s Free.   Map Ref: 24

Museum of Antiquities

University of Newcastle upon Tyne, Newcastle upon Tyne NE1 7RU   Tel: 0191 222 7849
Fax: 0191 222 8561   Email: l.allason-jones@ncl.ac.uk   Web: www.ncl.ac.uk/antiquities

Ideal place to start visit to Hadrian's Wall. Artefacts from 8000BC to 1600AD give the visitor a unique insight into the history of the north of England.

Opening Times: Mon to Sat 10:00-17:00. Closed Sun, Xmas & New Year and Good Friday.
Admission: Free. Location: In town centre. One minute walk from Haymarket.   Map Ref: 24

Newcastle Discovery Museum

Blandford Square, Newcastle upon Tyne NE1 4JA   Tel: 0191 232 6789   Fax: 0191 233 1088
Web: www.twmuseums.org.uk

Explore Newcastle's past from Romans to the present day. Tyneside inventions that changed the world, a fun approach to science, a soldier's life, and take a walk through fashion. The museum is currently undergoing an exciting £12.25 million transformation to introduce spectacular new displays, including a whole floor of galleries devoted to life on the River Tyne.

Opening Times: Mon to Sat 10:00-17:00, Sun 14:00-17:00. Admission: Free. Location: Ten minutes from city centre and central station.   Map Ref: 24

Shefton Museum of Greek Art & Archaeology

The Armstrong Building, University of Newcastle upon Tyne, Newcastle upon Tyne NE1 7RU
Tel: 0191 222 8996   Fax: 0191 222 8561   Email: l.allason-jones@ncl.ac.uk
Web: www.ncl.ac.uk/shefton-museum

The most important collection of archaeological material from the Greek world in the north of England.

Opening Times: Mon to Fri 10:00-16:00. Closed Sat, Sun and BH.   Admission: Free.
Location: In town centre, one minute walk from Haymarket.   Map Ref: 24

Stephenson Railway Museum

Middle Engine Lane, West Chirton, North Shields NE29 8DX   Tel / Fax: 0191 200 7145   Web: www.twmuseums.org.uk

Relive the glorious days of the steam railway at Stephenson Railway Museum. The Museum is home to George Stephenson's 'Billy', a forerunner of the world-famous Rocket and many other engines from the great age of steam including 'Jackie Milburn', named after the Newcastle United legend. A ride on a real steam train can be taken and the story of coal and electricity is also told.

Opening Times: Seasonal - call for details.   Admission: Free.
Map Ref: 25

Kirkleatham Old Hall Museum

Kirkleatham, Redcar TS10 5NW   Tel: 01642 479500

Local history collection reflecting life in Redcar and Cleveland: archaeology; social history (working and domestic life - ironstone mining; iron and steel making; fishing; shipbuilding; sea rescue); paintings; photographs. Permanent Galleries, temporary exhibitions, associated activities and events. Programme for schools and other groups. Housed in early 18th century listed building in important conservation area.

Kirkleatham Old Hall

Opening Times: Apr to Sep Tue to Sun 10:00-17:00, Oct to Mar Tue to Sun 10:00-16:00. Closed Mon (except BH) and Xmas to New Year.   Admission: Free.
Location: Kirkleatham Village, near Redcar.   Map Ref: 26

Zetland Lifeboat Museum

5 King Street, Redcar TS10 3PF   Tel: 01642 494311   Web: www.lifeboats.org.uk

Displays relating to Zetland Lifeboat, the oldest surviving lifeboat, and the Royal National Lifeboat Institution. 200th Anniversary of 'The Zetland' lifeboat in 2002.

Opening Times: Daily during summer. Closed Nov to Mar.   Admission: Free.   Map Ref: 26

Cragside

Rothbury NE65 7PX   Tel: 01669 620150   Fax: 01669 620066
Email: ncrvmx@smtp.ntrust.org.uk

Norman Shaw's high Victorian mansion with original furniture and fittings including William Morris stained glass and earliest wallpapers. Built for the great inventor-industrialist Lord Armstrong, who installed the world's first hydro-electric lighting.

Opening Times: House: 23 Mar to Sep 13:00-17:30, Oct to 3 Nov 13:00-16:30. Last admission one hour before closing.   Admission: Adult £6.90, Child £3.50, Family £17.30. Group rates available.   Location: Entrance one mile north of Rothbury on B6341, 15 miles north west of Morpeth, 13 miles south west of Alnwick.   Map Ref: 27

SHILDON *Durham*

Timothy Hackworth
Victorian & Railway Museum

Hackworth Close, Shildon DL4 1PQ   Tel / Fax: 01388 777999
Web: www.hackworthmuseum.co.uk

Dedicated to railway pioneer Timothy Hackworth; his former home built in 1830s contains Hackworth memorabilia, early railway exhibits and period rooms. 1830s Hackworth locomotive contained in shed built c1837. 1939 Peckett steam locomotive 'Merlin' gives occasional passenger rides. 1829 replica Sanspareil, also Steamingon special event days.

Opening Times: Easter to last Sun in Oct, Wed to Sun 10:00-17:00, also BH. Closed Xmas & New Year. Admission: Adult £2.00, Child £1.00, OAP £1.50. Groups by arrangement. Location: South east of Shildon town centre, two minutes from railway station. Exhibitions & Events 2003 : Please phone for brochure or visit website.   Map Ref: 28

SOUTH SHIELDS *Tyne & Wear*

Arbeia Roman Fort & Museum

Baring Street, South Shields NE33 2BB   Tel: 0191 456 1369   Fax: 0191 427 6862
Web: www.twmuseum.org.uk

Situated four miles east of the end of Hadrian's Wall at South Shields, Arbeia Roman Fort guarded the entrance to the River Tyne. Built about AD160 the stone fort played an essential role in the mighty frontier system. Originally built to house a garrison Arbeia soon became the military supply base for the 17 forts along the Wall. Today, the excavated remains, stunning reconstructions of original buildings and finds from the fort show what life was like in Roman Britain. Arbeia

combines the excavated remains of this Roman military supply base with reconstructions of the fort's buildings and stunning finds unearthed from the site to show what life was like on Hadrian's Wall. The fort's West Gate has been reconstructed and work is currently under way to reconstruct the Commanding Officer's house and a soldiers' barrack block. Nowhere else on Hadrian's Wall can the sheer scale of the Romans' achievements be better understood than here at Arbeia. The museum displays feature finds excavated at Arbeia, which are amongst the most impressive found along the World Heritage Site. TimeQuest gives visitors the chance to find out what it's like to be an archaeologist.

Opening Times: Easter to Sep Mon to Sat 10:00-17:30, Sun 13:00-17:00. Oct to Easter Mon to Sat 10:00-16:00, closed Sun. Admission: Free. Location: Near town centre 10-15 minutes walk from metro and bus. Exhibitions & Events 2003 : For Exhibitions and Events please telephone for details.   Map Ref: 29

South Shields Museum & Art Gallery

Ocean Road, South Shields NE33 2TA   Tel: 0191 456 8740   Fax: 0191 456 7850
Web: www.twmuseums.org.uk

The Museum is currently closed as it undergoes an exciting £1 million transformation. It will re-open in 2004 with: new display reflecting upon the experiences of local people during the last century and featuring the life of the world-famous author Catherine Cookson; an art adventure centre which will feature stunning paintings combined with hands-on diplays; a refurbished education room, a lift to all floors and toilets to make your visit more comfortable. For more information please contact Susan Raikes on 0191 456 8740

Opening Times: Re-opening in 2004. Admission: Free. Location: In centre of town.   Map Ref: 29

Northumberland, Tyne & Wear, Durham

Green Dragon Museum   ♿ ▓

Theatre Yard, off High Street, Stockton-on-Tees TS18 1AT   Tel: 01642 393938   Fax: 01642 393936

Incorporating the focus at photography gallery. The museum offers a lively mix of the best in contemporary photography and history as told through photography.

Opening Times: Mon to Sat 09:00-17:00. Closed Sun & BH.   Admission: Free.
Location: Town centre off High Street.   Map Ref: 30

Preston Hall Museum   ♿ ▓ 🅿 🚜

Yarm Road, Stockton-on-Tees TS18 3RH   Tel: 01642 781184

The museum illistrates Victorian social history with reconstructions of period rooms and a street with working craftsmen; collection includes costume, toys, arms, armour. There are 112 acres of parkland with riverside walks.

Opening Times: Easter to Sep daily 10:00-17:30, Oct to Easter Mon to Sat 10:00-16:30, Sun 14:00-16:30. Closed Good Friday, Xmas & New Year.   Admission: Adult £1.20, Child/Concession 60p.   Location: Set in 112 acres of parkland, between Stockton and Yarm on A135.   Map Ref: 31

Booking Office

Monkwearmouth Station Museum   ♿ ▓ 🚜

North Bridge Street, Sunderland SR5 1AP   Tel: 0191 567 7075
Fax: 0191 510 9415   Web: www.twmuseum.org.uk

This splendid Victorian railway station recreates a sense of rail travel in times past. Explore the ticket office as it would have looked in Victorian times, see the guard's van and goods wagon in the railway sidings and watch today's trains zoom past Platform Gallery. The Children's Gallery has a range of toys, books and dressing-up clothes.

Opening Times: Mon 10:00-15:45, Tue to Sat 10:00-17:00, Sun 14:00-17:00.   Admission: Free.   Location: Ten minute walk from city centre.   Map Ref: 32

North East Aircraft Museum   ▓ 🚜

Washington Road, Sunderland SR5 3HZ   Tel: 0191 5190662
Web: www.members.tripod.com/~BDaugherty/neam.html

A collection of 35 aircraft including the Vulcan Bomber and Pucara from the Falkland Islands. Aero engines, aeronautica and a large display of models from the early days of flight to the present day.

Opening Times: Apr to Sep daily 10:00-17:00, Oct to Mar 10:00-16:00. Closed Xmas & New Year.   Admission: Adult £3.00, Child/OAP £1.50. Please phone for Family and Group Concessions.   Location: Brown signposted off the A19 west of Sunderland, near to the Nissan Car Assembly Plant.   Map Ref: 32

Sunderland Museum & Winter Gardens   ♿ ▓ 🅿 ◑

Mowbray Gardens, Burdon Road, Sunderland SR1 1AF   Tel: 0191 553 2323   Fax: 0191 553 7828   Web: www.twmuseums.org.uk

11 exciting hands-on exhibits and interactive displays tell the story of Sunderland from its prehistoric past through to the present day. The Art Gallery features paintings by L S Lowry alongside Victorian masterpieces and artefacts from the four corners of the world. The displays look at traditional industries including shipbuilding coal mining, pottery, glass and textile crafts through to the prehistoric, medieval and 20th century history of the City. The natural world is also explored through stunning wildlife displays and live animals. The newly refurbished museum features a striking new glazed entrance; visitor facilities such as a large shop, a brasserie, toilets and lifts to all floors form a significant part of the scheme. The stunning new Winter Gardens is home to over 1,000 of the world's most exotic flowers, plants and

SUNDERLAND *Tyne & Wear (continued)*

trees. Some of the amazing plants include an 80 year old Sicilian olive tree, a 3.5 metre-high Palm tree and a 6.5 metre-high Yucca elaphanties from Honduras, the world's largest type of Yucca. The Gardens also feature sculptures, a waterfall, Koi carp and a stunning treetop walkway, from which visitors can look on to the displays.

Opening Times: Mon 10:00-16:00, Tue to Sat 10:00-17:00, Sun 14:00-17:00. Admission: Free. Location: In town centre. Exhibitions & Events 2003 : For Exhibitions and Events please telephone for details.   Map Ref: 32

WALLSEND *Tyne & Wear*

Segedunum Roman Fort, Baths & Museum

Buddle Street, Wallsend NE28 8HR   Tel: 0191 236 9347   Fax: 0191 295 5858
Web: www.twmuseums.org.uk

In AD122 the Emperor Hadrian ordered a mighty frontier system to be built across Britain to defend the Roman Empire from the barbarians to the north. Segedunum Roman Fort stood on the banks of the River Tyne and was

the last outpost of Hadrian's Wall. Today, Segedunum is once again the gateway to this world-famous heritage site. The excavated remains of the fort with spectacular reconstructions and exciting,

hands-on museum displays show what life was like in Roman Britain. The remains represent the most extensively excavated site in the Empire and the reconstructed bath-house is the only one of its kind in Britain. No other site on Hadrian's Wall can match the views from the 100 feet-high tower. The museum features finds excavated from the fort with the latest technology to show what life was like for the soldiers who lived at the fort. The history of the fort and Wallsend after the decline of the Roman Empire is also explored.

Opening Times: 1 Apr to 31 Oct daily 10:00-17:00. 1 Nov to 31 May daily 10:00-15:30.
Admission: Adult £3.50, Child/Concession £2.95. Location: One minute walk from Wallsend Metro.   Map Ref: 33

WYLAM *Northumberland*

Wylam Railway Museum

The Falcon Centre, Falcon Terrace, Wylam NE41 8EE   Tel: 01661 852174/853520
Email: wylampc@btinternet.com

George Stephenson 'The Father of Railways' was born in Wylam and historic locomotive 'Puffing Billy' worked on Wylam Colliery waggonway. Displays in this attractive small museum illustrate Wylam's unique place in railway history.

Opening Times: Tue & Thu 14:00-17:00 & 17:30-19:30, Sat 09:00-12:00. Admission: Free. Donations welcome. Location: The Falcon Centre, off Main Street at Fox & Hounds Inn.
    Map Ref: 34

Oxfordshire

The county is not renowned for its large cities and towns with Oxford, the county town, being the largest. However, the city is an important commercial, residential and industrial centre dominated by its university, the colleges of which, both ancient and modern, have their own particular character and treasures.

Oxford boasts museums and galleries of international fame and there are interesting collections to be found in Banbury, Henley and Woodstock.

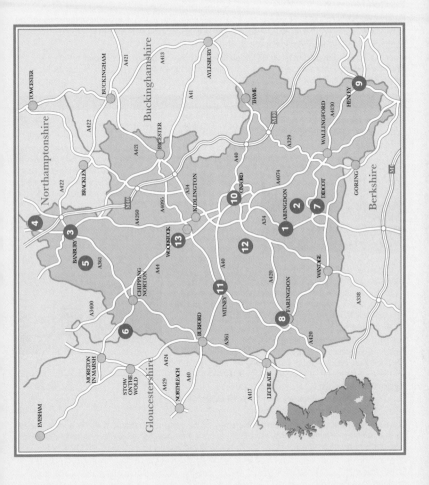

The Red Map References should be used to locate Museums etc on the pages that follow

Oxfordshire

Abingdon Museum
County Hall, Market Place, Abingdon OX14 3HG   Tel: 01235 523703   Fax: 01235 536814

The County Hall was built between 1678-1682 by Christopher Kempster, master mason who worked with Christopher Wren on St Paul's Cathedral. The museum contains local history from 'England's oldest town'.

Opening Times: Daily 10:30-16:00. Please telephone to check BH. Roof top closed during winter.   Admission: Free. (Roof top £1.00).   Location: In town centre.   Map Ref: 1

Pendon Museum
Long Wittenham, Abingdon OX14 4QD   Tel: 01865 407365   Web: www.pendonmuseum.com

Rural life in the Vale of the White Horse in the 1930s, recreated in miniature, together with the railways that ran through the Vale.

Opening Times: Sat & Sun 14:00-17:00, also Wed during Jul & Aug. Open from 11:00 on all Bank Holiday weekends except Xmas.   Admission: Adult £4.00, Child £2.00, Under 7s Free, OAP £3.50, Family £12.00.   Map Ref: 2

Banbury Museum
Spiceball Park Road, Banbury OX16 2PQ   Tel: 01295 259855   Fax: 01295 269469

Banbury's new canal-side museum is open. The stunning new displays illustrate Banbury's history, beginning with some of the stories and events that have made Banbury famous, such as the nursery rhyme 'ride a cock horse to Banbury Cross'. The principal displays tell four stories: the English Civil War and how it affected Banbury; the development of the plush weaving industry (plush is a velvet like fabric); the Victorian Town; and Banbury in the 20th century. Also on display is a rare collection of cost-

ume dating from the 17th century. A separate gallery interprets the Tooley's Boatyard and the Oxford Canal. Tooley's Boatyard is a scheduled ancient monument that is attached to the museum and can be visited on a guided tour. Excellent visitor facilities are available including a canal-side café.

Opening Times: Mon to Sat 09:30-17:00, Sun 10:30-16:00.   Admission: Free.   Location: Town centre, main entrance Castle Quay Shopping Centre.   Map Ref: 3

Bygones Museum
Butlin Farm, Claydon, Banbury OX17 1EP   Tel: 01295 690258
Email: bygonesmuseum@yahoo.com

Local Banbury shops, display centre. Victorian kitchen and work shops. Traction engine, steam roller, stationary engines, tractors etc. War and craft memorabilia, typewriters, sewing machines, jars, bottles and lots more.

Opening Times: Apr to Oct Wed to Sun 10:30-16:30. Closed Mon & Tue.   Admission: Adult £2.50, Child £1.75, OAP £2.00, Family £7.50.   Location: In the centre of a small village, six miles north of Banbury.   Map Ref: 4

Oxfordshire

Swalcliffe Barn

Shipston Road, Swalcliffe, Banbury
Tel: 01295 788278 Email: jcdemmar@btinternet.com
Web: www.oxfordshire.gov.uk

A magnificent 15th century barn with an original half-cruck timber roof structure. It was built in 1401 for the Rectorial Manor of Swalcliffe by New College, Oxford. The barn houses a collection of trade vehicles and agricultural machinery from Oxfordshire used in the 19th & 20th centuries.

Bread delivery hand cart,
Headington, Oxford

Opening Times: Easter to Oct Sun 14:00-17:00 or by appointment. Admission: Free. Location: In village centre. Exhibitions & Events 2003 : Easter to Oct: Swalcliffe Village History Exhibition. Map Ref: 5

Swalcliffe Barn from the west

Chastleton House

Chastleton, near Stow-on-the-Wold GL56 0SU Tel / Fax: 01608 674355
Email: tchgen@smtp.ntrust.org.uk Web: www.nationaltrust.org.uk/regions/thameschilterns

One of England's finest and most complete Jacobean houses, filled with a mixture of rare and everyday objects, especially tapestries.

Opening Times: Apr to Sep Wed to Sat 13:00-17:00, Oct Wed to Sat 13:00-16:00.
Admission: Adult £5.40, Child £2.70, Family £13.50, National Trust Members Free.
Location: Six miles from Stow-on-the-Wold. Approach only from A436 between A44 (west of Chipping Norton) and Stow-on-the-Wold. Map Ref: 6

Didcot Railway Centre

Didcot OX11 7NJ Tel: 01235 817200 Fax: 01235 510621 Email: didrlyc@globalnet.co.uk
Web: didcotrailwaycentre.org.uk

See the steam trains of the Great Western Railway, the original engine shed and a recreation of Brunel's broad gauge railway. Programme of Steamdays and special events including 'Day out with Thomas' during the year.

Opening Times: 27 May to 7 Sep daily 10:00-17:00, rest of the year Sat & Sun 10:00-16:00.
Admission: Adult £4.00-£7.50, Child £3.00-£6.00, OAP £3.50-£6.50, Family £12.00-£19.00.
Location: At Didcot Parkway rail station, signed from M4 junction 13 and A34. Map Ref: 7

Buscot Park

THE NATIONAL TRUST

Estate Office, Faringdon SN7 8BU
Tel: 0845 345 3387/01367 240786 Fax: 01367 241794
Email: estbuscot@aol.com Web: www.buscot-park.com

The 18th century house houses the Faringdon Collection of fine paintings, including works by Rembrandt, Murillo, Reynolds, Rossetti and the famous Briar Rose series by Burne-Jones. Also furniture with important pieces by Adam, Thomas Hope and others, together with porcelain and objets d'art. It is set in attractive parkland with lakes, a water garden by Peto and a walled garden. A tea room serves home-made cream teas and cakes from 14:30-17:30.

Opening Times: 2 Apr to 28 Sep Wed to Fri 14:00-18:00. Also BH inc Good Friday and 2nd & 4th weekends in each month, phone infoline for exact dates. Admission: Adult £5.00, Child £2.50, National Trust Members Free. Location: On A417 between Faringdon & Lechlade. Map Ref: 8

The Hall, with 'Egyptian' furniture by Thomas Hope

Oxfordshire

HENLEY-ON-THAMES

The Rowing Gallery

River & Rowing Museum ♿ 🏪 📷 🅿 🚌

River & Rowing Museum
Henley on Thames

Mill Meadows, Henley-on-Thames RG9 1BF
Tel: 01491 415600 Fax: 01491 415601
Email: museum@rrm.co.uk Web: ww.rrm.co.uk

Visit the award winning River & Rowing Museum with its stunning architecture and unique interpretation of the River Thames from its source to sea, the riverside town of Henley-on-Thames with its famous Royal Regatta and the sport of Rowing from the days of the Ancient Greek Trireme to the recent success of the Sydney Coxless Four. History is brought to life with interactive displays and fascinating exhibits for all the family. Special exhibitions, family activities and events are held throughout the year and its Riverside Café offers excellent food in distinctive surroundings.

Henley Gallery

Opening Times: Sep to Apr daily 10:00-17:00, May to Aug daily 10:00-17:30. Closed 24-25 Dec & 31 Dec-1 Jan. Admission: Adult £4.95, Concession £3.75, Family £13.95. Location: Off A4130, signposted to Mill Meadows. A short walk from Henley Town Centre, five minutes from Henley on Thames Railway Station.
Exhibitions & Events 2003 : 7 Dec to 16 Mar: Canoe Pioneers: Adventures with Rob Roy, 14 Dec to 2 Mar: Henley in the Frame: Lucy Cooper's views of the town, Mid Mar to Jun: ROMANS: They came, they saw, they stayed, 12 Apr to 2 Nov: Thames at War: The story of the river during WWII, 10 May to 1 Jun: Artweeks Exhibition, 28 Jun to 19 Oct: Everyday Images: Naive painting of daily life 1750-1900.
Map Ref: 9

OXFORD

Ashmolean Museum of Art & Archaeology 📷 ♿ 🏪 📷 🅿 Ashmolean

Beaumont Street, Oxford OX1 2PH Tel: 01865 278000
Fax: 01865 278018 Web: www.ashmol.ox.ac.uk

Uccello, The Hunt in the Forest

The Ashmolean houses the Oxford University's collections of art and antiquities. They range over four millennia - from Ancient Egypt, Greece and Rome to Renaissance Europe and the 20th century, plus an extensive Far Eastern collection. Sculpture, paintings, ceramics, glass, coins and musical instruments are all on show.

Opening Times: Tue to Sat 10:00-17:00, Sun 14:00-17:00. Admission: Free. Location: Town centre, five minutes walk from bus station, ten minutes walk from Railway Station. Exhibitions & Events 2003 : 7 Jan to 20 Apr: The Arts of Japan: Acquisitions from the Story Fund, 22 Jan to 25 May: The Four Seasons: This small but beautiful exhibition is an introduction to the skills and meaning of Chinese landscape painting, 19 Feb to 23 Mar: New 20th Century Prints: Two sets of prints from the artists Huey O'Donoghue and Georg Baselitz, 16 Apr to 14 Sep: Old Master Prints: A selection including works by Rembrandt, 22 Apr to 20 Jul: An Englishman's Travels in Egypt: Edward Lane in Cairo (1825 - 35), 30 Apr to 27 Jul: The Rothschild Collection of Ancient Coins, 11 Jun to 28 Sep: The Reyes Collection of Modern Chinese Painting, 22 Jul to 5 Oct: Tibetan Thangka Paintings: A display of Tibetan Buddhist scroll paintings.
Map Ref: 10

Bate Collection of Musical Instruments 📷 ♿ 🏪

Faculty of Music, St Aldate's, Oxford OX1 1DB Tel: 01865 276139 Fax: 01865 276128
Email: bate.collection@music.ox.ac.uk Web: www.ashmol.ox.ac.uk/bcmipage.html

A collection of over a thousand historic woodwind, brass and percussion instruments, a dozen historic keyboards including what may have been Handel's harpsichord; a unique bow-maker's workshop and fine collection of bows.

Opening Times: Mon to Fri 14:00-17:00, Sat 10:00-12:00. (During Oxford full term only)
Admission: Free. Location: Near town centre, next to Christ Church College. Map Ref: 10

Oxfordshire

Christic Church Picture Gallery

Christ Church, Oxford OX1 1DP   Tel: 01865 276172   Fax: 01865 202429
Email: dennis.harrington@christ-church.ox.ac.uk   Web: www.chch.ox.ac.uk

Christ Church Picture Gallery was designed in 1968 by Powell and Moya and holds 300 paintings and 2000 drawings by famous artists such as Van Dyck, Leonardo and Michelangelo.

Opening Times: Oct to Mar Mon to Sat 10:30-13:00 & 14:00-16:30, Sun 14:00-16:30. Easter to Sep daily 10:30-17:30.   Admission: Adult £2.00, OAP/Student/Concession £1.00. Free on Mon.
Location: Near the town centre.   Map Ref: 10

Modern Art Oxford

30 Pembroke Street, Oxford OX1 1BP   Tel: 01865 722733   Fax: 01865 722573
Web: www.modernartoxford.org.uk

Located in the heart of historic Oxford, the Modern Art Oxford presents outstanding exhibitions of modern and contemporary art from all over the world. Exhibitions include painting, sculpture, photography, video, film and architecture. It's a great place to add to your 'must see' list in Oxford. The Café serves delicious, freshly cooked food and is child and baby friendly.

Opening Times: Tue to Sat 10:00-17:00, Sun 12:00-17:00, Closed Mon. Late openings on event nights.
Admission: Free. Location: City centre, ten minutes walk from railway station, five minutes from High Street.   Map Ref: 10

A Victorian Kitchen c.1880

Museum of Oxford

St Aldates, Oxford OX1 1DZ
Tel: 01865 252761   Fax: 01865 202447
Email: museum@oxford.gov.uk   Web: www.oxford.gov.uk/museum

Discover Oxford's history by visiting the Museum of Oxford, the only museum in Oxford to tell the story of the city and its people from prehistoric times to the present day. The exhibits range from a mammoth's tooth to a 'Morris Motor' car engine. Archaeological treasures including a preserved Roman pottery kiln and a whole pavement made of cattle bones. There are six Oxford rooms recreated inside the museum from an Elizabethan inn to a Victorian kitchen. A full programme of workshops and activities for schools and families is available - term time, school holiday and weekends.

Hythe Bridge/Oxford Castle
by Michael Angelo Rooker c.1790

Opening Times: Tue to Fri 10:00-16:00, Sat 10:00-17:00, Sun 12:00-16:00. Admission: Adult £2.00, Child 50p, Concession £1.50. Location: Centre of town, five minute walk from bus station, ten minutes walk from train station.
Exhibitions & Events 2003 : May to Jun: Oxfordshire Artweeks, May: Museum & Galleries Month - Free admission and activities on specified days, All Year: Museum of Oxford Kids Club - Special events, workshops and competitions.   Map Ref: 10

Oxfordshire

Museum of the History of Science

Broad Street, Oxford OX1 3AZ   Tel: 01865 277280
Fax: 01865 277288   Email: museum@mhs.ox.ac.uk
Web: www.mhs.ox.ac.uk

Outstanding collection of early scientific instruments, astrolabes, sundials, telescopes, microscopes, etc. Displayed in Britain's first museum building includes globes, navigation, physics, chemistry and some of the earliest surviving instruments from a range of countries and cultures.

Opening Times: Tue to Sat 12:00-16:00, Sun 14:00-17:00. Closed Xmas. Admission: Free. Location: Broad Street, next to Sheldonian Theatre.   Map Ref: 10

Islamic Astrolabe

Oxford University
Museum of Natural History

Parks Road, Oxford OX1 3PW   Tel: 01865 272950   Fax: 01865 272970   Email: info@oum.ox.ac.uk   Web: www.oum.ox.ac.uk

The Oxford University Museum of Natural History houses Oxford University's extensive collection of entomological, geological, mineralogical and zoological material of international importance. Current displays include the remains of Alice's Dodo Bird and a splendid display of Dinosaurs.

Opening Times: Daily 12:00-17:00. Closed Xmas and Easter. Admission: Free. Location: Central Oxford on Parks Road immediately opposite Keble College.   Map Ref: 10

T-rex in Victorian Court

Pitt Rivers Museum 

Parks Road, Oxford OX1 3PP   Tel: 01865 270927   Fax: 01865 270943
Web: www.prm.ox.ac.uk

This unique museum is one of Oxford's most popular attractions, famous for its period atmosphere and outstanding collections. Founded in 1884, the displays still retain much of the original layout and appearance; cases are crowded with amulets, beads, pots, masks, shrunken heads, textiles, toys and more, from many cultures around the world past and present. Many objects still carry their first tiny hand-printed label.

Opening Times: Mon to Sat 12:00-16:30, Sun 14:00-16:30. Admission: Free. Location: Ten minutes walk from city centre. Entrance through Oxford University Museum of Natural History.   Map Ref: 10

The Pitt Rivers Museum from the Upper Gallery

Bishop's Palace Site

Mount House, Church Green, Witney   Tel: 01993 814114   Fax: 01993 813239
Email: martyn.brown@oxfordshire.gov.uk   Web: www.oxfordshire.gov.uk

The archaelogical site of the Bishop of Winchester's Palace at Witney.

Opening Times: Easter to Sep Sat & Sun 14:00-16:00. Admission: Free. Location: East of the church on the Green.   Map Ref: 11

Oxfordshire Museums Store

Witney Road, Standlake, Witney OX28 7QG   Tel: 01865 300972   Fax: 01865 300519
Email: martyn.brown@oxfordshire.gov.uk   Web: www.oxfordshire.gov.uk

Purpose built store and collections centre for conservation and museum support services. Contains natural science, archaeology, social history, transport, agricultural, crafts, textiles, arts - all relating to Oxfordshire.

Opening Times: Mon to Fri 9:00-17:00 by appointment. Public open days in May & Sep. Admission: Free. Location: A415 four miles south of Witney.   Map Ref: 12

Oxfordshire

Blenheim Palace
Woodstock OX20 1PX   Tel: 01993 811325
Fax: 01993 813527   Email: administrator@blenheimpalace.com
Web: www.blenheimpalace.com

Blenheim Palace, home of the 11th Duke of Marlborough and birthplace of Sir Winston Churchill, is an English Baroque masterpiece, with fine furniture, sculpture, paintings and tapestries set in magnificent gilded state rooms overlooking sweeping lawns and formal gardens. The Palace is set in 2100 acres of parkland landscaped by 'Capability' Brown and offering walks with beautiful views over the lake and through the trees.

Opening Times: Mid Mar to end Oct 10:30-16:45.
Admission: Adult £10.00, Child £5.00, OAP/Student £7.50.
Location: A44 eight miles from Oxford.   Exhibitions & Events 2003

Blenheim Palace, South Front

: 19 to 22 Jun: Blenheim Palace Flower Show, 4 to 7 Sep: Blenheim Petplan International Horse Trials.

Map Ref: 13

Oxfordshire Museum
Fletchers House, Park Street, Woodstock OX20 1SN   Tel: 01993 811456
Fax: 01993 813239   Email: oxonmuseum@oxfordshire.gov.uk
Web: www.oxfordshire.gov.uk

Located in a fine town house in the historic centre of Woodstock, the museum provides a window on Oxfordshire's rich history. Following a major Heritage Lottery funded extension and refurbishment the museum's new displays celebrate Oxfordshire in all its diversity. Featured collections reflect the archaeology, local history, landscape and wildlife of the county as well as providing an introduction to the astonishing range of ideas and technologies developed in Oxfordshire. Gallery interactives provide hands-on enjoyment for children and new computer programmes enable visitors to explore a variey of information about the objects on display. Visitors to the museum can also enjoy its peaceful garden whilst sampling a range of light refreshments in the new coffee shop.

The Oxfordshire Museum
entrance from Park Street

The Coffee Shop extension
adjoining Fletchers House

Opening Times: Tue to Sat 10:00-17:00, Sun 14:00-17:00.
Admission: Adult £2.50, Child 50p, OAP/Concession £1.00, Family £4.50.   Location: In town centre, adjacent gates to Blenheim Palace.

Map Ref: 13

Shropshire

Shrewsbury, the county town, almost encircled by the River Severn, was from Norman times strategically important as the gateway to Wales. In the eighteenth century it became a popular centre of fashionable society and boasts a wealth of fine Georgian buildings. Despite being primarily a rural agricultural county, it was here in the eighteenth century that the Industrial Revolution was born, in the Ironbridge Gorge of the Severn.

Shropshire can be justifiably proud of its first class museums concerned with the archaeology, natural history, social and industrial history of the region.

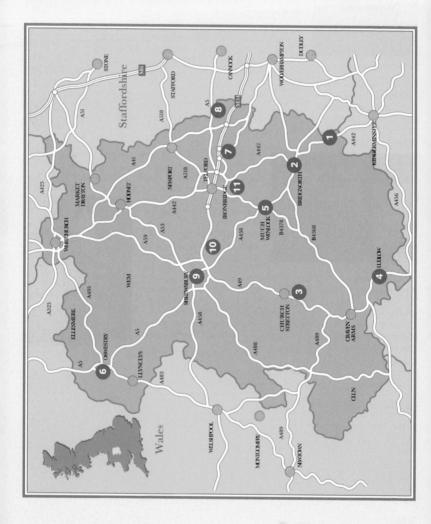

The Red Map References should be used to locate Museums etc on the pages that follow

Shropshire

Dudmaston

Quatt, Bridgnorth WV15 6QN   Tel: 01746 780866   Fax: 01746 780744

A late 17th century house, intimate family rooms, fine furniture, Dutch oil paintings and sculpture. 'Sir George La Bouchure' Collection of modern art. Collections of watercolours and botanical art. Nine acres garden with lakeside and Dingle Walk.

Opening Times: Apr to Sep Sun, Tue, Wed & BH Mon - House: 14:00-17:30 Garden: 12:00-18:00. Garden only Mon.   Admission: House & Garden: Adult £3.95, Child £1.30, Family £9.00. Garden: Adult £2.80.   Location: Four and a half miles south of Bridgnorth on A442 Telford to Kidderminister road.   Map Ref: 1

Northgate Museum

Burgess Hall, Northgate, Bridgnorth WV16 4ER   Tel: 01746 762830

Special features - local pictures, working 17th century turret clock, firemarks, coats-of-arms, coins, tokens, carpet loom, cameras, Victorian basinet, clay pipes, 17th century chest lock, man trap.

Opening Times: Easter to Oct Sat & Sun 14:00-16:00. School holidays Mon to Wed 14:00-16:00, extended openings, from 11:30 where possible.   Admission: Free, donation welcome.
Location: Near town centre, five minutes from car parks in 13th century gatehouse.   Map Ref: 2

Acton Scott Historic Working Farm Museum

Wenlock Lodge, Acton Scott, Church Stretton SY6 6QN   Tel: 01694 781306/7   Fax: 01694 781569   Email: acton.scott.museum@shropshire-cc.gov.uk
Web: www.actonscottmuseum.co.uk

Acton Scott Historic Working Farm demonstrates farming and rural life in South Shropshire at the close of the 19th century. This is achieved not only by collecting, renovating and exhibiting implements and other agricultural items, but also by farming as it would have been farmed in the period from about 1875 to the 1920s.

Opening Times: 26 Mar to 27 Oct Tue to Sun & BH 10:00-17:00. Closed Mon except BH.
Admission: Adult £3.95, Child £1.50, Under 5s Free, OAP £3.50. Groups: Adult £3.00, Child £1.25, Under 5s Free, OAP £2.50.   Location: Four miles south of Church Stretton off A49, 17 miles south of Shrewsbury of A49, 14 miles north of Ludlow off A49 at Marshbrook.   Map Ref: 3

Ludlow Museum

11/13 Castle Street, Ludlow SY8 1AS   Tel: 01584 875384   Web: www.shropshire-cc.gov.uk/museum.nsf

Make a visit to Ludlow Museum and unlock the natural and social history of this fascinating planned town and the surrounding region.

Opening Times: Apr to Oct Mon to Sat 10:30-13:00 14:00-17:00. Jun, Jul & Aug also open Sun.
Admission: Free.   Location: In town centre.   Map Ref: 4

Much Wenlock Museum

High Street, Much Wenlock TF13 6HR   Tel: 01952 727773
Web: www.shropshire.cc.gov.uk/museum.nsf

Displays of archaeology, natural history, social history, Wenlock Olympian Society, Wenlock Edge Geology.

Opening Times: Apr to Sep Mon to Sat 10:30-13:00 & 14:00-17:00. Jun, Jul & Aug also open Sun.   Admission: Free.   Location: In the centre of town.   Map Ref: 5

Oswestry Transport Museum

Oswald Road, Oswestry SY11 1RE   Tel: 01691 671749   Email: hignetts@enterprise.net

Collection of Cambrian Railways related artefacts dating from 1880s up to present day. Small collection of bicycles and motorbikes.

Opening Times: Daily 10:00-16:00.   Admission: Adult £1.00, Concession 50p.
Location: Near town centre.   Map Ref: 6

SHIFNAL

Royal Air Force Museum Cosford

Cosford, Shifnal TF11 8UP   Tel: 01902 376200   Fax: 01902 376211
Email: cosford@rafmuseum.com   Web: www.rafmuseum.com

The RAF Museum at Cosford houses over 80 aircraft in three wartime hangars. Fine examples of our aviation heritage are displayed in the Transport, Research and Development, Warplanes, Missiles and Aero-engine Collections.

Opening Times: Daily 10:00-18:00 (last admission 16:00). Closed Xmas & New Year.
Admission: Free admission.   Location: On A41, less than one mile from junction 3 on M54.

Map Ref: 7

Weston Park

Weston-under-Lizard, Shifnal TF11 8LE   Tel: 01952 852100   Fax: 01952 850430
Email: enquiries@weston-park.com   Web: www.weston-park.com

Weston Park

Weston Park is a magnificent Stately Home set in 1000 acres of Parkland. Built in 1671 the house boasts a superb collection of paintings including works by Van Dyck, Constable and Stubbs, furniture and objets d'art. Outside, visitors can explore the glorious parkland, meander through the formal gardens, take a variety of woodland walks before relaxing for lunch in The Stables Restaurant.

Opening Times: Easter, Apr, May, Jun & Sep weekends, Jul & Aug daily. Admission: Adult £4.50, Child £2.50, OAP £3.50. Location: Situated on A5 at Weston-under-Lizard, three miles off junction 3 on M54 and eight miles off junction 12 on M6.

Map Ref: 8

SHREWSBURY

Shrewsbury Museum & Art Gallery

Rowley's House, Barker Street, Shrewsbury SY1 1QH   Tel: 01743 361196   Fax: 01743 358411
Email: museums@shrewsbury-atcham.gov.uk   Web: www.shrewsburymuseums.com

Major regional museum; archaeology, geology, Shropshire ceramics, costume and social history, special exhibition programme linking historic collections and contemporary artists, including national and international names.

Opening Times: May BH to end of Sep Tue to Sat 10:00-17:00, Sun & Mon 10:00-16:00. Oct to May Tue to Sat 10:00-16:00. Admission: Free. Location: Town centre, five minutes from bus and railway stations.

Map Ref: 9

Wroxeter Roman City

Wroxeter Roman Site, Wroxeter, Shrewsbury SY5 6PH   Tel: 01743 761330

Wroxeter was once the fourth largest city in Roman Britain, with an impressive bath house, the remains of which are still visible today. The museum includes a column capital carved in the shape of a hare.

Opening Times: Apr to Sep daily 10:00-18:00, Oct daily 10:00-17:00, Nov to Mar daily 10:00-13:00 & 14:00-16:00. Closed Xmas & New Year. Admission: Adult £3.70, Child £1.90, Concession £2.80, Family £8.80   Location: At Wroxeter, five miles east of Shrewsbury on B4380.

Map Ref: 10

Shropshire

Blists Hill Victorian Town

Telford   Tel: 01952 586063/583003   Email: info@ironbridge.org.uk
Web: www.ironbridge.org.uk

Working factories, shops and cottages in a beautiful wooded landscape where life is lived - and demonstrated - as it was in Victorian times. Victorian industry, crafts and traditions are brought to life by the townsfolk who illustrate Britain's fascinating industrial history and social life in the streets and buildings of the town.

Opening Times: Apr to Nov daily 10:00-17:00, Nov to Mar 10:00-16:00. Admission: Please call for details. Group rates available.
Location: Situated five miles from Telford Central.   Map Ref: 11

Broseley Pipe Works

Duke Street, Broseley, Telford   Tel: 01952 882445
Email: info@ironbridge.org.uk   Web: www.ironbridge.org.uk

Once home to one of the most prolific clay tobacco pipe factories in Britain. Production ceased in the 1950s when the works were abandoned and left untouched until reopened as a museum in 1996. During its restoration little has been changed since the workers left, a wonderfully preserved 'time capsule' of an ancient local industry.

Opening Times: Apr to Nov daily 13:00-17:00. Closed Nov to Mar. Admission: Please call for details. Group rates available. Location: Five miles from Telford Central.   Map Ref: 11

Coalport China Museum & Youth Hostel

Coalport, Telford   Tel: 01952 580650
Email: info@ironbridge.org.uk   Web: www.ironbridge.org.uk

The national collections of Caughley and Coalport china are displayed in the restored factory buildings and bottle kilns of the old Coalport China Works. Galleries show the beautiful china and explore the hardships of factory life. Enjoy the children's gallery, workshops and speciality china shop.

Opening Times: Daily 10:00-17:00. Closed Xmas.
Admission: Please call for details. Group rates available.
Location: Five miles from Telford Central.   Map Ref: 11

Darby Houses & Quaker Burial Ground

Darby Road, Coalbrookdale, Telford   Email: info@ironbridge.org.uk
Web: www.ironbridge.org.uk

Rosehill and Dale House are restored Quaker Ironmasters' homes, built overlooking the Darby Furnace in Coalbrookdale. Rosehill is fully restored as it would have been when the Darby family lived there, housing personal belongings of the family.

Opening Times: Apr to Nov daily 10:00-17:00. Closed Nov to Mar. Admission: Please call for details. Group rates available. Location: Five miles from Telford Central.   Map Ref: 11

Iron Bridge & Tollhouse

Ironbridge, Telford   Tel: 01952 884391 Email: info@ironbridge.org.uk   Web: www.ironbridge.org.uk

The great symbol of success for the iron industry is the Iron Bridge, located in the heart of the designated world heritage site. The Toll House houses an exhibition about the Bridge and its fascinating history.
(continued over page)

235

Opening Times: Iron Bridge: open year round. Toll House: Apr to Nov daily 10:00-17:00. Closed Nov to Mar. Admission: Please call for details. Group rates available. Location: Located in Ironbridge Town Centre - five miles from Telford Central. Map Ref: 11

Jackfield Tile Museum

Jackfield, Telford   Tel: 01952 882030
Email: info@ironbridge.org.uk   Web: www.ironbridge.org.uk

Jackfield boasts magnificent displays of decorative tiles and ceramics throughout its gas-lit galleries within the restored Victorian factory buildings. Witness modern tile making combining drop-in workshops to make this a fascinating visit.

Opening Times: Closed for refurbishment until Autumn 2003.
Admission: Please call for details. Group rates available.
Location: Five miles from Telford Central. Map Ref: 11

Museum of Iron & Darby Furnace

Coalbrookdale, Telford   Tel: 01952 433418
Email: info@ironbridge.org.uk   Web: www.ironbridge.org.uk

The museum interprets the beginnings of industry and the lives of those who lived and worked in Coalbrookdale. The galleries now house an exhibition dedicated to the Great Exhibition of 1851. There is also a chance to see the original iron smelting furnace of Abraham Darby I.

Opening Times: Daily 10:00-17:00. Closed Xmas.
Admission: Please call for details. Group rates available.
Location: Five miles from Telford Central. Map Ref: 11

Museum of the Gorge

Ironbridge, Telford   Tel: 01952 432405   Email: info@ironbridge.org.uk
Web: www.ironbridge.org.uk

The Old Severn Warehouse is a short walk alongside the River Severn from the Iron Bridge. Built in the 1830s it was used as a riverside warehouse by the Coalbrookdale Company. Inside is an exhibition covering the whole history of the Gorge including a scaled model of the River Valley as it was in 1796.

Opening Times: Daily 10:00-17:00. Closed Xmas.
Admission: Please call for details. Group rates available.
Location: Five miles from Telford Central. Map Ref: 11

Tar Tunnel

Coalport Road, Coalport, Telford   Tel: 01952 580827   Email: info@ironbridge.org.uk
Web: www.ironbridge.org.uk

A feature that presents the first natural source of bitumen that was discovered over 200 years ago. Visitors can don a hard hat to witness this spectacular monument.

Opening Times: Apr to Nov daily 10:00-17:00. Closed Nov to Mar. Admission: Please call for details. Group rates available. Map Ref: 11

Taunton, the county town, has been the centre of county life since Saxon times and it was here in 1685 that the Duke of Monmouth was declared King of England. Glastonbury is closely associated with the Arthurian legends and stories of the Holy Grail and the miraculous Christmas flowering Glastonbury Thorn.

Somerset is an intriguing county of strange places and strange happenings, well reflected in its excellent museums.

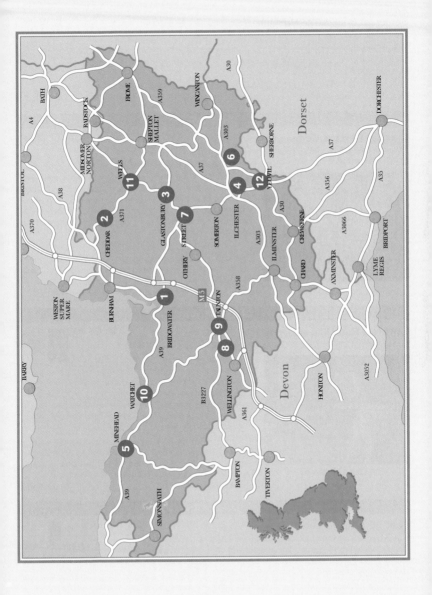

The Red Map References should be used to locate Museums etc on the pages that follow

Somerset

Blake Museum

Blake Street, Bridgwater TA6 3NB   Tel: 01278 456127   Fax: 01278 446412
Email: museums@sedgemoor.gov.uk   Web: www.sedgemoor.gov.uk

Bridgwater's museum of local history and archaelogy. Special features include Robert Blake (1598-1657), The Monmouth Rebellion (1685). Bridgwater's colourful and exciting carnival, maritime history and the brick and tile industry.

Opening Times: Tue to Sat 10:00-16:00.   Admission: Free.   Location: In the town centre.
Map Ref: 1

Somerset Brick & Tile Museum

East Quay, Bridgwater TA6 3NB   Tel: 01278 426088

The only remaining tile kiln in Bridgwater and an impressive survivor of a major Somerset industry. Visitors can enter the kiln and see some of the many varied patterns of bricks, tiles and other wares made here.

Opening Times: Thu & Fri 09:00-16:00 or by arrangement.   Admission: Free.   Location: In East Quay, ten minutes from town centre.
Map Ref: 1

CHEDDAR

Cheddar Caves & Gorge

Cheddar BS27 3QF   Tel: 01934 742343   Fax: 01934 744637
Email: caves@cheddarcaves.co.uk   Web: www.cheddarcaves.co.uk

'Cheddar Man' Museum connected with show caves and other attractions. Museum features Britain's oldest complete skeleton (9000 years old) and evidence of late upper palaeolithic life in Gough's Cave. Come and see how your ancestors lived in our caves. Ticket includes entry to all attractions.

Opening Times: Daily May to mid Sep 10:00-17:00, mid Sep to Apr 10:30-16:30.   Admission: Adult £7.90, Child £5.00, Under 5s Free.   Location: In Britain's biggest gorge, one mile from Cheddar village centre.   Map Ref: 2

Cox's Cave

GLASTONBURY

Somerset Rural Life Museum

Abbey Farm, Chilkwell Street, Glastonbury BA6 8DB   Tel: 01458 831197

In the Abbey Farmhouse the social and domestic life of Victorian Somerset is described in reconstructed rooms and an exhibition which tells the life story of a farm worker, John Hodges. The magnificent 14th century Abbey barn is the centrepiece of the Museum. The barn and farm buildings surrounding the courtyard contain displays illustrating the tools and techniques of farming in Somerset until the 1940s.

Opening Times: Tue to Fri & BH Mon 10:00-17:00, Sat & Sun 14:00-18:00. Closed Good Friday.   Admission: Free.   Location: In Glastonbury, follow signs to the Tor and Shepton Mallet A361.
Map Ref: 3

Repairing a wagon wheel

ILCHESTER

Fleet Air Arm Museum

Box D6, RNAS Yeovilton, Ilchester BA22 8HT   Tel: 01935 840565
Fax: 01935 842630   Email: info@fleetairarm.com   Web: www.fleetairarm.com

FLEET AIR ARM
MUSEUM

The Fleet Air Arm Museum is the only British museum sited next to an operational military airfield. From the viewing galleries you may well see some of the Royal Navy's aircraft flying. The museum shows over 40 aircraft within the many exhibitions throughout the four large halls. 'Leading Edge' tells the story of aircraft from early biplane to Concorde and the Sea Harrier. Innovative touch screen displays show you how aircraft fly and tell the stories of the aircraft and

Somerset

The Merlin experience

the men who flew them. 'Fly on board' the museum's own aircraft carrier, 'refitted' for 2003; tour the carrier's nerve centre and experience at close hand the thrills and noises of a working flight deck. New for 2003 is 'Projecting Power' the stories of the last 55 years of 'peacetime', and two temporary exhibitions, 'The Queen and Her Navies' and '100 years of Flight', in addition to major permanent displays covering the two World Wars and many other campaigns in which shipborne aircraft have played their part.

Concorde 002 and interactives within Leading edge

Opening Times: Apr to Oct daily 10:00-17:30, Nov to Mar daily 10:00-16:30. Closed 24-26 Dec. Admission: Adult £8.00, Child £5.75, OAP £6.75, Family (2 adults and 3 children) £25.00. Prices subject to change 1 Apr 03. Group and school prices on request. Location: On the B3151, just off the A303 near Ilchester. Exhibitions & Events 2003 : 22 Feb: Fleet Air Arms Seventh Model Show - one of the largest in the UK.   Map Ref: 4

MINEHEAD

West Somerset Railway

The Railway Station, Minehead TA24 5BG   Tel: 01643 704996
Fax: 01643 706349   Email: info@west-somerset-railway.co.uk
Web: www.west-somerset-railway.co.uk

7828 'Odney Manor' arrives at Minehead Station

Britain's longest Heritage Railway running 20 miles between Bishop's Lydeard (near Taunton) and Minehead, through the Quantock Hills and along the Exmoor Coast. Ten stations serving a variety of destinations.

Opening Times: Mar to Dec (selected dates) 09:30-17:30. Admission: Adult £10.00, Child £5.00, OAP £8.00. Party rates on application. Location: Four miles from Taunton (junction 25 on M5). Nearest main line railway station - Taunton.   Map Ref: 5

SPARKFORD

Haynes Motor Museum

Sparkford BA22 7LH   Tel: 01963 440804   Fax: 01963 441004
Email: info@haynesmotormuseum.co.uk   Web: www.haynesmotormuseum.co.uk

300 historic cars, over 50 motorcycles, military and commerical vehicles plus memorabilia displayed in spectacular style. Exhibits include Schumacher's F1 Ferrari and a Jaguar XJ220 supercar. Awarded 'Motor Museum of the Year'.

Opening Times: Mar to Oct 09:30-17:30, Nov to Feb 10:00-16:30. Open 09:30-18:30 during summer school holidays. Closed Xmas Day and New Year's Day. Admission: Adult £6.00, Child £3.50, Concession £5.00, Family from £7.50. Location: Conveniently located just off A303 at Sparkford in Somerset.   Map Ref: 6

STREET

The Shoe Museum

40 High Street, Street BA16 0YA   Tel: 01458 842169   Email: janet.targett@clarks.com

Contains shoes from Roman times to the present, buckles, fashion plates, machinery, hand tools and advertising material. Early history of Clarks Shoes and its role in the town.

Opening Times: Mon to Fri 10:00-16:45, Sat 10:00-17:00, Sun 11:00-17:00. Admission: Free. Location: Close to Clarks Village.   Map Ref: 7

Somerset

Sheppy's Farm & Cider Museum

Three Bridges Farm, Bradford-on-Tone, Taunton TA4 1ER   Tel: 01823 461233   Fax: 01823 461712   Email: info@sheppyscider.com   Web: www.sheppyscider.com

A small private collection of agricultural and cider-making artefacts and machinery. Includes a video of the cider-maker's year.

Opening Times: Mon to Sat (all year) 08:30-18:00, Sun (Easter to Xmas) 12:00-14:00.
Admission: Adult £2.00, Child £1.50, OAP £1.75.   Location: A38 half way between Taunton and Wellington, Junction 26 of M5.   Map Ref: 8

Somerset County Museum

The Castle, Castle Green, Taunton TA1 4AA
Tel: 01823 320201

There is a rich variety of objects on show at the Museum relating to the County of Somerset to intrigue and stir the imagination. There are toys and dolls, fossils, fine silver and pottery, and a rich collection of archaeological items from pre-historic and Roman Somerset. You can follow the fortunes of the Somerset Light Infantry in part of the Somerset Military Museum.

Opening Times: Tue to Sat & BH Mon 10:00-17:00. Closed Good Friday. Admission: Free. Location: Five minute walk from Taunton Town Centre.   Map Ref: 9

Somerset Military Museum

County Museum, The Castle, Taunton TA1 4AA   Tel: 01823 320201

The history of the County Regiments, especially the Somerset Light Infantry (Prince Albert's) from the 18th to the 20th century, illustrated through their uniforms, equipment, medals and memorabilia.

Opening Times: Tue to Sat & BH Mon 10:00-17:00. Closed Good Friday. Admission: Free.
Location: Within the Somerset County Museum, five minute walk from Taunton Town Centre.
                                                                                                     Map Ref: 9

Watchet Market House Museum

Market Street, Watchet TA23 0AN   Tel: 01984 631345

Watchet from pre-history to present day. Fossils and Saxon Mint, iron ore mines, railways and harbour trade and industries. Maritime paintings, photographs and models.

Opening Times: Easter to Sep daily 10:30-12:30 & 14:30-16:30, Jul & Aug 19:00-21:00.
Admission: Free. Location: Close to harbour.   Map Ref: 10

Wells Museum

8 Cathedral Green, Wells BA5 2UE   Tel: 01749 673477   Email: wellsmuseum@ukonline.co.uk

Wells Museum exhibits Medieval Cathedral statuary at close quarters, an insight into the social and natural history of Wells and the Mendip area and the varied artefacts excavated from the archaeological dig in the museum gardens.

Opening Times: Easter to Oct 10:00-17:30. Oct to Easter 11:00-16:00. Jul and Aug open until 20:00. Closed Tue (in winter) and Xmas Day. Admission: Adult £2.50, Child £1.00, Concession £2.00, Family £6.00. Location: Adjacent to Wells Cathedral.   Map Ref: 11

Museum of South Somerset

Hendford, Yeovil BA20 1UN   Tel: 01935 424774

Pre-historic and Roman occupation through to agricultural and industrial revolutions, South Somerset's association with leather and glove manufacturing. You can also see the Linotype setter which was in use for newspaper production.

Opening Times: Apr to Sep Tue to Sat 10:00-16:00, Oct to Mar Tue to Fri 10:00-16:00.
Admission: Free. Location: Near town centre.   Map Ref: 12

Suffolk

The superb landscape of this county has been immortalised in the paintings of John Constable who delighted in painting the lovely Stour Valley. The county is also renowned for the work of another great painter, Thomas Gainsborough.

The Suffolk museums and galleries are mostly concerned with local history and indeed the beauty of the county but other subjects include horseracing, transport, mechanical music, historic aircraft, and clocks and watches.

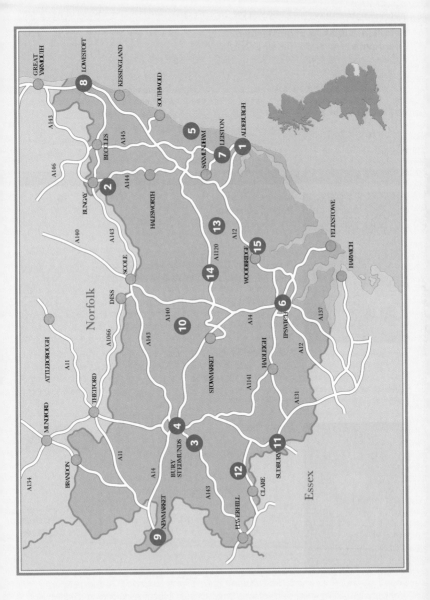

The Red Map References should be used to locate Museums etc on the pages that follow

Suffolk

Moot Hall Museum

Market Cross Place, Aldeburgh IP15 5BT   Tel: 01728 453295

Local history, Anglo Saxon urns etc. Shape Cemetery excavation 1862. Tudor building - paintings and finds from river and sea resulting from coastal erosion. Local flora and fauna, flints etc.

Opening Times: Easter to May Sat & Sun 14:30-17:00, Jun, Sep & Oct daily 14:30-17:00, Jul & Aug 10:30-12:30 14:30-17:00. Closed Nov to Easter. Admission: Adult £1.00, Child Free.
Location: Near centre of town.
Map Ref: 1

Norfolk & Suffolk Aviation Museum:
East Anglia's Aviation Heritage Centre

Buckeroo Way, The Street, Flixton, Bungay NR35 1NZ   Tel: 01986 896644
Email: nsam.flixton@virgin.net   Web: ww.aviationmuseum.net

Historic aircraft, indoor exhibitions - both civil and military, from the pioneer years through World War I to the present day. Special displays on Boulton & Paul, World War II Decoy Sites & Nature Walk.

Opening Times: Apr to Oct Sun to Thu 10:00-17:00, Nov to Mar Sun, Tue & Wed 10:00-16:00.
Closed 15 Dec to 15 Jan. Admission: Free. Location: On B1062 off A143, one mile west of Bungay.
Map Ref: 2

Ickworth House, Park & Gardens

THE NATIONAL TRUST

The Rotunda, Horringer, Bury St Edmunds IP29 5QE
Tel: 01284 735270 Fax: 01284 735175
Email: aihusr@smtpntrust.org.uk Web: www.nationaltrust.org.uk

The eccentric Earl of Bristol created this equally eccentric house, with its central rotunda and curved corridors, to house his collections. These include paintings by Titian, Gainsborough and Velasquez and a magnificent Georgian silver collection. The house is surrounded by an Italianase garden and set in a Capability Brown park with woodland walks, deer enclosure, vineyard, church, canal and lake.

The Pompeian Room

Opening Times: House: 22 Mar to 2 Nov 13:00-17:00. Closed Wed and Thu. Garden: 22 Mar to 2 Nov 10:00-17:00. Park: daily 07:00-19:00. Admission: Adult £6.10, Child £2.75, National Trust Members Free. Location: Located in the village of Horringer, two miles from the town of Bury St Edmunds. Exhibitions & Events 2003 : For full events list, call 01284 735961.
Map Ref: 3

Manor House Museum

Honey Hill, Bury St Edmunds IP33 1RT
Tel: 01284 757076 Fax: 01284 747231
Email: saskia.stent@manorhse.stedmundsbury.gov.uk
Web: www.stedmundsbury.gov.uk/manorhse

The Manor House Museum consists of clocks, watches, paintings, furniture and costume. We are renowned for having the finest collections of clocks and watches in England. The House was built in the Georgian period of 1738, purely as an entertaining home for Lady Elizabeth Hervey, the wife of the first Earl of Bristol.

Opening Times: Wed to Sun 11:00-16:00. Admission: Adult £2.50, Child/OAP £2.00, Free to residents of St Edmundsbury.
Location: Five minute walk from the Town Centre, through the Abbey gardens and churchyard.
Map Ref: 4

Suffolk

Moyses Hall Museum

Cornhill, Bury St Edmunds IP33 1DX   Tel: 01284 706183   Fax: 01284 765373
Email: moyses.hall@stedsbc.gov.uk   Web: www.stedmundsbury.gov.uk/moyses.htm

Recently extended and refurbished local history museum includes Suffolk Regiment Gallery, history of Bury St Edmunds display in a wonderful 800 year old building.

Opening Times: Daily 10:30-16:30, Sat & Sun 11:00-16:00   Admission: Free for residents of Bury St Edmunds, non-residents £2.50 Adult, Concessions £2.00   Location: Town centre.
Map Ref: 4

DUNWICH

The Museum

St James Street, Dunwich IP17 3EA   Tel: 01728 648796

History of town of Dunwich from Roman times with local wildlife and social history.

Opening Times: Mar Sat & Sun 14:00-16:30, Apr to Sep daily 11:30-16:30, Oct daily 12:00-16:00. Closed Nov to Feb.   Admission: Free. Donations welcome.   Location: In centre of village.
Map Ref: 5

IPSWICH

Christchurch Mansion

Christchurch Park, Ipswich IP4 2BE   Tel: 01473 433554

Period rooms from Tudor to Victorian. Wolsey Art Gallery has contemporary art exhibitions work by Constable, Gainsborough and other Suffolk artists.

Opening Times: Tue to Sat 10:00-17:00, Sun 14:30-16:30. Closes at dusk during winter.
Admission: Free.   Location: Town centre, one mile from railway station.   Map Ref: 6

Ipswich Museum

High Street, Ipswich IP1 3QH   Tel: 01473 433550   Fax: 01473 433568

IPSWICH

Romans in Suffolk; Anglo-Saxons in Ipswich; mankind galleries; local and world geology; Victorian natural history gallery; Suffolk wildlife; British birds.

Opening Times: Tue to Sat 10:00-17:00.
Admission: Free.   Location: Town centre, one mile from railway station.   Map Ref: 6

Anglo-Saxon Gallery

Ipswich Transport Museum

Cobham Road, Ipswich IP3 9JD   Tel: 01473 715666
Web: www.ipswichtransportmuseum.co.uk

Believed the largest collection in the UK devoted to the transport and engineering heritage of one town - Ipswich. Includes bicycles, cranes, prams, fire engines, buses etc.

Opening Times: Apr to Nov Sun & BH 11:00-16:30. School holidays, Mon to Fri 13:00-16:00.
Admission: Adult £2.50, Child £1.50, Concession £2.00, Family £7.00.   Location: South east
Ipswich, close to A14.   Map Ref: 6

LEISTON

Long Shop Museum

Main Street, Leiston IP16 4ES   Tel / Fax: 01728 832189   Email: longshop@care4free.net
Web: www.longshop.care4free.net

Two hundred years of the Garrett family history from the first production line to the first woman doctor. Housed in original Garrett Works buildings including Grade II* long shop.

Opening Times: Apr to Oct Mon to Sat 10:00-17:00, Sun 11:00-17:00.   Admission: Adult £3.50, Child £1.00, Under 5s Free, Concession £3.00.   Location: Near town centre.   Map Ref: 7

Suffolk

Lowestoft & East Suffolk Maritime Museum
Whapload Road, Lowestoft NR32 1XG   Tel: 01502 561963

Tells the history of the Lowestoft fishing fleet, models of boats, replica of aft cabin of steam drifter, RNLB display, collection of shipwrights' tools, picture gallery and photographs.

Opening Times: Easter 18 Apr to 5 Oct daily 10:00-16:30.   Admission: Adult 75p, Child 25p, OAP 50p.   Location: 30 minute walk from railway station, 25 minute walk from bus station.
Map Ref: 8

Lowestoft Museum
Broad House, Nicholas Everitt Park, Lowestoft NR33 9JR   Tel: 01502 511457

Third largest collection in the world of Lowestoft porcelain as well as the history of the area going back to the Stone Age and beyond.

Opening Times: 25 Mar to 6 Oct Mon to Fri 10:30-17:00, Sat/Sun 14:00-17:00. 12 Oct to 3 Nov Sat & Sun 14:00-16:00. Half term week Mon to Fri 10:30-16:00.   Admission: Free.   Location: In beautiful Nicholas Everitt Park in Oulton Broad, one mile inland from town centre.   Map Ref: 8

British Sporting Art Trust
BSAT Gallery, 99 High Street, Newmarket CB8 8LU   Tel: 01264 710344   Fax: 01264 710114
Email: BSATrust@aol.com   Web: www.BSATrust.com

Annually changing exhibition of sporting paintings. Library of books relating to sporting art and field sports.

Opening Times: Easter to end Oct Tue to Sun 10:00-17:00.   Admission: Adult £3.00.
Location: Near town centre, above National Horseracing Museum, next door to Jockey Club.
Map Ref: 9

National Horseracing Museum
99 High Street, Newmarket CB8 8JH   Tel: 01638 667333   Fax: 01638 665600
Web: www.nhrm.co.uk

The story of racing told through the museum's permanent collections, featuring the horses, people, events and scandals that made it so colourful. New: At the Races Gallery, hands on fun with Channel 4.

Opening Times: 15 Apr to 2 Nov Tue to Sun 11:00-17:00, also open Mon in Jul, Aug & BH.   Admission: Adult £4.50, Child £2.50, Concession £3.50, Family ticket £10.00.   Location: In town centre. Bus stop opposite, 15 minute walk from station.   Map Ref: 9

Mechanical Music Museum & Bygones
Blacksmiths Road, Cotton, Stowmarket IP14 4QN   Tel: 01449 613876
Email: museum@davidivory.co.uk   Web: www.davidivory.co.uk

Unique collection of music-boxes, gramophones, polyphons, organettes, street pianos, barrel organs, fair organs, Wurlitzer Theatre Pipe Organ, many unusual items all played, plus large collection of teapots and memorabilia.

Opening Times: Jun to Sep Sun only 14:30-17:30. Groups by arrangement during the week. Fair Organ Enthusiasts Day 5 Oct 10:00-17:00.   Admission: Adult £4.00, Child £1.00.   Location: Six miles north of Stowmarket, just off B1113 road. Nearest railway station: Stowmarket.   Map Ref: 10

Limonaire Fairground Organ circa 1850

Suffolk

Gainsborough's House

46 Gainsborough Street, Sudbury CO10 2EU   Tel: 01787 372958   Fax: 01787 376991
Email: mail@gainsborough.org   Web: www.gainsborough.org

Georgian fronted townhouse, birthplace of Thomas Gainsborough RA, displaying much of his work, together with 18th century furniture and memorabilia. Varied programme of contemporary exhibitions throughout the year. Attractive walled garden.

Opening Times: Tue to Sat 10:00-17:00, Sun & BH Mon 14:00-17:00. Closing time Nov to Mar 16:00. Closed Good Friday, Xmas & New Year.   Admission: Adult £3.50, Child £1.80, Concessions £2.80, Family £8.00.   Location: In the heart of Sudbury.   Map Ref: 11

Sue Ryder Museum

P O Box 5736, Cavendish, Sudbury CO10 8RN   Tel: 01787 282591   Fax: 01787 282991

Includes original exhibits from Nazi Concentration Camps. Also embroidery and handicrafts made by patients in Sue Ryder homes.

Opening Times: Daily 10:00-17:00. Closed Xmas.   Admission: Adult 80p, Child/OAP 40p.
Location: On A1092 between Clare and Long Melford; Sudbury eight miles; Bury St Edmunds 16 miles; Cambridge 29 miles.   Map Ref: 12

Lanman Museum

Framlingham Castle, Framlingham, Woodbridge IP13 9BP   Tel: 01728 723214

Part of a visit to the castle and telling the social history of Framlingham, this museum has all the copies of the Framlingham Weekly News (1859-1938) recording fascinating local happenings.

Opening Times: Winter 10:00-16:00. Summer 10:00-18:00.   Admission: Part of admission ticket to the castle.   Map Ref: 13

Saxstead Green Post Mill

The Mill House, Saxstead Green, Framlingham, Woodbridge IP13 9QQ   Tel: 01728 685789

This is a fine example of a post mill, where the superstructure turns on a great post to face the wind. There has been a mill here since 1287, as Framlingham was a thriving farming community.

Opening Times: Apr to Sep Mon to Sat 10:00-13:00 & 14:00-18:00, Oct Mon to Sat 10:00-13:00 & 14:00-17:00. Please check times before visiting in early part of season.   Admission: Adult £2.30, Child £1.20, Concession £1.70.   Location: Two and a half miles north west of Framlingham on A1120.   Map Ref: 14

Sutton Hoo

Tranmer House, Sutton Hoo, Woodbridge IP12 3DJ   Tel: 01394 389700   Fax: 01394 389702
Email: asoksx@smtp.ntrust.org.uk
Web: www.nationaltrust.org.uk/places/suttonhoo

Sutton Hoo is the burial ground of the pagan Anglo Saxon kings of East Anglia. It is the site of the famous excavations and discovery of treasure in 1939. The site has a large visitor centre and exhibition hall displaying some of the stunning original artefacts. There is also peaceful walks to the burial mounds and around the 250 acre estate.

Opening Times: Estate open daily. Exhibitions open 22 Mar to 31 May & Oct Wed to Sun 10:00-17:00. 1 Jun to 30 Sep daily 10:00-17:00. 1 Nov to 29 Feb 04 Sat & Sun 10:00-17:00.
Admission: National Trust Members Free. Adult £4.00, Child £2.00.
Location: Signed off A12 North Woodbridge. Site located off B1083 Bawdsey Road. Map Ref: 15

Britain's most wooded county can still claim countryside of outstanding beauty. The magnificent North Downs cross the county from east to west and include Box Hill, a famous beauty spot for over 200 years. To the south is the fertile Surrey Weald, while to the north is the low-lying belt of the Thames Valley.

The museums and galleries of Surrey are extremely varied in topics ranging from local history, geology and archaeology, to rural life and local crafts.

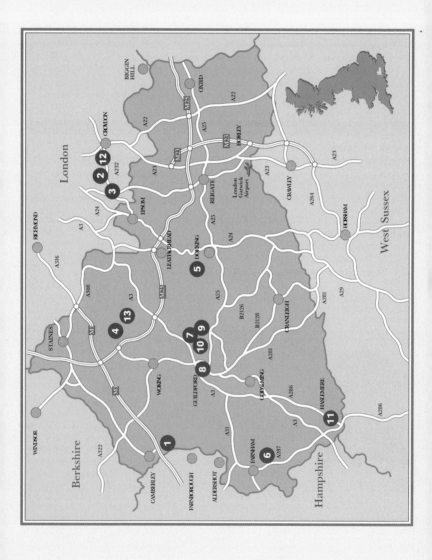

The Red Map References should be used to locate Museums etc on the pages that follow

Surrey

Royal Logistic Corps Museum

Princess Royal Barracks, Deepcut, Camberley GU16 6RW   Tel: 01252 833371   Fax: 01252 833484   Email: query@rlcmuseum.freeserve.co.uk

Formed in 1993, the museum houses the collection of the Royal Corps of Transport, Royal Army Ordnance Corps, Royal Pioneer Corps, Army Catering Corps and Royal Engineers' Postal & Courier Service.

Opening Times: Apr to Dec Tue to Fri 10:00-16:00, first & third Sat in month. Closed Dec 2002 to Apr 2003 for refurbishment.   Admission: Free.   Location: Deepcut village near Frimley Green.
Map Ref: 1

Honeywood Heritage Centre

Honeywood Walk, Carshalton SM5 3NX   Tel: 020 8770 4297   Fax: 020 8770 4777
Email: lbshoneywood@ukonline.co.uk   Web: www.sutton.gov.uk/lfl/heritage/honeywood

The recently restored interior of this historic building contains a wealth of period detail from the Victorian and Edwardian eras. Themed displays include Tudor life, the local River Wandle and its industries, and children's toys and games.

Opening Times: Wed to Fri 11:00-17:00, Sat, Sun & BH 10:00-17:00. Tea room open Tue to Sun 10:00-17:00.   Admission: Adult £1.20, Child 60p. Groups by prior arrangement.
Location: Next to Carshalton Ponds, off A232. Four minutes walk to Carshalton Station.
Map Ref: 2

Little Holland House

40 Beeches Avenue, Carshalton SM5 3LW   Tel: 020 8770 4781   Fax: 020 8770 4777
Email: valary.murphy@sutton.gov.uk   Web: www.sutton.gov.uk/lfl/heritage/lhh

Built between 1902-04 by Frank Dickinson, an ardent devotee of the Arts & Crafts Movement, the Grade II* interior contains Dickinson's paintings, hand-made furniture, carvings and metal work in an eclectic style which is unique.

Opening Times: First Sun every month plus Sun & Mon of BH weekends 13:30-17:30. Closed Xmas & New Year.   Admission: Free. Group visits outside opening times by prior arrangement only - include talks and guided tour £3.00 per person.   Location: On B278 four minute walk south of Carshalton Beeches Station.
Map Ref: 2

Whitehall

1 Malden Road, Cheam SM3 8QD   Tel: 020 8643 1236   Fax: 020 8770 4777
Email: curators@whitehallcheam.fsnet.co.uk   Web: www.sutton.gov.uk/lfl/heritage/whitehall

A Tudor timber-framed house, built c1500, which contains displays on various aspects of its history including the Killick family, who lived here for over 250 years.

Opening Times: Wed to Fri & Sun 14:00-17:00, Sat 10:00-17:00. BH 14:00-17:00. Closed Xmas & New Year.   Admission: Adult £1.20, Child 60p. Group rates available.   Location: On A2043 just north of junction with A232. Five minute walk from Cheam station. Pay and display car park off Park Road, opposite.
Map Ref: 3

Chertsey Museum

The Cedars, 33 Windsor Street, Chertsey KT16 8AT   Tel: 01932 565764   Fax: 01932 571118
Email: curator@chertseymuseum.org.uk   Web: www.chertseymuseum.org.uk

Collection displays explore the history of the Runnymede area and British fashion, including Thames Valley archaeology, clocks, social history, decorative art, Greek pottery, Chertsey Abbey and 'The Matthews Dress Collection'.

Opening Times: Tue to Fri 12:30-16:30, Sat 11:00-16:00. Closed Xmas & New Year and Good Friday.   Admission: Free.   Location: Near town centre, one minute walk from bus stop, 15 minute walk from train station.
Map Ref: 4

Surrey

DORKING

Polesden Lacey

    THE NATIONAL TRUST

Great Bookham, Dorking RH5 6BD   Tel: 01372 452048/458203
Fax: 01372 452023   Email: polesdenlacey@ntrust.org.uk   Web: www.nationaltrust.org.uk

In an exceptional setting on the North Downs, this originally Regency house was extensively remodelled in 1906-9 by the Hon Mrs Ronald Grenville, a well known Edwardian hostess. Her collection of fine paintings, furniture, porcelain and silver are displayed in the reception rooms and galleries, as they were at the time of her celebrated house parties.

The Library which is decorated in neo-classical. National Trust Photo Library

Opening Times: House: 23 Mar to 3 Nov Wed to Sun 11:00-17:00. Open BH Mon and Tue 4 Jun. Garden: Daily 11:00-18:00 or dusk if earlier. Admission: House: Adult £7.00, Family £17.50. Garden, grounds & walks: Adult £4.00, Family £10.00.   Map Ref: 5

FARNHAM

Rural Life Centre

Reeds Road, Tilford, Farnham GU10 2DL   Tel / Fax: 01252 795571
Email: rural.life@lineone.net   Web: www.rural-life.org.uk

Village life collection covering the last two hundred years of the 20th century set in large arboretum. Special events. Light railway, Sundays. Coaches and schools welcome by appointment.

Opening Times: Apr to Oct Wed to Sun & BH 11:00-18:00. Oct to Mar Wed 11:00-16:00.
Admission: Adult £5.00, Child £3.00, OAP £4.00, Family £12.00. Location: Mid-way between Frensham and Tilford, off the A287, three miles south of Farnham.   Map Ref: 6

GUILDFORD

Clandon Park

    THE NATIONAL TRUST

West Clandon, Guildford GU4 7RQ   Tel: 01483 222482 Fax: 01483 223479   Email: clandonpark@ntrust.org.uk   Web: www.nationaltrust.org.uk/clandonpark

Clandon Park was built by the Venetian architect Leoni in the 1730s and is considered to have one of the finest Marble Halls in Europe. The house is filled with an amazing collection of 18th century furniture, porcelain, textiles and carpets acquired in the 1920s by the connoisseur Mrs Gubbay. The attractive gardens contain a grotto, sunken Dutch garden and a fascinating Maori Meeting House.

Opening Times: Apr to Oct Tue, Wed, Thu, Sun & BH 11:00-17:00. Admission: Adult £6.00, Child £3.00, Family £15.00, Party £5.00. National Trust Members Free. Location: East of Guildford on A247. Buses - 479, 463 from Guildford Friary Bus Station (489 Sun & BH service).   Map Ref: 7

Guildford Cathedral Treasury

Stag Hill, Guildford GU2 7UP   Tel: 01483 565287 Fax: 01482 303350
Email: visits@guildford-cathedral.org   Web: www.guildford-cathedral.org

Out of 215 parishes, 35 Churches have lent 135 different artefacts to the Cathedral. The display represents nearly 450 years of ecclesiastical history and wonderful examples of art and craftmanship.

Opening Times: Daily 08:30-17:30. Admission: Free - donation welcome. Small fee for Groups. Location: Ten minute walk from mainline station.   Map Ref: 8

Guildford House Gallery

155 High Street, Guildford GU1 3AJ   Tel: 01483 444740 Fax: 01483 444742
Email: guildfordhouse@remote.guildford.gov.uk   Web: www.guildfordhouse.co.uk

Fascinating 17th century Grade I listed building. Original features include a finely carved

GUILDFORD (continued)

staircase, panelled rooms, decorative plaster ceilings and wrought iron window fittings. Varied temporary exhibition programme throughout the year.

Opening Times: Tue to Sat 10:00-16:45. Closed Mon.   Admission: Free.   Location: Guildford Town Centre.   Map Ref: 8

Guildford Museum

Castle Arch, Guildford GU1 3SX   Tel: 01483 444751   Fax: 01483 532391
Email: museum@remote.guildford.gov.uk   Web: www.guildfordmuseum.co.uk

The Museum was founded in 1898. It now houses the largest collection of archaeology, local history and needlework in Surrey. The archaeology collection contains objects from Palaeolithic hand axes to Roman Priests' head dresses. The needlework collections include most types of sewing. Objects and pictures covering local trades and industries, social life and customs, childhood and the home. Also local characters such as Lewis Carroll and Gertrude Jekyll.

Opening Times: Mon to Sat 11:00-17:00. Closed Sun.
Admission: Free.   Exhibitions & Events 2003 : 8 Mar: Women's Festival Study Day entitled 'Warrior Queens in the Roman World', 21 Jun: Tudor day, with re-enactment group and procession led by Queen Elizabeth I, Jun to Aug: Exhibition on the River Wey, 20 Aug to 9 Sep: Exhibition on the Cokelers - a local religious group, 10 to 12 Oct: Family Learning Weekend on the Medieval theme, Dec: Edwardian Christmas Party.   Map Ref: 8

Hatchlands Park

East Clandon, Guildford GU4 7RT   Tel: 01483 222482   Fax: 01483 223176   THE NATIONAL TRUST
Email: hatchlands@ntrust.org.uk   Web: www.nationaltrust.org.uk/hatchlands

Hatchlands is set in a beautiful 430 acre Repton Park offering a variety of walks. The house was built for the naval hero Admiral Boscawen in 1756 and can boast the earliest surviving interiors by Robert Adam. Inside explore the world's largest collection of composer related keyboards upon which J C Bach, Chopin, Mahler and Elgar (to mention but a few) have played.

Opening Times: Apr to Oct. House: Wed, Thu, Sun & BH, also Fri in Aug 14:00-17:30. Park: 11:00-18:00.
Admission: House: Adult £6.00, Child £3.00, Family £15.00. Park: Adult £2.50, Child £1.25, Family £5.00.
National Trust Members Free.   Location: East of Guildford on A246. Buses - 478, 479 from Guildford Friary Bus Station (489 Sun & BH service).   Map Ref: 9

Loseley Park

Guildford GU3 1HS   Tel: 01483 304440   Fax: 01483 302036   Email: enquiries@loseley-park.com   Web: www.loseley-park.com

Loseley House is a fine example of Elizabethan Architecture featuring many fine works of art including paintings, tapestries, chalk fireplace and panelling from Henry VIII's Nonsuch Palace.

Opening Times: Walled Garden: 6 May to 29 Sep Wed to Sun 11:00-17:00. Loseley House: 3 Jun to 26 Aug Wed to Sun 13:00-17:00. (Guided tours)   Admission: Garden: Adult £3.00, Child £1.50, OAP £2.50. House & Garden: Adult £6.00, Child £3.00, OAP £5.00.
Location: Three miles from Guildford Town Centre, five minutes drive from A3.   Map Ref: 8

Queen's Royal Surrey Regiment Museum

Clandon Park, Guildford GU4 7RQ   Tel: 01483 223419   Fax: 01483 224636
Email: queenssurrey@care4free.net   Web: www.surrey-online.co.uk/queenssurrey

Set in the National Trust mansion, Clandon Park, this museum tell the story of the long and distinguished service of the Infrantry Regiments of Surrey. Spectacular medal display. Exhibitions refurbished in 2002.

Opening Times: Apr to Oct Tue to Thu, Sun & BH Mon 12:00-17:00.   Admission: Free.
Location: West Clandon, four miles from Guildford Town Centre.   Map Ref: 10

Surrey

The Watts Gallery

Down Lane, Compton, Guildford GU3 1DQ   Tel: 01483 810235
Email: wattsgallery@freeuk.com   Web: www.wattsgallery.org.uk

The studio collection of G F Watts OMRA, the famous Victorian artist, including portraits, symbolist paintings and sculpture. Nearby is the Watts Chapel, designed and built by his wife, Mary.

Opening Times: Oct to Mar Mon, Tue, Fri & Sun 14:00-16:00, Sat & Wed 11:00-13:00 & 14:00-16:00. Apr to Sep Mon, Tue, Fri & Sun 14:00-18:00, Sat & Wed 11:00-13:00 & 14:00-18:00.
Admission: Free.   Location: In Compton, five minutes drive from Guildford.   Map Ref: 8

HASLEMERE

Haslemere Educational Museum

78 High Street, Haslemere GU27 2LA   Tel: 01428 642112   Fax: 01428 645234
Email: haslemeremuseum@compuserve.com   Web: www.haslemeremuseum.co.uk

Permanent exhibitions in refurbished galleries include geology, natural history, archaeology and human history. Popular features are Egyptian mummy, stuffed bear, wild flower table, and observation beehive. Attractive grounds with ha-ha, gazebo, pond and some unusual trees.

Opening Times: Tue to Sat 10:00-17:00.   Admission: Free.   Location: High Street location - ten minutes walk from station.   Map Ref: 11

WALLINGTON

Carew Manor Dovecote

Church Road, Beddington, Wallington SM6 7NH   Tel: 020 8770 4781   Fax: 020 8770 4777
Email: valary.murphy@sutton.gov.uk   Web: www.sutton.gov.uk/lfl/heritage/carew

The Great Hall at Carew Manor is Sutton's only Grade I listed building. Tours include the Great Hall with its arch-braced hammer-beam roof, cellars and eighteenth century dovecote.

Opening Times: Tours at 14:00 and 15:30 on Sun 11 May, 29 Jun, 20 Jul & 28 Sep.
Admission: Adult £3.00 per tour.   Location: Just off A232 at entrance to Beddington Park.
                                                                                    Map Ref: 12

WEYBRIDGE

Brooklands Museum Trust Ltd

Brooklands Road, Weybridge KT13 0QN   Tel: 01932 857381   Fax: 01932 855465
Email: info@brooklandsmuseum.com   Web: www.brooklandsmuseum.com

The birthplace of British motorsport and aviation, features a fine collection of historic racing and sports cars and aircraft. Including the Loch Ness Wellington bomber 'R' for 'Robert' and the Napier-Railton built for John Cobb.

Opening Times: Tue to Sun 10:00-17:00 (summer), 10:00-16:00 (winter).   Admission: Adult £7.00, Child £5.00, OAP/Student £6.00, Family £18.00. NB. Extra charges may be levied on events.   Location: A 20 minute walk from Weybridge station and ten minutes from Junction 10 on A3.   Map Ref: 13

Sussex

Much has been said and written about 'Sussex by the Sea', ever since Rudyard Kipling praised its glories. Brighton, the queen of Sussex seaside towns and the largest town in East Sussex, was mentioned in Domesday Book. The county town of West Sussex is Chichester, a Roman town retaining something of its Roman grid-iron street plan.

The cream of Sussex's museums and galleries and palaces are located in the coastal towns and have outstanding collections as well as covering the county's social and archaeological history.

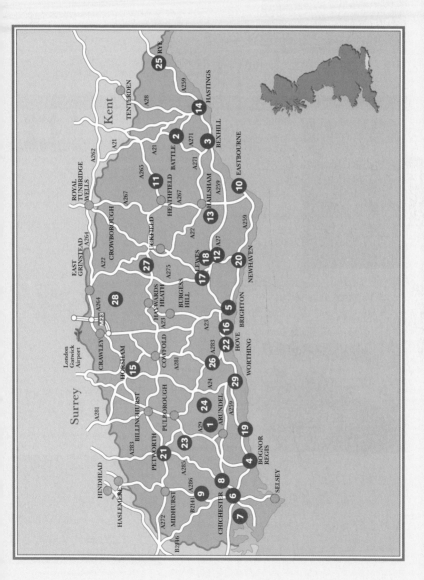

The Red Map References should be used to locate Museums etc on the pages that follow

Sussex

Amberley Working Museum

Amberley, Arundel BN18 9LT   Tel: 01798 831370   Fax: 01798 831831
Email: office@amberleymuseum.co.uk   Web: www.amberleymuseum.co.uk

A 1920 Leyland bus, providing free transport around Amberley

Amberley Working Museum is a 36 acre open-air site dedicated to preserving the industrial heritage of the south-east. Exhibits include a narrow-gauge railway and vintage bus collection (both of which provide free travel around site). Besides the SEEBOARD electricity hall, a printing workshop and a roadmarker's exhibition, the museum is also home to traditional craftspeople, such as a blacksmith, potter and broom-maker.

Opening Times: 20 Mar to 3 Nov Wed to Sun 10:00-17:00. Open BH and daily through school holidays.
Admission: Adult £6.75, Child £3.75, OAP/Student £6.00, Group rates available.   Location: On the B2139, between Arundel and Storrington. Adjacent to Amberley Railway Station.   Map Ref: 1

Battle Abbey

Battle TN33 0AD   Tel: 01424 773792

Battle Abbey was founded around 1070 by William the Conqueror, on the site of the Battle of Hastings. The best-preserved and most impressive part of the abbey is the great gate-house, the finest of all surviving Medieval abbey entrances, which was built around 1338. There is an exhibition on the build-up to the Battle of Hastings. Collections include architectural stonework and archaeological finds.

Opening Times: Apr to Sep daily 10:00-18:00, Oct daily 10:00-17:00, Nov to Mar daily 10:00-16:00. Closed Xmas & New Year.
Admission: Adult £5.00, Child £2.50, Concession £3.80, Family £12.50.   Location: In Battle, at south end of High Street.

Great Gatehouse from South © English Heritage   Map Ref: 2

Buckleys Yesterdays World

Next to Battle Abbey, 89/90 High Street, Battle TN33 0AQ   Tel: 01424 775378
Fax: 01424 775174   Email: info@yesterdaysworld.co.uk
Web: www.yesterdaysworld.co.uk

Step into the world of yesterday today

Step into the world of yesterday - today at the South East's No 1 top visitor attraction. Experience the sights, sounds and smells of a bygone age, as you journey through a hundred glorious years of shopping and social history. Discover what life was like from the 1850s onwards, and capture the charm of yesteryear as you explore over forty rooms and shop settings. Your nostalgia experience takes you along the 'high street' as you bump into many colourful life-sized characters in the various stores, ranging from the 1900s general store to the 1960s television shop. On the home front, the exhibition concentrates on Victorian life and you'll be thankful for today's labour saving gadgets when you see all the hard work going on in the kitchen and laundry. You'll be 'most amused' when you meet Queen Victoria in her throne room, surrounded by a host of regal memorabilia, including items belonging to Queen Victoria herself and letters written by Queen Elizabeth II. The fun continues with the Children's Play Village, Toddlers Activity Area and Miniature Golf. Indulge yourself at the Tea Terrace or Fudge Fayre overlooking the beautiful English Country Garden.

Meet colourful lifesized characters from 1850 onwards

Opening Times: Daily 09:30-18:00 (17:00 in winter).   Admission: Adult £4.95, Child £3.50, OAP £4.50, Family £15.75.   Location: Battle High Street, opposite Abbey.   Map Ref: 2

Sussex

BEXHILL *E Sussex*

Bexhill Museum

Egerton Road, Bexhill TN39 3HL   Tel / Fax: 01424 787950   Email: museum@rother.gov.uk
Web: bexhillmuseum.co.uk

Housed in an Edwardian Park Pavilion, collections reflect the fascinating history of Bexhill - important collections include local dinosaur remains, architect's model of De La Pavilion and much more. New access centre.

Opening Times: Feb to Dec Tue to Fri 10:00-17:00. Sat & Sun & BH 14:00-17:00.
Admission: Adult £1.00, Child Free, Concession 50p, Group 50p. School Groups Free.
Location: Just off Bexhill Seafront (B2182) by the Clock Tower, quarter mile railway station.

Map Ref: 3

BOGNOR REGIS *W Sussex*

Bognor Regis Museum/Bognor Regis Wireless Museum

69 High Street, Bognor Regis PO21 1RY   Tel: 01243 865636

The main museum houses displays of local history, also included is an independent wireless museum.

Opening Times: Tue to Sun 10:30-16:30. Closed Mon (except BH).   Admission: Free.
Location: In the town centre.

Map Ref: 4

BRIGHTON *E Sussex*

Booth Museum of Natural History

194 Dyke Road, Brighton BN1 5AA   Tel: 01273 292777   Fax: 01273 292778
Web: www.virtualmuseum.info

Over half a million specimens and natural history literature and data extending back over three centuries are housed in this fascinating museum, including hundreds of British birds, butterflies, skeletons, whale and dinosaur bones.

Opening Times: Mon to Sat 10:00-17:00, Sun 14:00-17:00. Closed Thu, Good Friday, 25-26 Dec, 1 Jan.   Admission: Free.   Location: 15 minute bus ride from town centre, five to ten minute walk from Brighton Station. Buses 27 & 27A.

Map Ref: 5

Brighton Museum & Art Gallery

Royal Pavilion Gardens, Brighton BN1 1EE   Tel: 01273 290900
Fax: 01273 292871   Web: www.virtualmuseum.info

Spine Chair (des.1986) by Andre Dubreuil

Brighton Museum & Art Gallery has re-opened following a £10 million redevelopment which has transformed it into a state-of-the-art visitor attraction. Dynamic and innovative new galleries feature exciting interactive displays appealing to all ages. Brighton Museum is famous for its collection of 20th century furniture, glass, textiles and jewellery, including examples by leading designers. The extensive ceramics collection includes the famous Willett Gallery, exploring 18th and 19th century British social history through earthenware. The museum's spectacular collection of non-western arts is of national importance and it also boasts stunning collections of fashion and fascinating local history collections. The

Frank Stella (1936) Red Scramble, 1977, Oil on Canvas

museum also has an extensive collection of fine art, ranging from the 15th to the 20th century.

Opening Times: Tue 10:00-19:00, Wed, Thu, Fri & Sat 10:00-17:00. Sun 14:00-17:00. Closed Mon, 24-26 Dec & 1 Jan.   Admission: Free.   Location: Royal Pavilion Gardens, Town Centre, Brighton.

Map Ref: 5

Preston Manor

Preston Drove, Brighton BN1 6SD   Tel: 01273 292770   Fax: 01273 292771
Email: visitor.services@brighton-hove.gov.uk   Web: www.prestonmanor.virtualmuseum.info

Delightful manor house, powerfully evoking the atmosphere of an Edwardian gentry home both upstairs and downstairs. Explore over 20 rooms on four floors from superbly renovated servant's

Sussex

quarters to the attic bedrooms.

Opening Times: Mon 13:00-17:00, Tue to Sat 10:00-17:00, Sun 14:00-17:00 and BH 10:00-17:00. Closed Mon 10:00-13:00 Good Friday, 25 & 26 Dec. Admission: Please phone for details.   Location: 10 minute bus ride from town centre. Buses 5 & 5A   Map Ref: 5

The Royal Pavilion, Brighton

Royal Pavilion
4/5 Pavilion Buildings, Brighton BN1 1EE
Tel: 01273 290900 Fax: 01273 292871
Email: visitor.services@brighton-hove.gov.uk
Web: www.royalpavilion.org.uk

The Royal Pavilion, the famous seaside palace of King George IV, is one of the most exotically beautiful buildings in the British Isles. Originally a simple farmhouse, in 1787 architect Henry Holland created a neoclassical villa on the site. From 1815-1822, the Pavilion was transformed by John Nash into its current distinctive Indian style complete with Chinese inspired interiors. Magnificent decorations and fantastic furnishings have been re-created in an extensive restoration programme. From the opulence of the main State rooms to the charm of the first floor bedroom suites, the Royal Pavilion is filled with astonishing colours and superb craftsmanship. Witness the magnificence of the Music Room with a domed ceiling of gilded shell shapes, and the dramatic Banqueting Room lit by a huge crystal chandelier held by a silvered dragon. Visitors can discover more about life behind the scenes at the Palace during the last 200 years with an interactive multimedia visitor interpretation programme and join public guided tours daily at 11:30 and 14:30 (for a small extra charge). The Royal Pavilion is an ideal location for filming and photography, from fashion shoots to corporate videos. Rooms are also available for hire for corporate and private functions and civil wedding ceremonies.

The Music Room at the
Royal Pavilion, Brighton

Opening Times: Daily Oct to May 10:00-17:15, Jun to Sep 09:30-17:45. Closed 25-26 Dec.
Admission: Please phone for details.   Location: Situated in town centre.   Exhibitions & Events 2003 : Family days, special interest talks and tours based on the collection an history of the Royal Pavilion.   Map Ref: 5

Chichester District Museum
29 Little London, Chichester PO19 1PB   Tel: 01243 784683   Fax: 01243 776766
Email: districtmuseum@chichester.gov.uk   Web: www.chichester.gov.uk/museum

Find out about the archaeology and local history of the Chichester district through displays and hands-on activities. Changing exhibitions and events for all ages.

Opening Times: Tue to Sat 10:00-17:30. Closed Sun, Mon and all Public Holidays. Admission: Free. Location: Off East Street, Chichester. 15 minutes from Bus and Train Stations. Map Ref: 6

Fishbourne Roman Palace
Salthill Road, Fishbourne, Chichester PO19 2QR   Tel: 01243 785859 Fax: 01243 539266   Email: adminfish@sussexpast.co.uk   Web: www.sussexpast.co.uk

Britain's finest collection of in situ Roman mosaics are on display at Fishbourne Roman Palace along with a museum of finds from this internationally important site, and a Roman garden replanted to its original plan. An audio-visual presentation helps bring the site back to life.

Opening Times: Jan & 16 Dec to 31 Dec Sat & Sun 10:00-16:00, Feb & Nov to 15 Dec daily 10:00-16:00, Mar to Jul & Sep to Oct daily 10:00-17:00, Aug daily 10:00-16:00. Admission: Adult £5.00, Child £2.60, Concession £4.30, Family £12.90, Disabled £3.90. Location: 5 minutes walk from Fishbourne Railway Station. North of A259 off Salthill Road in Fishbourne village. Bus services stop near end of Salthill Road.   Map Ref: 7

Trajan's Column

Sussex

Guildhall Museum

Priory Park, Chichester   Tel: 01243 784683   Fax: 01243 776766
Email: districtmuseum@chichester.gov.uk   Web: www.chichester.gov.uk/museum

A Grade I listed building and an ancient scheduled monument which dates from 1269 and was built as the church for the Grey Friars. Now displays large local history material.

Opening Times: Sat only Jun to Mid Sep 12:00-16:00.   Admission: Free.   Location: In Priory Park, located to the north-east of the City.   Map Ref: 6

Pallant House Gallery

9 North Pallant, Chichester PO19 1TJ   Tel: 01243 774557   Fax: 01243 536038
Email: pallant@pallant.co.uk   Web: www.pallanthousegallery.com

Predominantly British 20th century paintings. Superb collection in Queen Anne townhouse setting. Regular temporary exhibitions throughout the year.

Opening Times: Tue to Sat 10:00-17:00, Sun & BH 12:30-17:00.   Admission: Adult £4.00, Child Free, Concession £3.00, Student £2.50.   Location: Near city centre, take East Street from City Cross and turn right at Marks & Spencer.   Map Ref: 6

Royal Military Police Museum

Roussillon Barracks, Broyle Road, Chichester PO19 4BN   Tel: 01243 534225   Fax: 01243 534288   Email: museum@rhqrmp.freeserve.co.uk   Web: www.rhqrmp.freeserve.co.uk

Tracing military police history from Tudor origins, the museum displays artefacts from conflicts including World War I and World War II, Northern Ireland, the Gulf and NATO operations in the former Yugoslavia. Uniforms, badges, medals, videos.

Opening Times: Apr to Sep Tue to Fri 10:30-12:30 & 13:30-16:30, Sat & Sun 14:00-17:00. Oct to Mar Tue to Fri 10:30-12:30 & 13:30-16:30. Closed Xmas to end Jan.   Admission: Free.
Location: 15 minute walk from bus and railway station, on A286 Chichester to Midhurst road.
Map Ref: 6

Tangmere Military Aviation Museum

Tangmere, Chichester PO20 2ES   Tel: 01243 775223   Fax: 01243 789490
Email: admin@tangmere-museum.org.uk   Web: www.tangmere-museum.org.uk

The museum tells the story of military flying from the earliest days to the present time with special emphasis on the air war over southern England 1939-45.

Opening Times: Feb & Nov daily 10:00-16:30, Mar to Oct daily 10:00-17:30.   Admission: Adult £4.00, Child £1.50, OAP £3.00, Family £9.50.   Location: Three miles east of Chichester off A27.
Map Ref: 8

Weald & Downland Open Air Museum

Singleton, Chichester PO18 0EU   Tel: 01243 811348/811363
Fax: 01243 811475   Email: office@wealddown.co.uk   Web: www.wealddown.co.uk

Discover a very special place in the heart of the South Downs, an open air museum where you can explore the homes and gardens, farms and rural workplaces of the past 500 years in South East England. Enjoy demonstrations of rural crafts and trades. See traditional farming in action heavy horses at work, a watermill producing flour, and 'The Downland Gridshell' - a spectacular new greenoak building to house the Museum's conservation workshop, an inspiring embodiment of the Museum's strapline 'learning from the past'.

Opening Times: 2 Jan to 28 Feb Sat & Sun 10:30-16:00.
1 Mar to 31 Oct daily 10:30-18:00. 1 Nov to 24 Dec Sat & Sun 10:30-16:00. School half terms daily. Closed Xmas.   Admission: Adult £7.00, OAP £6.50, Child £4.00, Family £19.00.
Location: Off A286 in Singleton Village, on Chichester to Midhurst Road.   Exhibitions & Events 2003 : 20 & 21 Apr: Fine Food Fair, 1 Jun: Heavy Horse Spectacular, 28 & 29 Jun: Out of the Wood Show, 20 Jul: Rare & Traditional Breeds, 30 Jul to 27 Aug: Children's Activity Wednesdays, 21 to 25 Aug: Rural History Re-enactment, Oct: Autumn Countryside Celebration, Half Terms: Lots of countryside skills and crafts to get to grips with.   Map Ref: 9

Sussex

Filching Manor & Motor Museum
& Karting Track Campbell Circuit

Filching Manor, Filching Nr Polegate, Eastbourne BN26 5QA   Tel: 01323 487838   Fax: 01323 486331   Email: campbellcurcuit@aol.com   Web: www.campbellcurcuit.co.uk

Set in 15th century Wealden Hall House. 100 top historic cars, motorcycles, boats and aircraft, including Sir Malcolm Campbell's 1937 Bluebird and many classics.

Opening Times: Sat & Sun 11:00-14:30. Tours Easter to Oct & BH.   Admission: Adult £5.00, Child/OAP £3.50.   Location: One mile from A22 and A27 at Polegate. Brown tourist board signs A22 and A259 Friston. Map Ref: 10

'How We Lived Then' Museum of Shops

20 Cornfield Terrace, Eastbourne BN21 4NS   Tel: 01323 737143

Visit the famous south coast museum of shops, see over 100,000 exhibits collected during the past 40 years, on four floors of old shops, room-settings and displays.

Opening Times: Daily 10:00-17:00. Closed Xmas.   Admission: Adult £3.00, Child £2.00, Under 5s Free, OAP £2.50. Group rates available.   Location: Just off seafront, near town centre.

Map Ref: 10

Museum of the Royal National Lifeboat Institution

King Edward Parade, Eastbourne BN21 4BY   Tel: 01323 730717

Showing the history of Eastbourne lifeboats from 1824. Many photos of past crews and of epic rescues. Various items of lifeboat memorabilia. A small selection of lifeboat models.

Opening Times: 25 Mar to 28 Apr & 30 Sep to end Dec daily 10:00-16:00. 29 Apr to 29 Sep daily 10:00-17:00.   Admission: Free.   Location: On seafront, at The Wish Tower.   Map Ref: 10

Queens Royal Irish Hussars Museum

c/o Sussex Combined Services Msum, Redoubt Fortress,Royal Parade, Eastbourne BN22 7AQ   Tel: 01323 410300

Tracing history of cavalry regiments who took part in the Charge of the Light Brigade, up to their involvement in the Gulf War. Collections include rare uniforms.

Opening Times: Apr to 5 Nov 09:45-17:30.   Admission: £1.60.   Location: Half a mile east of pier on seafront. Map Ref: 10

Royal Sussex Regiment Museum

c/o Sussex Combined Services Musm, Redoubt Fortress, Royal Parade, Eastbourne BN22 7AQ   Tel: 01323 410300

Collections of local infantry regiment, including uniforms, medals, regimental silver and a German General's staff car.

Opening Times: Apr to 5 Nov 09:45-17:30.   Admission: £1.60.   Location: Half a mile east of pier on seafront. Map Ref: 10

Sussex Combined Services Museums & Redoubt Fortress

Royal Parade, Eastbourne BN22 7AQ   Tel: 01323 410300

The history of the Army, Navy and RAF in the Sussex area. Displays include uniforms and medals, set in a Napoleonic fortress.

Opening Times: Apr to 5 Nov 09:45-17:30.   Admission: £1.60. Map Ref: 10

Sussex

Bateman's (Kiplings House)

🕭 🕭 📷 🕭 🚌　　　🦋

Burwash, Etchingham TN19 7DS　Tel: 01435 882302　Fax: 01435 882811　THE NATIONAL TRUST
Email: kbaxxx@smtp.ntrust.org.uk　Web: www.nationaltrust.org.uk

A 17th century Ironmaster's house, which was the former home of Rudyard Kipling. This family house with plenty of atmosphere nestles in the beautiful Sussex countryside. A working water mill, gardens and Kipling's Rolls Royce all enhance this house's appeal. Each season this house hosts concerts and events, one of the most popular being 'Last Night of the Proms', when over 4000 people gather.

Opening Times: 23 Mar to 29 Sep Sat to Wed 11:00-17:30.　Admission: Adult £5.20, Child £2.60, Group £4.40, Family £13.00.　Location: Etchingham Station

Bateman's (Kiplings House)

three miles.　　　　　　　　　　　　　　Map Ref: 11

Firle Place

🕭 🕭 🕭 📷 🕭 🚌

Firle BN8 6LP　Tel: 01273 858567　Fax: 01273 858570

The house contains a magnificent collection of Old Master paintings, fine English and European furniture and an impressive collection of Sèvres porcelain.

Opening Times: 12 May to 29 Sep Wed, Thu, Sun & BH 13:45-16:15.　Admission: Adult £5.00, Child £2.50, OAP £4.50.　Location: Four miles south of Lewes.　　　　Map Ref: 12

Michelham Priory & Gardens

🕭 🕭 📷 🕭 🚌

Upper Dicker, Hailsham BN27 3QS　Tel: 01323 844224　Fax: 01323 844030
Email: adminmich@sussexpast.co.uk　Web: www.sussexpast.co.uk

With nearly 800 years of history on display, Michelham Priory offers visitors a wealth of fascinating exhibitions inside and out. Of particular interest are the remains of a former Augustinian Priory that evolved into a splendid Tudor mansion, a 14th century gatehouse, a rope museum, a working watermill and England's longest water-filled Medieval moat.

Opening Times: 1 Mar to 31 Oct Tue to Sun. Times: Mar & Oct 10:30-16:00, Apr to Jul & Sep 10:30-17:00, Aug 10:30-17:30.　Admission: Adult £5.00, Child £2.60, Concession £4.30, Family £12.90, Disabled £2.50.　Location: At Upper Dicker, approx two miles west of Hailsham and eight miles north-west of Eastbourne.　　　　　　　　　　　　　Map Ref: 13

Fishermans Museum

🕭 🕭 🕭

Rock-a-Nore Road, Hastings TN34 3DW　Tel: 01424 461446

Opened as a museum in 1956, the centrepiece is the 'Enterprise' one of the last Hastings sailing luggers (worked 1912-1954). Exhibits also include model ships and boats, fishing gear, historic paintings and photographs illustrating the local fishing industry. Outside are four other types of Hastings fishing boats and some examples of the unique net shops.

Opening Times: Apr to Oct daily 10:00-17:00. Nov to Mar daily 11:00-16:00. Closed Xmas.　Admission: Free. Donations welcome. Location: In and around Old Fishermen's

Model of a Hastings Lugger

Church, on beach at eastern end of Hastings Old Town.
　　　　　　　　　　　　　　　　　　　　Map Ref: 14

Hastings Museum & Art Gallery

🕭 🚌

Bohemia Road, Hastings TN34 1ET　Tel: 01424 781155　Fax: 01424 781165
Email: vwilliams@hastings.gov.uk　Web: www.hastings.gov.uk/museum

Paintings, ceramics, fossils, native Americans, special features on John Logie Baird, Robert Tressell and Grey Owl, exhibitions of contemporary art. The Durbar Hall was built as part of an Indian Palace in 1886.

Opening Times: Mon to Sat 10:00-17:00, Sun 14:00-17:00.　Admission: Free.　Location: Ten minute walk from town centre and railway station.　　　　　　　Map Ref: 14

Sussex

Museum of Local History

Old Town Hall, High Street, Hastings TN34 1EW   Tel: 01424 781166
Email: vwilliams@hastings.gov.uk   Web: www.hastings.gov.uk/museum

A walk back in time through the history of Hastings Old Town from the 1960s to pre-history. Subjects covered include seaside entertainment, the Napoleonic Garrison, smuggling, the Armada and the Cinque Ports.

Opening Times: Apr to Sep Mon to Sun 10:00-17:00, Oct to Mar Mon to Sun 11:00-16:00.
Admission: Free.   Map Ref: 14

Shipwreck Heritage Centre

Rock-a-Nore Road, Hastings TN34 3DW   Tel / Fax: 01424 437452

Displayed are the remains of a Roman ship, the complete hull of a Victorian river barge and many relics from a 1749 Dutch merchant ship whose wreck is visible off St Leonards at low tide.

Opening Times: Mar to Oct daily 10:30-17:00, Nov to Feb daily 11:00-16:00. Admission:
Suggested donation Adult £1.00. Guided Tours for Groups £1.00 per person.   Map Ref: 14

Horsham Museum

9 Causeway, Horsham RH12 1HE   Tel: 01403 254959   Fax: 01403 217581
Email: museum@horsham.gov.uk

Set in a timber framed Medieval house with over 20 galleries, two walled gardens, the museum displays costume, dinosaur bones, bicycles, toys, packaging, art and crafts as well as books by Shelley, the poet.

Opening Times: Mon to Sat (excluding BH & Sun) 10:00-17:00. Admission: Free.
Location: Near town centre, in historic street leading to Parish Church.   Map Ref: 15

Hove Museum & Art Gallery

19 New Church Road, Hove BN3 4AB   Tel: 01273 290200   Fax: 01273 292827
Web: www.virtualmuseum.info

Hove Museum & Art Gallery re-opens in early 2003 after major re-development works. New features include the installation of a lift and new displays of the craft, toy, film and fine art collections.

Opening Times: Tue to Sat 10:00-17:00, Sun 14:00-17:00. Admission: Free. Location: Five
minute walk from Hove Station.   Map Ref: 16

West Blatchington Windmill

Holmes Avenue, Hove BN3 7LE   Tel: 01273 776017   Web: www.virtualmuseum.info

Dating from the 1820s, this grade II listed building still has the original mill workings in place over five floors. Discover how grain is turned into flour in a traditional windmill.

Opening Times: May to Sep Sun & BH only 14:30-17:00, groups can be taken around at other
times of the year by arrangement. Admission: Please phone for details. Location: Ten minute
walk from Aldrington Station, 30 minutes bus ride from town centre. Buses 5A & 5B Map Ref: 16

Anne of Cleves Museum

52 Southover High Street, Lewes BN7 1JA   Tel: 01273 474610
Email: anne@sussexpast.co.uk   Web: www.sussexpast.co.uk

The house given to Anne by Henry VIII as part of their divorce settlement. See the old kitchen and the oak furnished main chamber, and investigate the history of the Sussex iron industry.

Opening Times: Jan & Feb, Nov & Dec Tue to Sat 10:00-17:00. Mar to Oct Tue to Sat 10:00-
17:00, Sun & Mon 11:00-17:00. Closed Xmas. Admission: Adult £2.80, Child £1.40,
Concession £2.50, Family £7.00. Location: Near town centre, about ten minutes walk from
Lewes Castle and eight minutes walk from Lewes Railway Stn. Bus stops nearby.   Map Ref: 17

Glynde Place

Glynde, Lewes BN7 6SX   Tel / Fax: 01273 858224
Email: hampden@glyndeplace.co.uk

A magnificent Elizabethan manor house set in the heart of the South Downs. Glynde Place was built in 1589 from local flint and stone from Normandy and extensively added to in the 18th century. There is a collection of Old Masters, family portraits, furniture, embroidery and silver all belonging to the family who had lived there for over 400 years.

Opening Times: Jun & Sep Sun & Wed, Jul & Aug Sun, Wed, Thu & BH 14:00-17:00. Admission: Adult £5.00, Child £2.50, Groups (25+) £3.00. Location: Three miles to the east of Lewes. Follow the brown tourist board signs off the A27 or the B2192. Map Ref: 18

Lewes Castle & Barbican House Museum

169 High Street, Lewes BN7 1YE   Tel: 01273 486290   Fax: 01273 486990
Email: castle@sussexpast.co.uk   Web: www.sussexpast.co.uk

Explore the Castle built soon after the Conquest of 1066 and see the spectacular views from the top. Next door Barbican House Museum displays a range of exhibitions plotting the history of the area along with a sound and light show based around a scale town model, and an interactive touch-screen computer.

Opening Times: Tue to Sat 10:00-17:30 Sun, Mon BH 11:00-17:30. Closed Mon in Jan & Xmas.
Admission: Adult £4.20, Child £2.10, Concession £3.70, Family £11.40. Location: In town centre, ten minutes walk from bus and railway stations. Map Ref: 17

LITTLEHAMPTON *W Sussex*

Littlehampton Museum

Manor House, Church Street, Littlehampton BN17 5EW   Tel: 01903 738100   Fax: 01903 731690   Email: littlehamptonmuseum@arun.gov.uk

Varied collection of archaeology, social history artefacts and art relating to the Littlehampton area. Also, special displays of photographic and maritime history - over 200 ship models on show!

Opening Times: Tue to Sat 10:30-16:30. Admission: Free. Location: 50 metres from High Street, seven minutes walk from train. Map Ref: 19

NEWHAVEN *E Sussex*

Newhaven Fort

Fort Road, Newhaven BN9 9DS   Tel: 01273 517622   Fax: 01273 512059
Email: enquiries@newhavenfort.org.uk   Web: www.newhavenfort.org.uk

Victorian clifftop fortress commanding superb views that really brings history to life. Experience what it was like in the First and Second World Wars, through exciting life size and interactive exhibitions.

Opening Times: 23 Mar to 3 Nov daily 10:30-18:00. Admission: Adult £4.75, Child £3.25, OAP £4.25, Family £14.00. Location: One mile from Newhaven Town Centre. Map Ref: 20

Museums • Galleries • Historic Houses

Please let us know of any collections that are not listed in this guide that you feel should be listed. E-mail us on *editor@tomorrows.co.uk* or return the Report Form on page 448

Sussex

Planet Earth Museum & Sussex History Trail

Paradise Park, Avis Road, Newhaven BN9 0DH   Tel: 01273 512123
Fax: 01273 616005   Email: enquiries@paradisepark.co.uk   Web: paradisepark.co.uk

Iguanodon Bridge

Planet Earth is one of the finest museums of its type in the country with life size moving dinosaurs, interactive displays and a spectacular collection of fossils, minerals and crystals. Handcrafted models of Sussex landmarks are the setting for the Sussex History Trail which is set in beautiful themed gardens.

Opening Times: Daily 10:00-18:00.   Admission: Adult £4.99, Child £3.99, Family £16.99. Group rates available. Location: Signposted from A26 and A259. Short walk from Newhaven Railway Station and Denton Corner bus stop.   Map Ref: 20

Petworth House & Park

THE NATIONAL TRUST

Petworth GU28 0AE   Tel: 01798 342207   Fax: 01798 342963
Email: petworth@ntrust.org.uk   Web: www.nationaltrust.org.uk/petworth

View of Petworth House taken from the Deer Park

Enjoy the National Trust's finest painting and sculpture collection including works by Van Dyck, Reynolds, Blake and Turner displayed in a magnificent 17th century mansion set in a beautiful deerpark landscaped by 'Capability' Brown. Superb state rooms containing fine furniture, ceramics and Grinling Gibbons' finest limewood carvings. Fascinating servants' quarters show the domestic side of life.

Opening Times: 29 Mar to 2 Nov Sat to Wed 11:00-17:30.   Admission: Adult £7.00, Child £4.00, Family £18.00. National Trust Members Free.

Location: Located in the centre of Petworth.   Map Ref: 21

Foredown Tower

Foredown Road, Portslade-by-Sea BN41 2EW   Tel: 01273 292092
Web: www.virtualmuseum.info

A converted Edwardian water tower, home to the only operational 'camera obscura' in the south east with outstanding views over the surrounding countryside.

Opening Times: Thu to Sun 10:00-17:00. Closed 24 Dec to 3 Jan (inc). Groups can visit on other days by prior arrangement.   Location: 30 minute bus ride from town centre. Buses 6 & 6A
                                                                    Map Ref: 22

Bignor Roman Villa

Bignor, Pulborough RH20 1PH   Tel / Fax: 01798 869259
Email: bignorromanvilla@care4free.net

All under cover. Discovered 1811. Some of the finest mosaics in Great Britain including Venus and Cupid Gladiators, Medusa and Ganymede. Remains of Hypocaust system. Guided tours must be pre-booked.

Opening Times: Mar to Apr Tue to Sun & BH 10:00-17:00, May daily 10:00-17:00, Jun to Sep daily 10:00-18:00, Oct daily 10:00-17:00.   Admission: Adult £3.80, Child £1.60, OAP £2.70. Group rates available.   Location: Six miles north of Arundel on A29. Six miles from Petworth A285.   Map Ref: 23

Guided or Private Tours	Disabled Access	Gift Shop or Sales Point	Café or Refreshments	Restaurant	Car Parking

Sussex

Parham House and Gardens

Parham Park, Pulborough RH20 4HS
Tel: 01903 742021 Fax: 01903 746557
Email: enquiries@parhaminsussex.co.uk
Web: www.parhaminsussex.co.uk

A beautiful Elizabethan house with 11 acres of award winning gardens in the heart of a medieval deer park, on the slopes of the South Downs. The house contains an important collection of paintings, furniture and needlework shown in the light panelled rooms, including a long gallery, with stunning arrangements of flowers, cut from the four acre walled garden.

Opening Times: Easter Sun to end Sep Wed, Thu, Sun & BH Mon, also Tue & Fri in Aug. Admission: House & Garden: Adult £6.00, Child £2.00, OAP £5.50, Family (2 adult and 2 children) £14.00. Garden only: Adult/OAP £4.00, Child £1.00, Family £9.00. Exhibitions & Events 2003 : 12 & 13 Jul: 10th Annual Garden Weekend - over 70 specialist nurseries and horticultural sundriesmen selling direct to the public; NAFAS floral art competition, no charge Plant Doctor consultant; Folk/Morris Dancing; licenced food tent, 6 & 7 Sep: Autumn Flowers at Parham House - a celebration of flower arranging, Parham Style. Map Ref: 24

Rye Art Gallery

Ockman Lane, East Street, Rye TN31 7JY   Tel: 01797 223218/222433   Fax: 01797 225376

Two buildings linked by a courtyard. Easton Rooms holds a programme of exhibitions by contemporary artists and craftsmen. Stormant Studio holds the permanent collection of over 400 pieces shown in rotation together with in-house exhibitions.

Opening Times: Daily 10:30-13:00 & 14:00-17:00. Admission: Free. Location: High Street location. Map Ref: 25

Rye Castle Museum

3 East Street, Rye TN31 7JY   Tel: 01797 226728

Rye 18th century fire engine, Rye Pottery, uniforms, smuggling items, paintings, etc. All about Rye's long and illustrious history.

Opening Times: Both sites: Apr to Oct Thu to Mon 10:30-13:00 & 14:00-17:00. Ypres Tower: Nov to Mar Sat & Sun 10:30-13:00 & 14:00-15:30. Closed 13:00-14:00. Admission: Both sites Adult £2.90, Child £1.50, Concession £2.00, Family £5.90. Single site Adult £1.90, Child £1.00, Concession £1.50, Family £4.50. Location: In town centre. Map Ref: 25

Steyning Museum

Church Street, Steyning BN44 3YB   Tel: 01903 813333

The museum charts the fluctuations in Steyning's fortunes over 2000 years. Its people, buildings, railway and 400 year old school occupy centre stage in the displays. Temporary exhibitions, displays for children and research facilities.

Opening Times: Tue, Wed, Fri, Sat & Sun PM only. Summer: 10:30-12:30 14:30-16:30, winter: 10:30-12:30 14:30-16:00. BH & other days by appointment. Admission: Free. Location: Near town centre, four minute walk. Map Ref: 26

Sussex

Bluebell Railway

Sheffield Park Station, Sheffield Park, Uckfield TN22 3QL   Tel: 01825 720800
Fax: 01825 7720804   Web: www.bluebell-railway.co.uk

USA Class 0-6-0 Tank No 30064

The Bluebell Railway is a working steam heritage museum. Large collection of working locomotives travel 18 mile round trip through Sussex countryside. Small, detailed collection of railway memorabilia, stations from Victorian, 1930s and 1950s style.

Opening Times: Sheffield Park Station - Trains run daily Apr to Sep & school holidays 10:00-17:00. Closed Xmas. Admission: Adult £8.00, Child £4.00, OAP £6.40, Family £21.50. Includes all-day travel. Location: Sheffield Park Station - access from East Grinstead to Kingscote via special bus service. A275 East Grinstead Lewes road, two miles north junction with A272   Map Ref: 27

The Priest House

The North Lane, West Hoathly RH19 4PP   Tel: 01342 810479   Email: priest@sussexpast.co.uk
Web: www.sussexpast.co.uk

Built in the 15th century, The Priest House has been open as a museum since 1908. Its furnished rooms contain a fascinating array of 17th and 18th century domestic furniture, needlework and household items. Outside a formal herb garden contains over 150 culinary, medicinal and household herbs.

Opening Times: Mar to Oct Tue to Sat 10:30-17:30, Sun 12:00-17:30. Admission: Adult £2.60, Child £1.30, Concession £2.30. Location: In centre of village of West Hoathly.   Map Ref: 28

Worthing Museum & Art Gallery

Chapel Road, Worthing BN11 1HP   Tel: 01903 239999   Fax: 01903 236277
Email: museum@worthing.gov.uk   Web: www.worthing.gov.uk

This beautiful building is home to a fascinating collection of toys, costume, art and decorative art, local history and archaeology. There's so much to see that one visit just won't be enough. The Studio, Art Gallery, Norwood Gallery and Sculpture Garden feature work by local, national and international artists.

Opening Times: Mon to Sat 10:00-17:00. Closed Sun & some BH. Admission: Free.
Location: In town centre, ten minute walk from Worthing Central Railway Station.   Map Ref: 29

Warwickshire & West Midlands

Warwickshire is the quintessential English county in a region rich in history and blessed with some of the country's loveliest scenery. Warwick was rebuilt following a disastrous fire in 1694 and possesses a wondrous castle and some fine buildings. Stratford-upon-Avon is a magnet to the thousands who flock to see Shakespeare's birthplace. Birmingham dominates the West Midlands.

There is an interesting selection of quality museums and galleries throughout the region.

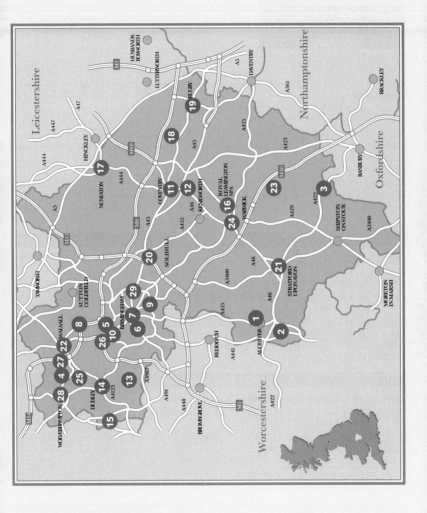

The Red Map References should be used to locate Museums etc on the pages that follow

Warwickshire & West Midlands

Coughton Court

Alcester B49 5JA Tel: 01789 400777   Fax: 01789 765544
Email: andrew@throckmortons.co.uk   Web: www.coughtoncourt.co.uk

Home of Throckmorton family since 1530. Close connections with the Gunpowder Plot. Still of Roman Catholic faith with exhibitions/material on recusancy and Catholic emancipation. Excellent collection of family portraits from Tudor times to present day plus family memorabilia, furniture, porcelain and books.

Opening Times: 23 Mar to Sep Wed to Sun, BH Mon & Tue in Jul & Aug 11:30-17:00. Oct Sat & Sun 11:30-17:00. Closed Good Friday & Sat 22 Jun & 20 Jul.
Admission: House & Garden: Adult £9.45, Child £4.75, Under 5s Free. Location: Two miles north of Alcester on A435. Map Ref: 1

Coughton Court - The Courtyard from the East.
Tudor Gatehouse c.1530

Ragley Hall

Alcester B49 5NJ Tel: 01789 762090 Fax: 01789 764791 Email: info@ragleyhall.com
Web: www.ragleyhall.com

Built in 1680 by Robert Hooke, Ragley has England's finest Baroque plasterwork by James Gibbs, 1750. Wood carvings by Grinling Gibbons, family portraits by Sir Joshua Reynolds. Sheraton and Louis XVI furniture and Minton, Copeland and Meissen china amongst others. 20th century mural by Graham Rust completed 1969-1983.

Opening Times: 10 Apr to 28 Sep Thu to Sun & BH Mon 11:00-18:00 (last admission 16:30).
Admission: Adult £6.00, Child £4.50, OAP £5.00, Family £22.00 (2 adults and 4 children). £1.00 entry fee for State Rooms on first floor. Location: Two miles south west of Alcester, off the A46/A435. Map Ref: 2

Upton House

Banbury OX15 6HT   Tel / Fax: 01295 670266   Email: vuplan@smtp.ntrust.org.uk
Web: www.nationaltrust.org.uk

An impressive 17th century house with fine collections and a magnificent terraced garden.

Opening Times: 23 Mar to 3 Nov Sat to Wed 13:00-17:00 (last admission 16:30). Closed Thu and Fri, but open Good Friday. Admission: House and Garden: Adult £6.00, Child £3.00, Family (2 adults and 3 children) £15.00. Garden only: Adult £3.00, Child £1.50. Location: On A422 seven miles from Banbury, 12 miles from Statford-on-Avon. Follow signs from junction 12 on M40. Map Ref: 3

Bilston Craft Gallery & Museum

Mount Pleasant, Bilston WV14 7LU Tel: 01902 552507   Fax: 01902 552504
Web: www.wolverhamptonart.org.uk

The gallery hosts an exciting programme of contemporary craft exhibitions with workshops and events. Craftplay, an activity room for pre-school children is open for groups by appointment and in summer the sculpture gardens are a popular attraction.

Opening Times: Tue to Fri 10:00-16:00, Sat 11:00-16:00. Admission: Free. Location: Four miles from Wolverhampton and five minutes from Bilston Metro Stop. Map Ref: 4

Aston Hall

Trinity Road, Aston, Birmingham B6 6JD Tel: 0121 327 0062 Web: www.bmag.org.uk

One of the last great houses to be built in a Jacobean style, Aston Hall hosts a fine collection of paintings, textiles and furniture and a 136ft Long Gallery.

Opening Times: Apr to Oct Tue to Fri 13:00-16:00, Sat & Sun 12:00-16:00. Closed Mon except BH. Admission: Free. Location: Three miles from city centre, near junction 6 off M6.
Map Ref: 5

Barber Institute of Fine Arts

University of Birmingham, Edgbaston, Birmingham B15 2TS   Tel: 0121 4147333   Fax: 0121 4143370   Email: info@barber.org.uk   Web: www.barber.org.uk

One of the finest small art galleries in the world housing an outstanding collection of Old Master and Modern paintings, including masterpieces by Rubens, Murillo, Rossetti, Monet and Magritte.

Opening Times: Mon to Sat 10:00-17:00, Sun 12:00-17:00.   Admission: Free.   Location: On University of Birmingham Campus, three miles south of city centre.   Map Ref: 6

Birmingham Museum
and Art Gallery

Birmingham Museum and Art Gallery

Chamberlain Square, Birmingham B3 3DH   Tel: 0121 303 2834   Fax: 0121 303 1394   Email: bmag_enquiries@birmingham.gov.uk   Web: www.bmag.org.uk

Home to the largest collection of Pre-Raphaelite art in Europe, Birmingham Museum & Art Gallery also host a fine collection of 18th and 19th century art, silver, sculpture, ceramics and archeology. Also houses the Waterhall Gallery of modern art and local history galleries. Gas Hall has a range of temporary exhibitions across the year.

Opening Times: Mon to Thur & Sat 10:00-17:00, Fri 10:30-17:00, Sun 12:30-17:00. Closed Xmas & New Year. Admission: Free - voluntary contribution. Location: Five minutes from New Street and Snow Hill Stations. Short walk from any city centre bus stop.

Map Ref: 7

Bishop Asbury Cottage

Newton Road, Great Barr, Birmingham B43 6HN   Tel: 0121 553 0759   Fax: 0121 525 5167   Email: oakhouse@sandwell.gov.uk   Web: www.smbc.sandwell.gov.uk

18th century furniture and artefacts connected with Bishop Frances Asbury, the first Methodist Bishop of America.

Opening Times: Open by appointment only, two open days a year. Admission: Groups £2.50 per person (min charge £25.00 per group). Location: On the A4041, Newton Road. Parking at Maltshovel Public House next door.   Map Ref: 8

Museum of the Jewellery Quarter

75/79 Vyse Street, Hockley, Birmingham B18 6HA   Tel: 0121 554 3598   Email: 6mag_enquiries@birmingham.gov.uk   Web: www.bmag.org.uk

A perfectly preserved jewellery workshop little changed since the early part of this century. The Museum tells the story of jewellery making in Birmingham, through guided tours and demonstrations.

Opening Times: Mon to Fri 10:00-16:00, Sat 11:00-17:00. Close Sun. Admission: Adult £3.00, Concession £2.50, Joint ticket with Soho House Adult £5.00, Concession £4.00.
Location: Short bus ride from city centre. Jewellery Quarter Railway Station five minutes away.

Map Ref: 7

Sarehole Mill

Cole bank Road, Hall Green, Birmingham B13 0BD   Tel: 0121 777 6612   Email: 6mag_enquiries@birmingham.gov.uk   Web: www.bmag.org.uk

Sarehole is the only surviving example of the 60 or so watermills that once existed in Birmingham. It was also the childhood haunt of JRR Tolkien and inspiration for the mill in 'The Hobbit'.

Opening Times: Easter to Oct Tue to Fri 13:00-16:00, Sat & Sun 12:00-16:00. Closed Mon except BH. Admission: Free. Location: Five miles from city centre off A34. 15 minutes from Hall Green Station or a short walk from the 11A/11C bus stop.   Map Ref: 9

Soho House

Soho Avenue, Handsworth, Birmingham B18 5LB   Tel: 0121 554 9122   Fax: 0121 554 5929   Email: 6mag_enquiries@birmingham.co.uk   Web: www.bmag.org.uk

Soho House was Matthew Boulton's 18th century home, restored with original items from the

BIRMINGHAM W Midlands (continued)

house. You can find out about this fascinating inventor and the great thinkers that met at the house - the Lunar Society.

Opening Times: Tue to Sat 10:00-17:00, Sun 12:00-17:00. Closes Mon except BH.
Admission: Adult £3.00, Child £2.50. Joint ticket with Museum of Jewellery Quarter Adult £5, Child £4.00. Location: Ten minutes from city centre by bus or train. Ring for more details.
Map Ref: 10

COVENTRY Warwicks

Coventry Toy Museum
Whitfriars Gate, Much Park Street, Coventry CV1 2LT Tel: 024 7622 7560

A collection of toys of every description housed in a 14th century monastery gatehouse.

Opening Times: Daily 13:00-17:00 Admission: Adult £1.50, Child/OAP £1.00.
Location: Coventry City Centre.
Map Ref: 11

Herbert Art Gallery & Museum
Jordan Well, Coventry CV1 5QP Tel: 024 7683 2565 Fax: 024 7683 2410
Email: artsandheritage@coventry.gov.uk Web: www.coventrymuseum.org.uk

Coventry City Council

Jacquard Loom dating from 1845
in Godiva City Exhibition

The Herbert Art Gallery and Museum is situated in the heart of Coventry City Centre a couple of minutes walk away from Coventry Cathedral. The award winning Godiva City exhibition tells the story of the city from before Lady Godiva to the present. The rest of the Gallery is used for temporary exhibitions using objects from the museum collections and provided by other organisations and individuals. Items from the Museum's permanent collection of Lady Godiva paintings and drawings and sketches for Graham Sutherland's Cathedral tapestry are invariably on display. The collections cover visual arts, natural history, archaeology, industrial and social history.

Coventry's 20th Century Industries
in Godiva City Exhibition

Opening Times: Mon to Sat 10:00-17:30, Sun 12:00-17:00. Admission: Free. Location: City centre near Tourist Information Centre and Coventry Cathedral. Exhibitions & Events 2003 : Permanent:: Godiva City - history of Coventry, 7 Dec to 16 Feb: Expressions in Stich, 13 Jan to 2 Mar: Retrospective: Ian Bamford, To 2 Feb: Sky Blue Heaven - Coventry City Football Club, To 16 Feb: The Building of Coventry Cathedral, 15 Feb to 16 Mar: Picasso: Histoire Naturelle, 15 Mar to 10 Apr: Coventry & Warwickshire Society of Artists, Mid Jul to 5 Oct: Tim Threlfall 4 Oct to Feb 04: Phil Maxwell, 1 Nov to Feb 04: The Coventry Open Art Exhibition 2003, 23 Nov to 18 Jan: Made in the Middle.
Map Ref: 11

Jaguar Daimler Heritage Trust
Jaguar Cars, Browns Lane, Coventry CV5 9DR Tel: 024 76402121

Display of 30+ Jaguars, collection totals 130+ available to view if required. Archive housing original factory records and photographic collection and picture gallery.

Opening Times: Mon to Fri 08:30-16:45 and last Sun of month 10:00-16:00. Admission: Free.
Location: On bus route from city centre, good access to motorways.
Map Ref: 11

Lunt Roman Fort
Coventry Road, Baginton, Coventry Tel: 024 7683 2381 Fax: 024 7683 2410
Email: artsandheritage@coventry.gov.uk Web: www.coventrymuseum.org.uk

Once inhabited by the Roman Army, this ancient site includes the Granary building which contains a museum of Roman Life with archaeological finds.

Opening Times: 30 Mar to 27 Oct Sat, Sun & BH. 1 Jun to 9 Jun daily except Wed. 20 Jul to 1 Sep daily except Wed. All 10:00-17:00. Admission: Adult £2.00, Concession £1.00.
Location: Baginton Village is on the south side of Coventry, just off the A45 and A46. The fort is situated off the Coventry Road.
Map Ref: 12

Warwickshire & West Midlands

Museum of British Road Transport

Hales Street, Coventry CV1 1PN Tel: 024 7683 2425 Fax: 024 7683 2465
Email: museum@mbrt.co.uk Web: www.mbrt.co.uk

Largest collection of British road transport in the world. Designated as a collection of National Importance with 200 cars and commercial vehicles, 200 cycles and 90 motorcycles and Thrust 2 and Thrust SSC land speed record cars.

Opening Times: Daily 10:00-17:00. Closed 24-26 Dec. Admission: Free. Location: Town centre, one minute walk from bus station, ten minutes from train station.   Map Ref: 11

Priory Visitor Centre

Priory Gardens, Coventry CV1 5EX Tel: 024 7655 2242 Fax: 024 7683 2410
Email: artsandheritage@coventry.gov.uk Web: www.coventrymuseum.org.uk

On the site of Coventry's medieval Priory and Cathedral. It tells the story of the site from the time of Lady Godiva to the Dissolution by King Henry VIII using archaeological finds from recent excavations.

Opening Times: Mon to Sat 10:00-17:30, Sun 12:00-16:00. Admission: Free. Location: In city centre, near Holy Trinity Church and Coventry Cathedral.   Map Ref: 11

St Mary's Guildhall

Bayley Lane, Coventry Tel: 024 7683 2381 Fax: 024 7683 2410
Email: artsandheritage@coventry.gov.uk Web: www.coventrymuseum.org.uk

St Mary's Guildhall is one of the finest surviving medieval Guildhalls in England. It dates from the 1340s and includes the imposing Great Hall with its stained glass windows and a Tournai tapestry dated 1500.

Opening Times: Easter to end Sep Sun to Thu 10:00-16:00. Admission: Free. Location: City centre, near Coventry Cathedral.   Map Ref: 11

Haden Hill House

Off Barrs Road, Cradley Heath Tel: 01384 569444 Email: oakhouse@sandwell.gov.uk
Web: www.smbc.sandwell.gov.uk

A Victorian furnished house with a collection of social history relating to the borough of Sandwell.

Opening Times: Mon to Thu 10:00-17:00, Fri 10:00-16:30, Sat & Sun 13:00-17:00
Admission: Free Location: Off Barrs Road, Cradley Heath near the Leisure Centre
Map Ref: 13

Black Country Living Museum

Tipton Road, Dudley DY1 4SQ Tel: 0121 557 9643 Fax: 0121 557 4242
Email: info@bclm.co.uk Web: www.bclm.co.uk

Policeman

The Black Country Living Museum was established in 1975 to collect, preserve research and display items relating to the social and industrial history of the Black Country. There is a collection of well over 30,000 items, ranging from hand made nails to whole buildings. Together, the mine, the foundry and the many houses, shops and workshops rebuilt on its 26 acre site represent the Black Country when it was the heart of industrial Britain. Much of the collection consists of the fixtures and fittings that make these buildings complete and accurate to the last detail, but in addition, Black Country products, both past and present, are continually being added to the collection. The most recent addition is a representative collection of cars and motorcycles made in Wolverhampton, an important centre of the automotive industry in the 1920s and 30s. The modern exhibition halls, opened in 2000, display selections of Black Country

St. James's School

Warwickshire & West Midlands

products. The centrepiece is a permanent display of items that defined the area across the world: chain and anchor made in Netherton for the great ocean liners, world class saddles made in Walsall, crystal glass made in Stourbridge and hardware made in Cradley Heath and exported throughout the British Empire.

Opening Times: Mar to Oct daily 10:00-17:00, Nov to Feb Wed to Sun 10:00-16:00.
Admission: Adult £8.25, Child £4.75, OAP £7.25, Family (2 adults and 3 children) £22.50.
Location: Three miles from junction 2 of the M5, six miles from junction 10 of the M6, ten miles from Birmingham City Centre. Exhibitions & Events 2003 : For details please contact.

Map Ref: 14

Dudley Museum & Art Gallery

St James's Road, Dudley DY1 1HU Tel: 01384 815575 Fax: 01384 815576
Web: www.dudley.gov.uk

Geological gallery with definitive collection of local Silurian and carboniferous fossils. Brooke Robinson museum of European paintings, furniture and ceramics. Temporary exhibitions throughout the year.

Opening Times: Mon to Sat 10:00-16:00. Closed BH Mon. Admission: Free. Location: Town centre.

Map Ref: 14

Broadfield House Glass Museum

Compton Drive, Kingswinford DY6 9NS Tel: 01384 812745 Fax: 01384 812746
Email: glass.museum@dudley.gov.uk Web: www.dudley.gov.uk

Situated in the historic glass quarter, Broadfield House celebrates the art of glassmaking. Glass artists can be watched in the studio and attractive gifts bought from the shop.

Opening Times: Tue to Sun 14:00-17:00, BH Mon 12:00-17:00. Admission: Free.
Location: Near town centre, on main bus route.

Map Ref: 15

Leamington Spa Art Gallery & Museum, Royal Pump Rooms

The Parade, Leamington Spa CV32 4AA Tel: 01926 742700

Award winning art gallery and museum with services on offer including: fine art collection, exhibition on the history of Royal Leamington Spa, cabinet of curiosities, gallery of interactive exhibits, Hammam (restored Turkish bathroom), changing programme of visual arts, history and local interest exhibitions and educational parties by arrangement. Fine art collection includes 16th and 17th century Dutch and Flemish, 19th and 20th century British artists, local artists, sculpture, ceramics and glassware. Recent acquisitions include works of art by Mark Quinn, Mark Francis and Catherine Yass. Other key artists in the collection include Stanley Spencer, L S Lowry, Gillian Wearing, Vanessa Bell, Patrick Caulfield, Sir Terry Frost, Walter Sickert and Graham Sutherland. Facilities at The Royal Pump Rooms also include a café, library, Tourist Information Centre and assembly rooms.

Opening Times: Tue, Wed, Fri & Sat 10:30-17:00, Thu 13:30-20:00, Sun 11:00-16:00. Closed Mon. Admission: Free. Location: 500 metres from Leamington Spa Railway Station. The Royal Pump Room is situated on The Parade, two minute walk from the main shopping area. Exhibitions & Events 2003 : For Exhibitions and Events please telephone for details.

Map Ref: 16

Guided or Private Tours	Disabled Access	Gift Shop or Sales Point	Café or Refreshments	Restaurant	Car Parking

Warwickshire & West Midlands

Museum & Art Gallery

Riversley Park, Nuneaton CV11 5TU Tel: 024 7635 0720 Fax: 024 7634 3559
Email: museum@nuneaton-bedworthbc.gov.uk Web: www.nuneatonandbedworth.gov.uk

The Museum and Art Gallery boasts a varied collection which includes George Eliot memorabilia, local history and paintings. As well as the permanent displays of its collections, there is a lively temporary exhibition programme showing regional artists, quality touring displays and subjects of local interest.

Opening Times: Tue to Sat 10:30-16:30, Sun 14:00-16:30. Closed Mon except BH. Admission: Free.
Location: Pleasant location in Riversley Park close to town centre. Map Ref: 17

Recreation of George Eliot's Drawing Room

HM Prison Service Museum

Newbold Revel, Stretton under Fosse, Rugby CV23 0TH Tel: 01788 834168/7 Fax: 01788 834186 Email: museum@breathemail.net Web: hmprisonservice.gov.uk

Visit HM Prison Service Museum to find out about punishment and imprisonment from medieval times to the present day.

Opening Times: Mon to Fri 09:00-20:00. Group visits and tours by arrangement.
Admission: Free. Location: Situated on the B4027 near Stretton under Fosse. Both the M1 and M6 pass within reasonable travelling distance. Map Ref: 18

James Gilbert Rugby Football Museum

5 St Matthews Street, Rugby CV21 3BY Tel: 01788 333889 Fax: 01788 540795
Email: pat@james-gilbert.com Web: www.gilbertrugby.com

Visit the museum and trace the history of the game and its evolution. Soak up the history of this noble game through memorabilia from its beginnings to the World Cup of 1999. Multi-screen show, The Rugby Experience.

Opening Times: Mon to Sat 09:00-17:00. Admission: Free. Location: Opposite Rugby School. Map Ref: 19

Rugby Art Gallery & Museum

Little Elborow Street, Rugby CV21 3BZ Tel: 01788 533201 Fax: 01788 533204
Email: rugbyartgallery&museum@rugby.gov.uk Web: www.rugbygalleryandmuseum.org.uk

Tripontium collection of Roman artefacts. Rugby's social history including touchscreen kiosk about Rugby's industrial heritage. Rugby Collection of 20th century and contemporary British art. Changing programme of contemporary art and craft exhibitions.

Opening Times: Tue & Thu 10:00-20:00, Wed & Fri 10:00-17:00, Sat 10:00-16:00, Sun & BH 13:00-17:00. Closed Mon. Admission: Free. Location: Town centre. Map Ref: 19

National Motorcycle Museum

Coventry Road, Bickenhill, Solihull B92 0EJ Tel: 01675 443311 Fax: 01675 443310
Email: sales@nationalmotorcylemuseum.co.uk Web: nationalmotorcyclemuseum.co.uk

The National Motorcycle Museum houses a breathtaking collection of over 700 British motorcycles dating from 1898, each painstakingly restored to its original specification. Facilities at the Museum include a restaurant/snack bar, bookshop and souvenir shop.

Opening Times: Daily 10:00-18:00. Closed Xmas.
Admission: Adult £4.50, Child/OAP £3.25.
Location: The Museum is situated on the A45 junction 6 of M42, opposite the National Exhibition Centre.

Wartime machines on view Map Ref: 20

Warwickshire & West Midlands

Royal Shakespeare Company Collection

Royal Shakespeare Theatre, Waterside, Stratford-upon-Avon CV37 6BB   Tel: 01789 262870/412617   Fax: 01789 262870   Email: info@rsc.org.uk   Web: www.rsc.org.uk

Exhibition featuring costumes worn by famous actors in past productions. Historic paintings, drawings and prints of scenes and characters. Regularly updated to complement repertoire. Displays of memorabilia and theatre history.

Opening Times: Mon to Fri 13:30-18:30, Sat 10:30-18:30, Sun 12:00-16:00. Admission: Adult £1.50, Concession £1.00. Location: Near town centre on the banks of River Avon. Map Ref: 21

Shakespeare Birthplace Trust

The Shakespeare Centre, Henley Street, Stratford-upon-Avon CV37 6QW
Tel: 01789 204016   Fax: 01789 263138   Email: info@shakespeare.org.uk
Web: www.shakespeare.org.uk

The Trust administers the five Shakespeare properties which house the museum collections: Shakespeare's Birthplace, Anne Hathaway's Cottage, New Place/Nash's House, Mary Arden's House and the Shakespeare Countryside Museum and Halls Croft. The collections include Elizabethan and Jacobean domestic furniture, ceramic, metal ware and textiles; Shakespeare memorabilia; archaeological and social history material relating to the Stratford-upon-Avon district; local craft and agricultural tools,

Elizabethan mans's signet ring which may have belonged to Shakespeare

vehicles and machinery; coins and medals; oil and watercolours paintings, including important portraits of Shakespeare. The Trust also administers Harvard House and the Museum of British Pewter with a large collection of pewter dating from Romano-British times. The Trust also has an important Shakespeare Library and a Records Office.

Reconstruction of John Shakespeare's glove-making workshop

Opening Times: Nash's House/New Place and Hall's Croft: Nov to Mar Mon to Sat 11:00-16:00, Sun 11:00-16:00, Apr to May & Sep to Oct daily 11:00-17:00, Jun to Aug Mon to Sat 09:30-17:00, Sun 10:00-17:00. Anne Hathaway's Cottage: Nov to Mar Mon to Sat 10:00-16:00, Sun 10:30-16:00, Apr to May & Sep to Oct Mon to Sat 09:30-17:00, Sun 10:00-17:00, Jun to Aug Mon to Sat 09:00-17:00, Sun 09:30-17:00. Mary Arden's House: Nov to Mar Mon to Sat 10:00-16:00, Sun 10:30-16:00, Apr to May & Sep to Oct Mon to Sat 10:00-17:00, Sun 10:30-17:00, Jun to Aug Mon to Sat 09:30-17:00, Sun 10:00-17:00. Shakespeare's Birthplace: Nov to Mar Mon to Sat 10:00-16:00, Sun 10:30-16:00, Apr to May & Sep to Oct Mon to Sat 10:00-17:00, Sun 10:30-17:00, Jun to Aug Mon to Sat 09:00-17:00, Sun 09:30-17:00. Admission: Nash's House/New Place and Hall's Croft: Single Ticket Adult £3.50, Child £1.70, Concession £3.00, Family £9.00. Anne Hathaway's Cottage Single Ticket: Adult £5.00, Child £2.00, Concession £4.00, Family £12.00. Mary Arden's House Single Ticket: Adult £5.00, Child £2.00, Concession £5.00, Family £13.50. Shakespeare's Birthplace Single Ticket: Adult £6.50, Child £2.50, Concession £5.50, Family £15.00. Multiple House Tickets - Three In-Town Houses: Adult £9.00, Child £4.50, Concession £8.00, Family £20.00. All Five Houses: Adult £13.00, Child £6.50, Concession £12.00, Family £29.00. Group rates available telephone 01789 201806. Map Ref: 21

Birchills Canal Museum

Old Birchills, Walsall WS3 8QD   Tel: 01922 645778

This is housed in a former Boatman's Mission built in 1900. It aimed to improve the physical and spiritual lives of its visitors. The Museum contains a reconstruction of a narrowboat cabin and examples of canal decorative artwork along with other canal related objects. It provides an introduction to the history of canals in Walsall and the people who have worked on them.

Opening Times: Tue to Wed 09:30-12:30, Thur to Sun 13:00-16:00. Closed BH.
Admission: Free. Location: Off A34 Green Lane. Map Ref: 22

Warwickshire & West Midlands

Jerome K Jerome Birthplace Museum

Belsize House, Bradford Street, Walsall WS1 1PN
Tel: 01922 653116

Jerome K Jerome is Walsall's most distinguished literary figure, born here on 2 May 1859. The Museum, located on the ground floor, includes an 1850s Victorian parlour and an exhibition charting his life and times. Items on display include his World War One ambulance driver's uniform and first editions of his work.

Opening Times: Mon to Fri 09:00-17:00, Sat 12:00-14:00. Closed BH. Admission: Free. Location: Bradford Street, two minutes walk from the Bridge. Map Ref: 22

Jerome's birthplace, Belsize House

New Art Gallery Walsall

Gallery Square, Walsall WS2 8LG Tel: 01922 654400/info 637575
Fax: 01922 654401 Email: wilkinsonc@walsall.gov.uk
Web: www.artatwalsall.org.uk

On permanent display is The Garman Ryan Collection which was donated to the people of Walsall by Lady Kathleen Garman, widow of sculptor Sir Jacob Epstein, in 1973. The gallery is also home to a Discovery Gallery, which creates an introduction to a three storey children's house, including an artist's studio and activity room. The temporary exhibition galleries are dedicated to exhibiting the best of contemporary and historic art.

The Garman Ryan Collection

Opening Times: Tue to Sat 10:00-17:00, Sun 12:00-17:00. Open BH. Admission: Free. Location: Two minutes away from the town centre and is sign posted from all major routes into Walsall Town Centre and M6 junction 7, 8 & 10. Map Ref: 22

Heritage Motor Centre

Banbury Road, Gaydon, Warwick CV35 0BJ Tel: 01926 641188 Fax: 01926 641555
Email: enquiries@heritagemotorcentre.org.uk Web: www.heritage-motor-centre.co.uk

Home to the largest collection of historic British cars in the world. With the Land Rover off-road demonstration track (open everyday), and children's quad bikes and electric cars running at weekends and school holidays.

Opening Times: Daily 10:00-17:00. Closed 24-26 Dec. Admission: Adult £8.00, Child £6.00, OAP £7.00, Family (2 adults and 3 children) £25.00. Location: Two minutes from junction 12 on M40. Map Ref: 23

The Queen's Own Hussars Museum

Lord Leycester Hospital, High Street, Warwick CV34 4BH Tel / Fax: 01926 492035
Email: trooper@qohm.tsnet.co.uk

The Early Years display includes Sheriffmuir, the first action in which both the 3rd and 7th Hussars took part. The Wars against the French include Dettingen and the story of Thomas Brown. The Napoleonic War cases highlight Peninsular Campaign and lead up to Waterloo. 19th century and Colonial Wars are illustrated through life sized tableaux. In the Guildhall section there are numerous displays including one on the Second World War.

Opening Times: Summer Tue to Sun 10:30-17:00. Winter Tue to Sun 10:30-16:00. Closed Xmas.

Admission: Hospital: Adult £3.00, Child £2.00, OAP £2.50. No charge to enter Museum.
Location: Housed in Lord Leycester Hospital, one minute walk from Market Square. Map Ref: 24

Royal Regiment of Fusiliers Museum (Royal Warwickshire)

St Johns House, Warwick CV34 4NF   Tel: 01926 491653   Fax: 01869 257633

Museum tells the story of the Sixth Foot (Royal Warwickshire Regiment) from its origins in 1674 to the Fusiliers of today. The displays are an exciting mix of real objects, models and activities. You can see uniforms, weapons, equipment, medals, documents, paintings and curios from all ranks of soldier - Private to Field Marshal.

Opening Times: Jan to Dec, Tue to Sat 10:00-17:00, May to Sep, Sun 14:30-17:00
Admission: Free.   Location: Five minute from Warwick Railway Station, near town centre.
Map Ref: 24

St Johns House

St Johns, Warwick CV34 4NF   Tel: 01926 412021/412132   Fax: 01926 419840
Email: museum@warwickshire.gov.uk   Web: www.warwickshire.gov.uk/museum

Social history of Warwickshire, displayed in a 17th century house with gardens. Victorian schoolroom and kitchen, costume gallery, Discovery Room for the under 5s.

Opening Times: Tue to Sat & BH Mon 10:00-17:00, May to Sep also Sun 14:30-17:00.
Admission: Free.   Location: Near town centre and St Nicholas Park, two minute walk from Warwick Railway Station.   Map Ref: 24

Warwick Castle

Warwick CV34 4QU   Tel: 0870 442 2000   Fax: 01926 401692
Email: customer.information@warwick-castle.com   Web: www.warwick-castle.co.uk

Experience over 1000 years of history at Warwick Castle. Attractions include the Medieval 'Kingmaker - A Preparation for Battle', the Victorian 'Royal Weekend Party' and the newly opened Mill and Engine House.

Opening Times: Apr to Sep daily 10:00-18:00, Oct to Mar daily 10:00-17:00. Closed Xmas Day. Admission: Please telephone for details on 0870 442 2000. Location: The Castle is well signposted and less than two miles from junction 15 of the M40. Events 2003 : There are a number of special events taking place throughout the year.   Map Ref: 24

Warwick Doll Museum

Okens House, Castle Street, Warwick CV34 4BP   Tel: 01926 495546/412500   Fax: 01926 419840   Email: museum@warwickshire.gov.uk   Web: www.warwickshire.gov.uk/museum

Dolls, teddies, toys and games from days gone by, displayed in Okens House - a 15th century timber-framed building. Shop catering for serious doll collectors and casual visitors.

Opening Times: Apr to Oct Mon to Sat 10:00-17:00, Sun 11:30-17:00, Nov to Mar Sat only 10:00-16:00. Admission: Adult £1.00, Child/Concession 70p, Family £3.00. Location: Near town centre, on route from Warwick Castle.   Map Ref: 24

Warwickshire Museum

Market Place, Warwick CV34 4SA   Tel: 01926 412500   Fax: 01926 419840
Email: museum@warwickshire.gov.uk   Web: www.warwickshire.gov.uk/museum

Displays on the archaeology, geology and natural history of Warwickshire and a temporary exhibition gallery. Highlights include a huge brown bear, the Sheldon Tapestry Map of Warwickshire, live bees, fossils and ancient jewellery.

Opening Times: Tue to Sat & BH Mon 10:00-17:00, May to Sep also Sun 11:30-17:00.
Admission: Free.   Location: Town centre, in the Market Square.   Map Ref: 24

Warwickshire & West Midlands

Wednesbury Museum & Art Gallery

Holyhead Road, Wednesbury WS10 7DF   Tel: 0121 556 0683
Email: oakhouse@sandwell.gov.uk   Web: www.smbc.sandwell.gov.uk

Houses a Fine art collection and the world's largest public collection of Ruskin Pottery. Also has a Family fun room, changing exhibition and workshop programme.

Opening Times: Mon, Wed & Fri 10:00-17:00, Thu & Sat 10:00-13:00, closed Sun.
Admission: Free. Location: Off the old A41 in Wednesbury, three minute walk from bus station, five minute walk from Great Western Street Metro Station.   Map Ref: 25

Oak House Museum

Oak Road, West Bromwich B70 8HJ   Tel: 0121 553 0759   Email: oakhouse@sandwell.gov.uk
Web: www.smbc.sandwell.gov.uk

A Yeoman farmer's residence surrounded by pleasant grounds, housing Jacobean and Tudor furniture.

Opening Times: Apr to Sep, Mon, Tue, Wed & Fri 10:00-17:00, Sat & Sun 14:00-17:00. Oct to Mar, Mon, Tue, Wed & Fri 10:00-16:00, Sat 13:30-16:00. Closed Sun and Thu. Admission: Free
Location: Near Town Centre, Ten minutes walk from Lodge Road Metro Station   Map Ref: 26

Willenhall Museum

Willenhall Library, Walsall Street, Willenhall   Tel: 01922 653116

Situated in the former Town Hall, the Museum provides a brief introduction to the history of Willenhall, showing how the community has developed from a small rural village to a large industrial centre. During the Industrial Revolution, Willenhall's traditional craft of lock making was transformed and locks were exported worldwide.

Opening Times: Mon 10:00-19:00, Tue 09:30-17:00, Thu 09:30-19:00, Fri 09:30-17:00, Sat 09:30-16:00. Closed BH.
Admission: Free. Location: Above Willenhall Library.
Map Ref: 27

Willenhall Library Building

Bantock House & Park

Finchfield Road, Wolverhampton WV3 9LQ   Tel: 01902 552195   Fax: 01902 552196
Web: www.wolverhamptonart.org.uk

Visitors can discover the history of Wolverhampton, from market town to metropolis, as well as finding out the history of the 19th century house and park. There are activities for all ages throughout.

Opening Times: Nov to Mar Fri to Sun 12:00-16:00, Apr to Oct Tue to Sun 10:00-17:00.
Admission: Free. Location: One mile from the centre of Wolverhampton, good bus links.
Map Ref: 28

Wightwick Manor

Wightwick Bank, Wolverhampton WV6 8EE   Tel: 01902 761400   Fax: 01902 764663
Email: mwtman@smtp.ntrust.org.uk   Web: www.nationaltrust.co.uk

Victorian manor house and garden owned by the Mauder family. The house is a wonderful example of the influence of William Morris and the Arts and Craft Movement. Pre-Raphaelite Art Collection, 17 acre Thomas Mawson garden with formal areas and woodland.

Opening Times: Mar to Dec Thu & Sat 13:30-17:00, BH Sun & Mon 13:30-17:00.
Admission: Adult £5.60, Child/Student £2.80, Family £13.00, National Trust Members Free.
Location: Off A454, three miles west of Wolverhampton.   Map Ref: 28

Warwickshire & West Midlands

Wolverhampton Art Gallery

Lichfield Street, Wolverhampton WV1 1DU   Tel: 01902 552055   Fax: 01902 552053
Email: info.wag@dial.pipex.com   Web: www.wolverhamptonart.org.uk

Wolverhampton Art Gallery has become renowned for its innovative programme of temporary exhibitions, backed up by a lively programme of workshops and events. The contemporary collection is the finest in the region. The gallery also houses an outstanding collection of British and American Pop Art along with traditional 18th and 19th century paintings by artists such as Gainsborough, Turner and Landseer.

Opening Times: Mon to Sat 10:00-17:00.
Admission: Free.   Location: Centre of city, two minute walk from bus and train stations.   Map Ref: 28

Blakesley Hall

Blakesley Road, Yardley B25 8RN   Tel: 0121 4642193   Web: www.bmag.org.uk

Built in 1590 Blakesley Hall contains period furniture and fittings including the table in the great hall that is original to the house. Recently renovated it is one of the few remaining timber framed buildings left in Birmingham.

Opening Times: Please telephone for seasonal opening times.   Admission: Free.   Map Ref: 29

Wiltshire

Salisbury, built where the rivers Avon, Bourne and Nadder meet is arguably the most perfect cathedral city in England. Salisbury Plain contains Britain's leading concentration of major prehistoric sites, the main one being Stonehenge. Malmesbury in the north boasts some of the finest Roman architecture in the country and Avebury is one of the most important megalithic monuments in Europe.

Wiltshire's heritage is well recorded in its museums and stately homes.

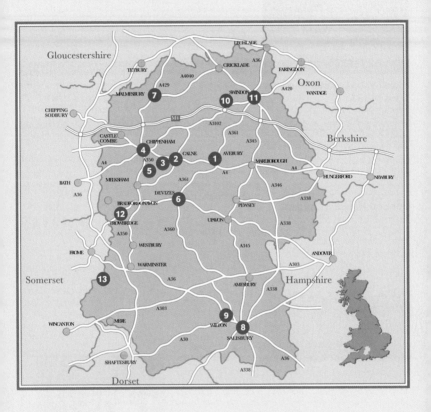

The Red Map References should be used to locate Museums etc on the pages that follow

Wiltshire

Alexander Keiller Museum

High Street, Avebury SN8 1RF   Tel: 01672 539250   Fax: 01672 539388
Email: wavgen@smtp.ntrust.org.uk

THE NATIONAL TRUST

Contains prehistoric collections from the Avebury complex of monuments, which are of similar age to Stonehenge. Admission charge also covers 'Avebury, 6000 Years of Mystery', an interactive exhibition.

Opening Times: Apr to Oct daily 10:00-18:00. Nov to Mar daily 10:00-16:00. Closed Xmas. Admission: Adult £4.00, Child £2.00. National Trust and English Heritage Members Free. Location: Next to prehistoric stone circles. Parking five minutes walk.   Map Ref: 1

The Alexander Keiller Museum

Atwell-Wilson Motor Museum

Downside, Stockley Lane, Calne SN11 0NF   Tel / Fax: 01249 813119   Web: www.atwell-wilson.org

The collection began in 1962 with the Buick and Singer, Vauxhall and a Model T arrived later, and welding work commenced in 1972. The large hall was built in 1989 when the museum opened. The contents are varied with vehicles from the 1920s to the 1980s.

Opening Times: Apr to Oct Mon to Thu & Sun 11:00-17:00. Open Good Friday. Nov to Mar Mon to Thu & Sun 11:00-16:00. Admission: Adult £2.50, Child £1.00, OAP £2.00. Location: The site is also the location of a 17th century water meadow, which is being preserved. Map Ref: 2

Bowood House & Gardens

Estate Office, Bowood House, Calne SN11 0LZ   Tel: 01249 812102
Fax: 01249 821757 Email: houseandgardens@bowood.org
Web: www.bowood.org

BOWOOD
HOUSE & GARDENS

Front elevation of Bowood House

Bowood House, the family home of the Marquis and Marchioness of Lansdowne, was built during the 18th century, to the designs of Henry Keene and Robert Adam. The Chapel and famous Italianate terraced gardens were added in the 19th century. The House contains important paintings and classical and 19th century sculpture. There is a fascinating collection of Indiana (the 5th Marquis was Viceroy 1888-94). The Exhibition Rooms contain Victoriana, costume, jewellery, miniatures and fine porcelain. Among the most interesting items are the Napoleonic Collection, including Napoleon's death mask and Imperial porcelain, and one of the finest private collections of British watercolours, especially notable for works by Bonington, Roberts, Lear and Turner. Those who are interested in garden history will enjoy 'Capability' Brown's Park and the late 18th century 'picturesque' rockwork garden.

The Chapel, designed by Sir Charles Cockerall, decorated for Christmas

Opening Times: 23 Mar to 3 Nov daily 11:00-17:30.
Admission: Adult £6.05, Child £3.85, Under 4s £3.00, Under 2s Free, OAP £3.00. Group rates on request. Location: Off the A4 in Derry Hill village, midway between Calne and Chippenham. Exhibitions & Events 2003 : Please telephone for details.
                                                                                             Map Ref: 3

Guided or Private Tours	Disabled Access	Gift Shop or Sales Point	Café or Refreshments	Restaurant	Car Parking

Wiltshire

Chippenham Museum & Heritage Centre
10 Market Place, Chippenham SN15 3HF   Tel: 01249 705020   Fax: 01249 705025
Email: heritage@chippenham.gov.uk

Chippenham's new museum tells the story of this historic market town. Displays focus on Saxon Chippenham, Alfred the Great, Brunel's railway, and much more.

Opening Times: Mon to Sat 10:00-16:00. Closed Sun.   Admission: Free.   Location: Near town centre, at the historic Market Place.   Map Ref: 4

Fox Talbot Museum
High Street, Lacock, Chippenham SN15 2LG   Tel: 01249 730459   Fax: 01249 730501

The Museum commemorates the achievements of a former resident of Lacock Abbey, William Henry Fox Talbot (1800-77), inventor of the photographic process and whose decendants gave the Abbey and village to the Trust in 1944.

Opening Times: 1 Mar to 2 Nov daily 11:00-17:00 & winter weekends 11:00-16:00. Closed 20-28 Dec.   Admission: Adult £4.20, Child £2.50, Family £11.80.   Location: Three miles south of Chippenham off A350.   Map Ref: 5

Kennet & Avon Canal Museum
Canal Centre, The Wharf, Devizes SN10 1EB   Tel: 01380 721279/729489
Email: administrator@katrust.org

The museum has been described as 'the best little canal museum in the country'. It tells the story of the waterway from its beginnings to the present day. There is also a shop with videos, books, maps and souvenirs.

Opening Times: Feb to Xmas daily 10:00-17:00.   Admission: Adult £1.50, Child 50p, OAP £1.00.   Location: Near town centre, situated at The Wharf, beside the canal.   Map Ref: 6

Wiltshire Heritage Museum
41 Long Street, Devizes SN10 1NS   Tel: 01380 727369   Fax: 01380 722150
Email: wanhs@wiltshireheritage.org.uk   Web: www.wiltshireheritage.org.uk

The Museum is designated for its outstanding collections, which tell the story of Wiltshire from its earliest origins at the time of the dinosaurs, up to the present day. The Museum is especially strong in prehistory, and displays some of the most important artefacts from the Bronze Age, associated with Stonehenge.

Opening Times: Mon to Sat 10:00-17:00, Sun 12:00-16:00. Closed Xmas & BH.   Admission: Free Sun & Mon. Adult £3.00, Under 16s Free, Concession £2.00.   Location: Near town centre, three minute walk from Market Place.   Map Ref: 6

Bronze age gold regalia found near Stonehenge

Athelstan Museum
Town Hall, Cross Hayes, Malmesbury SN16 9BZ   Tel / Fax: 01666 829258
Email: athelstanmuseum@northwilts.gov.uk

Collections include displays of archaeology, coins and tokens, maps, photographs. Malmesbury lace, costume, early bicycles and tricycles. Also an 18th century fire engine, Romano-British burial of a child, Malmesbury branch railway, the civil war and philosopher Thomas Hobbs.

Opening Times: Apr to Sep Tues to Sat 10:00-14:00. Oct to Mar Thu 10:00-14:00, Sat 10:00-12:00. Closed Sun and BH. Telephone for opening hours.   Admission: Free.   Location: The museum is situated within the Town Hall, Cross Hayes, one minute walk from the Abbey and centre of Malmesbury. Buses stop opposite the museum.   Map Ref: 7

Wiltshire

John Creasey Museum/Edwin Young Gallery

Salisbury Library & Galleries, Market Place, Salisbury SP1 1BL   Tel: 01722 410614
Fax: 01722 413214   Email: peterriley@wiltshire.gov.uk

Permanent collection of contemporary art by leading artists. Temporary exhibitions on various themes from the collection plus loan exhibitions. We also hold the Edwin Young Collection of art (twice a year), which consists of watercolour and drawings of Salisbury and environs produced primarly by Edwin Young in the 19th century.

Opening Times: Mon 10:00-19:00, Tue, Wed & Fri 09:00-19:00, Thu 10:00-17:00, Sat 09:00-16:00. Admission: Free.   Location: Near Market Place, five minutes from bus station.

Map Ref: 8

Royal Gloucestershire, Berkshire & Wiltshire Regiment (Salisbury) Museum

The Wardrobe, 58 The Close, Salisbury SP1 2EX   Tel: 01722 414536
Web: www.thewardrobe.org.uk

Three in one attraction of historic house, lanscaped garden to River Avon and Museum of Berkshire and Wiltshire Infantry Regiments. Museum on ground floor. Licensed tea room on site.

Opening Times: Apr to Oct 10:00-17:00, Nov Tue to Sun 10:00-17:00.   Admission: Adult £2.75, Child 75p, Concession £2.00, Family £6.00, Garden 75p.   Location: Within Salisbury's Cathedral Close and walking distance from car parks and stations.

Map Ref: 8

Salisbury & South Wiltshire Museum

The King's House, 65 The Close, Salisbury SP1 2EN   Tel: 01722 332151   Fax: 01722 325611
Email: museum@salisburymuseum.freeserve.co.uk   Web: www.salisburymuseum.org.uk

Award-winning Museum designated as having outstanding archaeology collections of national importance. Home of the re-designed Stonehenge Gallery, Warminster Jewel and Monkton Deverill gold torc. Displays of pre-history, Romans, Saxons, the medieval history of Old Sarum and Salisbury (with the renowned Giant and Hob Nob), the Pitt Rivers collection, ceramics and costume. Pictures throughout, including Turner watercolours. Temporary exhibitions all year round.

Opening Times: Mon to Sat 10:00-17:00, Sun Jul & Aug 14:00-17:00. Admission: Adult £3.50, Child £1.00, Concession £2.30, Family £7.90.   Location: Situated in Salisbury Cathedral Close opposite the west front of the Cathedral.

Map Ref: 8

Wilton House

The Estate Office, Wilton, Salisbury SP2 0BJ   Tel: 01722 746720   Fax: 01772 744447
Email: tourism@wiltonhouse.com   Web: www.wiltonhouse.com

Inigo Jones designed house, Double Cube room arguably the finest state room in England. A very fine art collection, including many Van Dycks, important Roman, Greek and 17th century sculpture.

Opening Times: 27 Mar to 27 Oct 10:30-17:30. Admission: Adult £9.25, Child £5.00, OAP £7.50.   Location: Three miles west of Salisbury.

Map Ref: 9

Lydiard House

Lydiard Park, Lydiard Tregoze, Swindon SN5 3PA   Tel: 01793 770401   Fax: 01793 877909
Web: www.swindon.gov.uk

Rescued from delapidation and now beautifully restored ancestral home of the Bolingbrokes. Fine furniture and family picture collection, painted glass window and 15th century Lady Diana Spencer Room. Audio guides and gift shop.

Opening Times: Mon 10:00-13:00 & 14:00-17:00, Sat 10:00-17:00, Sun 14:00-17:00. Nov to Feb closes 16:00. Closed Good Friday, Xmas & New Year.   Admission: Adult £1.40, Child/Concession 70p.   Location: From Swindon, follow signs to West Swindon and then pick up brown signs to Lydiard Park. From junction 16 on M4, follow brown signs.

Map Ref: 10

Steam - Museum of the Great Western Railway   ♿ 🏛 ☕ ⓘ 🚂

Kemble Drive, Swindon SN2 2TA   Tel: 01793 466646   Fax: 01793 466615
Email: steampostbox@swindon.gov.uk   Web: www.steam-museum.org.uk

King George V at the reconstructed Station Platform

Isambard Kingdom Brunel

STEAM is located in a beautifully restored railway building in the heart of Swindon works where seven generations of men and women built the great locomotives and made the Great Western Railway in its heyday, the most important employer in Swindon. STEAM - Museum of the Great Western Railway, which received European Museum of the Year Special Commendation 2002, tells the story of the men and women who built, operated and travelled on 'God's Wonderful Railway'. Hands on displays, world-famous locomotives, archive film footage and the testimonies of the ex-railway workers bring the story to life.

Experience the sounds, sights and smells of the Railway Works where huge locomotives were built. Walk underneath the 'Caerphilly Castle' step up on the station platform and climb aboard the famous 'King George V'. Discover the romance and excitement of holiday travel by rail, explore hands on displays and computer interactives and discover what it was like to drive a train. Located next door the McArthurGlen Designer Outlet Great Western, STEAM offers a great day out for all. With excellent value group packages, special events and exhibitions, shop and café.

Opening Times: Apr to Oct Mon to Sat 10:00-17:30, Sun 11:00-17:30. Nov to Mar Mon to Sat 10:00-17:00, Sun 11:00-17:00.
Admission: Adult £5.70, Child £3.60, OAP £3.70, Family (2 Adults & 2 Children) £14.00, Groups (15+) £4.80 per person.
Location: Ten minutes walk from town centre, through Railway Village.   Exhibitions & Events 2003 : Storehouse: New attraction displaying hundreds of unique railway objects from the museum stores.   Map Ref: 11

Swindon Museum & Art Gallery   ♿ 🏛

Bath Road, Old Town, Swindon SN1 4BA   Tel: 01793 466556   Fax: 01793 484141
Web: www.swindon.gov.uk

Situated in an elegant early 19th century house, Swindon's oldest museum contains a variety of displays on the history, archaeology and geology of Swindon and surrounding area. The Art Gallery houses an outstanding collection of 20th century British art, a selection of which is on display.

Opening Times: Mon to Sat 10:00-17:00, Sun 14:00-17:00. Closed BH.   Admission: Free.   Location: In Old Town, near town centre. Easily accessible by buses.
Map Ref: 11

Wiltshire

Step back in time at
Trowbridge Museum

Trowbridge Museum

The Shires, Court Street, Trowbridge BA14 8AT
Tel: 01225 751339 Fax: 01225 754608
Email: clyall@trowbridgemuseum.co.uk
Web: www.trowbridgemuseum.co.uk

Housed in a former woollen mill, museum displays tell the fascinating story of Trowbridge Town and its people. Working looms still produce cloth, which is sold within the museum. Other displays include reconstruction of Trowbridge Castle, a Victorian schoolroom, a weaver's cottage and a draper's shop. There are plenty of hands-on activities including a mouse-trail and history hunt.

Opening Times: Tue to Fri 10:00-16:00, Sat 10:00-17:00. Closed Sun, Mon & BH. Admission: Free. Location: In the Shires Shopping Centre, five minutes from bus picking-up points and ten minutes from railway station.   Map Ref: 12

Longleat House

Warminster BA12 7NW Tel: 01985 844400 Fax: 01985 844885
Email: enquiries@longleat.co.uk Web: www.longleat.co.uk

Longleat House

Nestling within 900 acres of 'Capability' Brown landscaped grounds, Longleat House is widely regarded as one of the best examples of high Elizabethan architecture in Britain. Priceless collections of paintings, including works by Tintoretto and Wootton, series of magnificent ceilings by John Dibblee Crace and exquisite 17th century Flemish tapestries. Also the Safari Park, 'World's Longest Hedge Maze', Safari Boats and numerous other attractions.

Opening Times: All attractons open daily from 5 Apr to 2 Nov. Longleat House: 1 Jan to 4 Apr Sat & Sun, 5 Apr to 31 Dec daily. Closed Xmas day. Admission: Adult £16.00, Child £13.00, OAP £13.00. Location: Just off the A36 between Bath & Sailsbury (A362 Warminster to Frome).   Map Ref: 13

Yorkshire

North Yorkshire is mainly rural in character, whereas South Yorkshire is industrial. West Yorkshire, on the other hand, is a mixture of both and offers magnificent Pennine and moorland scenery including the dramatic Bronte Country. Dominating the Vale of York is the historic city of York.

A fine collection of museums and galleries record the achievements of the towns and industries created by the Industrial Revolution. The artistic and cultural aspects of Yorkshire life are also well catered for.

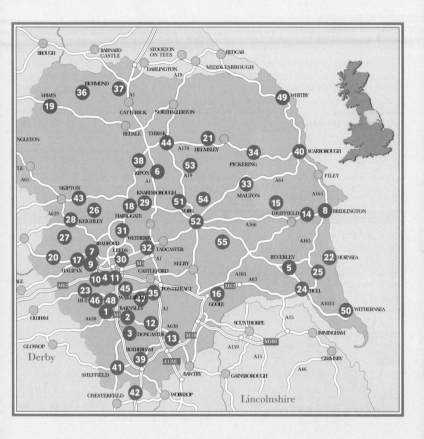

The Red Map References should be used to locate Museums etc on the pages that follow

Yorkshire

Cannon Hall Museum

Bark House Lane, Cawthorne, Barnsley S75 4AT   Tel: 01226 790270   Fax: 01226 792117
Email: cannonhall@barnsley.co.uk   Web: www.barnsley.co.uk

The museum has fine collections of Moorcroft Pottery, furniture and glass. It is also home to the 13th/18th Royal Hussars Military Museum and William Harvey Collection of Dutch and Flemish paintings.

Opening Times: Apr to Oct Wed to Fri 10:30-17:00, Sat & Sun 12:00-17:00. Nov,Dec & Mar Sun only 12:00-17:00. Closed Jan & Feb.   Admission: Free from April 2002.   Location: Seven miles from Barnsley Town Centre, off junction 38 on M1.   Map Ref: 1

Cooper Gallery

Church Street, Barnsley S70 2AH   Tel: 01226 242905   Fax: 01226 297283
Email: coopergallery@barnsley.gov.uk   Web: www.barnsley.gov.uk

The Gallery holds a programme of contemporary art exhibitions, crafts and is home to the Trustees Collection of 17th-20th century paintings. There is also a cafe with a range of home made soups, sandwiches and delicious cakes.

Opening Times: Mon to Fri 10:30-16:00, Sat 10:00-15:00.   Admission: Free.   Map Ref: 2

Worsbrough Mill Museum

Worsbrough Bridge, Barnsley S70 5LJ   Tel: 01226 774527

A 17th century working water powered corn mill, milling wholemeal and white flour on sale through the mill shop.

Opening Times: Apr to Oct Wed to Sun 10:00-17:00. Nov to Mar Wed to Sun 10:00-16:00.
Admission: Adults 50p, all others 25p.   Location: One mile junction 36 of M2. Three miles from Barnsley Town Centre.   Map Ref: 3

Bagshaw Museum

Wilton Park, Batley WF17 0AS   Tel: 01924 326155   Fax: 01924 326164
Web: www.kirkleesmc.gov.uk

Step straight from the mystery of an Egyptian tomb into the tropical enchantment of the rainforest, taming mythical beasts on the way. With local history collections and Gothic decor.

Opening Times: Mon to Fri 11:00-17:00, Sat & Sun 12:00-17:00. Please ring for Xmas closing.
Admission: Free.   Map Ref: 4

Batley Art Gallery

Market Place, Batley WF17 5DA   Tel: 01924 326021   Web: www.kirkleesmc.gov.uk

Changing, temporary exhibitions.

Opening Times: Please ring for opening times.   Admission: Free.   Location: Town centre.
Map Ref: 4

Oakwell Hall & Country Park

Nutter Lane, Birstall, Batley WF17 9LG   Tel: 01924 326240   Fax: 01924 326249
Web: www.kirkleesmc.gov.uk

Built in 1583, the Hall is set out as a 1690s home, giving valuable insight into late 17th century life. One hundred acres of the original grounds are now managed as a country park.

Opening Times: Mon to Fri 11:00-17:00, Sat & Sun 12:00-17:00. Please call for Xmas closing.
Admission: There is a small admission charge from Mar to Oct.   Map Ref: 4

Beverley Art Gallery

Champney Road, Beverley HU17 8HE   Tel: 01482 883903   Fax: 01482 392778

The Gallery runs a lively temporary exhibition programme of art and craft. Selections from the permanent collection, which includes work by local Edwardian artists Fred and Mary Elwell, are displayed at times during the year.

Opening Times: Wed to Fri 10:00-17:00, Sat & Sun 10:00-12:30 & 13:30-17:00. Closed Mon & Tue.   Admission: Free.   Location: Short walk from the town centre on Champney Road, above the main Beverley Library.   Map Ref: 5

Yorkshire

Museum of Army Transport

Flemingate, Beverley HU17 0NG   Tel: 01482 860445   Fax: 01482 872767
Web: www.museum-of-army-transport.co.uk

The museum covers an area of over two acres giving the history of military transport from the Boer War to modern day. The museum also houses the last remaining Blackburn Beverley aircraft.

Opening Times: Daily 10:00-17:00. Closed Xmas.   Admission: Adult £4.50, Child £3.00, OAP £3.00, Family £12.00, Under 5s Free.   Location: Near town centre, ten minute walk from central bus station, five minute walk from railway station.   Map Ref: 5

BOROUGHBRIDGE *S Yorks*

Aldborough Roman Town & Museum

Main Street, Boroughbridge YO5 9EF   Tel: 01423 322768

Aldborough was once the rich Roman city Isurium Brigantum, the principal town of the Brigantes - the largest tribe in Roman Britain. The museum displays a remarkable collection of finds from the town.

Opening Times: Apr to Sep daily 10:00-13:00 & 14:00-18:00, Oct daily 10:00-13:00 & 14:00-17:00.   Admission: Adult £1.80, Child 90p, Concession £1.40.   Location: In Aldborough, three quarters of a mile south east of Boroughbridge.   Map Ref: 6

BRADFORD *W Yorks*

Bradford Industrial Museum & Horses At Work

Moorside Road, Eccleshill, Bradford BD2 3HP   Tel: 01274 435900

Moorside Mills, an original spinning mill, is alive with magnificent machinery which once converted raw wool into the world's worsted cloth. The mill yard rings to the sound of iron on stone as the Shire horses give rides, pull a horse tram or haul a horse-bus. In the mill, you can experience the sounds and smells of the engines which once powered the mills throughout Yorkshire.

Opening Times: Tue to Sat 10:00-17:00, Sun 12:00-17:00.
Admission: Free.   Location: Signposted from the Bradford ring road and Harrogate Road (A568).

Norman and the Tram

Map Ref: 7

Cartwright Hall

Lister Park, Bradford BD9 4NS   Tel: 01274 431212

Our collections reflect the cultural mix that makes Bradford unique, from sumptuous Indian silks and embroideries to the challenge of contemporary art and the delights of Victorian painting. The upper galleries are reserved for display of the permanent collection of Bradford Art Galleries and Museums with paintings, sculpture and decorative arts from the 19th and 20th centuries. The lower galleries are changing exhibitions.

Opening Times: Tue to Sat 10:00-17:00, Sun 13:00-17:00.
Admission: Free.   Location: In Lister Park on the A650 Keighley Road, about one mile from city centre.

Francis Derwent Wood's "Humanity overcoming War"

Map Ref: 7

National Museum of Photography, Film & Television

Bradford BD1 1NQ   Tel: 01274 202030   Fax: 01274 394540   Email: talk.nmpft@nmsi.ac.uk
Web: www.nmpft.org.uk

Experience the past, present and future of photography, film and television with ten interactive galleries and a spectacular IMAX Cinema plus, the treasures of the Museum's Collections in Insight: Collections & Research Centre.

Opening Times: Tue to Sun 10:00-18:00. Also open BH and school holiday Mon.
Admission: Permanent Galleries Free. Charges for Imax and some exhibitions.   Map Ref: 7

Yorkshire

Sewerby Hall Museum & Art Gallery

Sewerby Hall, Church Lane, Sewerby, Bridlington YO15 1EA   Tel: 01262 677874   Fax: 01262 674265   Email: sewerbyhall@yahoo.com   Web: www.bridlington.net/sewerby

East Yorkshire history and east coast maritime art. Amy Johnson collection and temporary exhibitions of regional art and photography.

Opening Times: 18 Mar to 3 Nov daily 10:00-17:30. 4 Nov to 22 Dec Sat to Tue 11:00-16:00. Admission: Adult £3.10, Child £1.20, Over 60s £2.30, Groups half price.   Location: Two miles north of Bridlington. Map Ref: 8

Smith Art Gallery

Halifax Road, Brighouse HD6 2AF   Tel / Fax: 01484 719222
Email: Karen.Belshaw@calderdale.gov.uk   Web: www.calderdale.gov.uk

Permanent displays of 19th century art works. Also has temporary exhibition space in back gallery.

Opening Times: Mon, Tue, Thu and Fri 10:00-12:30 & 13:00-18:00, Sun 10:00-12;30 & 13:00-16:00.   Admission: Free.   Location: Two minutes walk from Brighouse Bus Station, ten minutes walk from Brighouse Railway Station. Map Ref: 9

Red House

Oxford Road, Gomersal, Cleckheaton BD19 4JP   Tel: 01274 335100   Fax: 01274 335105
Web: www.kirkleesmc.gov.uk

Home of Mary Taylor, friend of Charlotte Bronte, who featured the house as 'Briarmains' in 'Shirley'. Each room brings you closer to the 1830s and two permanent exhibitions shed light on the Brontes and life in the Spen Valley.

Opening Times: Mon to Fri 11:00-17:00, Sat & Sun 12:00-17:00. Please phone to check Xmas closing.   Admission: Free. Map Ref: 10

Dewsbury Museum

Crow Nest Park, Heckmondwike Road, Dewsbury WF13 2SA   Tel: 01924 325100
Web: www.kirkleesmc.gov.uk

Remember growing up? Dedicated to the magical theme of childhood, Dewsbury Museum will not only take you back to yours, it will give you insight into the childhood of past and future generations.

Opening Times: Mon to Fri 11:00-17:00, Sat & Sun 12:00-17:00. Please ring for Xmas closing. Admission: Free. Map Ref: 11

Brodsworth Hall

Brodsworth, Doncaster DN5 7XJ   Tel: 01302 722598

Brodsworth Hall has survived almost completely intact since the 1860s with an extraordinary collection of 17,000 objects. These include an important group of Italian marble sculptures, an impressive collection of paintings, silver and furniture. The gardens are spectacular including a special collection of old rose varieties.

Opening Times: 1 Apr to 26 Oct Tue to Sun & BH 13:00-18:00. Pre-booked guided tours in mornings Apr to Oct. Admission: Adult £6.00, Child £3.00, Concession £4.50. Location: In Brodsworth, 5 miles NW of Doncaster off A635 Barnsley Rd, from jct 37 of A1(M).   Map Ref: 12

Cusworth Hall - The Museum of South Yorkshire Life

Cusworth Hall, Cusworth Lane, Doncaster DN5 7TU   Tel / Fax: 01302 782342
Email: museum@doncaster.gov.uk   Web: www.doncaster.gov.uk

The Museum illustrates the changing home, work and social life of local people and communities. Set in an imposing 18th century country house in extensive landscaped parklands.

Opening Times: Mon to Fri 10:00-17:00, Sat 11:00-17:00, Sun 13:00-17:00. Dec & Jan closing 16:00. Please ring beforehand to confirm opening times if travelling from outside the local area. Admission: Free.   Location: Approximately two miles north from centre (off A638), nearest railway station Doncaster. Map Ref: 13

Yorkshire

Doncaster Museum & Art Gallery

Chequer Road, Doncaster DN1 2AE   Tel: 01302 734293   Fax: 01302 735409
Email: museum@doncaster.gov.uk   Web: www.doncaster.gov.uk

The Museum depicts various aspects of natural history, archaeology, local history and fine and decorative art.

Opening Times: Mon to Sat 10:00-17:00, Sun 14:00-17:00.   Admission: Free.   Location: Near town centre, five minute walk from Southern Bus Station.   Map Ref: 13

Kings Own Yorkshire Light Infantry Regimental Museum

Doncaster Museum and Art Gallery, Chequer Road, Doncaster DN1 2AE   Tel: 01302 734293
Fax: 01302 735409   Email: museum@doncaster.gov.uk   Web: www.doncaster.gov.uk

Situated in the same building as Doncaster Museum & Art Gallery, in its own extension, the Museum reflects the history of this famous local regiment.

Opening Times: Mon to Sat 10:00-17:00, Sun 14:00-17:00.   Admission: Free.
Location: Located as part of Doncaster Museum, near town centre.   Map Ref: 13

Burton Agnes Hall

Estate Office, Burton Agnes, Driffield YO25 0ND   Tel: 01262 490324   Fax: 01262 490513
Web: www.burton-agnes.com

Elizabethan house with original carving and plasterwork. China, paintings and furniture collected over four centuries with a notable collection of modern and Impressionist paintings.

Opening Times: Apr to Oct daily 11:00-17:00.   Admission: Adult £5.20, Child £2.60, OAP
£4.70.   Map Ref: 14

Sledmere House

Sledmere, Driffield YO25 3XG   Tel: 01377 236637   Fax: 01377 236500

Sledmere House is a stunning 18th century Georgian Mansion set admist the Yorkshire Wolds in a Capability Brown Park. The magnificent plasterwork was designed by Joseph Rose, the most famous plasterer of the 18th century, his finest work was carried out at Sledmere. The house contains a fine collection of Chippendale and French furniture, antique statuary and paintings, the blue tiled Turkish room is unique in Britain. Sledmere is home to one of Britain's finest country house Organs, the console is housed at the base of the grand staircase, the pipes in a great glass dome which dominates the main staircase. The organ is played for visitors Wednesday to Friday and Sunday afternoons.

Opening Times: Easter weekend & May to Sep 11:30-16:30. Closed Mon & Fri.
Admission: Adult £5.00, OAP £4.50, Child £2.00.   Location: Sledmere House is situated an approximate half an hour drive form York, Beverley, Scarborough and Bridlington, off the A166 between York and Bridlington.   Exhibitions & Events 2003 : 18 to 21 Apr: Charity Flower Festival, 13 Jul: MG Car Rally, 29 Jun: Vintage Care Rally - 500 vehicles on display, 23 to 25 Aug: Charity Flower Festival.   Map Ref: 15

Goole Museum & Art Gallery

Carlisle Street, Goole DN14 5DS   Tel: 01405 768963   Fax: 01482 392782
Email: janet.tierney@eastriding.gov.uk

History of the development of the town and port of Goole, including ship models, photographs, social history and marine paintings by Goole-born artist Reuben Chappell.

Opening Times: Mon 14:00-17:00, Tue to Fri 10:00-17:00, Sat 09:00-13:00. Closed BH and Xmas & New Year.   Admission: Free.   Location: Town centre 12 minutes from bus station, five minutes from railway station.   Map Ref: 16

Yorkshire

Bankfield Museum

Boothtown Road, Halifax HX3 6HG   Tel: 01422 352334   Fax: 01422 349020
Email: Bankfield.Museum@calderdale.gov.uk   Web: www.calderdale.gov.uk

Once the home of a mill owner, the magnificent Renaissance style Victorian mansion houses one of the finest collections of costumes and textiles in the country. There are also temporary exhibitions, workshops and activities. The museum also houses the Duke of Wellington's Regimental Collection.

Opening Times: Tue to Sat and BH Mon 10:00-17:00, Sun 14:00-17:00   Admission: Free
Location: 20 Minutes walk from Halifax Bus Station   Map Ref: 17

Eureka! The Museum for Children

Discovery Road, Halifax HX1 2NE   Tel: 01422 330069

Eureka! Is the interactive children's museum in Halifax, where you can touch, hear, smell, and discover hundreds of fascinating things about yourself and the world around you in the only hands-on museum in the UK designed and built especially for 3-12 year old children. With more than 400 hands-on exhibits, games and challenges, you'll be amazed at all the fun things you can do. Activities are designed to encourage the natural curiosity of young minds. From operating TV cameras and reading the news, to saving a yacht, riding a skeleton bike and meeting Scoot the Robot everyone will have a fun packed visit. A varied programme of special events provides different activities all year from song and dance to journeys into outer space.

Opening Times: Daily 10:00-17:00. Closed Xmas.
Admission: Adult & Child £5.50, Under 3s Free.   Location: Near town centre and station. Exhibitions & Events 2003 : Please telephone for details.   Map Ref: 17

Piece Hall Art Gallery

Piece Hall, Halifax HX1 1RE   Tel: 01422 358300   Fax: 01422 300878
Email: Karen.Belshaw@calderdale.gov.uk   Web: www.calderdale.gov.uk

An exciting and diverse range of temporary exhibitions of art, crafts and local history situated in the historic Piece Hall.

Opening Times: Tue to Sun and BH 10:00-17:00.   Admission: Free.   Location: Two minutes walk from Halifax Bus Station and railway station.   Map Ref: 17

Shibden Hall

Listers Road, Halifax HX3 6XG   Tel: 01422 321455/352246   Fax: 01422 348440
Email: shibden.hall@calderdale.gov.uk

Built in 1420, Shibden Hall with its oak panelled interiors and atmospheric room settings is Halifax's Historic Home. The Folk Museum and Barn also offer you a world without electricity, where craftsmen worked in wood and iron.

Opening Times: Mar to Nov Mon to Sat 10:00-17:00, Sun 12:00-17:00. Dec to Feb Mon to Sat 10:00-16:00, Sun 12:00-16:00.   Admission: Adult £3.50, Concession £2.50, Family £10.00.
Prices are subject to change.   Map Ref: 17

Harlow Carr Museum of Gardening

Crag Lane, Harrogate HG3 1QB   Tel: 01423 565418

The Museum, which is situated within the Plant Centre at RHS Garden Harlow Carr, houses displays of gardening equipment, tools and related items such as catalogues and seed packets. It includes a 1930s 'potting shed'.

Opening Times: Daily 09:30-17:30.   Admission: Adult £4.50, Child £1.00, Under 11s Free, OAP £4.00, RHS Members Free. NB. charge is for Gardens entrance, no charge for Museum.
Location: Off B6162, on the outskirts of Harrogate.   Map Ref: 18

Yorkshire

Mercer Art Gallery

Swan Road, Harrogate HG1 2SA   Tel: 01423 566188   Fax: 01423 556130
Email: lg12@harrogate.gov.uk   Web: www.harrogate.gov.uk/museums

Originally built in 1806 as Harrogate's first spa building, 'The Promenade Room' has been restored to its former glory. The Gallery hosts a diverse programme of events and exhibitions, ranging from national touring shows of painting, photography, sculpture and crafts, to the display of work by Yorkshire artists. Also home to Harrogate's fine art collection.

Opening Times: Tue to Sat 10:00-17:00, Sun & BH 14:00-17:00. Closed Mon, 24-26 Dec & New Year.
Admission: Free.   Location: Near town centre.

Mercer Art Gallery

Map Ref: 18

Royal Pump Room Museum

Crown Place, Harrogate HG1 2RY   Tel: 01423 556188   Fax: 01423 556130
Email: lg12@harrogate.gov.uk
Web: www.harrogate.gov.uk/museums

Housed in Harrogate's premier Spa building and site of Europe's strongest Sulphur Well, the Royal Pump Room Museum tells the story of Harrogate as a spa. You can still see the sulphur wells, and no visit to the museum is complete without a taste of the water.

Opening Times: Mon to Sat 10:00-17:00 (except Nov to Mar close 16:00), Sun 14:00-17:00 (Sun in Aug open 11:00). Closed 24-26 Dec & New Year.   Admission: 2002 prices: Adult £2.00, Child £1.25, Concession £1.50, Family £5.50. Group rates, season and combined tickets available.   Location: Near town centre.

Royal Pump Room Museum

Exhibitions & Events 2003 : 2003: 1950s Exhibition.   Map Ref: 18

Dales Countryside Museum

Station Yard, Hawes DL8 3NT   Tel: 01969 667494   Fax: 01969 667165
Email: dcm@yorkshiredales.org.uk

Fascinating museum telling the story of the people and landscape of the Yorkshire Dales, past and present. Static steam locomotive and carriages with video and displays. Interactive area. Special events, demonstrations and temporary exhibitions. Tourist information and National Park Centre.

Opening Times: Daily 10:00-17:00, except Xmas.   Admission: Adult £3.00, OAP £2.00, Family £8.00, Group rate available.   Location: East end of market town centre.   Map Ref: 19

Heptonstall Museum

Heptonstall, Hebden Bridge   Tel: 01422 843738   Web: www.calderdale.gov.uk

17th century building with original school furniture and items of local, domestic, historic and agricultural interest including a coins exhibition.

Opening Times: Easter to Oct Sat, Sun & BH 13:00-17:00.   Admission: Adult £2.00, Concession £1.00.   Location: Buses from Hebden Bridge and Halifax. A646 to Hebden Bridge, then up to Heptonstall.   Map Ref: 20

Rievaulx Abbey

Rievaulx, Helmsley YO6 5LB   Tel: 01439 798228

Founded in 1132, Rievaulx Abbey was the first Cistercian abbey in the north of England. The collection includes medieval floor tiles, stone sculpture, late medieval cutlery and other finds from the abbey.

Opening Times: Apr to Sep daily 10:00-18:00, Oct daily 10:00-17:00, Nov to Mar daily 10:00-16:00. Closed Xmas & New Year.   Admission: Adult £3.80, Child £1.90, Concession £2.90.
Location: In Rievaulx, just over two miles west of Helmsley.   Map Ref: 21

Yorkshire

Hornsea Museum

11 Newbegin, Hornsea HU18 1AB   Tel: 01964 533443   Web: www.hornseamuseum.com

Historic farmhouse, home of the Burns family for 200 years. Rooms, including Victorian farmhouse kitchen and parlour are displayed to show how the Burns lived worked and played 100 years ago. Also large garden, school room and Hornsea pottery collection.

Opening Times: Tue to Sat 11:00-17:00, Sun 14:00-17:00. Closed Mon except School Holidays.
Admission: Adult £2.00, Concession £1.50, Family Ticket £6.00.   Location: Near town centre.
Map Ref: 22

Colne Valley Museum

Cliffe Ash, Golcar, Huddersfield HD7 4PY   Tel: 01484 659762

Experience the atmosphere of a hand weaver's home and working life c.1840-50, with working hand looms and spinning jenny, a gas lit Cloggers Shop that's fully equipped with period tools and equipment from 1910.

Opening Times: Sat, Sun & BH 14:00-17:00. Closed Xmas & New Year.   Admission: Adult £1.40, Child/OAP 70p.
Map Ref: 23

Huddersfield Art Gallery

Princess Alexandra Walk, Huddersfield HD1 2SU   Tel: 01484 221964
Web: www.kirkleesmc.gov.uk

A lively programme, showcasing the best contemporary art from regional, national and international artists. In addition, the Kirklees Collection contains over 2000 items representing British art of the past 150 years.

Opening Times: Mon to Fri 10:00-17:00, Sat 10:00-16:00.   Admission: Free.   Location: Town centre.
Map Ref: 23

Tolson Memorial Museum

Wakefield Road, Huddersfield HD5 8DJ   Tel: 01484 223830   Fax: 01484 223843
Web: www.kirkleesmc.gov.uk

The history book of a typical Yorkshire town. Tolson Museum draws a vivid and intriguing picture of Huddersfield and its people, from the prehistoric to the present.

Opening Times: Mon to Fri 11:00-17:00, Sat & Sun 12:00-17:00.   Admission: Free.
Map Ref: 23

Victoria Tower

Castle Hill, Lumb Lane, Almondbury, Victoria Tower, Huddersfield   Tel: 01484 223830
Web: www.kirkleesmc.gov.uk

Shrouded by myth, history and legend, the story of Castle Hill goes back thousands of years. Despite its castle-like appearance, the Tower is a comparative newcomer. Breathtaking panoramic views of the Pennines and Peak District.

Opening Times: Easter & May Day weekends. Every Sat & Sun from Spring Bank until early Sep 12:00-16:00.   Admission: There is a small charge to the Tower.   Map Ref: 23

Artic Corsair

Wilberforce House, High Street, Hull HU1 1NQ   Tel: 01482 613902   Fax: 01482 613710
Email: museums@hullcc.gov.uk   Web: www.hull.cc.gov.uk.museums

Welcome aboard Hull's last side-winder trawler. Take guided tours by experts around this historic vessel moored on the River Hull.

Opening Times: Apr to Oct Wed & Sat 10:00-17:00, Sun 13:30-16:30.   Admission: Adult £2.00, Child/OAP £1.00.   Location: In the old town, 15 minutes walk from the bus and train stations.
Map Ref: 24

Yorkshire

Burton Constable Hall

Burton Constable Foundation, Burton Constable, Skirlaugh, Hull HU11 4LN
Tel: 01964 562400   Fax: 01964 563229
Email: enquiries@burtonconstable.com   Web: www.burtonconstable.com

Burton Constable Hall, West Front

With nearly 30 rooms open, the public are offered a unique insight into the patronage of the Constable family, who have lived here since the house was built. Superb 18th and 19th century interiors, including a gallery, Great Hall, dining and drawing rooms, bedrooms, chapel, Chinese room and lamp room. Pictures and prints, architectural drawings, Chippendale furniture, scientific instruments, cabinet of curiosities and sporting guns.

Opening Times: Easter Sun to Oct. Closed Fri. Grounds: 12:30-17:00. Hall: 13:00-17:00.   Admission: Adult £5.00, Child £2.00, OAP £4.50, Family £11.00. Grounds only: Adult £1.00, Child 50p.   Location: From Beverley (14 miles) follow A165 Bridlington Road. From Hull (seven miles) follow B1238 Sproatley. Follow Historic House signs.   Map Ref: 25

Ferens Art Gallery

Queen Victoria Square, Hull HU1 3RA   Tel: 01482 613902   Fax: 01482 613710
Email: museums@hullcc.gov.uk   Web: www.hullcc.gov.uk/museums

An award winning gallery, featuring Dutch Old Masters, contemporary works, an interactive children's gallery and live art space. A wide variety of workshops, exhibitions and events.

Opening Times: Mon to Sat 10:00-17:00, Sun 13:30-16:30.   Admission: Free.   Location: In city centre, five minutes walk from the bus and train stations.   Map Ref: 24

Hands on History

South Church Side, Market Place, Hull HU1 1RR   Tel: 01482 613902   Fax: 01482 613710
Email: museums@hullcc.gov.uk   Web: www.hullcc.gov.uk/museums

The story of Hull and its people. Victorian and Egyptian collections, features the only replicas of King Tutenkhamun's grave goods and an Egyptian mummy.

Opening Times: Sat 10:00-17:00, Sun 13:30-16:30.   Admission: Free.   Location: In the city centre, five minutes walk from the bus and train stations.   Map Ref: 24

Hull & East Riding Museum

36 High Street, Hull HU1 1PS   Tel / Fax: 01482 613902   Email: museums@hullcc.gov.uk
Web: www.hullcc.gov.uk/museums

From pre-history to the Romans. Geology, archaeology and natural history collections; important Roman mosaics, the Hasholme Boat and Roos Carr figures.

Opening Times: Mon to Sat 10:00-17:00, Sun 13:30-16:30.   Admission: Free.   Location: In town centre, five minutes walk from the bus and train stations.   Map Ref: 24

Maritime Museum

Queen Victoria Square, Hull HU1 3RA   Tel: 01482 613902   Fax: 01482 613710
Email: museums@hullcc.gov.uk   Web: www.hullcc.gov.uk/museums

Whales and whaling, ships and shipping - a collection showcasing Hull's maritime history. Features maritime art and important Scrimshaw collection.

Opening Times: Mon to Sat 10:00-17:00, Sun 13:30-16:30.   Admission: Free.   Location: In town centre, five minutes walk from the bus and train stations.   Map Ref: 24

Spurn Lightship

Hull Marina, Hull   Tel: 01482 613902   Fax: 01482 613710   Email: museums@hullcc.gov.uk
Web: www.hullcc.gov.uk/museums

The Spurn Lightship - discover how the crew lived abroad, feature of the Lightship and the work of the Humber Conservancy Board.

Opening Times: Apr to Oct Mon to Sat 10:00-17:00, Sun 13:30-16:30.   Admission: Free.
Location: Near town centre, moored at Hull Marina.   Map Ref: 24

HULL E Riding (continued)

Streetlife - Hull Museum of Transport   ♿ ♦

High Street, Hull HU1 1PS   Tel: 01482 613902   Fax: 01482 613710
Email: museums@hullcc.gov.uk   Web: www.hullcc.gov.uk/museums

200 years of transport history displayed in an exciting, hands-on environment, including an innovative carriage display and street scenes.

Opening Times: Mon to Fri 10:00-17:00, Sun 13:30-16:30.   Admission: Free.   Location: In the old town, 15 minutes walk from the bus and train stations.   Map Ref: 24

University of Hull Art Collection   ♿ ♦ ☕ ♿

The University of Hull, Cottingham Road, Hull HU6 7RX   Tel: 01482 465035   Fax: 01482 465192   Web: www.hull.ac.uk/artcoll/

Includes works by Beardsley, Sickert, Steer, Lucien Pissarro, John, Spencer, Wyndham Lewis and Ben Nicholson, with sculpture by Epstein, Gill, Gaudier-Brzeska and Moore. Also two important collections of Chinese ceramics covering the period c.618-1850.

Opening Times: Mon, Tue, Thu & Fri 14:00-16:00, Wed 12:30-16:00. Closed Sat, Sun & BH. Admission: Free.   Location: 20 minute bus ride from town centre.   Map Ref: 24

Wilberforce House Museum   ♦

25 High Street, Hull HU1 1NQ   Tel: 01482 613902   Fax: 01482 613710
Email: museums@hullcc.gov.uk   Web: www.hullcc.gov.uk/museums

Birthplace of William Wilberforce, showcases his campaign to abolish slavery, also collections of costume, Hull silver and clocks. Set in Georgian house and garden.

Opening Times: Mon to Fri 10:00-17:00, Sun 13:30-16:30.   Admission: Free.   Location: In the old town, 15 minutes walk from the bus and train stations.   Map Ref: 24

ILKLEY W Yorks

Manor House Art Gallery & Museum   ♦

Castle Yard, Ilkley LS29 9DT   Tel: 01943 600066

A small museum specialising in local pre-history and artefacts from the area during Roman occupation. The museum is on the site of a Roman Fort. Parts of the Manor House date back to the 15th century and the building is of architectural interest.

Opening Times: Wed to Sat 11:00-16:00, Sun 13:00-16:00. Closed Mon (except BH), Tue and Xmas. Admission: Free.   Location: Five minutes from rail/bus station.   Map Ref: 26

KEIGHLEY W Yorks

Front entrance of the Parsonage

Brontë Parsonage Museum   ♦

Church Street, Haworth, Keighley BD22 8DR   Tel: 01535 642323
Fax: 01535 647131   Email: bronte@bronte.org.uk
Web: www.bronte.org.uk

Charlotte, Emily and Anne Brontë, were the authors of some of the greatest books in the English language. Haworth Parsonage was their much-loved home and Jane Eyre, Wuthering Heights and The Tenant of Wildfell Hall were all written here. Set between the unique village of Haworth, and the wild moorland beyond, this homely Georgian house still retains the atmosphere of the Brontë time. The rooms they once used daily are filled with Brontës furniture, clothes and personal possessions. Here you can marvel at the handwriting in their tiny manuscript books, admire Charlotte's wedding bonnet and imagine meeting Emily's pets from her wonderful lifelike drawings. Gain an insight into the place and objects that inspired their work. The writing desks belonging to the three sisters are always on display, but their other personal possessions are changed on a yearly basis so you can always be sure of seeing something new. In addition to the main house, the Wade Wing houses a permanent exhibition about the

Mr Bronte's Bedroom

Yorkshire

whole of this remarkable creative family. Downstairs in our temporary exhibition gallery there is a changing display of manuscripts and art works from the Brontë Society collection.

Opening Times: Apr to Sep 10:00-17:00, Oct to Mar 11:00-16:30. Closed Xmas and Jan to 1 Feb 03. Admission: Adult £4.80, Child £1.50, Concession £3.50, Family £10.50. Location: Behind the church off Haworth Main Street. Exhibitions & Events 2003 : For Exhibitions and Events please telephone for details. Map Ref: 27

Cliffe Castle

Spring Gardens Lane, Keighley BD20 6LH Tel: 01535 618230/1

Former Victorian mansion set in parkland, housing displays of rocks, crystals, fossils, local natural hsitory, bygones, Morris stained glass, original house furniture and temporary exhibitions. Aviaries, childrens play area and education room.

Opening Times: Tue to Fri 10:00-17:00, Sun 12:00-17:00. Closed Mon except BH. Admission: Free. Location: Ten minutes walk from town centre, surrounded by park with playground. Map Ref: 28

East Riddlesden Hall

Bradford Road, Keighley BD20 5EL Tel: 01535 607075 Fax: 01535 691462 Email: yorker@smtp.ntrust.org.uk Web: www.visitbrontecountry.com

A homely 17th century merchant's house set in delightful grounds. The house has a wonderful collection of embroideries and textiles. The Great Barn with its oak frame, is one of the finest in the north of England.

Opening Times: 23 Mar to 3 Nov Sat 13:00-17:00, Sun, Tue & Wed 12;00-17:00 and BH 12:00-17:00. Additional openings school holidays. Admission: Adult £3.60, Child £1.80, Family £9.00. Location: One mile north east of Keighley. Bus stop 100 yards - 662 Bradford bus. Map Ref: 28

Knaresborough Castle & Museum

HARROGATE
MUSEUMS & ARTS

Castle Grounds, Knaresborough HG5 8AS
Tel: 01423 556188 Fax: 01423 556130
Email: lg12@harrogate.gov.uk
Web: www.harrogate.gov.uk/museums

The home of Medieval kings, the imposing castle built by Edward III has many tales to tell. Join a guided tour and discover the mysterious underground Sallyport or explore on foot the keep and its dungeon. The castle museum houses a rare Tudor courtroom and galleries looking at Knaresborough's past, particularly the Civil War.

Opening Times: Good Friday to end Sep daily 10:30-17:00. Admission: Adult £2.00, Child £1.25, Concession £1.50, Family

Knaresborough Castle

£5.50. (2002 prices) Group rates and Combined and Season tickets available. Location: Town centre. Map Ref: 29

St Roberts Cave

Abbey Road, Knaresborough Tel: 01423 556188 Fax: 01423 556130 Email: lg12@harrogate.gov.uk Web: www.harrogate.gov.uk/museums

St Robert's Cave and Chapel are rare survivals of a medieval heritage. Cut out of magnesian limestone bedrock and consists of a cave, domestic area and a small chapel area which contains the grave and altar.

Opening Times: All year. Admission: Free. Location: On Abbey Road in Knaresborough, just off the Wetherby Road. Best access is to walk out of Abbey Road from Briggate, about 20 mins. Restricted access for cars. Map Ref: 29

Guided or Private Tours	Disabled Access	Gift Shop or Sales Point	Café or Refreshments	Restaurant	Car Parking

Yorkshire

Abbey House Museum

Abbey Walk, Abbey Road, Kirkstall, Leeds LS5 3EH   Tel: 0113 230 5492   Fax: 0113 230 5499
Email: abbeyhouse.museum@virgin.net   Web: www.leeds.gov.uk

Reopened to public following complete refurbishment, new displays include an interactive childhood gallery, displays devoted to Kirkstall Abbey and a gallery exploring life in Victorian Leeds. Three reconstructed streets allow visitors to immerse themselves in the sights and sounds of late 19th century, from the glamorous art furnishers shop to the impoverished widow washerwoman and the sombre workshop of the undertaker.

Abbey House Museum

Opening Times: Tue to Fri 10:00-17:00, Sat 12:00-17:00, Sun 10:00-17:00. Closed Mon.   Admission: Adult £3.00, Child £1.00, Concession £2.00. Group rates available.   Location: Three miles west of Leeds City Centre on A65.   Map Ref: 30

Armley Mills Industrial Museum

Canal Road, Armley, Leeds LS12 2QF   Tel: 0113 263 7861
Email: armleymills.indmuseum@virgin.net   Web: www.leeds.gov.uk

Formerly largest woollen mill in the world, Armley Mills now houses Leeds Industrial Museum. Located beside the River Aire, the museum explores the city's rich industrial past. Displays cover local textiles and clothing industries, printing, cinematography, photography and engineering. Working exhibits include a 1904 spinning mule and a 1920s style cinema.

Opening Times: Tue to Sat 10:00-17:00, Sun & BH 13:00-17:00.   Admission: Adult £2.00, Child 50p, Concession £1.00, Family £5.00   Location: Two miles west of Leeds City Centre of A65.   Map Ref: 30

Harewood House

Harewood, Leeds LS17 9LQ   Tel: 0113 218 1010   Fax: 0113 218 1002
Email: business@harewood.org   Web: www.harewood.org

HAREWOOD

A stunning house designed by John Carr with exquisite interiors by Robert Adam. Renowned for its stunning collections including Renaissance masterpieces, Turner watercolours and fine porcelain; furnished throughout by Thomas Chippendale including the spectacular State Bed; set in magnificent Capability Brown landscape and gardens, including a lakeside Bird Garden. One of the great Treasure Houses of England - and a Designated Museum.

'The North Front' at Harewood House

Opening Times: Daily 26 Mar to 2 Nov and Sat & Sun Nov to 14 Dec.   Admission: Mon to Sat: Adult £9.50, Child £5.25, OAP £7.75, Family £29.00. Sun: Adult £10.50, Child £5.75, OAP £8.75, Family £32.00.   Location: On the A61 between Leeds and Harrogate, five mile from A1, 22 miles from York.   Map Ref: 31

Henry Moore Institute

74 The Headrow, Leeds LS1 3AH   Tel: 0113 246 7467   Fax: 0113 246 1481
Email: info@henry-moore.ac.uk   Web: www.henry-moore-fdn.ac.uk

A centre for the study of sculpture with a programme of temporary historical and contemporary exhibitions, accompanied by a series of talks, symposia and conferences.

Opening Times: Daily 10:00-17:30, Wed 10:00-21:00. Closed BH.   Admission: Free.
Location: In the centre of Leeds, a short walk from the city train station.   Map Ref: 30

Yorkshire

Kirkstall Abbey

Abbey Walk, Kirkstall Road, Leeds LS5 3EH   Tel: 0113 230 5492   Fax: 0113 230 5499
Email: abbeyhouse.museum@virgin.net   Web: www.leeds.gov.uk

One of Britain's best preserved abbeys sits on the edge of the city by the River Aire. Founded in 1152 by a party of Cistercian monks but closed down in 1539 by Henry VIII, its buildings were given over to new use and were to become of the most spectacular, picturesque ruins, sought out by artists such as JMW Turner and Thomas Griffin.

Opening Times: Dawn to dusk all year. Admission: Free. Guided Tours: Adult £2.00, Child 50p, Concession £1.00. Location: Three miles west of Leeds City Centre on A65. Map Ref: 30

Leeds City Art Gallery

The Headrow, Leeds LS1 3AA   Tel: 0113 247 8248   Web: www.leeds.gov.uk

One of the premier venues for visual arts in the north. Its nationally designated fine art collections range from early 19th to late 20th centuries. An outstanding collection of English watercolours; fine Victorian academic and pre-Raphaelite painting; late 19th century pictures as well as one of the most extensive collections of modern art. A changing exhibition programme represents reviews and explorations of 20th century art.

Opening Times: Mon to Sat 10:00-17:00, Wed 10:00-20:00, Sun 13:00-17:00. Closed BH. Admission: Free.

Location: City Centre Civil Quarter, next to the Town Hall, junction 4 on City Centre Loop.

Map Ref: 30

Lotherton Hall

Lotherton Lane, Aberford, Leeds LS25 3EB   Tel: 0113 281 3259   Fax: 0113 281 2100
Web: www.leeds.gov.uk

The interiors of the former home of the colliery-owning Gascoigne family traces a world of high Edwardian living as well as providing rich locations for collections of costume, original art and ceramics. Also bird gardens and a deer park.

Opening Times: Tue to Sat 10:00-17:00, Sun 13:00-17:00. Admission: Adult £2.00, Child 50p, Concession £1.00, Family £5.00. Location: 13 Miles north east of Leeds City Centre and two and a half miles east of junction 47 on A1. Map Ref: 32

Royal Armouries Museum

Armouries Drive, Leeds LS10 1LT   Tel: 0113 220 1940/1860 Fax: 0113 220 1955
Email: debbie.jones@armouries.org.uk

3000 years of history covered by over 8000 spectacular exhibits in stunning surroundings make this world famous collection of arms and armour a must see attraction. Experience an exciting combination of breathtaking displays, costumed demonstrations and dramatic interpretations, live action events, entertaining films, interactive technology and thrilling exhibitions. There really is something for everybody with five magnificent galleries themed

on War, Tournament, the Orient, Self-defence and Hunting. You'll marvel at these priceless displays including Henry VIII's magnificent tournament armour and the awesome 16th century Mughal elephant armour. With authentic demonstrations of jousting, falconry and pollaxe combat, you are guaranteed an unforgettable day out from start to finish.

Opening Times: Daily 10:00-17:00. Closed Xmas.
Admission: Adult £4.90, Child/OAP/Concession Free.

Map Ref: 30

Yorkshire

Temple Newsam House

Temple Newsam Road, off Selby Road, Leeds LS15 0AE   Tel: 0113 264 7321

Over 1500 acres of parkland, woodland, farmland and gardens make up this historic estate which is landscaped by 'Capability' Brown in the 18th century. Temple Newsam House is closed until autumn 2003 for Heritage Lottery funded work to the fabric of the building and the courtyard. There will be a new interpretation programme available from the re-opening.

Opening Times: Summer Tue to Sun 10:00-17:00. Winter Tue to Sun 10:00-16:00. Closed Xmas Day. Admission: Free.   Map Ref: 30

Thackray Museum

Beckett Street, Leeds LS9 7LN   Tel: 0113 244 4343   Fax: 0113 247 0219
Email: info@thackraymuseum.org   Web: www.thackraymuseum.org

Award-winning displays bring the history of medicine to life for all ages. Walk through the slums of 1840 Leeds, visit the quack doctor, explore the giant gut in Bodyworks.

Opening Times: Daily 10:00-17:00. Closed 24-26 Dec & New Year. Admission: Adult £4.40, Child £3.30, Concession £3.60, Family £14.00. Group rates available. Location: Two miles from Leeds City Station.   Map Ref: 30

Thwaite Mills Watermill

Thwaite Lane, Stourton, Leeds LS10 1RP   Tel: 0113 249 6453   Fax: 0113 277 6737
Web: www.leeds.gov.uk

Lying between river and canal, this island-based water-powered mill once sustained a small self-sufficient community. A tour of the early 19th century mill with its two giant turning waterwheels, is a journey back in time, telling of life and times of mill workers and a working partnership between nature and industry.

Opening Times: Sat, Sun and BH. Please ring to check times. Admission: Adult £2.00, Child 50p, Concession £1.00, Family £5.00. Location: Two miles south of Leeds City Centre off A61, one and a half miles from junction 7 of M621.   Map Ref: 30

Malton Museum

Market Place, Malton YO17 7LP   Tel: 01635 695136

Renowned for its splendidly displayed Roman collection, gathered from many years of local excavations. Also objects from the Wharram Percy deserted medieval village. Also a temporary exhibition in upper gallery each year.

Opening Times: Easter Sat to 31st Oct Mon to Sat 10:00-16:00. Admission: Adult £1.50, Child/OAP/Student £1.00, Family £4.00. Location: In the town centre, a five minute walk from the railway and bus stations.   Map Ref: 33

Beck Isle Museum of Rural Life

Bridge Street, Pickering YO18 8DU   Tel: 01751 473653   Fax: 01751 475996
Email: beckislemuseum@aol.com   Web: www.beckislemuseum.co.uk

The museum is housed in a Regency mansion. 27 rooms containing Victorian collections, typical shops and workshops. A central yard contains farming equipment. An exhibition of Sydney Smith photographs on display all season.

Opening Times: 22 Mar to 3 Nov daily 10:00-17:00. Admission: Adult £3.00, Child £1.50, Concession £2.50, Family £7.50. Group prices available. Location: Opposite Memorial Hall just around the corner from the North Yorkshire Moors Railway Station.   Map Ref: 34

Pontefract Museum

Salter Row, Pontefract WF8 1BA   Tel: 01977 722740   Fax: 01977 722742
Web: www.wakefield.gov.uk

Chronological look at the history of Pontefract so far, including history of liquorice, life in the work house and living in old Pontefract. Hands-on exhibits and children's activities.

Opening Times: Mon to Fri 10:00-16:30, Sat 10:30-16:30. Closed Xmas Day. Admission: Free. Location: Centre of town, next door to the library.   Map Ref: 35

Yorkshire

Swaledale Folk Museum

Reeth Green, Reeth DL11 6QT   Tel: 01748 884373

Shows how hill farming and lead mining shaped life in this beautiful Dale. Exhibits include: blacksmiths shop; joiner; tin smith; poor Law; schools; chapels; horse back doctor; crafts; pubs; clogs; brass bands; toys.

Opening Times: Good Friday to 31 Oct 10:30-17:00.   Admission: Adult £2.00, Child 50p.
Location: Reeth.   Map Ref: 36

Green Howards Museum

Trinity Church Square, Richmond DL10 4QN   Tel: 01748 822133   Fax: 01748 826561
Web: www.greenhowards.org.uk

One of the finest small military museums in the country with a unique collection of regimental uniforms, headdress, weapons, medals and silver. Display cabinets on four floors tell the story of the Green Howards in peace and war from 1688-2003. They are enhanced by touch-screen videos of WWI, WWII and the Regiment today.

Grandad explains the Crimean War (1854-56)

Opening Times: Feb, Mar & Nov Mon to Fri 09:00-17:00. Apr to May Mon to Sat 09:00-17:00. May to Sep Mon to Sat 09:00-17:00 & Sun 14:00-17:00. Oct Mon to Sat 09:00-17:00.   Admission: Adult £2.00, Child Free, OAP £1.50, Group £1.50 per person.   Location: Situated in medieval church in centre of Richmond's cobbled market place.   Map Ref: 37

Richmondshire Museum

Ryders Wynd, Richmond DL10 4JA   Tel: 01748 825611
Email: angus.goodfellow@btinternet.com

Displays trace the history of Richmond and Richmondshire and cover leadmining, transport, domestic bygones, needlework, geology and archaeology. Features include a Dales post office, chemist shop and the vet's surgery set from television's 'All Creatures Great and Small'.

Opening Times: Apr to Oct daily 10:30-16:30.
Admission: Adult £1.50, Child/OAP £1.00, Family £4.00.
Location: Near Market Place.   Map Ref: 37

Period Chemist's Shop from Catterick Garrison

Newby Hall

Ripon HG4 5AE   Tel: 01423 322583   Fax: 01423 324452
Email: info@newbyhall.com   Web: www.newbyhall.com

A unique collection of sculptures, displayed in its own gallery, and chamber pots dating from the 16th century can be viewed in Newby Hall. Within the 25 acres of award winning gardens is the national collection of cornus or dogwoods.

Opening Times: Hall: 1 Apr to 28 Sep Tue to Sun & BH Mon 12:00-17:00. Garden: 1 Apr to 28 Sep Tue to Sun & BH Mon 11:00-17:30. Admission: Adult £7.20, Child £4.70. Garden only: Adult £5.70, £4.20.   Location: Between Ripon and Boroughbridge off B6265. Exhibitions & Events 2003 : From May: Sculpture Park, 11 May: Spring Plant Fair, 7 to 8 Jun: Rainbow Craft Fair, 20 Jul: Historic Vehicle Rally, 3 Aug: Harrogate MG Club.   Map Ref: 38

Part of the rare collection of Chamber Pots at Newby Hall

Yorkshire

Yorkshire Law & Order Museums at Ripon

Allhallowgate, Ripon HG4 1LE   Tel: 01765 690799   Email: ripon.museums@btclick.com
Web: www.ripon.co.uk/museums

Walk the law and order trail and discover life for the poor, the homeless and the law-breaker in Victorian Ripon. The Workhouse Museum of Poor Law - 'vacancies for vagrants', bath, bed and board; payment in chopping wood and breaking stones. The Courthouse Museum - free transportation to Australia, licence to sell ale, or a term in the debtors' gaol (recognise Ashfordly Magistrates Court from on YTV's Heartbeat?). The Prison & Police Museum - solitary confinement, hard labour, whipping post, pillory and handcuffs. Major refurbishment/access improvements will start Nov 2002 and should be completed Spring 2003.

'Your Worship, I wish to apply
for a licence to sell ale'

Opening Times: 1 Apr to 26 Oct daily 13:00-16:00.
School holidays, Jul & Aug 11:00-16:00.   Admission: 3 in 1 Ticket - Adult £4.00, Child Free,
Concession £3.00.   Map Ref: 38

Rotherham Art Gallery

Rotherham Arts Centre, Walker Place, Rotherham S65 1JH   Tel: 01709 823621
Fax: 01709 823653   Email: Andy.Pollard@rotherham.gov.uk   Web: www.rotherham.gov.uk

A continuous programme of temporary exhibitions of contemporary arts and crafts. When Clifton Park Museum closes, Rotherham Art Gallery will be re-launched as a learning resource centre in January 2003, and will be used to deliver educational activities until the museum re-opens in 2004.

Opening Times: Mon to Sat 09:30-17:00. Closed Sun & BH.   Admission: Free.
Location: Town centre, three minute walk from bus station.   Map Ref: 39

York & Lancaster Regimental Museum

Rotherham Arts Centre, Walker Place, Rotherham S65 1JH   Tel: 01709 323621   Fax: 01709
823653   Email: georgina.kersey@rotherham.gov.uk   Web: www.rotherham.gov.uk

The York and Lancaster Regimental Museum tells the 200 year story of the men who served in the York and Lancaster Regiment.

Opening Times: Mon to Fri 09:30-17:00, Sat 09:30-16:00. Closed Sun & BH.   Admission: Free.
Location: In town centre, three minute walk from central bus station.   Map Ref: 39

Rotunda Museum of Archaeology & Local History

Museum Terrace, Vernon Road, Scarborough YO11 2NN   Tel: 01723 232323

Finest purpose-built museum of its age in the UK, built to a design suggested by 'Father of English Geology', William Smith. The museum displays archaeological finds from the internationally important site at Star Carr and 'Gristhorpe Man' a Bronze Age tree trunk burial. Also items of Victorian Scarborough.

Opening Times: Jun to Sep Tue to Sun 10:00-17:00. Oct to May Tue, Sat & Sun 11:00-16:00.
Summer opening school holidays and BH.   Admission: Museum 'S' Pass, valid 12 months all
three Scarborough museum/gallery sites. Adult £2.00, Concession £1.50, Family £5.00.
Location: On Foreshore, less than 100 yards from the South Bay beach.   Map Ref: 40

Scarborough Art Gallery

The Crescent, Scarborough YO11 2PW   Tel: 01723 232323

Displays of Scarborough's fine art collection which features seascapes and views of Scarborough including works by Grimshaw, HB Carter, Frank Mason and Ernest Dade. Lively temporary exhibitions programme featuring both contemporary work from the region and works from the permanent collection.

Opening Times: Jun to Sep Tue to Sun 10:00-17:00. Oct to May Thu, Fri & Sat 11:00-16:00.
Additional opening during school holidays and BH.   Admission: Museum 'S' Pass, valud 12
months all three Scarborough museum/gallery sites. Adult £2.00, Concession £1.50, Family
£5.00.   Location: Near town centre.   Map Ref: 40

Wood End Museum

The Crescent, Scarborough YO11 2PW   Tel: 01723 367326

Displays featuring local wildlife, rocks and fossils and tunny fishing. Also, 'Making Sense', four large scale artworks to stimulate the senses inspired by the natural world.

Opening Times: Jun to Sep Tue to Sun 10:00-17:00. Oct to May Wed, Sat & Sun 11:00-16:00. Summer opening for school holidays & BH.   Admission: Museum 'S' Pass, valid 12 months all three Scarborough museum/gallery sites. Adult £2.00, Concession £1.50, Family £5.00. Location: Near town centre.   Map Ref: 40

SHEFFIELD *S Yorks*

Bishops' House

Norton Lees Lane, Sheffield S8 9BE   Tel: 0114 278 2600
Fax: 0114 278 2604 Email: info@sheffieldgalleries.org.uk
Web: www.sheffieldgalleries.org.uk

Bishops' House

Bishops' House dates from around 1500 and is the best surviving timber-framed house in Sheffield. It retains many of its original features and gives visitors a tantalising flavour of Stuart England. The Great Parlour is restored as a typical dining room and the first floor chamber contains the original bedroom furniture and fittings listed in a 17th century inventory of contents.

Opening Times: Sat 10:00-16:30 & Sun 11:00-16:30. Mon to Fri pre-booked groups only. Admission: Free. Location: Approx two miles from Sheffield City Centre.   Map Ref: 41

Graves Art Gallery

Surrey Street, Sheffield S1 1XZ   Tel: 0114 278 2600   Fax: 0114 273 4705
Email: info@sheffieldgalleries.org.uk   Web: www.sheffieldgalleries.org.uk

Graves Art Gallery

The Graves Art Gallery is home to Sheffield's outstanding collection of British and European 19th and 20th century art, including works by artists such as Stanley Spencer, Matisse, Picasso and Cezanne. The gallery also shows a superb range of touring exhibitions chosen to complement the permanent displays.

Opening Times: Mon to Sat 10:00-17:00.
Admission: Free. Location: In the town centre.
Graves Art Gallery   Map Ref: 41

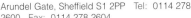

Millennium Galleries

Arundel Gate, Sheffield S1 2PP   Tel: 0114 278 2600 Fax: 0114 278 2604
Email: info@sheffieldgalleries.org.uk
Web: www.sheffieldgalleries.org.uk

Millennium Galleries

Four different galleries mean there is something to please every visitor. Enjoy blockbuster exhibitions from Britain's national galleries and museums, including the Victoria & Albert Museum and Tate. See the best craft and design, both contemporary and historical. Be dazzled by Sheffield's internationally important collection of metalwork and silverware and discover a wonderful array of treasures inside the world-renowned Ruskin Gallery.

Opening Times: Mon to Sat 10:00-17:00, Sun 11:00-17:00.
Admission: Free, apart from Special Exhibition Gallery: Adult £4.00, Child £2.00, Concession £3.00, Family £9.00. Location: In the city centre.   Map Ref: 41

Guided or Private Tours	Disabled Access	Gift Shop or Sales Point	Café or Refreshments	Restaurant	Car Parking

Yorkshire

Renishaw Hall Museum, Art Gallery & Performing Art Gallery

Renishaw Hall Estate Office, Renishaw Hall, Renishaw Park, Sheffield S21 3WB Tel: 01246
432310 Fax: 01246 430760 Email: info@renishawhall.free-online.co.uk
Web: www.sitwell.co.uk

Performing Art Gallery - this unique gallery contains pictures, gowns and personal mementoes of the stars of the silver screen and stage. John Piper Art Gallery - this gallery contains paintings by the war time artist John Piper. Costume Gallery - gowns, uniforms and staff clothing belonging to the Sitwell family, along with personal items.

Opening Times: First Fri in Apr to last Sun in Sep Fri, Sat, Sun and BH Mon 10:30-16:30. Admission: Adult £3.00, Concession £2.50. Location: Sheffield six miles, junction 30 on M1 only two miles away. Chesterfield six miles on A6135 between Eckington and Renishaw.

Map Ref: 42

Embsay & Bolton Abbey Steam Railway

Bolton Abbey Station, Bolton Abbey, Skipton BD23 6AF Tel: 01756 710614
Fax: 01756 710720 Email: embsay.steam@btinternet.com
Web: www.embsayboltonabbeyrailway.org.uk

Travel between Embsay Station built in 1888 and the new award-winning station at Bolton Abbey. The journey takes you through picturesque Yorkshire Dales scenery. Bolton Abbey Station is the ideal stopping off point, with pleasant walks, beautiful countryside for picnics or exploring the 12th century priory.

Opening Times: For the Talking Timetable phone 01756 795189. Admission: Return fares: Adult £6.00, Child £3.00, Family £16.00.

Map Ref: 43

Vintage train on the Embsay & Bolton Abbey Steam Railway

Thirsk Museum

14/16 Kirkgate, Thirsk YO7 1PQ Tel: 01845 527707 Email: thirskmuseum@supanet.com
Web: www.thirskmuseum.org

Local history in birthplace of Thomas Lord; life and times of James Herriot's town. Bones of the Saxon giant and finds from Castle Garth. Legend of the Busby Stoop Chair.

Opening Times: Easter to end Oct Mon to Wed, Fri & Sat 10:00-16:00. Admission: Adult £1.50, Child 75p, Family £3.50. Location: In Kirkgate, off Market Place - free car park 100 yards.

Map Ref: 44

Clarke Hall

Aberford Road, Wakefield WF1 4AL Tel: 01924 302700 Fax: 01924 302701
Email: info@clarke-hall.co.uk Web: www.clarke-hall.co.uk

Clarke Hall is completely furnished as the family home of a late 17th century gentleman, Benjamin Clarke who owned it between 1677 and 1688. It includes a knot garden, maze and herb garden. New exhibition centre and café open 2003.

Opening Times: Please telephone. Admission: Open days: Adult £3.50, Child Free, Concession £2.00. Group rates available. Location: One mile from the centre of Wakefield and three miles from junction 30 of M62. Opposite Pinderfields Hospital.

Map Ref: 45

National Coal Mining Museum For England

Caphouse Colliery, New Road, Overton, Wakefield WF4 4RH Tel: 01924 848806 Fax: 01924 840694 Email: info@ncm.org.uk Web: www.ncm.org.uk

A unique opportunity to go 450 feet underground, where models and machinery depict methods

of mining from the 1800s to the present day. Above ground, visit the pit ponies, exhibitions, steam winder and pit head baths.

Opening Times: Daily 10:00-17:00. Closed 24-26 December & New Years Day.
Admission: Free. Location: On the main A642 Wakefield to Huddersfield road. Map Ref: 46

Nostell Priory

Doncaster Road, Wakefield WF4 1QE Tel: 01924 863892 Fax: 01924 865282

Built in 1733 the house is an architectural masterpiece by James Paine. The State Rooms were later completed by Robert Adam, and are magnificent examples of 18th century interior style and Chippendale furniture.

Opening Times: House: 31 Mar to 4 Nov Wed to Sun & BH 13:00-17:30. 10 Nov to 9 Dec Sat & Sun 12:00-16:30. Grounds: open same days as house 11:00-18:00. Admission: House & Gardens: Adult £4.50, Child £2.20, Family £11.00. Grounds only: Adult £2.50, Child £1.20.
Map Ref: 47

Wakefield Art Gallery

Wentworth Terrace, Wakefield WF1 3QW Tel: 01924 305796 Fax: 01924 305770
Web: www.wakefield.gov.uk/communitymuseumsarts

Collection of 20th century art, fine examples of work by international sculptors Henry Moore and Barbara Hepworth - both born locally. There is also an important collection of 19th and 20th century paintings.

Opening Times: Tue to Sat 10:30-16:30, Sun 14:00-16:30. Closed Mon. Admission: Free.
Location: Approximately one mile from town centre, near to Wakefield College. Map Ref: 45

Wakefield Museum

Wood Street, Wakefield WF1 2EW Tel: 01924 305356
Fax: 01924 305353
Web: www.wakefield.gov.uk/community/museumsarts

Discover the world of Charles Waterton, conservationist and creator of the first nature reserve. Follow him on his journey through the rainforest of South America. Upstairs is the 'Story of Wakefield' - from ancient man through to the miners' strikes in the 1980s. 8000 photographs to view and print.

Opening Times: Mon to Sat 10:30-16:30, Sun 14:00-16:30.
Admission: Free. Location: Close to town centre, next to Town Hall and opposite main Police Station. Map Ref: 45

Exploring the Touchy Feely Tree in the Waterton Gallery

Yorkshire Sculpture Park

West Bretton, Wakefield WF4 4LG Tel: 01924 830302 Fax: 01924 832600
Email: info@ysp.co.uk Web: www.ysp.co.uk

Set in the beautiful grounds of the 18th century Bretton Estate, Yorkshire Sculpture Park is one of the world's leading open-air galleries presenting a changing programme of international sculpture exhibitions. Its new Centre opened in June 2002 providing all-weather facilities.

Opening Times: Daily 10:00-16:00 in winter, 10:00:18:00 in summer. Closed Xmas.
Admission: Free (£1.50 car parking a day). Location: One mile from junction 38 on the M1.
Map Ref: 48

Captain Cook Memorial Museum

Grape Lane, Whitby YO22 4BA Tel / Fax: 01947 601900
Email: captcookmuseumwhitby@ukgateway.net Web: www.cookmuseumwhitby.co.uk

House on the harbour where the young James Cook lodged as an apprentice and learnt his seamanship. Superb collections about his explorations. Paintings, models, special exhibition. Stunning site.

Opening Times: Mar Sat & Sun 11:00-15:00. Apr to end Oct daily 09:45-17:00.
Admission: Adult £3.00, Child £2.00, OAP £2.50, Student £2.00, Family £8.50. School rate £1.50 per pupil. Location: Town centre near swing bridge. Map Ref: 49

Yorkshire

Museum of Victorian Whitby

4 Sandgate, Whitby YO22 4DB   Tel: 01947 601221

Displays representing a stimulating re-creation of daily life in Victorian Whitby. Scenes including fisherman's cottage, barber's shop, cooper's yard and tallow chandlers, to mention but a few. The Bridge of the 19th Century Whaling Ship is also featured.

Opening Times: Daily 09:00-18:00.   Admission: Adult £1.50, Child £1.00.   Location: Museum is situated on first floor and basement of property.   Map Ref: 49

The RNLI Whitby Lifeboat Museum

Pier Road, Whitby YO21 3PU   Tel: 01947 602 001   Web: www.lifeboats.org.uk

Last pulling and sailing lifeboat in service on display, Robert & Ellen Robson. Models, photographs, memorabilia.

Opening Times: Easter to Oct.   Admission: Free.   Location: Pier Road.   Map Ref: 49

Whitby Abbey

Whitby YO22 4JT   Tel: 01947 603568

Whitby Abbey was founded by St Hilda in 657. The original community was destroyed by the Danes, but was refounded as a Benedictine priory in 1078. The new museum and visitor centre contains excavated finds and replicas.

Opening Times: Apr to Sep daily 10:00-18:00, Oct daily 10:00-17:00, Nov to Mar daily 10:00-16:00. Closed Xmas & New Year. Admission: Adult £3.80, Child £1.90, Concession £2.90.
Location: On cliff top east of Whitby. Railway station half a mile away.   Map Ref: 49

Whitby Museum

Pannett Park, Whitby YO21 1RE   Tel: 01947 602908   Fax: 01947 897638
Email: graham@durain.demon.co.uk   Web: www.whitby-museum.org.uk

An Edwardian/Victorian 'museum within a museum' with a very wide set of collections, relating to Whitby and the surrounding area.

Opening Times: May to Sep Mon to Fri 09:30-17:30, Sun 14:00-17:00. Oct to Apr Tue 10:00-13:00, Wed to Sat 10:00-16:00, Sun 14:00-16:00, closed Mon. Admission: Adult £2.50, Child £1.00, Family £6.00. OAP £2.00, Group/School rates available.   Location: Near town centre.
Map Ref: 49

Withernsea Lighthouse Museum

Hull Road, Withernsea HU19 2DY   Tel: 01964 614834

Maritime exhibits - RNLI and HM Coastguard, photos of shipwrecks, local history, photos of Victorian and Edwardian Withernsea including pier and promenade. Also model railway. Kay Kendall Memorial including wedding dress and excerpts of films on video.

Opening Times: Mar to Oct Sat, Sun & BH 13:00-17:00. Mid Jun to mid Sep Mon to Fri 11:00-17:00. Closed Good Friday.   Admission: Adult £2.00, Child £1.00, Under 5s Free, OAP £1.50, Family £5.50.   Location: Centre of town.   Map Ref: 50

Beningbrough Hall & Gardens

York YO30 1DD   Tel: 01904 470666   Fax: 01904 470002

THE NATIONAL TRUST

This wonderful Georgian house is filled with 18th century treasures including portraits loaned by the National Portrait Gallery. There are beautiful gardens and parkland. All complemented by Victorian laundry, potting shed, excellent facilities for children, shop and restaurant.

Opening Times: 23 Mar to 3 Nov Sat to Wed, also Fri in Jul, Aug, 25 Oct & 1 Nov and Good Friday.
Admission: House, Garden & Exhibition: Adult £5.20, Child £2.60, Family £13.00. Garden & Exhibition: Adult £3.60, Child £1.80, Family £9.00.   Location: Eight miles northwest of York signposted off A19 & A59.   Map Ref: 51

Beningbrough Hall

Yorkshire

Castle Howard

York YO60 7DA   Tel: 01653 648333   Fax: 01653 648501
Email: house@castlehoward.co.uk   Web: www.castlehoward.co.uk

Magnificent 18th century house with extensive collection and breathtaking grounds featuring temples, lakes and fountains. Additional attractions include historical characters, outdoor daily tours, archaeological dig and summer events programme.

Opening Times: Feb to Nov daily 10:00.
Admission: Adult £9.00, OAP £8.00, Child £6.00.
Location: 25 minutes north east of York, just off the A64.

Map Ref: 52

Castle Museum

Eye of York, York YO1 9RY   Tel: 01904 653611   Fax: 01904 671078
Email: castle.museum@york.gov.uk   Web: www.york.gov.uk

'Kirkgate' York Castle Museum

Venture into the prison cell of notorious highwayman Dick Turpin. Wander through Victorian and Edwardian streets and experience four hundred years of fascinating social history. Famous for its collections of costume, textiles, military and social history, York Castle Museum brings history back to life. With over 100,000 items on show you'll be amazed at what's here!

Opening Times: Nov to Mar daily 09:30-16:30, Apr to Oct 09:30-17:00. Closed Xmas & New Year.
Admission: Adult £5.75, Child/Concession £3.50, Family £16.00.   Location: Centre of York, close to Clifford's Tower and the Coppergate Shopping Centre.

Map Ref: 52

Impressions Gallery of Photography

29 Castlegate, York YO1 9RN   Tel: 01904 654724   Fax: 01904 651509
Email: enquiries@impressions-gallery.com   Web: www.impression-gallery.com

Installation of Blackthorne wall paper by Diane House, photo Jerry Hardman-Jones

Impressions Gallery opened in 1972 as one of the first specialist contemporary photography galleries in Europe. Since then we have established ourselves as a leading international exhibition space for photography and digital art. We support and promote innovative and creative work that extends the boundaries of current photographic practice. Digital imagery, film and video are essential resources for the contemporary artist, and this is reflected in our programme.

Opening Times: Apr to Oct Mon to Sat 10:00-18:00 (Tue & Thu to 20:00). Nov to Mar Mon to Sat 10:00-17:30.
Admission: Free.

Location: Located in the Coppergate Centre, near Clifford's Tower and the Jorvik Centre.   Exhibitions & Events 2003 : 7 Oct to 30 Nov: 30th Anniversary Show, 7 Dec to 1 Feb: A Film & Video Umbrella Commission: Julie Henry, 8 Feb to 28 Mar: Ten Thousand Li: Yeu-Lai Mo, Pamela So, Dinu Li, Yeun-Yi Lo, 5 Apr to 31 May: Illustration of Life: Max Kandhola, 7 Jun to 2 Aug: Innocent Landscapes: David Farrell, 9 Aug to 27 Sep: Grounded: Helen Sear, 4 Oct to 31 Jan: Intrigue: Simon Warner, Marco Dellacand, 7 Feb to 3 Apr: New Work: Trish Morrisey

From the series Slow Glass by Naoya Hatekeyama

Map Ref: 52

Yorkshire

JORVIK - The Viking City

Coppergate, York YO1 9WT Tel: 01904 543403/643211 Fax: 01904 627097
Email: enquiries@vikingjorvik.com Web: www.vikingjorvik.com

Experience a faithful recreation of Viking-age York, developed following 20 years of archaeological research. Also see 800 of the Viking finds uncovered on site in the state-of-the-art Artefact Gallery.

Opening Times: Apr to Oct daily 09:00-17:30, Nov to Mar daily 10:00-16:30. Closed Xmas Day. For full details please phone 01904 643211. Admission: Please ring for details. Location: In York City Centre, railway station and Park & Ride stops all within easy walking distance.

Map Ref: 52

GREAT WESTERN RAILWAY

National Railway Museum

Leeman Road, York YO26 4XJ Tel: 01904 621261
Fax: 01904 631319

National Railway Museum is 'European Museum of the Year 2001'. Our collection includes 103 locomotives and 177 other items of rolling stock and tells the story of the train from Rocket to Eurostar. Permanent displays include 'Palace on Wheels' with royal saloons dating back to pre Victorian times. We also have on display the only Bullet Train outside Japan.

Opening Times: Daily 10:00-18:00. Closed Xmas.
Admission: Free, except during 'Thomas Friends' events.
Location: 540 metres from York Railway Station. Map Ref: 52

The Royal Dragoon Guards

3 Tower Street, York YO1 9SB Tel / Fax: 01904 642036 Email: rdgmuseum@onetel.net.uk
Web: www.rdg.co.uk

Artefacts, standards and medals of four famous cavalry regiments covering all their battles of the past 300 years. A new six seat cinema showing 20 minute films has recently been installed. Co-located with The Prince of Wales's Own Regiment of Yorkshire.

Opening Times: Mon to Sat 09:30-16:30. Closed 22 Dec to 2 Jan. Admission: Adult £2.00, Child/OAP £1.00. Groups 2 for the price of 1. Location: Centre of town, next to Cliffords Tower.

Map Ref: 52

Shandy Hall

Coxwold, York YO61 4AD Tel / Fax: 01347 868465 Web: www.shandy-hall.org.uk

Shandy Hall houses the world's foremost collection of editions of Laurence Sterne's novels, plus an interesting background of contemporary prints and paintings illustrating his work.

Opening Times: House: May to Sep Wed 14:00-16:30, Sun 14:30-16:30. Garden: May to Sep Sun to Fri 11:00-16:30. Admission: House & Garden £4.50. Garden £2.50. Location: Above church, last house west end of village. Map Ref: 53

Sutton Park

Sutton-on-the-Forest, York YO61 1DP Tel: 01347 810249 Fax: 01347 811251
Email: suttonpark@fsbd.co.uk Web: www.statelyhome.co.uk

Rich collection of 18th century furniture and paintings. Important collection of porcelain. Plaster work by Cortese, rare Chinese wallpaper.

Opening Times: Good Friday to Easter Mon then Wed, Sun & BH Mon until 29 Sep.
Admission: Adult £5.00, Child £2.50, OAP £4.00. Group rates available. Location: Eight miles north of York on B1363 York to Helmsley Road. Map Ref: 54

Treasurer's House

Minster Yard, York YO1 7JL Tel: 01904 624247 Fax: 01904 647372
Email: yorkth@smtp.ntrust.org.uk

Named after the Treasurer of York Minster and built over a Roman Road, the house is not all that it seems. Carefully restored and presented with 16th to 20th century decoration, furniture, china and glass.

Opening Times: Apr to Oct Sat to Thu 11:00-16:30. Admission: Adult £3.80, Child £2.00, Family £9.50. Group rates available. Location: York City Centre, behind York Minster. Map Ref: 52

Yorkshire

York City Art Gallery

Exhibition Square, York YO1 7EW   Tel: 01904 551861   Fax: 01904 551866
Email: art.gallery@york.gov.uk   Web: www.york.gov.uk/heritage/museums/art

Seven centuries of European painting from early Italian gold-ground panels to the art of the present day. Changing exhibitions of modern and contemporary art. Events for all the family.

Opening Times: Daily 10:00-17:00.   Admission: Free to York residents; Adult £2.00, Concession £1.50.
Location: Three minutes from Minster, ten minutes from railway station.   Map Ref: 52

William Marlow (1740-1813): Ouse Bridge, York

York Minster Undercroft Treasury & Crypt

YORK MINSTER

York Minster, Deangate, York YO1 7JF   Tel: 01904 557216   Fax: 01904 557218   Email: visitors@yorkminster.org
Web: www.yorkminster.org

York Minster is the chief church in the Northern Province of the Church of England and is the seat of the Archbishop of York. The present building is the largest Gothic cathedral in Northern Europe, and is the setting for some of the finest 14th and 15th century stained

The West End of York Minster

glass windows in existence. Whether you come to York Minster as a tourist or pilgrim, we hope that as you walk round you will understand why the cathedral has inspired people of every generation since its completion. Prayer has been offered to God on this site for nearly 1,000 years. We invite you to join us in worship and experience the real purpose for which the Minster was built. Newly refurbished, the Undercroft and Crypt uncovers the remarkable history of York Minster from its early Norman foundations to the 20th century engineering that supports the central tower. The Undercroft also contains the remains of York's Roman Legionary fortress, Viking gravestones and historic artefacts from the Minster's collection.

12th Century Stained Glass depicting Christ

Opening Times: Winter 10:00-16:45 (last entry 16:00). Jun, Jul & Aug 09:30-18:00 (last entry 17:15)   Admission: Adult £3.80, Child £1.50, OAP/Student £2.80, Family £8.00. Price includes free audio tour.   Location: City centre.   Map Ref: 52

Yorkshire Air Museum & Allied Air Forces Memorial

Halifax Way, Elvington, York YO41 4AU   Tel: 01904 608595   Fax: 01904 608246
Email: museum@yorkshireairmuseum.co.uk   Web: www.yorkshireairmuseum.co.uk

A fascinating museum authentically based on a former World War II Bomber Command Station. Experience the atmosphere of the original restored control tower and appreciate the interesting collections of squadron memorabilia. Other displays pay tribute to the Air Gunners, Royal Observer Corps, Airborne Forces and much more. The aircraft collection contains more than 40 historic airframes and includes the unique Halifax Bomber and the Cayley Glider.

Opening Times: Mon to Fri 10:30-16:00, Sat, Sun & BH 10:30-17:00. Times may vary in winter - please check.   Admission: Adult £4.00, Child/OAP £3.00, Family £12.00. (2002 prices) Group rates available.   Location: Five miles south east of York, good regional road access.   Map Ref: 55

Yorkshire Museum   ♿ ❖

Museum Gardens, York YO1 7FR   Tel: 01904 551800   Fax: 01904 551802
Email: yorkshire.museum@york.gov.uk   Web: www.york.gov.uk/heritage/museums/yorkshire

Set in ten acres of botanical gardens, the Yorkshire Museum houses some of the richest archaeological finds in Europe and covers over 1000 years of local history. Discover Roman, Anglo-Saxon, Viking and Medieval life and meet the Jurassic sea-dragons. Exciting temporary exhibitions on display throughout the year. Call for details.

Opening Times: Daily 10:00-17:00. Admission: Adult £4.50, Child/Concession £2.95. Group rates available. Location: City centre location, five minute walk from York Railway Station.   Map Ref: 52

Yorkshire Museum of Farming, Murton Park   ♿ ❖ ⬚ ⬚

Murton Park, Murton Lane, York YO19 5UF   Tel: 01904 489966   Fax: 01904 489159
Email: info@murtonpark.co.uk   Web: www.murtonpark.co.uk

Covers 200 years of agriculture, including machinery, equipment and domestic items. Land Army display, James Herriot surgery, working blacksmith's forge, paddocks with rare breeds, farm animals and poultry. Large reference library.

Opening Times: Mar to Oct 10:00-17:00, Nov to Feb 10:00-16:00. Closed Xmas & New Year. Admission: Adult £3.60, Child £1.80, Under 5s Free, Concessions £3.00, Family £10.00. Season ticket: Adult £12.00, Family £25.00.   Location: Three miles from York, just off York ring road (A64), first left from roundabout off Bridlington Road - A166.   Map Ref: 55

Edinburgh, Glasgow & Southern Scotland

This is the region of Sir Walter Scott and Robert Burns, writers who did much to familiarise the world with romantic Scotland. Edinburgh is a stunning city renowned for its castle and the architecture of the city displayed at its best in New Town, the most impressive area of Georgian architecture in the whole of Europe. Glasgow now rates as the second favourite city to visit in Britain, the cathedral being the central point of the oldest part of the city.

Scotland is a nation with a proud and ancient heritage, and the world-class museums and galleries of Edinburgh and Glasgow provide a wonderful source of culture but there is also a wealth of smaller museums throughout southern Scotland each with their particular story to tell.

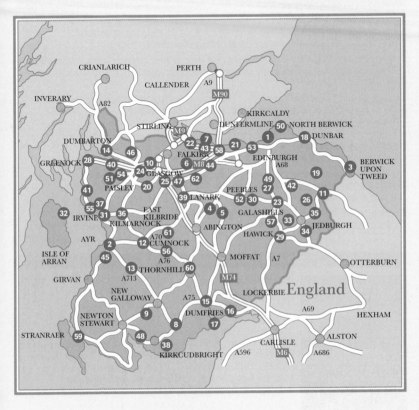

The Red Map References should be used to locate Museums etc on the pages that follow

ABERLADY *East Lothian*

Myreton Motor Museum

Aberlady EH32 0PZ Tel: 01875 870288/07947 066666

Established in 1966, Myreton has on show cars, motorcycles, commercials from 1899 to 1969. There is also a large collection of period advertising, posters and enamel signs etc.

Opening Times: Easter to Sep daily 10:30-16:30, Oct to Easter Sun 12:00-15:00.
Admission: Adult £5.00, Child £2.00, OAP/Student £3.50. Location: One mile from village of Aberlady, East Lothian.
Map Ref: 1

AYR

Burns Cottage & Museum

Burns Cottage, Alloway, Ayr KA7 4PY Tel: 01292 441215 Fax: 01292 441750
Email: burnscottage@netscapeonline.co.uk Web: www.robertburns.org

Birthplace of Robert Burns (1759-96), Scotland's National Poet. Museum contains many exhibits of Burns' songs, poems, letters and personal belongings. Original manuscripts of 'Auld Lang Syne' and 'Tam O'Shanter'.

Opening Times: Apr to Sep daily 09:00-17:30. Oct to Mar 10:00-17:00. Admission: Adult £3.00, Child/OAP £1.50, Family £9.00. Location: Two miles south of Ayr. One mile off A77 Glasgow to Stranraer.
Map Ref: 2

Rozelle House Gallery

Rozelle Park, Monument Road, Ayr KA7 4NQ Tel: 01292 445447

The Goudie Collection, an exciting series of paintings which vividly depict Burn's haunting tale of Tam O'Shanter is the focus for Rozelle Galleries. Interspersed with this will be a programme of art, craft and museum exhibitions and there is a craft shop.

Opening Times: Mon to Sat 10:00-17:00, Apr to Oct also Sun 14:00-17:00. Admission: Free.
Location: Approximately two miles from Ayr Town Centre in Robert Burns Birthplace, Alloway.
Map Ref: 2

BERWICK-UPON-TWEED *Scottish Borders*

Paxton House

Berwick-upon-Tweed TD15 1SZ Tel: 01289 386291
Fax: 01289 386660 Email: info@paxtonhouse.com
Web: www.paxtonhouse.com

One of the finest 18th century palladian country houses in Britain, featuring Adam Interiors and Chippendale. Largest picture gallery in a Scottish country house, with 70 paintings from National Galleries of Scotland. 12 period rooms, 80 acres of gardens, woodland and riverside walks, shops, stables, tearoom and exhibitions.

Opening Times: 1 Apr to 31 Oct daily 11:00-17:00. Grounds close at sunset. Admission: Adult £5.00, Child £2.50, Concession £4.75, Group £4.00, Family £13.00. Location: Signposted three miles from A1 Berwick-upon-Tweed Bypass on B6461. Berwick East Coast line 10 minutes, no. 32 'Paxton House' bus from Berwick daily except Sun. Exhibitions & Events 2003 : 22 Jun: Paxton House 3rd Vintage Rally, 18 to 20 Jul: Summer Music Festival of Classical Music.
Map Ref: 3

BIGGAR *Lanarkshire*

Biggar Gasworks Museum

Moat Park, Biggar ML12 6DT Tel / Fax: 01899 221050
Email: margaret@bmtrust.freeserve.co.uk Web: www.biggar-net.co.uk

The only remaining gas works in Scotland. By 1839 Biggar had its own gasworks. A major reconstruction in 1914 brought Biggar Gasworks more or less into its present form. Closed down in 1973, but not demolished, it has been preserved for future generations.

Opening Times: May to Sep Mon to Sun 14:00-17:00. Admission: £1.00. Location: Near town centre.
Map Ref: 4

Edinburgh, Glasgow & Southern Scotland

Gladstone Court Museum   ♿ ❖

North Back Road, Biggar ML12 6DT   Tel / Fax: 01899 221050
Email: margaret@bmtrust.freeserve.co.uk   Web: www.biggar-net.co.uk

Gladstone Court is for all the family, its small shops and offices displaying small town life as the old remember it and the young imagine it. Here is an ironmonger's store, a bank, photographers, chemist, dressmaker, watchmaker, millner, printer and bootmaker, together with a village library and schoolroom.

Opening Times: Easter to mid Oct Mon to Sat 10.30:17:00, Sun 14:00-17:00. Admission: Adult £2.00, Child £1.00, Concessions £1.50, Family £4.00, Group discounts. Location: Near town centre.   Map Ref: 4

Greenhill Farmhouse Museum

Burn Braes, Biggar ML12 6DT   Tel / Fax: 01899 221050
Email: margaret@bmtrust.freeserve.co.uk   Web: www.biggar-net.co.uk

Rebuilt in the lovely Burn Braes, Biggar, stands Greenhill Farmhouse. The Museum Trust rescued it in a derelict condition and moved the house to Biggar as a home for its Covenanting Museum.

Opening Times: May to Sep Sat & Sun 14:00-17:00 or by appointment weekdays.
Admission: Adult £1.00 Child 50p Concession 75p. Location: Near town centre, five minutes walk.   Map Ref: 4

John Buchan Centre   ♿ ❖ 🚜

Broughton, Biggar ML12 6HQ   Tel / Fax: 01899 221050
Email: margaret@bmtrust.freeserve.co.uk   Web: www.biggar-net.co.uk

In the Old Free Kirk at Broughton, John Buchan, a young supply clergyman, met his wife, Helen Masterton. The Kirk now houses a display commemorating the life and work of their eldest son, John, poet, statesman and author of many popular novels. Broughton was his childhood holiday home, held in great affection by himself and his sister Anna, who also wrote under the pen name of O Douglas.

Opening Times: May to Sep daily 14:00-17:00. Admission: Adult £1.50, Child 50p.
Location: Old Free Kirk, Broughton.   Map Ref: 5

Moat Park Heritage Centre   ☞ ♿ ❖ 🚜

Moat Park, Kirkstyle, Biggar ML12 6DT   Tel / Fax: 01899 221050
Email: margaret@bmtrust.freeserve.co.uk   Web: www.biggar-net.co.uk

The Moat Park Heritage Centre was opened by HRH The Princess Royal in June 1988. One can see here how the Clyde and Tweed valleys were formed millions of years ago, rub shoulders with an Iron Age family or encounter a blood thirsty Roman soldier and other figures from our past. Splendid models display early dwellings, mottes, castles and farmhouses. There is also a magnificent Victorian patchwork.

Opening Times: Easter to mid Oct Mon to Sat 10:30-17:00, Sun 14:00-17:00. Admission: Adult £2.00, Child £1.00, Concession £1.50, Family £4.00. Location: Near town centre.   Map Ref: 4

Blackridge Community Museum   ♿ 🚜

Craig Inn Centre, Blackridge EH48 3RJ   Tel: 01501 752396
Email: museums@westlothian.gov.uk   Web: www.wlonline.org

Display on the origins of the village as a coaching stop and its subsequent development. Programme of temporary community exhibitions.

Opening Times: Tue & Thu 14:00-18:30, Wed 09:30-12:30 & 13:30-16:30, alternate Sat 09:30-12:30. Admission: Free. Location: In centre of village, enter through library in Craig Inn Centre.   Map Ref: 6

☞	♿	❖	☕	🍴	🚜
Guided or Private Tours	Disabled Access	Gift Shop or Sales Point	Café or Refreshments	Restaurant	Car Parking

Scottish Railway Preservation Society

Bo'ness & Kinneil Railway, Bo'ness Station, Union Street, Bo'ness EH51 9AQ
Tel: 01506 822298/825855   Fax: 01506 828766   Email: srps@srps.org.uk
Web: www.srps.org.uk

Bo'ness & Kinneil Railway is home to an exciting collection of railway buildings, locomotives, equipment, carriages and wagons. Your journey through the Forth Valley takes you to the Caverns of Birkhill Fireclay Mine. On your return you can visit the Scottish Railway Exhibition depicting the history of railways in Scotland.

Opening Times: Weekends Apr to Oct. July & Aug Tue to Sun 11:00-16:15. Admission: Entry to museum is free, Rail Fares - Adult £4.50, Child £2.00, Concession £3.50, Family (2 adults and 2 children) £11.00. Location: In town of Bo'ness. From Edinburgh M9 leave junction 3,

Caledonian Railway Locomotive CR419 at Bo'ness Station

follow signs to Bo'ness. Exhibitions & Events 2003 : Special events include Easter Egg Specials, Diesel Galas, Day out with Thomas Weekends, Caledonian Weekend, Vehicle Rallies, Santa Steam Specials and Black Bun Specials.   Map Ref: 7

Castle Douglas Art Gallery

Market Street, Castle Douglas DG7 1BE   Tel / Fax: 01557 331643
Email: davidd@dumgal.gov.uk   Web: www.dumgal.gov.uk/museums

The Gallery plays host to an annual programme of exhibitions ranging from fine art, craft, photography. Touring exhibitions are regularly displayed at the Gallery.

Opening Times: Opening times may vary, please contact. Admission: Free. Location: Town centre.   Map Ref: 8

Clatteringshaw Visitor Centre

By New Galloway, Castle Douglas DG7 3SQ   Tel: 01671 402420   Fax: 01671 403708

See interpretive display of Galloway wildlife, touchy-feely sections. Tearoom and shop. Forest trails, cycle routes, forest drive nearby and CCTV on red Kites. Panoramic views of Clatteringshaw Loch to the wild Galloway Hills beyond.

Opening Times: Easter to 28 Sep daily 10:30-17:00. 29 Sep to 26 Oct daily 10:30-16:30.
Admission: Free. Location: Five miles south west of New Galloway on A712.   Map Ref: 9

Summerlee Heritage Park

Heritage Way, Coatbridge ML5 1QD   Tel: 01236 431261   Fax: 01236 440429

'4 star' graded visitor attraction. 22 acre site with operational tramway, re-created addit mine and miners' row. Exhibition hall with working machinery and extensive displays of social and industrial heritage.

Opening Times: Apr to Oct daily 10:00-17:00, Nov to Mar daily 10:00-16:00. Admission: Free.
Location: To the west of Coatbridge town centre, by the central station.   Map Ref: 10

Coldstream Museum

12 Market Square, Coldstream TD12 4BD   Tel: 01890 882630

Local history and Coldstream Guards.

Opening Times: Easter to Sep Mon to Sat 10:00-16:00, Sun 14:00-16:00. Oct Mon to Sat 13:00-16:00. Admission: Free. Location: Near town centre.   Map Ref: 11

Baird Institute Museum

3 Lugar Street, Cumnock KA18 1AD   Tel / Fax: 01290 421701

A local museum featuring temporary and permanent exhibitions. Displays include Cumnock

CUMNOCK *Ayrshire (continued)*

Pottery, Mauchline Boxware and Ayrshire Embroidery. A room is dedicated to Keir Hardy, founder of the Labour Party. Family history information is available.

Opening Times: Mon, Tue, Thu & Fri 10:00-13:00 & 13:30-16:30.   Admission: Free.
Location: Near Cumnock Town Centre.   Map Ref: 12

DALMELLINGTON *Ayrshire*

Cathcartston Visitor Centre
Cathcartston, Dalmellington KA6 7QY   Tel: 01292 550633   Fax: 01292 550937
Email: stanley.sarsfield@east-ayrshire.gov.uk

A local history museum with a fine collection of photographs and maps showing the Doon Valley over the centuries. Local history displays combined with changing art exhibitions and a weaving tableau.

Opening Times: Mon to Fri 10:00-16:30.   Admission: Free.   Location: In the centre of
Dalmellington, off the main square.   Map Ref: 13

DUMBARTON *Dunbartonshire*

Denny Ship Model Experimental Tank
Castle Street, Dumbarton G82 1QS   Tel: 01389 763444   Fax: 01389 743093

Step back into the world of the Victorian ship designer, fully restored and still used for testing ship designs.

Opening Times: Mon to Sat 10:00-16:00.   Admission: Adult £1.50, Child/OAP 75p, Family
£3.00.   Location: Near town centre, two minutes walk from railway station.   Map Ref: 14

DUMFRIES

Burns House
Burns Street, Dumfries DG1 2PS   Tel: 01387 255297   Fax: 01387 265081
Email: dumfriesmuseum@dumgal.gov.uk   Web: www.dumgal.gov.uk/museums

Simple sandstone house in a quiet Dumfries street where Robert Burns, Scotland's National Poet, spent the last years of his brilliant life.

Opening Times: Apr to Sep Mon to Sat 10:00-17:00, Sun 14:00-17:00. Oct to Mar Tue to Sat
10:00-13:00 & 14:00-17:00.   Admission: Free.   Location: One minute walk from Broons Road
car park.   Map Ref: 15

Dumfries & Galloway Aviation Museum
Former Control Tower, Heathhall Industrial Estate, Dumfries DG1 3PH   Tel: 01387 251623
Web: www.dgam.co.uk

Based around the original control tower of RAF Dumfries, the museum is a fascinating collection of aircraft and memorabilia from the earliest days of flight to recent times.

Opening Times: Easter to Oct Sat & Sun 10:00-17:00. Jun to Aug Wed 18:00-21:00.
Admission: Adult £2.00, Child £1.00.   Location: Heathhall Industrial Estate, off A701.
Map Ref: 15

Dumfries Museum & Camera Obscura
The Observatory, Dumfries DG2 7SW   Tel: 01387 253374   Fax: 01387 265081
Email: dumfriesmuseum@dumgal.gov.uk   Web: www.dumgal.gov.uk/museums

A treasure house of the history of Dumfries and Galloway telling the story of the land and people of the region.

Opening Times: Apr to Sep Mon to Sat 10:00-17:00, Sun 14:00-17:00. Oct to Mar Tue to Sat
10:00-13:00 & 14:00-17:00.   Admission: Museum free. Camera Obscura Adult £1.50
Concession 75p.   Location: Five minutes walk from Whitesands.   Map Ref: 15

Gracefield Arts Centre
29 Edinburgh Road, Dumfries DG1 1JQ   Tel: 01387 262084   Fax: 01387 255173

Gracefield presents a changing display of contemporary exhibitions by local, national and international artists and craftspeople. Selected exhibitions from the permanent collection of Scottish paintings, drawings and prints dating from the 1840s are shown 3 to 4 times per year.

Opening Times: Tue to Sat 10:00-17:00.   Admission: Free.   Location: Five minute walk from
train station and town centre.   Map Ref: 15

DUMFRIES (continued)

Old Bridge House

Mill Street, Dumfries DG2 7BE   Tel: 01387 256904   Fax: 01387 265081
Email: dumfriesmuseum@dumgal.gov.uk   Web: www.dumgal.gov.uk/museums

Built in 1660 into the sandstone of the 15th century Devorgilla Bridge, Dumfries' oldest house is now a museum of everyday life in the town.

Opening Times: Apr to Sep Mon to Sat 10:00-17:00. Sun 14:00-17:00.   Admission: Free.
Location: One minutes walk from Whitesands.   Map Ref: 15

Robert Burns Centre

Mill Road, Dumfries DG2 7BE   Tel / Fax: 01387 264808
Email: info@dumfriesmuseum.demon.co.uk   Web: www.dumgal.gov.uk/museums

Situated in the town's 18th century watermill on the West Bank of the River Nith, The Robert Burns Centre tells the story of Robert Burns' last years spent in the bustling streets and lively atmosphere of Dumfries in the late 18th century.

Opening Times: Apr to Sep Mon to Sat 10:00-20:00, Sun 14:00-17:00. Oct to Mar Tue to Sat 10:00-13:00 & 14:00-17:00.   Admission: Free.   Location: West Bank of River Nith, opposite Whitesands.   Map Ref: 15

Savings Banks Museum

Ruthwell, Dumfries DG1 4NN   Tel: 01387 870640   Email: tsbmuseum@btinternet.com
Web: www.lloydstsb.com/savingsbanksmuseum

International collection of money boxes and savings bank memorabilia. Social and family records and information on medieval Ruthwell Cross. History of savings banks and founder, the Rev Henry Duncan DD.

Opening Times: Daily 10:00-13:00 & 14:00-17:00. Closed Sun & Mon in winter.
Admission: Free.   Location: Six miles west of Annan on B724.   Map Ref: 16

Shambellie House
Museum of Costume

New Abbey, Dumfries DG2 8HQ   Tel: 01387 850375   Fax: 01387 850461   Email: info@nms.ac.uk
Web: www.nms.ac.uk/costume

Step back in time and experience Victorian and Edwardian grace and refinement. Set in attractive wooded grounds, Shambellie is a beautiful Victorian country house which offers visitors the chance to see period clothes, from the 1850s to the 1950s, in appropriate room settings, with accessories, furniture and decorative art.

Opening Times: Apr to Oct 11:00-17:00.   Admission: Adult £2.50, Child Free, Concession £1.50.   Location: Seven miles south of Dumfries, on the A710.   Map Ref: 17

Shambellie House display

DUNBAR East Lothian

Dunbar Town House Museum

Dunbar Town House, High Street, Dunbar EH42 1ER   Tel: 01368 863734   Fax: 01620 828201
Email: elms@eastlothian.gov.uk   Web: www.dunbarmuseum.org

Dunbar Town House Museum is based in a 16th century building. There is an archaeology display, a local history room and a different local history exhibition each year.

Opening Times: Apr to Sep 12:30-16:30. Admission: Free. Location: High Street.   Map Ref: 18

John Muir Birthplace

128 High Street, Dunbar EH42   Tel: 01368 860187   Fax: 01620 828201
Email: elms@elothian-museums.demon.co.uk   Web: www.muir-birthplace.org

The birthplace of the environmentalist John Muir, includes displays about Muir's life and ideas, and the conservation movement. The museum is due re-open in the summer of 2003 after a major refurbishment project.

Opening Times: Apr to Sep 11:00-13:00 & 14:00-17:00. Admission: Free. Location: High Street.
                                                                                          Map Ref: 18

Edinburgh, Glasgow & Southern Scotland

DUNS *Scottish Borders*

Jim Clark Room

44 Newton Street, Duns TD11 3AU   Tel: 01361 883960

Museum dedicated to local driver Jim Clark.

Opening Times: Easter to Sep daily 10:30-13:00 & 14:00-16:30, Sun 14:00-16:00. Oct Mon to Sat 13:00-16:00. Admission: Adult £1.30, SBC Residents Free. Location: In main town centre.   Map Ref: 19

EAST KILBRIDE *Lanarkshire*

Museum of Scottish Country Life

Wester Kittochside, East Kilbride G76 9HR   Tel: 01355 224181   Fax: 01355 571290   Email: info@nms.ac.uk   Web: www.nms.ac.uk/countrylife

This award-winning new Museum shows how country people lived and worked in Scotland in the past and how this has shaped the countryside of today. The site includes a new exhibition building housing the National Country Life Collections, the original Georgian farmhouse, historical working farm and events area.

Opening Times: Daily 10:00-17:00. Admission: Adult £3.00, Child Free, Concessions £1.50. Location: Situated between East Kilbride and Glasgow.   Map Ref: 20

EDINBURGH

Brass Rubbing Centre

Trinity Apse, Chambers Close, Royal Mile, Edinburgh EH1 1SS   Tel: 0131 556 4364

Web: www.cac.org.uk
The Brass Rubbing Centre occupies Trinity Apse, the sole surviving fragment of the Gothic Trinity College Church founded about 1460. It contains a fascinating collection of replicas moulded from ancient Pictish stones, and medieval church brasses. No experience is required to make a rubbing, and staff are on hand to assist. The Centre also stocks high-quality, ready-made rubbings and brass rubbing kits.

Edinburgh Brass Rubbing Centre

Opening Times: Apr to Sep Mon to Sat 10:00-17:00, Sun during the Edinburgh International Festival 12:00-17:00. Closed Oct to Mar. Admission: Free. Cost to make rubbing.   Map Ref: 21

City Art Centre

2 Market Street, Edinburgh EH1 1DE   Tel: 0131 529 3993 Fax: 0131 529 3986 Web: www.cac.org.uk

The City Art Centre is both home to Edinburgh's outstanding collection of Scottish art and one of the United Kingdom's premier temporary exhibition spaces. Since it opened in 1980, the City Art Centre has mounted a huge range of exhibitions, from rare Egyptian antiquities to the most innovative contemporary art, from Michelangelo drawings to Star Wars. The scale and range of the exhibition programme has made the gallery one of Britain's most visited exhibition centres. The city's fine art collection consists of almost 4,000 works of Scottish art: paintings, watercolours, drawings, prints, photographs, sculpture and tapestries, including work by McTaggart, Fergusson, Peploe and Eardley. The collection reflects all of the significant influences and movements in Scottish art, ranging from early portraiture, through the Glasgow Boys, the Edinburgh School and the Colourists.

The Blue Hat

Opening Times: Mon to Sat 10:00-17:00, Sun during Jul & Aug 12:00-17:00. Admission: Free. Charging for occasional exhibitions.   Map Ref: 21

Dean Gallery

73 Belford Road, Edinburgh EH4 3DS   Tel: 0131 624 6200   Fax: 0131 623 7126
Email: deaninfo@nationalgalleries.org   Web: www.nationalgalleries.org

The Dean Gallery just opposite the Gallery of Modern Art, holds an extensive collection of Dada and Surrealist art including works by Dali, Ernst, Magritte, Man Ray and Miro. It is also home to an impressive collection of works by Sir Eduardo Paolozzi including a substantial number of plaster sculptures, prints and drawings. Spectacular city views and beautiful sculpture park.

Opening Times: Daily 10:00-17:00, late night Thu until 19:00.   Admission: Free to permanent collection, admission charges for special exhibitions.   Location: Ten minutes walk from West End Princes Street, or catch free bus from Scottish National Portrait Gallery.   Exhibitions & Events 2003 : 26 Apr to 15 Jun: The Advertising Artist: The Collection and Archive of Ashley Havinden - under the professional name 'Ashley' Havinden (1903-73) was one of the most successful advertising artists and designers working in Britain in the 20th century.   Map Ref: 21

Edinburgh University - Historical Musical Instruments

Reid Concert Hall, Bistro Square, Edinburgh EH8 9AG   Tel: 0131 650 4367   Fax: 0131 650 2425   Email: euchmi@ed.ac.uk   Web: www.music.ed.ac.uk/euchmi

Outstanding display of over 1000 musical instruments showing 400 years of history of folk and domestic music, bands and orchestras, plus interactive devices.

Opening Times: Mon to Fri 14:00-17:00, Wed 15:00-17:00, Sat 10:00-13:00. Closed Xmas & New Year.   Admission: Free.   Location: Bristo Square, next to McEwan Hall   Map Ref: 21

The Fruitmarket Gallery

fruitmarket the gallery

45 Market Street, Edinburgh EH1 1DF   Tel: 0131 225 2383   Fax: 0131 220 3130   Email: annie@fruitmarket.co.uk   Web: www.fruitmarket.co.uk

Situated in one of the world's most beautiful cities, Edinburgh's Fruitmarket Gallery is an acclaimed international art space which has operated as a contemporary gallery since 1974. The gallery shows a programme of exciting, thought-provoking exhibitions of Scottish, British and international contemporary art. The Fruitmarket Gallery exhibition programme is complemented by an ambient, street-level glass fronted café and innovative bookshop.

The Fruitmarket Gallery, Edinburgh

Opening Times: Mon to Sat 11:00-18:00, Sun 12:00-17:00.   Admission: Most exhibitions free, small charge for festival exhibition.   Location: Very central location, next to Waverley Station.   Map Ref: 21

Georgian House

7 Charlotte Square, Edinburgh EH2 4DR   Tel / Fax: 0131 226 3318

The Georgian House is part of Robert Adam's masterpiece of urban design, Charlotte Square. It dates from 1776, when those who could afford it began to escape the cramped, squalid conditions of Edinburgh's Old Town to settle in the fashionable New Town. The house's beautiful china, shining silver, exquisite paintings and furniture all reflect the domestic surroundings and social conditions of the times.

Opening Times: 1-31 Mar & 1 Nov to 24 Dec daily 11:00-15:00, 1 Apr to 31 Oct daily 10:00-17:00.

Entrance to the Georgian House - 7 Charlotte Square

Admission: Adult £5.00, Concession £3.75, Family £13.50.   Location: Two minutes from west end of Princes Street, ten minutes from Tourist Information Centre.   Map Ref: 21

EDINBURGH *(continued)*

The Grand Lodge of Scotland Museum

Freemasons Hall, 96 George Street, Edinburgh EH2 3DH   Tel: 0131 225 5304   Fax: 0131 225 3953   Email: grandsecretary@sol.co.uk   Web: www.grandlodgescotland.com

All objects relating to Scottish Freemasonry, including glassware, ceramics, coins, photographs and books.

Opening Times: Mon to Fri 09:30-16:30. Closed Sat, Sun & BH.   Admission: Free.
Location: Town centre.   Map Ref: 21

Granton Centre

242 West Granton Road, Edinburgh EH5 1JA   Tel: 0131 247 4470   Fax: 0131 551 4106   Email: info@nms.ac.uk   Web: www.nms.ac.uk/granton

Visit the major store of the National Museums of Scotland; important conservation work is carried out here, preparing thousands of objects for display, as diverse as classic motorbikes, whale bones and ancient pottery.

Opening Times: Tue, tours at 10:30 and 14:00.   Admission: Free. Visits must be booked one day in advance.   Location: Half an hour from city centre, by car, by Lothian Buses 10, 8 & 32.
                                                                                             Map Ref: 21

Lauriston Castle

Cramond Road South, Davidson's Mains, Edinburgh EH4 5QD
Tel: 0131 336 2060   Web: www.cac.org.uk

A 16th century tower house with later additions, Lauriston Castle stands in tranquil grounds overlooking the Forth at Cramond. The preserved Edwardian interior is an ideal backdrop to the rich collection of fine and decorative art assembled by the last private owners. The Castle and its grounds are host to a year round programme of art and craft based workshops, study days and family events.

Opening Times: Guided tours only Apr to Oct 11:20, 12:20, 14:20, 15:20 & 16:20. Closed Fri. Nov to Mar Sat & Sun 14:20 & 15:20.
Admission: Adult £4.50, Concession £3.00.   Map Ref: 21
Photo Caption: Lauriston Castle

Lothian & Borders Fire Brigade, Museum of Fire

Brigade Headquarters, Lauriston Place, Edinburgh EH3 9DE   Tel: 0131 228 2401   Fax: 0131 229 8359   Email: csg@lothian.fire-uk.org   Web: www.lothian.fire-uk.org

The Museum tells the history of the oldest fire brigade in the UK (formed 1824), showing the development of fire fighting, displaying a range of engines along with many other fire related items.

Opening Times: Mon to Fri 09:00-16:30. Closed Xmas & New Year also first two weeks Aug.
Admission: Free.   Location: City Centre, next to Art College.   Map Ref: 21

Museum of Childhood

42 High Street, Royal Mile, Edinburgh EH1 1TG   Tel: 0131 529 4142   Web: www.cac.org.uk

It is a treasure house crammed full of memories of childhood past and present. There are toys and games galore from all around the world, ranging from dolls and teddy bears to train sets and tricycles. Listen to children chanting multiplication tables in the 1930s schoolroom. Watch the street games played by Edinburgh children filmed in 1951. Find out how children were brought up, dressed and educated in decades gone by.

Opening Times: Mon to Sat 10:00-17:00, Sun during Jul & Aug 12:00-17:00.   Admission: Free.   Map Ref: 21

Museum of Edinburgh

Huntly House, 142 Canongate, Royal Mile, Edinburgh EH8 8DD   Tel: 0131 529 4143
Web: www.cac.org.uk

Housing collections relating to the story of Edinburgh from pre-historic times to the present day, the museum's treasures include the National Covenant, the great charter demanding religious freedoms, signed in 1638. The museum also includes the feeding bowl and collar presented to 'Greyfriars Bobby', the little Skye Terrier dog that maintained a vigil by the grave of his master and won the hearts of the people of Edinburgh.

Opening Times: Mon to Sat 10:00-17:00. Sun during the Edinburgh International Festival 14:00-17:00.
Admission: Free.   Map Ref: 21

National Gallery of Scotland

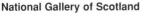

The Mound, Edinburgh EH2 2EL   Tel: 0131 624 6200   Fax: 0131 623 7126
Email: nginfo@nationalgalleries.org   Web: www.nationalgalleries.org

Scotland's greatest collection of European paintings, drawings and prints dating from the early Renaissance to the late 19th century. The collection includes works by Raphael, Titian, Velazquez, Poussin, Rembrandt, Vermeer, Rubens, Turner and the Impressionists. Also houses the national collection of Scottish art with works by Ramsay, Raeburn, Wilkie and McTaggart.

Opening Times: Daily 10:00-17:00, late night Thu until 19:00. Admission: Free to permanent collection, charges for special exhibitions. Location: Right in the centre of Edinburgh, just off Princes Street. Exhibitions & Events 2003 : 2 Aug to 26 Oct: Monet: The Seine and the Sea - Vétheuil and Normandy, 1878-1883 - This exhibition, the first at the newly refurbished Royal Scottish Academy, will bring together around 80 paintings by the Impressionist master, dating from the years he spent in Vétheuil.   Map Ref: 21

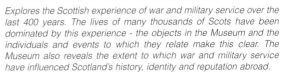

National War Museum of Scotland

Edinburgh Castle, Castlehill, Edinburgh EH1 2NG
Tel: 0131 225 7534   Fax: 0131 225 3848
Email: info@nms.ac.uk   Web: www.nms.ac.uk/war

Explores the Scottish experience of war and military service over the last 400 years. The lives of many thousands of Scots have been dominated by this experience - the objects in the Museum and the individuals and events to which they relate make this clear. The Museum also reveals the extent to which war and military service have influenced Scotland's history, identity and reputation abroad.

Opening Times: Apr to Oct 09:45-17:45, Nov to Mar 09:45-16:45.
Admission: Included in admission to Edinburgh Castle. Location: In city centre, five minutes walk from Princes Street.   Map Ref: 21

Nelson Monument

Calton Hill, Edinburgh EH7 5AA   Tel: 0131 556 2716
Web: www.cac.org.uk

High on Calton Hill, this monument to Admiral Lord Nelson and Trafalgar was built between 1807 and 1815. In 1853 a large time ball was introduced. It is lowered each day as the one o'clock gun is fired from Edinburgh Castle. The panoramic view from the monument is framed by Fife to the north, the Forth estuary to the east, the Moorfoot Hills to the south and the Forth Rail and Road Bridges to the west.

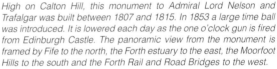

Opening Times: Apr to Sep Mon 13:00-18:00, Tue to Sat 10:00-18:00. Oct to Mar Mon to Sat 10:00-15:00. Admission: Adult £2.00.   Map Ref: 21

Newhaven Heritage Museum

24 Pier Place, Newhaven Harbour, Edinburgh EH6 4LP   Tel: 0131 551 4165

Web: www.cac.org.uk

What was it like to live in the tightly-knit fishing community of Newhaven, earning a living as a fishwife or fisherman braving the sea to bring home the catch? Discover the answer in the historic fishmarket, next to Harry Ramsden's fish and chip restaurant, overlooking picturesque Newhaven Harbour.

Opening Times: Mon to Sun 12:00-17:00.
Admission: Free.   Map Ref: 21

The lively and informative Newhaven Heritage Museum

The People's Story

Canongate Tolbooth, Royal Mile, Edinburgh EH8 8BN   Tel: 0131 529 4057

Web: www.cac.org.uk

Situated in the Canongate Tolbooth, opposite the Museum of Edinburgh in the Royal Mile, The People's Story Museum uses oral history, reminiscence, written sources and reconstructed set to tell the story of the lives, work and leisure of the ordinary people of Edinburgh from the late 18th century to the present day.

Opening Times: Mon to Sat 10:00-17:00. Sun during the Edinburgh International Festival 14:00-17:00.
Admission: Free.   Map Ref: 21

The People's Story Museum

The Queen's Gallery

Palace of Holyroodhouse, Edinburgh EH8 8DX   Tel: 0131 556 5100

Email: information@royalcollection.org.uk   Web: www.royal.gov.uk

The new Queen's Gallery will host a programme of changing exhibitions from the Royal Collection. Exhibitions include Leonardo da Vinci: The Divine and the Grotesque, Fabergé and King of the World: The Padshahnama, An Imperial Mughal Manuscript.

Opening Times: Daily Apr to Oct 09:30-18:00 (last admission 17:15). Nov to Mar 09:30-16:30 (last admission 15:45). Entry by timed ticket.   Admission: Adult £4.00, Child £2.00, Under 5s Free, OAP/Student £3.00, Family (2 adults and 3 children) £10.00.   Map Ref: 21

Royal Museum & Museum of Scotland

Chambers Street, Edinburgh EH1 1JF   Tel: 0131 227 4219/4422

Fax: 0131 220 4819   Email: info@nms.ac.uk   Web: www.nms.ac.uk

Royal Museum - presenting the world to Scotland: The Royal Museum houses outstanding international collections reflecting the diversity of life on Earth and the ingenuity of humankind. Explore this magnificent Victorian building, distinguished by its soaring glass-topped roof, which floods the elegant main hall with natural light. Museum of Scotland - presenting Scotland to the world: A striking new landmark adjacent to the Royal Museum, in Edinburgh's Historic Old Town. This stunning building presents for the first time, the history of Scotland, its land,

its people and their achievements. The series of galleries take you on a journey from Scotland's geological beginnings, through time, to the 20th century. The Royal Museum and Museum of Scotland have been awarded a five-star museum rating by the Scottish Tourist Board.

Opening Times: Mon to Fri 10:00-17:00, Tue 10:00-20:00, Sun 12:00-17:00. Admission: Free. Location: Near city centre, five minute walk from Princes Street and Royal Mile.   Map Ref: 21

Royal Scots Regimental Museum
The Castle, Edinburgh EH1 2YT Tel: 0131 310 5016/5017

The Royal Scots is the oldest Regiment in the British Army and as such is the Senior Infantry Regiment of the Line. It was raised in 1633 and through paintings, artefacts, silver and medals their fascinating story is told from formation to the present day.

Opening Times: Apr to Sep daily 09:30-17:30. Oct to Mar Mon to Fri 09:30-16:00.
Admission: Free. Location: Edinburgh Castle.   Map Ref: 21

Scott Monument
East Princes Street Gardens, Edinburgh EH2 2EJ Tel: 0131 529 4068 Web: www.cac.org.uk

Designed by George Meikle Kemp, this monument to the great Scottish writer opened in August 1846. In the years since then millions of people have climbed the 200 foot structure to admire its commanding views of the city, the exhibition on the life of Sir Walter Scott and the statuettes of characters from his works which adorn the monument.

Opening Times: 1 Apr to 30 Sep Mon to Sat 09:00-18:00, Sun 10:00-18:00. 1 Oct to 31 Mar Mon to Sat 09:00-15:00, Sun 10:00-15:00. Admission: £2.50.   Map Ref: 21

The Scott Monument, Edinburgh

Scottish National Gallery of Modern Art
75 Belford Road, Edinburgh EH4 3DR Tel: 0131 624 6200 Fax: 0131 623 7126
Email: gmainfo@nationalgalleries.org Web: www.nationalgalleries.org

Scotland's finest collection of 20th and 21st century paintings, sculpture and graphic art including works by Picasso, Matisse, Giacometti, Sickert and Hockney. Significant holdings of Surrealism and German Expressionism along with an unrivalled collection of 20th and 21st century Scottish art, from the Colourists right up to the present day. Sculptures by Moore, Hepworth and Paolozzi in surrounding grounds.

Opening Times: Daily 10:00-17:00, late night Thu until 19:00. Admission: Free to permanent collection,

Scottish National Gallery of Modern Art

admission charges for special exhibitions. Location: Ten minutes walk from West End Princes Street, or catch free bus from Scottish National Portrait Gallery. Exhibitions & Events 2003 : 12 Aug to 23 Nov: Boyle Family - This exhibition will focus on the work of the Boyle Family: Mark Boyle (b.1934), his wife Joan Hills (b.1931) and their children Sebastian (b.1962) and Georgia (b.1965). Boyle and Hills first began working together in the early 1960s, and the children have assisted them since the 1970s.   Map Ref: 21

| Guided or Private Tours | Disabled Access | Gift Shop or Sales Point | Café or Refreshments | Restaurant | Car Parking |

Edinburgh, Glasgow & Southern Scotland

Scottish National Portrait Gallery
1 Queen Street, Edinburgh EH2 1JD   Tel: 0131 624 6200
Fax: 0131 623 7126   Email: pginfo@nationalgalleries.org
Web: www.nationalgalleries.org

A visual history of Scotland from the 16th century to the present day, told through portraits of the people who shaped it: royals and rebels, poets and philosophers, heroes and villains. Among the most famous are Mary, Queen of Scots and Robert Burns. Also houses the National Photography Collection, including vast holdings of work by Hill and Adamson, the Scottish pioneers of photography.

Opening Times: Daily 10:00-17:00, late night Thu until 19:00.
Admission: Free to permanent collection, admission charges for special exhibitions.   Location: Just a two minute walk from Princes Street (Eastend) and one minute walk from central bus station in St Andrew Square.   Exhibitions & Events 2003 : 20 Jun to 14 Sep: High Society the life and art of Sir Francis Grant (1803-1878) - Celebrating the bicentenary of the painter's birth, this exhibition re-introduces a dominant figure in the Victorian art world, a leading society portrait painter and the only Scottish president of the Royal Academy - Sir Francis Grant, PRA.   Map Ref: 21

Talbot Rice Gallery
University of Edinburgh, Old College, South Bridge, Edinburgh EH8 9YL
Tel: 0131 6502211

A Georgian gallery with a collection of Italian and Dutch Old Master paintings and bronzes. The 'White Gallery' houses six contemporary exhibitions each year. The experimental 'Round Room' space has four installations each year.

Opening Times: Tue to Sat 10:00-17:00, please phone for further details. Admission: Free. Location: Five minutes walk from Royal Mile, next to Royal Museum of Scotland.   Map Ref: 21

The Torrie Collection

The Writers' Museum
Lady Stair's House, Lady Stair's Close,
Lawnmarket, Royal Mile, Edinburgh EH1 2PA
Tel: 0131 529 4901   Web: www.cac.org.uk

THE WRITERS' MUSEUM

The Museum is dedicated to Scotland's great literary figures: Robert Burns (1759-1796), Sir Walter Scott (1771-1832) and Robert Louis Stevenson (1850-1895). Other prominent Scottish writers are featured in the museum's temporary exhibition programme. In the adjacent Makars' Court, which takes its name from the Scots word for a writer or poet, commemorative flagstones celebrate the work of Scottish writers from the 14th century to the present day.

Opening Times: Mon to Sat 10:00-17:00. Sun during Edinburgh
Festival 14:00-17:00. Admission: Free.   Map Ref: 21
The Writers Museum, Edinburgh

Callendar House
Callendar Estate, Falkirk FK1 1YR
Tel: 01324 503770   Fax: 01324 503771

CALLENDAR
HOUSE

600 years of Scottish history; costumed interpreters, working Georgian kitchen, exhibitions, Georgian gardens, gift shop, conference facilities, tea shop at the stables, the Park Gallery and maginificent grounds. Open all year.

Opening Times: Mon to Sat all year 10:00-16:00, Apr to Sep Sun 14:00-17:00. Admission: Adults £3.00, Child £1.00, OAP £1.50   Map Ref: 22

GALASHIELS Scottish Borders

Old Gala House

Scott Crescent, Galashiels TD1 3JS   Tel / Fax: 01896 752611

Museum and art gallery, former home of Laird of Gala.

Opening Times: Easter to Sep Tue to Sat 10:00-16:00. Jul to Aug Mon to Sat 10:00-16:00, Sun 14:00-16:00. Oct Tue to Sat 13:00-16:00. Admission: Free. Location: Five minute walk from town centre.
Map Ref: 23

GLASGOW

The Warrick Vase from the Emperor Hadrian's villa of Tivoli

Burrell Collection

2060 Pollokshaws Road, Glasgow G43 1AT
Tel: 0141 287 2550   Fax: 0141 287 2597

The Burrell Collection consists of some 9000 items of European, Near Eastern and Oriental fine and decorative art. Highlights of the collection include the spectacular medieval European stained glass, tapestries and furniture; Egyptian, Greek and Roman antiquities; 19th century French art including works by Degas and Cezanne; Islamic art and Chinese art. The collections are housed in a award winning building in the woodland surroundings of Pollak Country Park. They were a gift to the city from the great ship owner and collector Sir William Burrell.

Rodin, The Thinker

Opening Times: 15 Mar to 6 Jan Mon to Fri 10:00-17:00, Sat & Sun 11:00-17:00. Admission: Free. Location: Pollok Country Park.
Exhibitions & Events 2003 : 15 Mar to 5 Jan: Knights and Castles.
Map Ref: 24

Clydebuilt - Scottish Maritime Museum

Kings Inch Road, Braehead, Glasgow G51 4BN   Tel: 0141 886 1013   Fax: 0141 886 1015
Email: clydebuilt@tinyworld.co.uk

The story of Glasgow, its river and people over 300 years from tobacco to shipbuilding with floating exhibits.

Opening Times: Mon to Thu & Sat 10:00-18:00 Sun 11:00-17:00. Closed Fri. Admission: Adult £3.50, Child/OAP £1.75, Family £8.00. Location: Next to Braehead Shopping Centre.
Map Ref: 24

Collins Gallery

University of Strathclyde, 22 Richmond Street, Glasgow G1 1XQ   Tel: 0141 548 2558
Fax: 0141 552 4053   Email: collinsgallery@strath.ac.uk
Web: www.collinsgallery.strath.ac.uk/collections

Lively, annual programme of temporary exhibitions covering contemporary Fine and Applied Art from British and International artists, both new and established. Artwork is usually for sale.

Opening Times: Mon to Fri 10:00-17:00, Sat 12:00-16:00. Closed Sun, public holidays and exhibition installations. Admission: Free. Location: City centre, five minute walk from railway stations and underground.
Map Ref: 24

David Livingstone Centre

165 Station Road, Blantyre, Glasgow G72 9BT   Tel: 01698 823140

Scotland's most famous explorer and missionary was born here in Shuttlerow in 1813. Today the 18th century tenement commemorates David Livingstone's life and work.

Opening Times: 1 Apr to 24 Dec Mon to Sat 10:00-17:00, Sun 12:30-17:00. Admission: Adult £3.50, Concession £2.60, Family £9.50. Location: Just off junction 5 of M74 via A725 and A724, in Blantyre.
Map Ref: 25

Fossil Grove

Victoria Park, Glasgow G14 1BN   Tel: 0141 950 1448

330 million year old fossilised tree stumps. The fossils represented the giant clubmoss, which grew in swampy tropical forests during the carboniferous or coal age. Designated a Site of Special Scientific Interest by Scottish National Heritage.

Opening Times: Apr to Sep. Admission: Free.
Location: Victoria Park.   Map Ref: 24

Gallery of Modern Art

Queen Street, Glasgow G1 3AZ   Tel: 0141 229 1996

Opened in 1996, the gallery is housed in the elegant, neo-classical Royal Exchange Building, in the heart of Glasgow city centre. The displays are constantly changing as a result of an active programme of temporary exhibitions and new acquisitions. The Gallery of Modern Art aims to widen public access to contemporary art; in particular targeting young adults aged 16-25 years. A thought-provoking programme of temporary exhibitions and workshops focuses upon contemporary social issues, often featuring groups marginalized in today's society.

Opening Times: Mon to Thu & Sat 10:00-17:00, Fri & Sun 11:00-17:00. Admission: Free. Location: In city centre. Exhibitions & Events 2003 : 11 Apr to 29 Sep: Sanctuary - an exhibition of contemporary art on themes around freedom & asylum, featuring works by major living artists.   Map Ref: 24

The Glasgow School of Art

167 Renfrew Street, Glasgow G3 6RQ   Tel / Fax: 0141 353 4526   Email: shop@gsa.ac.uk
Web: www.gsa.ac.uk

Charles Rennie MacKintosh's architectural masterpiece. Still a working art school, the regular guided tours let visitors see inside this fascinating building that includes the breathtaking MacKintosh Library.

Opening Times: Tour times: Mon to Fri 11:00 & 14:00, Sat 10:30 & 11:30. Additional times in Jul & Aug Sat 13:00, Sun 10:30, 11:30 & 13:00. Admission: Adult £5.00, Concession £4.00.
Location: City centre, 15 minute walk from Queen Street Station.   Map Ref: 24

Key to Classifications

see Classifications Index on page 413

Anthropology	Jewellery	Railway
Archaeological	Literature & Libraries	Religion
Art Galleries	Maritime	Roman
Arts, Crafts & Textiles	Military & Defence	Science - Earth
China, Glass & Ceramics	Mills - Water & Wind	& Planetary
Communications	Multicultural	Sculpture
Egyptian	Music & Theatre	Sporting History
Fashion	Natural History	Stately Homes
Geology	Oriental	Toy & Childhood
Health & Medicine	Palaces	Transport
Horticultural	Police, Prisons & Dungeons	Victoriana

The Mackintosh House

Hunterian Art Gallery   ♿ ●

University of Glasgow, Hillhead Street, Glasgow G12 8QQ
Tel: 0141 330 5434 Fax: 0141 330 3618
Email: hunter@museum.gla.ac.uk Web: www.hunterian.gla.ac.uk

The Hunterian Art Gallery holds a remarkable collection of European art. The founding collection of Dr William Hunter includes outstanding paintings by Rembrandt, Koninck, Chardin and Stubbs. Unrivalled holdings of work by James McNeil Whistler including paintings, pastels and prints. A popular feature of the Charles Rennie Mackintosh collection is the reconstruction of the interiors of The Mackintosh House. There are major displays of paintings by the Scottish Colourists, Fergussion, Peploe, Cadell and Hunter. The *graphics collection, one of the most important in Scotland, holds some 30,000 prints. These may be seen in the Print Room by prior appointment or in the Gallery's exhibition programme. Selections from the collection can be seen in regular exhibitions drawn from the Print Room.*

Red & Black: The Fan,
by J M Whistler

Opening Times: Mon to Sat 09:30-17:00. Closed Sun. Mackintosh House closes daily 12:30-13:30. Admission: Free. Location: In Westend of Glasgow, 15 minutes from city centre. Exhibitions & Events 2003 : For Exhibitions and Events please telephone for details. **Map Ref: 24**

Hunterian Museum   ♿

The University of Glasgow, University Avenue, Glasgow G12 8QQ Tel: 0141 330 4221
Fax: 0141 330 3617 Email: hunter@museum.gla.ac.uk Web: www.hunterian.gla.ac.uk

The Bearsden Shark: photo JK Ingham.

Scotland's first public museum was established in 1807 based on the vast collections of Dr William Hunter (1718-83). A student at Glasgow University in the 1730s, Dr Hunter later acquired fame and fortune as a physician and medical teacher in London. Many items from his valuable collect-ions are on display.
Since Dr Hunter's time, the collections have grown into one *of the largest collections in the United Kingdom with new and exciting additions every year. The Hunterian Museum is located within the Gothic splendour of the University of Glasgow. It has unique exhibits of Romans in Scotland, Scottish fossils including the world famous 330 million year old Bearsden shark, dinosaurs from Scotland, Scottish minerals including a large unique star sapphire, of the* other treasures from around the world and beyond. The new Kelvin Gallery occasionally houses spectacular temporary exhibitions.

One of the largest ancient
coin collections in Britain

Opening Times: Mon to Sat 09:30-17:00. Closed Sun & BH. Admission: Free. Location: In West End of Glasgow, part of University of Glasgow, campus. **Map Ref: 24**

Kelvingrove Art Gallery & Museum   ☞ ♿ ● ▯ 🛒

Kelvingrove, Glasgow G3 8AG
Tel: 0141 287 2699

Kelvingrove is home to one of the finest civic collections in Europe. The fine art displays offer Old Masters, including works by Filippino Lippi, Botticelli, and Rembrandt. There is also a notable collection of French 19th century paintings and of course of Scottish art, including works by
Kelvingrove Art Gallery & Museum

GLASGOW *(continued)*

Charles Rennie Mackintosh. The arms and armour displays are among the best outside London and include a set of horse armour made for the Earl of Pembroke, while other galleries feature Egyptology, Scottish archaeology and ethnography. The natural history collections range from the time of the dinosaurs to the present and feature, including amongst other animals Sir Roger the Elephant, a popular children's favourite.

Opening Times: Mon to Thu & Sat 10:00-17:00, Fri & Sun 11:00-17:00. Admission: Free. Location: 20 minutes from town centre. Exhibitions & Events 2003 : Kelvingrove Art Gallery & Museum is closing in July 2003 and will re-open in 2006. From April 2003 the art treasures of Kelvingrove will be displayed in the McLillan Galleries, 270 Sauchiehall Street, 0141 565 4100.   Map Ref: 24

Milanese Armour

Museum of Transport
Kelvin Hall, 1 Bunhouse Road, Glasgow G3 8DP   Tel: 0141 287 2720
Fax: 0141 287 2692

The history of transport and technology in Glasgow. Horse-drawn vehicles, the world's oldest bicycle, cars, fire engines, trains, locomotives and ship models illustrating the history of Clyde shipbuilding. Kelvin Way recreates an old Glasgow street with a cinema showing films about Glasgow transport.

Opening Times: Mon to Thu & Sat 10:00-17:00, Fri & Sun 11:00-17:00. Admission: Free.   Map Ref: 24

The Clyde Room: models from the great days of Glasgow shipyards

Peoples Palace Museum
Glasgow Green, Glasgow G40 1AT   Tel: 0141 554 0223
Fax: 0141 550 0892

The historical, social and cultural history of Glasgow, especially the East End, presented through a range of displays including audio-visual shows and reconstructions including a flat, a shop and an air-raid shelter. Objects range from suffragette banners to Billy Connolly's banana boots.

Opening Times: Mon to Thu & Sat 10:00-17:00, Fri & Sun 11:00-17:00. Admission: Free.   Map Ref: 24

The Big Yin: Billy Connolly's stage costume

Pollok House

2060 Pollokshaws Road, Glasgow G43 1AT   Tel: 0141 616 6410   Fax: 0141 616 6521

The Maxwell family is known to have been established at Pollok by 1269. The present house (c.1750) replaced three earlier structures and was extended in 1890. It is set within Pollok Country Park, also the home of the Burrell Collection. The house contains an internationally important collection of paintings, silver and ceramics, displayed as they were around 1931.

Opening Times: Daily 10:00-17:00. Closed Xmas & New Year. Admission: Adult £5.00, Concession £3.75, Family £13.50. Location: Off junctions 1 or 2 of M77, follow signs for Burrell Collection, three miles south of Glasgow's city centre.   Map Ref: 24

Guided or Private Tours	Disabled Access	Gift Shop or Sales Point	Café or Refreshments	Restaurant	Car Parking

Provands Lordship

3 Castle Street, Glasgow G4 0RB Tel: 0141 553 2557 Fax: 0141 552 4744

The oldest house in Glasgow, built in 1471 as a manse for the St Nicholas Hospital, just opposite Glasgow Cathedral. Period display and furniture. Tranquil recreated medieval herb garden.

Opening Times: Mon to Thu & Sat 10:00-17:00, Fri & Sun 11:00-17:00. Admission: Free. Map Ref: 24

Historic domestic interior

Royal Highland Fusiliers Regimental Museum

518 Sauchiehall Street, Glasgow G2 3LW Tel: 0141 332 0961 Fax: 0141 353 1493
Email: assregsec@rhf.org.uk Web: www.rhf.org.uk

The museum tells the story of three hundred and thirty years continuous service with the use of silver, weapons, artwork, medals, uniforms etc.

Opening Times: Mon to Fri 08:30-16:00. Admission: Free. Location: Charring Cross, three minutes from underground station. Map Ref: 24

St Mungo Museum of Religious Life & Art

2 Castle Street, Glasgow G4 0RH Tel: 0141 553 2557
Fax: 0141 552 4744

The museum explores the importance of religion in people's lives across the world and through time. There are galleries of religious art, including Dali's Christ of St John of the Cross, religious life (and death) and Britain's first permanent Zen garden, symbolising the harmony between people and nature.

Opening Times: Mon to Thu & Sat 10:00-17:00, Fri & Sun 11:00-17:00. Admission: Free. Map Ref: 24

Salvador Dali, Christ of St John of the Cross

Scotland Street School, Museum of Education

225 Scotland Street, Glasgow G5 8QB Tel: 0141 287 0500 Fax: 0141 287 0515

The building is a Glasgow Board School designed by Charles Rennie Mackintosh. The collection relates to education in the region from c.1830 to the present day, including furniture, books, photographs, documents, toys and costumes. Reconstructed period classroom and craft room.

Opening Times: Mon to Thu & Sat 10:00-17:00, Fri & Sun 11:00-17:00. Admission: Free. Location: On south side of city. Map Ref: 24

Classroom

Tenement House

145 Buccleuch Street, Glasgow G3 6QN Tel: 0141 333 0183

Glasgow is associated with tenements. This first-floor flat is a typical late Victorian example, consisting of four rooms and retaining most of its original features such as its bed recesses, kitchen range, coal bunker and bathroom.

Opening Times: 1 Mar to 31 Oct daily 12:00-17:00. Admission: Adult £3.50, Concession £2.60, Family £9.50. Map Ref: 24

Guided or Private Tours	Disabled Access	Gift Shop or Sales Point	Café or Refreshments	Restaurant	Car Parking

GORDON *Scottish Borders*

Mellerstain House

Gordon TD3 6LG Tel: 01573 410225 Fax: 01573 410636
Email: mellerstein.house@virgin.net   Web: www.muses.calligrafix.co.uk/mellerstain

Superb Adam Mansion. Fine interior decorations and plasterwork. Original period furniture. Art collection with portraits by Van Dyke, Ramsay, Gainsborough, Maes and Van Der Helst. Beautiful grounds, gardens and lakeside walk.

Opening Times: Easter weekend 1 May to 30 Sep Sun to Fri 12:30-17:00. Grounds: 11:30-18:00. Oct Sat & Sun 12:30-17:00. Admission: Adult £5.50, Child £3.00, Concession £5.00. Gardens £3.00.   Location: Six miles north of Kelso on A6089, 40 miles south of Edinburgh via A68.   Map Ref: 26

GOREBRIDGE *Midlothian*

Arniston House

Gorebridge EH23 4RY   Tel / Fax: 01875 830515   Email: henrietta.d.bekker2@btinternet.com
Web: www.arniston-house.co.uk

The Dundas family home, a William Adam mansion house. Fine stucco work, Scottish portraiture and period furniture.

Opening Times: Apr, May & Jun Tue & Wed tours at 14:00 & 15:30. Jul to Mid Sep Sun to Fri tours at 14:00 & 15:30. Grounds open at 12:00. Admission: Adult £5.00, Child £2.00, Concession £4.00.   Location: Turn off A7 onto B6372 towards Temple. Arniston is one mile on the right.   Map Ref: 27

GREENOCK *Inverclyde*

McLean Museum & Art Gallery

15 Kelly Street, Greenock PA16 8JX Tel: 01475 715624 Fax: 01475 715626
Email: val.boa@inverclyde.gov.uk Web: www.inverclyde.gov.uk/museum/index.htm

Permanent displays on local history, James Watt, ship and engine models, big game mounts and items from foreign lands. Temporary exhibition programme and fine art collection.

Opening Times: Mon to Sat 10:00-17:00. Closed Sun & BH. Admission: Free.
Location: West end of Greenock, close to bus station and Greenock West Railway Station.
Map Ref: 28

HAWICK *Scottish Borders*

Drumlanrigs Tower

High Street, Hawick Tel: 01450 377615 Fax: 01450 378506

Hawick's oldest building is a fortified tower enveloped inside an 18th century town house. The Tower displays the history of Hawick during medieval times, to the industrial revolution to the present day.

Opening Times: Easter to Oct Mon to Sat 10:00-17:00, Sun 12:00-17:00. Jun & Sep closed 17:30. Jul & Aug closed 18:00. Admission: Adult £2.50, SBC Residents Free.   Map Ref: 29

Hawick Museum & the Scott Gallery

Wilton Lodge Park, Hawick TD9 7JL Tel: 01450 373457 Fax: 01450 378506
Email: fionacolton@hotmail.com

The museum and custom-built art gallery house the Jimmie Guthrie Motorcycle exhibition and the Scott Art Gallery. The Museum and Scott Gallery reflect the town's history and provide a venue for visiting exhibitions.

Opening Times: Apr to Sep Mon to Fri 10:00-12:00 & 13:00-17:00, Sat & Sun 14:00-17:00. Oct to Mar Mon to Fri 13:00-16:00, Sun 14:00-16:00. Admission: Free. Location: In local park, ten minute walk from town centre.   Map Ref: 29

INNERLEITHEN *Scottish Borders*

Traquair House

Innerleithen EH44 6PW Tel: 01896 830323 Fax: 01896 830639
Email: enquiries@traquair.co.uk Web: www.traquair.co.uk

Where Alexander I signed a charter over 800 years ago and where the 'modern wings' were completed in 1680. Once a pleasure ground for Scottish kings in times of peace, then a refuge for Catholic priests in times of terror.

Opening Times: Jun to Aug 10:30-17:30, Oct 12:30-16:30.   Admission: Adult £5.50, Child £3.00, OAP £5.20, Family £16.00.   Location: Innerleithen, one and a half miles from Traquair.

Map Ref: 30

IRVINE *Ayrshire*

Scottish Maritime Museum
Laird Forge Buildings, Gottries Road, Irvine KA12 8QE   Tel: 01294 278283   Fax: 01294 313211   Email: smm@tildesley.fsbusiness.co.uk   Web: www.scottishmaritimemuseum.org

The museum holds Scotland's best collection of smaller ships and boats. Also displayed in former Alexander Stephens of Linthouse shipbuilding engine shop, shipyard machinery and tools.

Opening Times: Apr to Oct 10:00-17:00, Nov to Mar 10:00-16:00.   Admission: Adult £2.50, Child/OAP £1.75, Family £5.00.   Location: Near town centre, two minute walk from Irvine Railway Station.

Map Ref: 31

Vennel Gallery
10 Glasgow Vennel, Irvine KA12 0BD   Tel / Fax: 01294 275059
Email: vennel@globalnet.co.uk   Web: www.northayrshiremuseums.org.uk

The Gallery has a programme of changing exhibitions of contemporary art and crafts. The gallery includes the Heckling Shop and the Lodging House where Robert Burns worked and lived in 1781.

Opening Times: Fri to Sun 10:00-13:00 & 14:00-17:00. Closed Wed.   Admission: Free.
Location: Just down the lane from The Porthead Tavern.

Map Ref: 31

ISLE OF ARRAN *Ayrshire*

Arran Heritage Museum
Rosaburn, Brodick, Isle of Arran KA27 8DP   Tel: 01770 302636
Email: arranmuseum@biinternet.com

The museum reflects the social history, archaeology and geology of the island.

Opening Times: Apr to Oct daily 10:30-16:30.   Admission: Adult £2.25, Child £1.00, OAP £1.50, Family £6.00.   Location: One mile from ferry terminal on main road north.   Map Ref: 32

Brodick Castle Gardens & Country Park
Brodick, Isle of Arran KA27 8HY   Tel: 01770 302202   Fax: 01770 302312

The site of this ancient seat of the Dukes of Hamilton was a fortress even in Viking times. The 13th century fortified tower was developed in the 16th century and extended by Cromwell in the 17th century. Some furniture dates from the 17th century, with superb paintings, porcelain and silver collected by the Hamiltons and William Beckford, whose daughter was married to the 10th Duke of Hamilton.

Opening Times: 1 Apr to 31 Oct daily 11:00-16:30 (closes 15:30 in Oct). Reception centre, shop & restaurant - also open 1 Nov to 21 Dec Fri to Sun 10:00-15:30.   Admission: Adult £7.00, Concession £5.25, Family £19.00.   Location: Ferry from Ardrossan to Brodick and connecting bus to Reception Centre.

Brodick Castle - Entrance Hall

Map Ref: 32

JEDBURGH *Scottish Borders*

Harestanes Countryside Visitor Centre
Harestanes, Ancrum, Jedburgh TD8 6UQ   Tel: 01835 830306   Fax: 01835 830734

Countryside centre.

Opening Times: Easter to Oct Mon to Sun 10:00-17:00.   Admission: Free.   Location: Off main A68 road.

Map Ref: 33

Jedburgh Castle Jail & Museum

Castlegate, Jedburgh TD8 6QD   Tel: 01835 863254   Fax: 01835 864750

Comprehensive guide to Jedburgh's history. Also jail cells in two two-storey blocks. Garden and grounds for picnics and functions. Audio tours - touch screen and video.

Opening Times: Apr to Oct Mon to Sat 10:00-16:30, Sun 13:00-16:00.   Admission: Adult £2.00, Child Free, Concession £1.50.   Location: Within walking distance of the town.   Map Ref: 34

Mary Queen of Scots House

Queen Street, Jedburgh TD8 6EN   Tel / Fax: 01835 863331

Museum dedicated to Mary Queen of Scots.

Opening Times: Mar to Nov Mon to Sat 10:00-16:30, Sun 11:00-16:30.   Admission: Adult £2.50, SBC Residents Free.   Location: Five minute walk from town centre.   Map Ref: 34

Floors Castle

Roxburghe Estates Office, Kelso TD5 7SF
Tel: 01573 223333 Fax: 01573 226056
Email: marketing@floorscastle.com   Web: www.floorscastle.com

The largest inhabited castle in Scotland is home to the Duke of Roxburghe. The interiors are fiilled with outstanding collection o French 17th and 18th century furniture, magnifiicent tapestries Chinese and European porcelain and many other fiine works of art Enhanced with family photographs and beautiful estate grown plants.

Opening Times: 5 Apr to 26 Oct 10:00-16:30. Last admission 16:00.   Admission: Adult £5.75, Child £3.25, OAP/Student £4.75, Under 5s Free. Group rates available.   Location: Roxburghe Estate Office.   Map Ref: 35

Late 17th Century
Japanese Cabinet-on-Stand

Dean Castle

Dean Road, Kilmarnock KA3 1XB   Tel: 01563 574916   Fax: 01563 554720
Email: bruce.morgan@east-ayrshire.gov.uk

Dean Castle is a magnificent collection of restored buildings dating from the 1350s. Important collections of arms and armour, musical instruments and manuscripts by Robert Burns are on display in public rooms.

Opening Times: Apr to Oct 12:00-17:00. Oct to Apr Sat & Sun only 12:00-16:00. Admission: Free.   Location: 15 minutes walk from Kilmarnock Railway Station, set in grounds off the main road into Kilmarnock.   Map Ref: 36

Dick Institute

Elmbank Avenue, Kilmarnock KA1 3BU   Tel: 01563 554343   Fax: 01563 554344
Email: jason.sutcliffe@east-ayrshire.gov.uk

Temporary and permanent exhibitions over two floors of this grand Victorian building. Fine art, social and natural history collections are upstairs, whilst downstairs galleries house temporary exhibitions.

Opening Times: Mon & Tue, Thu & Fri 09:00-20:00, Wed & Sat 09:00-17:00.   Admission: Free.   Location: Near Kilmarnock town centre, ten minutes from railway station.   Map Ref: 36

Dalgarven Mill Museum of Ayrshire Country Life & Costume

Dalgarven Mill Trust, Dalgarven, Kilwinning KA13 6PL   Tel / Fax: 01294 552448
Email: admin@dalgarvenmill.org.uk   Web: www.dalgarvenmill.org.uk

Collection of machinery, memorabilia, furnishings and archives illustrating life in pre-industrial rural Ayrshire. Superb collection of costume spanning two centuries from 1775, beautifully displayed with changing exhibitions.

Opening Times: Easter to end Oct Tue to Sun 10:00-17:00. Nov to Easter Tue to Fri 10:00-16:00, Sat & Sun 10:00-17:00.   Admission: Admission charged.   Location: Rural situation, two miles from Kilwinning, two miles from Dalry on A737.   Map Ref: 37

KILWINNING *(continued)*

Kilwinning Abbey Tower
Main Street, Kilwinning   Tel / Fax: 01294 464174   Email: namuseum@globalnet.co.uk
Web: www.northayrshiremuseums.org.uk

The tower displays the fascinating history of the Abbey and town of Kilwinning. It is also the home of the world's oldest archery competition.

Opening Times: Jun to Sep Thu & Sun 14:00-16:00, Fri & Sat 10:30-12:30 & 14:00-17:00.
Admission: Free.   Location: In town centre in Abbey Grounds.   Map Ref: 37

KIRKCUDBRIGHT *Dumfries & Galloway*

Stewartry Museum
St Mary Street, Kirkcudbright DG6 4AQ   Tel / Fax: 01557 331643
Email: DavidD@dumgal.gov.uk   Web: www.dumgal.gov.uk/museums

The Stewartry Museum was founded in 1879. As the collections grew, the present purpose-built museum was opened in 1893 and it still retains its charm as a traditional late Victorian museum. Its collections chiefly relate to the human and natural history of the Stewartry. The permanent collection includes the 'Siller Gun' - Britain's earliest surviving sporting trophy, and works by Kirkcudbrightshire artists including Jessie M King. Temporary exhibitions highlight different aspects of the collection and Museums Service activities.

Opening Times: Mon to Sat 11:00-16:00. Longer hours Jun to Sep including Sun 14:00-17:00.
Location: Town Centre.   Map Ref: 38

Tolbooth Art Centre
High Street, Kirkcudbright DG6 4JL   Tel: 01557 331556   Fax: 01557 331643
Email: DavidD@dumgal.gov.uk   Web: www.dumgal.gov.uk/museums

The Tolbooth Art Centre is based in Kirkcudbright's 17th century Tolbooth. Find out about Kirkcudbright's famous artists, such as E A Hornel, Jessie M King, E A Taylor and Charles Oppenheimer in the audio-visual shows and see their works on permanent display. The top floor of the Tolbooth, formerly the debtor's prison, is now used as a gallery for ever changing contemporary art and craft exhibitions.

Opening Times: Mon to Sat 11:00-16:00. Longer hours Jun to Sep including Sun 14:00-17:00.
Admission: Adult £1.50, Child Free, Concession 75p.   Location: Town centre.   Map Ref: 38

LANARK

New Lanark Visitor Centre
New Lanark World Heritage Village, Mill 3, Lanark ML11 9DB   Tel: 01555 661345   Fax: 01555 665738   Email: development@newlanark.org   Web: www.newlanark.org

Close to the Falls of Clyde, the 200 year old cotton mill village of New Lanark has been saved for future generations as a living community and lasting monument to Robert Owen, mill owner and social pioneer.

Opening Times: Daily 11:00-17:00.   Admission: Adult £4.95, Concession £3.95.   Location: By Lanark, signposted from all major routes (M74 and M8).   Map Ref: 39

LANGBANK *Renfrewshire*

The Dolly Mixture
Finlaystone Country Estate, Langbank PA14 6TJ   Tel / Fax: 01475 540285
Email: info@finlaystone.co.uk   Web: www.finlaystone.co.uk

All sorts of dolls from around the world, collected since 1903 by mother and daughter Clare Spurgin and Jane MacMillan. Set within a country estate with extensive gardens and woodlands.

Opening Times: Apr to Sep 12:00-17:00. Oct to Mar Sat & Sun 12:00-17:00.
Admission: Estate: Adult £3.00, Child/OAP £2.00. Museum: 50p.   Location: Ten minutes west Glasgow Airport on A8.   Map Ref: 40

LARGS *Ayrshire*

Kelburn Castle

Fairlie, Largs KA29 0BE   Tel: 01475 568685   Fax: 01475 568121
Email: admin@kelburncountrycentre.com   Web: www.kelburncountrycentre.com

The home of the Earls of Glasgow, probably the oldest castle in Scotland to have been continuously inhabited by the same family, incorporating a Norman Keep (1200), a Z-plan castle (1580), a 1700 mansion house and a Victorian wing (1882). Famous glen, unique trees and historic gardens. Also exhibitions, riding school, falconry centre, children's play areas and the 'Secret Forest'.

Opening Times: Easter to Oct daily 10:00-18:00 (Castle open Jul & Aug or for booked groups).

Admission: Adult £4.50, Child/OAP £3.00 (£1.50 extra for castle).   Location: On the A78 between Largs and Fairlie.

Map Ref: 41

LAUDER *Scottish Borders*

Thirlestane Castle

Lauder TD2 6RU   Tel: 01578 722430   Fax: 01578 722761
Email: admin@thirlestancastle.co.uk   Web: www.thirlestanecastle.co.uk

Nestling in the gentle Border Hills, with its rose pink sandstone and fairytale turrets, Thirlestane Castle holds a uniquely important place in Scottish history. It is one of the oldest and finest castles in the land, and home to one of the country's most distinguished families.

Opening Times: Good Friday, Easter Monday, 1 May to end of second week in Oct Mon to Sun 10:30-16:50 (last admissions 15:30)   Admission: Castle & Grounds: Adult £5.50, Child £3.00, OAP £5.00, Family (2 adults and 3 children) £15.00. Grounds only: Adult £2.00, Child £1.00.

The Chinese Room

Map Ref: 42

LINLITHGOW *West Lothian*

Canal Museum

Linlithgow Canal Centre, Canal Basin, Manse Road, Linlithgow EH49 6AJ   Tel: 01506 671215
Email: info@lucs.org.uk   Web: www.lucs.org.uk

Display of photographs, documents, tools and other objects illustrating the history of the Union Canal, its construction, and its working life. Video.

Opening Times: Easter to mid Oct Sat & Sun 14:00-17:00. Jul & Aug daily 14:00-17:00.
Admission: Free.   Location: Five minute walk from Linlithgow Station.

Map Ref: 43

House of the Binns

Linlithgow EH49 7NA   Tel: 0150683 4255

The House of the Binns was built between 1612 and 1630 by Thomas Dalyell. In 1944 Eleanor Dalyell gifted the house to The National Trust for Scotland, along with a fine collection of furniture, porcelain and family portraits.

Opening Times: House: 1 Jun to 30 Sep daily expect Fri 14:00-17:00. Parkland: 1 Apr to 31 Oct daily 10:00-17:00, 1 Nov to 31 Mar daily 10:00-16:00.   Admission: Adult £5.00, Child/OAP/Concession/Student £3.75, Family £13.50, National Trust Member Free.
Location: On top of a hill, three quarters of a mile from main road, four miles east of Linlithgow and railway station.

Map Ref: 43

Almond Valley Heritage Trust

Livingston Mill, Millfield, Livingston EH54 7AR
Tel: 01506 414957 Fax: 01506 497771
Email: rac@almondvalley.co.uk Web: www.almondvalley.co.uk

An innovative museum exploring the history and environment of West Lothian. Includes displays of Scotland's Shale Oil industry and other local manufacturing. Health, food, sanitation and hands-on environment science. Working watermill, farm, narrow-gauge railway, nature trail and play areas.

Opening Times: Daily 10:00-17:00. Admission: Adult £2.80, Child/OAP £1.60, Family (2 adult and 4 children) £8.00.
Location: Two miles from junction 3 on the M8.   Map Ref: 44

Culzean Castle & Country Park

Maybole KA19 8LE Tel: 01655 884455 Fax: 01655 884503 Email: culzean@nts.org.uk
Web: www.culzeancastle.net

Robert Adam converted the fortified tower house into an elegant residence for David Kennedy, 10th Earl of Cassillis, between 1777 and 1792. The Castle contains a fine collection of paintings and furniture, and a display of weapons in the Armoury. The Country Park contains a wealth of natural and historical interest with garden areas including a Walled Garden and terraced Fountain Court.

Opening Times: Castle: 1 Apr to 31 Oct daily 10:30-17:00. Visitor Centre: 1 Apr to 31 Oct daily 09:00-17:30, 1 Nov to 31 Mar, Sat & Sun 11:00-16:00. Country Park: Daily 09:30 to sunset. Admission: Combined ticket: Adult £9.00, Concession £6.50, Family £23.00. Country Park only: Adult £5.00, Concession £3.75, Family £13.50. Location: 12 miles south of Ayr on A719, four miles west of Maybole, off A77.   Map Ref: 45

Lillie Art Gallery

East Dunbartonshire Museums, Station Road, Milngavie G62 8BZ Tel: 0141 578 8847

20th century Scottish paintings, drawing by Joan Eardley (1921-1963), paintings, watercolours and etchings by Robert Lillie (1867-1949) and a small collection of 20th century Scottish ceramics.

Opening Times: Tue to Sat 10:00-13:00 & 14:00-17:00. Admission: Free. Location: Opposite Milngavie Railway Station. A short drive from Glasgow City Centre, off the A81.   Map Ref: 46

Motherwell Heritage Centre

1 High Road, Motherwell ML1 3HU Tel: 01698 251000 Fax: 01698 268867
Email: devaneyr@northlan.gov.uk Web: motherwellheritage.freeserve.com

The gallery features a year round programme of both in-house and touring exhibitions. Don't miss the permanent 'Technopolis' display on the area's heritage. Also local history research library.

Opening Times: Wed to Sat 10:00-17:00, Thu 10:00-19:00. Sun 12:00-17:00. Closed Mon and Tue. Admission: Free. Location: Top of Hamilton Road, by Bentley Hotel, three minutes from Motherwell Station.   Map Ref: 47

Edinburgh, Glasgow & Southern Scotland

Creetown Gem Rock Museum

Chain Road, Creetown, Newton Stewart DG8 7HJ Tel: 01671 820357 Fax: 01671 820554
Email: gem.rock@btinternet.com Web: www.gemrock.net

Outstanding collection and displays of crystals, gemstones, minerals and fossil. With many world class examples including British and foreign. Hand carved gemstones.

Opening Times: Good Friday to Sep daily 09:30-17:30, Oct to Nov & Mar to Good Friday daily 10:00-16:00, Dec to Feb Sat & Sun 10:00-16:00. Closed Xmas & New Year. Admission: Adult £3.25, Concession £2.75, Child 5-15 years £1.75, Family £8.25. Location: In the village of Creetown, follow signposts from village square.
Map Ref: 48

Scottish Mining Museum

Lady Victoria Colliery, Newtongrange EH22 4QN Tel: 0131 663 7519 Fax: 0131 654 1618
Email: enquiries@scottishminingmuseum.com Web: www.scottishminingmuseum.com

Five star visitor attraction. Scotland's National Coal Mining Museum, historic buildings and extensive collections and archives. Retail, catering, events and hospitality venue.

Opening Times: Feb to Oct daily 10:00-17:00, Nov to Feb 10:00-16:00. Admission: Adult £4.00, Child/OAP £2.20, Family £10.00. Group: Adult £3.50, Concession £2.00.
Location: Newtongrange, eight miles from Edinburgh on A7.
Map Ref: 49

Museum of Flight

East Fortune Airfield, North Berwick EH39 5LF
Tel: 01620 880308 Fax: 01620 880355
Email: info@nms.ac.uk Web: www.nms.ac.uk/flight

Scotland's national aviation collection. Some of the most extraordinary machines in the world map the development of human flight. See the oldest aircraft in Britain, an original Wright Brothers' engine, Europe's biggest rocket and some of the finest machines ever built. Based at historic East Fortune Airfield - launch site of the R34 Airship, the first aircraft to cross the Atlantic, east to west.

Opening Times: Daily 10:00-17:00, Jul & Aug 10:00-18:00.
Admission: Adult £3.00, Child Free, Concessions £1.50.
Location: 20 miles east of Edinburgh.
Map Ref: 50

Coats Observatory

49 Oakshaw Street West, Paisley PA1 2DR Tel: 0141 889 2013 Fax: 0141 889 9240
Email: museum-els@renfrewshire.gov.uk Web: www.renfrewshire.gov.uk

Architecturally stunning, the Observatory was built by the Coats family in 1883 and is a working Victorian Observatory. Displays on astronomy, astronautics, seismology and meteorology. Meteorological and astronomical information has been recorded here since 1882. Public telescopic viewing, weather permitting, on Thursday evenings in winter. Very active Renfrewshire Astronomical Society.

Opening Times: Tue to Sat 10:00-17:00, Sun 14:00-17:00. Oct to Mar Thu 19:00-21:30.
Admission: Free. Location: Access via Oakshaw Street or through Paisley Museum. Less than ten minutes from railway station.
Map Ref: 51

Paisley Museum & Art Galleries

High Street, Paisley PA1 2BA Tel: 0141 889 3151
Fax: 0141 889 9240
Email: museum.els@renfrewshire.gov.uk
Web: www.renfrewshire.gov.uk

Home to the world's largest collection of Paisley Shawls, a selection of which are always on display. Art Galleries show 19th century Scottish paintings and studio ceramics. Also displays on local and natural history. Museum shop has wide range of Paisley pattern products and exclusive

PAISLEY Renfrewshire (continued)

gifts. A-listed historic 1871 building.

Opening Times: Tue to Sat 10:00-17:00, Sun 14:00-16:00, BH 10:00-17:00. Admission: Free. Location: Less than ten minute walk from Paisley Gilmour Street Railway Station. Map Ref: 51

PEEBLES Scottish Borders

Cornice Museum of Ornamental Plasterwork

Innerleithen Road, Peebles EH45 8BA   Tel / Fax: 01721 720212

Recreation of a plasterers casting workshop from around 1900 with probably the largest collection of plaster moulds in the country.

Opening Times: Mon to Thu 10:00-12:00 & 14:00-16:00, Fri 10:00-12:00 & 14:00-15:30. Closed Sat & Sun, 2 weeks at Xmas & New Year, 1 week in Apr, 1st 2 weeks of Aug. Admission: Free. Location: Near town centre, three minute walk from Peebles Town Centre bus stop. Map Ref: 52

Tweeddale Museum

Chambers Institute, High Street, Peebles EH45 8AJ   Tel: 01721 724820   Fax: 01721 724424 Email: rhannay@scotborders.gov.uk

Local history museum.

Opening Times: Mon to Fri 10:00-12:00 & 14:00-17:00, Apr to Oct also Sat 10:00-13:00 & 14:00-16:00. Closed Sun. Admission: Free. Location: In town centre. Map Ref: 52

PRESTONPANS East Lothian

Prestongrange Industrial Heritage Museum

Morison's Haven, Prestongrange, Prestonpans EH32 9RX   Tel: 0131 653 2904   Fax: 01620 828201   Email: elms@elothian-museums.demon.co.uk   Web: www.prestongrangemuseum.org

Prestongrange Museum is based in the Old Prestongrange Colliery at Morison's Haven, Prestonpans. There is a Cornish bean engine on site, unique to Scotland. We also feature an annual educational exhibition.

Opening Times: Apr to Sep 11:00-16:00. Admission: Free. Location: Between Musselburgh and Prestonpans, easily accessible from the A1 and on public transport. Map Ref: 53

RENFREW

Renfrew Community Museum

The Brown Institute, 41 Canal Street, Renfrew PA4 8QA   Tel: 0141 886 3149   Fax: 0141 886 2300   Email: museums.els@renfrewshire.gov.uk   Web: www.renfrewshire.gov.uk

This museum was opened for the Renfrew 600 Celebrations in 1997 in the former Brown Institute Building, when Renfrew celebrated 600 years of Royal Burgh status. Displays of local history.

Opening Times: Tue to Sat 10:00-13:00 & 14:00-17:00. Admission: Free. Location: Few minutes walk from centre of Renfrew. Map Ref: 54

SALTCOATS Ayrshire

North Ayrshire Museum

Manse Street, Kirkgate, Saltcoats KA21 5AA   Tel / Fax: 01294 464174 Email: namuseum@globalnet.co.uk   Web: www.northayrshiremuseums.org.uk

The Museum shows the history of North Ayrshire with displays on archaeology, costume, transport and popular culture. There is a maritime history section and a reconstruction of an Ayrshire cottage interior.

Opening Times: Mon to Sat 10:00-13:00 & 14:00-17:00, closed Wed. Admission: Free. Location: In church grounds between Safeways and the Post Office. Map Ref: 55

SANQUHAR Dumfries & Galloway

Sanquhar Tolbooth Museum

High Street, Sanquhar DG4 6BN   Tel: 01659 50186   Fax: 01387 265081 Email: dumfriesmuseum@dumgal.gov.uk   Web: www.dumgal.gov.uk/museums

Discover Sanquhar's world famous knitting tradition and the story of the mines and miners of Sanquhar and Kirkconnel. How did the ordinary people of Upper Nithsdale live and work? All this and more can be found in the town's fine 18th century Tolbooth.

Opening Times: Apr to Sep Tue to Sat 10:00-13:00 & 14:00-17:00, Sun 14:00-17:00. Admission: Free. Location: On High Street. Map Ref: 56

SELKIRK *Scottish Borders*

Bowhill House & Country Park
Bowhill, Selkirk TD7 5ET   Tel / Fax: 01750 22204   Email: bht@buccleuch.com

Scottish Borders home of the Duke and Duchess of Buccleuch set in magnificent scenery. Outstanding collection of art, silverware, porcelain and French furniture. Historic relics include Monmouth's saddle and execution shirt, Sir Walter Scott's plaid and some proof editions. Queen Victoria's letters and gifts to successive Duchess of Buccleuch, her Mistress of the Robes.

Opening Times: House: Jul daily 13:00-17:00. Country Park: May to Aug daily except Fri. Admission: Ho00, OAP/Group £4.00, Under 5s/Disabled Free. Country Park: Adult £1.00, Child £1.00, Under 5s/Disabled Free.

Bowhill set amid magnificent scenery

Location: Three miles west of Selkirk on A708.   Map Ref: 57

Halliwells House Museum
Halliwells Close, Market Place, Selkirk TD7 4BL   Tel: 01750 20096/20054

Recreated ironmongers shop and local Tourist Information Centre.

Opening Times: Easter to Sep Mon to Sat 10:00-17:00, Sun 14:00-16:00. Jul & Aug 9:30-17:30 Sun 14:00-17:00. Oct Mon-Sat 10:00-16:00. Admission: Free. Location: Off Market Place.
                                                                      Map Ref: 57

Sir Walter Scotts Courtroom (Selkirk Town Hall)
Market Place, Selkirk TD7 4BT   Tel: 01750 20096   Fax: 01750 23282
Email: dmabon@scotborders.gov.uk

Museum dedicated to local Sheriff of Selkirk - Sir Walter Scott.

Opening Times: Easter to Sep Mon to Sat 10:00-16:00, Jun to Sep also Sun 14:00-16:00, Oct Mon to Sat 13:00-16:00. Admission: Free. Location: In town centre.   Map Ref: 57

SOUTH QUEENSFERRY *West Lothian*

Dalmeny House
South Queensferry EH30 9TQ   Tel: 0131 331 1888   Fax: 0131 331 1788
Email: linda.edgar@dalmeny.co.uk   Web: www.dalmeny.co.uk

Rothschild 18th century French furniture, tapestries and porcelain. One of the world's most important Napoleonic collections, assembled by the fifth Earl, Prime Minister, historian and owner of three Derby winners.

Opening Times: Jul & Aug Sun, Mon & Tues 14:00-17:30. Last admission 16:30.
Admission: Adult £4.00.   Location: Seven miles from centre of Edinburgh.   Map Ref: 58

Queensferry Museum
53 High Street, South Queensferry EH30 9HP   Tel: 0131 331 5545
Web: www.cac.org.uk

QUEENSFERRY
MUSEUM

Situated in the historic former Royal Burgh of Queensferry, the museum commands magnificent views of the great bridges spanning the Forth. The museum traces the history of the people of Queensferry and Dalmeny, the historic ferry passage to Fife, the construction of the rail and road bridges and takes a look at the wildlife of the Forth estuary.

Opening Times: Mon, Thu, Fri & Sat 10:00-13:00 & 14:15-17:00, Sun 12:00-17:00. Closed Tue & Wed.
                                                                      Map Ref: 58

STRANRAER *Dumfries & Galloway*

Castle of St John
Castle Street, Stranraer DG9 7RT   Tel: 01776 705088   Fax: 01776 705544
Email: JohnPic@dumgal.gov.uk   Web: www.dumgal.gov.uk/museums

The Castle of St John is a medieval tower house. Over the centuries the Castle has been used as a home, a local court, a military garrison and a prison. Videos and reconstructions are used to tell the story of the Castle. There is an activity room for families and children.

Opening Times: Easter to mid Sep Mon to Sat 10:00-13:00 & 14:00-17:00. Admission: Adult £1.20, Child/Concession 60p, Family £3.00. Location: Town centre, within walking distance of ferry terminal.
Map Ref: 59

Stranraer Museum

The Old Town Hall, George Street, Stranraer DG9 7JP   Tel: 01776 705088   Fax: 01776 705835
Email: JohnPic@dumgal.gov.uk   Web: www.dumgal.gov.uk/museums

Displays on archaeology, local history, farming and dairying. Temporary exhibitions held throughout the year and activities for all the family.

Opening Times: Mon to Fri 10:00-17:00, Sat 10:00-13:00 & 14:00-17:00. Closed Xmas & New Year, Easter & May BH. Admission: Free. Location: Near town centre, a short walk from ferry terminal.
Map Ref: 59

Drumlanrig Castle, Gardens & Country Park

Thornhill DG3 4AQ   Tel: 01848 330248   Fax: 01848 331682
Email: bre@drumlanrigcastle.org.uk   Web: www.drumlanrigcastle.org.uk

Dumfriesshire home of the Duke of Buccleuch and Queensberry KT, built between 1679 and 1691 by William Douglas, 1st Duke of Queensberry. Magnificent art collection, including works by Rembrandt, Holbein and Leonardo. Associations with Bonnie Prince Charlie and Mary Queen of Scots. French furniture, 300 year old silver chandelier as well as cabinets made for Louis XIV's Versailles.

Opening Times: Castle: 18 Apr to 21 Apr & 3 May to 7 Sep Mon to Sat 11:00-16:00, Sun 12:00-16:00. Gardens & Country Park: 18 Apr to 30 Sep daily 11:00-17:00. Admission: Castle & Country Park: Adult £6.00, Child £2.00, OAP/Student £4.00, Family (2 adults and 4 children) £14.00. Country Park Only: Adult £3.00, Child £2.00, Family (2 adults and 4 children) £8.00. Location: 18 miles north of Dumfries on A76. 16 miles from M74 at Elvanfoot. Exhibitions & Events 2003 : 3 & 4 May: Drumlanrig Gathering in aid of Macmillian Cancer Relief - includes Vintage and Veteran Car Rally, craft stalls, food fayre, Macmile fun run, mass pipe bands and much more.
Map Ref: 60

Museum of Lead Mining

Wanlockhead ML12 6UT   Tel: 01659 74387   Fax: 01659 74481
Email: brianwmont@goldpan.co.uk   Web: www.leadminingmuseum.co.uk

Scotland's only visitor lead mine. Fabulous mineral collection. Visit 18th and 19th century miners' cottages. Scotland's second oldest miners' library.

Opening Times: Apr to end Oct daily 10:00-17:00. Admission: Adult £3.95, Child £2.50, Concession £2.75, Family £9.80. Group Adult £3.00, Group Child £2.00. Location: Situated in Wanlockhead, Scotland's highest village, signposted from junction 13 and 14 of M74 and A76.
Map Ref: 61

Whitburn Community Museum

Union Road, Whitburn EH47 0AR   Tel: 01501 678050   Email: museums@westlothian.gov.uk
Web: www.wlonline.org

Display on the mining history of the village and its later industrial and social development. Programme of temporary exhibitions.

Opening Times: Mon & Fri 09:30-17:30, Tue & Thu 09:30-20:00, Wed 10:00-17:30, Sat 09:30-13:00. Admission: Free. Location: In town centre, enter through library.
Map Ref: 62

There are few aspects of Scottish history, folklore and legend that cannot be examined within the great variety of museums in this central eastern region of Scotland. St Andrews, Aberdeen, Dundee, Perth and Stirling all have a variety of interesting museums, there are ancient Scottish castles with fine collections, and many smaller towns whose museums display the life, work and aspirations of their locality.

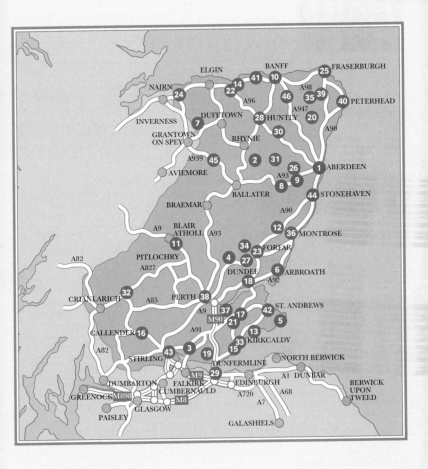

The Red Map References should be used to locate Museums etc on the pages that follow

Aberdeen Art Gallery

Schoolhill, Aberdeen AB10 1FQ   Tel: 01224 523700/523711
Fax: 01224 632133   Email: info@aagm.co.uk
Web: www.aberdeencity.gov.uk

One of the city's most popular tourist attractions, Aberdeen's splendid art gallery houses an important fine art collection with particularly good examples of 19th and 20th century works, a rich and diverse applied art collection and an exciting programme of special exhibitions.

Opening Times: Mon to Sat 10:00-17:00, Sun 14:00-17:00.
Admission: Free.   Location: Centrally located via Belmont Street, from Union Street.
Map Ref: 1

Aberdeen Maritime Museum

Shiprow, Aberdeen AB11 5BY   Tel: 01224 337700   Fax: 01224 213066
Email: info@aagm.co.uk   Web: www.aberdeencity.gov.uk

The city's award-winning maritime museum brings the history of the North Sea to life. View multi-media displays and exciting exhibitions on the offshore oil industry, shipbuilding, fishing and clipper ships, then visit the museum shop and licensed café.

Opening Times: Mon to Sat 10:00-17:00, Sun 12:00-15:00. Admission: Free. Location: Situated facing the harbour, accessible from Union Street via Adelphi.
Map Ref: 1

The Gordon Highlanders Museum

St Lukes, Viewfield Road, Aberdeen AB15 7XH   Tel: 01224 311200   Fax: 01224 319323
Email: museum@gordonhighlanders.com   Web: www.gordonhighlanders.com

Regimental collection of The Gordon Highlanders, including 12 Victoria Crosses. History of the Regiment told through audio-visual and traditional displays. Tea room, gardens and gift shop.

Opening Times: Apr to Oct Tue to Sat 10:30-16:30, Sun 13:30-16:30. Open by appointment only at all other times.   Admission: Adult £2.50, Child £1.00, OAP/Student £1.50. By appointment visits £3.50.   Location: West end of Aberdeen, just off Queens Road by Anderson Drive Roundabout.
Map Ref: 1

Marischal Museum

Marischal College, Aberdeen AB10 1YS   Tel: 01224 274301   Fax: 01224 274302
Email: museum@abdn.ac.uk   Web: www.abdn.ac.uk/marischal_museum

Major display of North-East identity from the first settlers to the present day; other gallery displays material from the rest of the world through the collections of donors - ancient Egypt, gold buddhas, African masks and Greek vases, etc.

Opening Times: Mon to Fri 10:00-17:00, Sun 14:00-17:00.   Admission: Free.   Location: In city centre.
Map Ref: 1

Provost Skene's House

Guestrow, Aberdeen AB10 1AS   Tel: 01224 641086   Fax: 01224 632133
Email: info@aagm.co.uk   Web: www.aberdeencity.gov.uk

Dating from 1545, Provost Skene's House now houses an attractive series of period room settings recalling the elegant furnishings of earlier times. Visitors can see an intriguing series of religious paintings in the Painted Gallery, changing fashions in the Costume Gallery and enjoy displays of local interest, coins and archaeology on the top floor.

Opening Times: Mon to Sat 10:00-17:00, Sun 13:00-16:00. Admission: Free. Location: Guestrow is off Broad Street, opposite Marischal College.   Map Ref: 1

Central, East & Northeast Scotland

Satrosphere Ltd

The Tramsheds, 179 Constitution Street, Aberdeen AB24 5TU Tel: 01224 640340 Fax: 01224 622211 Email: satrosphere@satrosphere.net
Web: www.satrosphere.net

Satrosphere's Plasma Dome

Scotland's original science centre. Light up a plasma dome, make shadow photos on the flash wall, feel forces at work in the spinning chair. Aberdeen's discovery place brings science alive with hands-on fun for all ages. Exhibits, interactive shows, workshops, special events, gift shop and the Tramsheds café.

Opening Times: Mon to Sat 10:00-17:00, Sun 11:30-17:00. Admission: Adult £5.00, Child/Concession £3.00, Family discounts available. Location: Near Aberdeen's fun Beach, five minutes from city centre. Map Ref: 1

Grampian Transport Museum Trust

Alford AB33 8AE Tel: 019755 62292 Fax: 019755 62180 Email: info@gtm.org.uk
Web: www.gtm.org.uk

The land travel and transport history of Aberdeenshire housed in a large road gallery and restored railway station. Road vehicles include the famous Craigievar Express, a 19th century steam tricycle and the world's oldest Sentinel Steam Waggon.

Opening Times: 31 Mar to 31 Oct daily 10:00-17:00. Admission: Adult £4.00, Child £1.60, OAP £3.10, Family (2 adults & up to 3 children) £9.60. Location: 25 miles west of Aberdeen, on the A944. Town centre, off free public car park. Map Ref: 2

Clackmannanshire Council Museum & Heritage Service

Speirs Centre, 29 Primrose Street, Alloa FK10 1JJ Tel: 01259 216913 Fax: 01259 721313
Email: smills@clacks.gov.uk Web: www.clacksweb.org.uk

Growing collections of archaeological, social and industrial history, including large assemblage of W & J A Bailey's/Alloa Pottery and artefacts from Patons & Baldwins, Alloa wool-spinning mill, memorabilia from breweries in Alloa. Expanding art collection.

Opening Times: Tue to Fri 13:30-17:00. Closed Sat, Sun & BH. Also open by arrangement or appointment. Admission: Free. Location: Near town centre, two minutes walk main car park & bus station. Map Ref: 3

Mill Trail Visitor Centre

Glentana Mill, West Stirling Street, Alva FK12 5EN
Tel: 01259 769696 Fax: 01259 763100
Email: milltrailvc@aillst.ossian.net
Web: www.visitscottishheartlands.org

Follow The Mill Trail and you are guaranteed a great shopping experience. A visit to Scotland's Mill Trail Visitor Centre takes you back 150 years to discover what life was like in the mill factories of the time. Relax in the Ochil View coffee shop before discovering a variety of shops - some factory, some not; from cashmere to chocolate.

Opening Times: Jan to Jun daily 10:00-17:00, Jul to Sep daily 09:00-17:00, Oct to Dec daily 10:00-17:00. Admission: Free.
Location: Only short drive from the historic town of Stirling.

Map Ref: 3

Central, East & Northeast Scotland

ALYTH *Perthshire*

Alyth Museum

Commercial Street, Alyth PH11 8AF   Tel: 01738 632488   Fax: 01738 443505
Email: museum@pkc.gov.uk   Web: www.pkc.gov.uk/ah

Collections relating to local history and life in and around Alyth.

Opening Times: May to Sep Wed to Sun 13:00-17:00.   Admission: Free.   Location: In town centre.
Map Ref: 4

ANSTRUTHER *Fife*

Kellie Castle

Pittenweem, Anstruther KY10 2RF   Tel: 01333 720271   Fax: 01333 720326

Kellie Castle is a very fine example of the domestic architecture of Lowland Scotland (dating from 1360). Sympathetically restored around 1878, it contains magnificent plaster ceilings, painted panelling and furniture designed by Sir Robert Lorimer.

Opening Times: Good Friday to Easter Monday & 1 Jun to 30 Sep daily 13:00-17:00.
Admission: Adult £5.00, Concession £3.75, Family £13.50.   Location: On B9171, three miles north west of Pittenweem.
Map Ref: 5

The Scottish Fisheries Museum Trust Ltd

St Ayles, Harbourhead, Anstruther KY10 3AB   Tel / Fax: 01333 310628
Email: andrew@scottish-fisheries-museum.org   Web: www.scottish-fisheries-museum.org

This award-winning National Museum tells the story of the Scottish fishing industry and its people from the earliest times to the present day.

Opening Times: Apr to Sep Mon to Sat 10:00-17:30, Sun 11:00-17:00. Oct to Mar Mon to Sat 10:00-16:30, Sun 12:00-16:30.   Admission: Adult £3.50, Accompanied Child Free, Concession £2.50. Group rates available.   Location: By Anstruther Harbour.
Map Ref: 5

ARBROATH *Angus*

Arbroath Art Gallery

Hill Terrace, Arbroath DD11 1AH   Tel: 01241 875598   Fax: 01241 439263
Email: signal.tower@angus.gov.uk   Web: www.angus.gov.uk/history.htm

Two galleries show temporary exhibitions of artists in the local area and from our Angus Council Collections which includes two works by 'Breughel the Younger' and works by James Watterston Herald.

Opening Times: Mon & Wed 09:30-20:00, Tues 10:00-18:00, Thu 09:30-18:00, Fri & Sat 09:30-17:00.   Admission: Free.   Location: Ten minute walk from bus and railway stations. Town centre location above Public Library.
Map Ref: 6

Arbroath Museum

Signal Tower, Ladyloan, Arbroath DD11 1PU   Tel: 01241 875598   Fax: 01241 439263
Email: signal.tower@angus.gov.uk   Web: www.angus.gov.uk/history.htm

Arbroath's fishing, flax, engineering and social history and the Bell Rock Lighthouse, the 1813 Shore Station of which is the museum building.

Opening Times: Mon to Sat 10:00-17:00 all year, Jul to Aug Sun 14:00-17:00.
Admission: Free.   Location: On A92 on seafront beside harbour. Seven minutes walk from bus/railway station.
Map Ref: 6

BALLINDALLOCH *Aberdeenshire*

Ballindalloch Castle

Ballindalloch AB37 9AX   Tel: 01807 500206   Fax: 01807 500210
Email: enquiries@ballindallochcastle.co.uk   Web: www.ballindallochcastle.co.uk

Ballindalloch Castle is the family home of the Macpherson-Grants, Lairds of Ballindalloch since 1546. This beautiful castle houses the most important private collection of 17th century Spanish paintings in Scotland.

Opening Times: Easter to Sep 10:30-17:00.   Admission: Charges on application.
Location: On A95 seven miles southwest of Aberlour.
Map Ref: 7

Central, East & Northeast Scotland

BANCHORY *Aberdeenshire*

Banchory Museum   ♿ ●

Bridge Street, Banchory AB31 5SX   Tel: 01224 664228

Exhibition on Banchory-born Scott Skinner - the 'Strathspey King'. Displays of Royal commemorative china, nineteenth century tartans and Deeside natural history.

Opening Times: May, Jun & Sep Mon to Sat 11:00-13:00 & 14:00-16:30. Jul to Aug Mon to Sat 11:00-13:00 & 14:00-16:30. Sun 14:00-16:30. For Apr & Oct - times 01771 622906.
Admission: Free.   Location: In Bridge Street, one minute walk from main car park in Dee Street.   Map Ref: 8

Crathes Castle   ♿ ● ◐ 🚿

Banchory AB31 5QJ   Tel: 01330 844525   Fax: 01330 844797

King Robert the Bruce granted the lands of Leys to the Burnett family in 1323. The ancient Horn of Leys was presented by Bruce to the family as a symbol of his gift. The castle, built in the 16th century, is an excellent example of a tower house of the period. Some rooms retain original painted ceilings and collections of family portraits and furniture.

Opening Times: 1 Apr to 30 Sep daily 10:00-17:30, 1 to 31 Oct daily 10:00-16:30.   Admission: Adult £9.00, Concession £6.50, Family £23.00.   Location: Three miles east of Banchory.

Crathes Castle - Muses Ceiling   Map Ref: 8

Drum Castle   ● 🗔 🚿

Drumoak, Banchory AB31 5EY   Tel: 01330 811204   Fax: 01330 811962

The keep is one of the three oldest tower houses surviving in Scotland. The house contains an excellent collection of portraits and good Georgian furniture.

Opening Times: 1 Apr to 31 May daily 12:30-17:30, 1 Jun to 31 Aug daily 10:00-17:30.
Admission: Adult £7.00, Concession £5.25, Family £19.00.   Location: Off A93, three miles west of Peterculter.   Map Ref: 9

BANFF *Aberdeenshire*

Banff Museum   ♿ ●

High Street, Banff AB45 1AE   Tel: 01771 622906

One of Scotland's oldest museums, founded in 1828. Award-winning natural history display and the life of Thomas Edward, the 'Banff Naturalist'. Nationally important collection of Banff silver.

Opening Times: Jun to Sep Mon to Sat 14:00-16:30.   Admission: Free.   Location: In High Street, one minute walk from St Mary's car park.   Map Ref: 10

BLAIR ATHOLL *Perthshire*

Blair Castle   🕮 ♿ ● 🗔 ◐ 🚿 🏛

Blair Atholl PH18 5TL   Tel: 01796 481207
Fax: 01796 481487   Email: office@blair-castle.co.uk
Web: www.blair-castle.co.uk

Five star attraction set in stunning Highland Perthshire, Blair Castle has been the ancient home and fortress of the Earls and Dukes of Atholl for over 725 years. Some 30 rooms of infinite variety display beautiful furniture, fine collections of paintings, arms and armour, china, costume, lace and embroidery, Jacobite relics and other unique treasures presenting a stirring picture of Scottish life from the 16th to 20th centuries.

Opening Times: 1 Apr to 31 Oct daily 09:30-17:00.
Admission: Adult £6.50, Child £4.00, OAP £5.50, Student £5.25, Family £16.75.   Map Ref: 11

Brechin Museum

Public Library, St Ninians Square, Brechin DD9 7AD   Tel: 01307 464123
Email: the.meffan@angus.gov.uk   Web: www.angus.gov.uk/history.htm

Social history of this tiny Cathedral City includes local ecclesiastical, industrial history and works of art by David Waterson.

Opening Times: Mon & Wed 09:30-20:00, Tues 10:00-18:00, Thu 09:30-18:00, Fri & Sat 09:30-17:00.   Admission: Free.   Location: Close to town centre, an annexe to Brechin Public Library.

Map Ref: 12

Buckhaven Museum

College Street, Buckhaven   Tel: 01592 412860   Fax: 01592 412870

The display features the town's history with a focus on the fishing industry. See the stained glass windows made by local people with the help of the community artist and a replica of a kitchen from the 1920s.

Opening Times: Open library hours.   Admission: Free.   Location: Above Buckhaven Library.

Map Ref: 13

The Buckie Drifter Maritime Heritage Centre

Freuchny Road, Buckie AB56 1TT   Tel: 01542 834646   Fax: 01542 835995
Email: buckie.drifter@moray.org.uk   Web: www.moray.org/area/bdrifter/mbdrifter.html

Enter the Buckie Drifter for a journey back in time to when the herring was king, glimpse the lives of the fishing communities, recreated fishing boat and quayside display. RNLI lifeboat on display.

Opening Times: Apr to Oct Mon to Sat 10:00-17:00, Sun 12:00-17:00.   Admission: Adult £2.75, Child/OAP £1.75. Group rates available.   Location: Situated at the harbour across the road from the lifeboat station.

Map Ref: 14

Peter Anson Gallery

Town House West, Cluny Place, Buckie AB56 1HB   Tel: 01309 673701   Fax: 01309 675863
Email: museums@moray.gov.uk   Web: www.moray.org/museums

Examples of drawings/paintings by maritime artist Peter Anson.

Opening Times: Mon to Fri 10:00-20:00, Sat 10:00-12:00. Closed Sun.   Admission: Free.
Location: Shared building with Buckie Library near town centre.

Map Ref: 14

Burntisland Museum

102 High Street, Burntisland   Tel: 01592 412860   Fax: 01592 412870

Visit the exciting reproduction Edwardian fairground display and find out more about Burntisland's history.

Opening Times: Open library hours.   Admission: Free.

Map Ref: 15

Rob Roy & Trossachs Visitor Centre

Ancaster Square, Callander FK17 8ED   Tel: 01877 330342

Highland Hero; Lowland Outlaw and Hollywood Legend - Rob Roy MacGregor has inspired authors and film makers for nearly 300 years. At the Rob Roy & Trossachs Visitor Centre, Callander, learn of the daring exploits which made him a hero to his own people - and Scotland's most notorious outlaw. Eavesdrop on Rob Roy McGregor as he plans another daring raid with one of his clansmen. Enjoy the fascinating audio visual presentation as it takes you through the life and times of Rob Roy. Walk into a farmhouse of that time, complete with byre and animals, finishing your experience with an cinematic

Central, East & Northeast Scotland

tour of the places where Rob Roy once roamed, narrated by well known Scots personality Jimmy McGregor.

Opening Times: Mar to May & Oct to Dec daily 10:00-17:00, Jun 09:30-18:00, Jul & Aug 09:00-20:00, Sep 10:00-18:00. Jan & Feb Sat & Sun 11:00-16:00. Admission: Adult £3.25, Child/OAP £2.25, Student £2.75, Family £9.75. Map Ref: 16

CUPAR *Fife*

Hill of Tarvit Mansion House
Cupar KY15 5PB   Tel: 01334 653127

Home to a notable collection including French, Chippendale-style and vernacular furniture, Dutch paintings and pictures by Raeburn and Ramsay, Flemish tapestries and Chinese porcelain and bronzes. The interior is very much in the Edwardian fashion.

Opening Times: 1 Apr to 30 Sep daily 13:00-17:00, 1 to 31 Oct Sat & Sun 13:00-17:00. Admission: Adult £5.00, Concession £3.75, Family £13.50.   Location: Off A916, two miles south of Cupar. Map Ref: 17

DUNDEE *Angus*

Broughty Castle Museum
Castle Approach, Broughty Ferry, Dundee DD5 2TF   Tel: 01382 436916   Fax: 01382 436951 Email: broughty@dundeecity.gov.uk   Web: www.dundeecity.gov.uk/broughtycastle

15th century fort at the mouth of the Tay Estuary, housing fascinating displays on the history and natural history of the local area. Enjoy magnificent views over the river from our Observation Gallery.

Opening Times: Apr to Sep Mon to Sat 10:00-16:00, Sun 12:30-16:00. Oct to Mar Tue to Sat 10:00-16:00, Sun 12:30-16:00.   Admission: Free.   Location: Situated on the seafront beside Broughty Ferry harbour. Three miles from Dundee City Centre off the A930. Map Ref: 18

McManus Galleries
Albert Square, Dundee DD1 1DA   Tel: 01382 432084   Fax: 01382 432052 Email: leisure.arts@dundeecity.gov.uk   Web: www.dundeecity.gov.uk/mcmanus

A remarkable Gothic building housing one of Scotland's most impressive collections of fine and decorative art and award-winning displays of local history, archaeology, wildlife and the environment. There's always something new to see and do with a changing programme of exhibitions, activities, events and displays. Café serving refreshments and a gallery shop selling a variety of prints, cards, books and gifts.

Opening Times: Mon to Sat 10:30-17:00, Thu 10:30-19:00, Sun 12:30-16:00.   Admission: Free.
Gallery 4 - 'Europe and Beyond'
Location: Situated in Dundee City Centre, ten minutes walk from bus and rail stations. Map Ref: 18

Mills Observatory
Glamis Road, Balgay Park, Dundee DD2 2UB   Tel: 01382 435846   Fax: 01382 435962 Email: mills.observatory@dundeecity.gov.uk   Web: www.dundeecity.gov.uk/mills

Mills Observatory is the UK's only full-time public observatory. See the stars and planets through an impressive Victorian telescope. Fascinating displays on astronomy and space exploration. Public planetarium shows take place monthly during the winter.

Opening Times: Apr to Sep Tue to Fri 11:00-17:00, Sat & Sun 12:30-16:00. Oct to Mar Mon to Fri 16:00-22:00, Sat & Sun 12:30-16:00.   Admission: Free.   Location: Balgay Park, one mile west of Dundee City Centre. Map Ref: 18

Central, East & Northeast Scotland

Royal Research Ship Discovery

Discovery Point, Discovery Quay, Dundee DD1 4XA   Tel: 01382 201245   Fax: 01382 225891
Email: info@dundeeheritage.sol.co.uk   Web: www.rrsdiscovery.com

Visit Discovery Point and Royal Research Ship Discovery where you can follow in the footsteps of Captain Scott and his crew. With brand new interactives and many historic artefacts you can experience first hand this great voyage of discovery.

Opening Times: Apr to Oct Mon to Sat 10:00-17:00, Sun 11:00-17:00. Nov to Mar Mon to Sat 10:00-16:00, Sun 11:00-16:00.   Admission: Adult £6.25, Child £3.85, Under 5s Free, Concession £4.70. Group rates available.   Location: Near town centre, one minute walk from central railway station.   Map Ref: 18

Verdant Works

West Hendersons Wynd, Dundee DD1 5BT   Tel: 01382 225282   Fax: 01382 221612
Email: admin@dundeeheritage.col.co.uk   Web: www.verdantworks.com

Verdant Works brings the past to life using audio visual displays, computer interactives, original machinery and film show which allows you to experience what life was like in the Jute Mill.

Opening Times: Apr to Oct Mon to Sat 10:00-17:00, Sun 11:00-17:00. Nov to Mar Wed to Sat 10:30-16:30, Sun 11:00-16:30. Closed Mon & Tue.   Admission: Adult £5.95, Child £3.85, Under 5s Free, Concession £4.45. Group rates available.   Map Ref: 18

Andrew Carnegie Birthplace Museum

Moodie Street, Dunfermline KY12 7PL   Tel: 01383 724302   Fax: 01383 721862
Email: carnegiebirthplace@hotmail.com   Web: www.carnegiebirthplace.com

Andrew Carnegie's birthplace, cottage and memorial hall house the many treasures which he acquired during his eventful life. They include freedom caskets, keys and items from his study in Skibo Castle.

Opening Times: Apr to Oct Mon to Sat 11:00-17:00, Sun 14:00-17:00.   Admission: Adult £2.00, Child (accompanied) Free, Concession £1.00.   Location: Near town centre, 400 yards downhill from Dunfermline Abbey.   Map Ref: 19

Dunfermline Museum

Viewfield Terrace, Dunfermline KY12 7HY   Tel: 01383 313838   Fax: 01383 313837
Email: lesley.botten@fife.gov.uk

Linen history and Dunfermline's civic and local history. Dunfermline Museum is the headquarters for West Fife Museums Service which also includes Pittencrieff House Museum, Inverkeithing Museum and St Margaret's Cave.

Opening Times: By appointment only.   Admission: Free.   Location: Five minutes walk from bus station.   Map Ref: 19

Pittencrieff House Museum

Pittencrieff Park, Dunfermline KY12 8QH   Tel: 01383 722935/313838

Temporary exhibition gallery, displays about local history and the Dunfermline Giant.

Opening Times: Good Friday to last Sun in Sep 11:00-17:00. Oct to Good Friday 11:00-16:00.
Admission: Free.   Location: In Pittencrieff Park, western edge of Dunfermline.   Map Ref: 19

Haddo House

Methlick, Ellon AB41 7EQ   Tel: 01651 851440   Fax: 01651 851888

Designed by William Adam in 1732, but refurbished in the 1880s, the House elegantly blends crisp Georgian architecture with sumptuous late Victorian interiors by Wright and Mansfield. Haddo is noted for its fine furniture, paintings and objets d'art.

Opening Times: 1 to 30 June Fri to Mon 11:00-16:30, 1 Jul to 31 Aug daily 11:00-16:30.
Admission: Adult £7.00, Concession £5.25, Family £19.00.   Location: Off B999, four miles north of Pitmedden.   Map Ref: 20

Central, East & Northeast Scotland

Falkland Palace & Garden
Falkland KY7 7BY   Tel: 01337 857397   Fax: 01337 857980

The Royal Palace of Falkland was the country residence of Stuart kings and queens. The palace contains fine portraits of the Stuart monarchs and two sets of 17th century tapestry hangings. The garden was designed and built by Percy Cane, and contains three herbaceous borders with many varieties of shrubs and trees.

Opening Times: 1 Mar to 31 Oct Mon to Sat 10:00-18:00, Sun 13:00-17:00.   Admission: Adult £7.00, Concession £5.25, Family £19.00.   Location: A912, ten miles from junction 8 of M90, 11 miles north of Kirkcaldy.

Falkland Palace - Chapel Royal

Map Ref: 21

Fochabers Folk Museum
High Street, Fochabers IV32 7DU   Tel: 01343 821204

Over 4000 items on display, horse drawn vehicles, costume, clocks and a varied collection of local items in this converted church. Something of interest for all the family.

Opening Times: Apr to Oct.   Admission: Free.

Map Ref: 22

The Meffan, Forfar Museum & Gallery
Meffan Institute, 20 West High Street, Forfar DD8 1BB   Tel: 01307 464123/467017   Fax: 01307 468451   Email: the.meffan@angus.gov.uk   Web: www@angus.gov.uk/history.htm

Stunning Pictish Stones and archaeology. A street of quaint old shops including weaver, shoemaker, sweet shop, clock maker and baker. Art galleries with frequently changing exhibitions. A witch's trial prior to her execution all in realistic life size displays.

Opening Times: Mon to Sat 10:00-17:00.   Admission: Free.   Location: In town centre.

Map Ref: 23

Brodie Castle

Brodie Castle, Brodie, Forres IV36 2TE   Tel: 01309 641371   Fax: 01309 641600

The house contains fine French furniture, English, Continental and Chinese porcelain and a major collection of paintings, including 17th century Dutch art, 19th century English watercolours, Scottish Colourists and early 20th century works.

Opening Times: 1 to 30 Apr & 1 Jul to 31 Aug daily 12:00-16:00, 1 May to 30 Jun & 1 to 30 Sep Sun to Thu 12:00-16:00.   Admission: Adult £5.00, Concession £3.75, Family £13.50.
Location: Off A96, four and a half miles west of Forres.

Map Ref: 24

Falconer Museum

Tolbooth Street, Forres IV36 1PH   Tel: 01309 673701   Fax: 01309 675863
Email: museums@moray.gov.uk   Web: www.moray.org/museums

Information about the Royal Burgh of Forres, its people and history. Collection about the popular folk singing duo 'The Corries'.

Opening Times: Apr to Oct Mon to Sat 10:00-17:00. Closed Sun. Nov to Mar Mon to Thu 11:00-12:30 & 13:00-15:30. Closed Fri, Sat, Sun.   Admission: Free.   Location: Just off the High Street on Tolbooth Street, opposite The Tolbooth.

Map Ref: 24

Nelson Tower
c/o Falconer Museum, Tolbooth Street, Forres IV36 1PH   Tel: 01309 673701   Fax: 01309 675863   Email: museums@moray.gov.uk   Web: www.moray.org/museums

Memorabilia associated with Lord Nelson and his various battles. Pictures of Forres and surrounding area in bygone days. Spectacular views of Forres and Findhorn Bay.

Opening Times: May to Sep Tue to Sun 14:00-16.00.   Admission: Free.   Location: Around a mile from town centre.

Map Ref: 24

Central, East & Northeast Scotland

FRASERBURGH *Aberdeenshire*

Museum of Scottish Lighthouses

Kinnaird Head, Fraserburgh AB43 9DU   Tel: 01346 511022   Fax: 01346 511033
Web: www.lighthousemuseum.co.uk

The new Museum of Scottish Lighthouses boasts the largest and best collection of lighthouse lenses and equipment in the UK. Discover the unique story of the Stevenson family, lighthouse engineers to the world.

Opening Times: Nov to Mar daily 10:00-16:00, Sun 12:00-16:00. Apr to Oct daily 10:00-18:00, Sun 12:00-18:00.   Admission: Adult £3.90, Child £2.00, Concession £3.25, Family £10.00/£11.00. Group rates available.   Location: Fraserburgh, 15 minute walk from bus station.
Map Ref: 25

Sandhaven Meal Mill

Sandhaven, Fraserburgh AB43 4EP   Tel: 01224 664228

Restored typical 19th century Scottish meal mill. Guided tours and working demonstration model.

Opening Times: May to Sep Sat & Sun 14:00-16:30.   Admission: Free.   Location: On B9031 at eastern end of Sandhaven village.
Map Ref: 25

GARLOGIE *Aberdeenshire*

Garlogie Mill Power House Museum

Garlogie AB32 6RX   Tel: 01224 664228

Unique beam engine - only one of its type still in situ - which powered this 19th century woollen spinning mill. Award-winning AV presentation and displays on the history of textiles in the area.

Opening Times: May to Sep Sat & Sun 14:00-16:30.   Admission: Free.   Location: At west end of Garlogie village, behind Village Hall.
Map Ref: 26

GLAMIS *Angus*

Angus Folk Museum

Kirkwynd Cottage, Glamis DD8 1RT   Tel: 01307 840288   Fax: 01307 840233

Housing one of Scotland's finest folk collection, this museum presents a vivid insight into how the rural workforce used to live.

Opening Times: 1 Apr to 31 Jun & 1 to 30 Sep Fri to Tue 12:00-17:00, 1 Jul to 31 Aug daily 12:00-17:00.   Admission: Adult £5.00, Concession £3.75, Family £13.50.   Location: Off A94 in Glamis, five miles south west of Forfar.
Map Ref: 27

Glamis Castle

Glamis DD8 1RJ   Tel: 01307 840393

Family home of the Earls of Strathmore and Kinghorne since 1372. Childhood home of Her Majesty Queen Elizabeth the Queen Mother and setting for Shakespeare's famous play 'Macbeth'.

Opening Times: 29 Mar to 27 Oct 10:30-17:30, Jul & Aug from 10:00.   Admission: Adult £6.50, Child £3.20, OAP/Student £4.80. Group rates available.
Map Ref: 27

HUNTLY *Aberdeenshire*

Brander Museum

The Square, Huntly AB54 8AE   Tel: 01224 664228

Display on Huntly-born author George Macdonald. Extensive collection of communion tokens. 19th century arms and armour from Sudan. Archaeological finds from Huntly Castle and other aspects of local history.

Opening Times: Tue to Sat 14:00-16:30. Closed BH.   Admission: Free.   Location: In The Square, town centre.
Map Ref: 28

Leith Hall

Huntly AB54 4NQ   Tel: 01464 831216   Fax: 01464 831594

Leith Hall is at the centre of a 279 acre estate which was the home of the head of the Leigh family from 1650. The house contains personal possessions of successive lairds.

Opening Times: Good Friday to Easter Monday daily 12;00-17:00, 1 May to 30 Sep Fri to Tue 12:00-17:00.   Admission: Adult £7.00, Concession £5.25, Family £19.00.   Location: On B9002, one mile west of Kennethmont.
Map Ref: 28

Central, East & Northeast Scotland

INVERKEITHING *Fife*

Inverkeithing Museum

The Friary, Queen Street, Inverkeithing KY11 1LS   Tel: 01383 313838/313594

Local history displays and local collections, featuring Admiral Samuel Greig, 'Father of the Russian Navy'.

Opening Times: Thu to Sun 11:00-12:30 & 13:00-16:00.   Admission: Free.   Location: Upstairs in The Friary, just off the High Street.   Map Ref: 29

INVERURIE *Aberdeenshire*

Carnegie Museum

The Square, Inverurie AB51 3SN   Tel: 01771 622906/01224 664228

Extensive archaeological displays, showing finds from New Stone Age to Bronze Age, as well as Early Christian carved stones. Displays on Inverurie's canal and railway history and the 19th century Volunteer Movement.

Opening Times: Mon & Wed to Fri 14:00-16:30, Sat 10:00-13:00 & 14:00-16:00. Closed BH.
Admission: Free.   Location: In The Square, above Inverurie Library, in town centre.

Map Ref: 30

Castle Fraser

Sauchen, Inverurie AB51 7LD   Tel: 01330 833463

The most elaborate Z-plan castle in Scotland was begun in 1575 by the sixth laird, Michael Fraser. The castle contains many Fraser family portraits, including one by Raeburn, and fine 18th and 19th century carpets, curtains and bed hangings.

Opening Times: 1 Apr to 30 Jun & 1 to 30 Sep Fri to Tue 12:00-17:30, 1 Jul to 31 Aug daily 11:00-17:30. Admission: Adult £7.00, Concession £5.25, Family £19.00.   Location: Off A944, four miles north of Dunecht.   Map Ref: 31

KILLIN *Perthshire*

Breadalbane Folklore Centre

Falls of Dochart, Killin FK21 8XE   Tel: 01567 820214   Fax: 01567 820764
Email: killin@aillst.ossian.net

Folklore Centre, history of clans MacNab and MacGregor and area with two audio visual screens, short film and story of Saint Fillan. Sales shop and information centre.

Opening Times: Mar to May & Oct daily 10:00-17:00. Jun & Sep daily 10:00-18:00. Jul & Aug daily 09:30-18:30. Closed Nov to Feb.   Admission: Adult £2.00, Child/OAP £1.25, Student £1.50, Family £5.25. Group discounts available. Location: At Falls of Dochart, Killin. Map Ref: 32

KIRKALDY *Fife*

John McDouall Stuart Museum

Rectory Lane, Dysart, Kirkaldy   Tel: 01592 412860   Fax: 01592 412870

This house is the birthplace of John McDouall Stuart, the first European explorer to make a return journey across Australia in 1861-1862. Displays describe his harrowing journeys, the Australian wilderness and the Aborigines who made a life there.

Opening Times: 1 Jun to 31 Aug 14:00-17:00.   Admission: Free.   Location: In town centre.

Map Ref: 33

Blue and White Teapot by S J Peploe

Kirkaldy Museum & Art Gallery

War Memorial Gardens, Kirkaldy KY1 1YG   Tel: 01592 412860   Fax: 01592 412870

Set in lovely grounds, Kirkaldy Museum & Art Gallery, features superb collection of 19th and 20th century Scottish paintings, an award-winning permanent local history and a lively changing exhibition programme. Gallery shop for cards, crafts and local publications. Café incorporating Wemyss Ware Pottery displays. Enquiry and outreach service.

Opening Times: Mon to Sat 10:30-17:00, Sun 14:00-17:00. Closed Xmas & New Year. Admission: Free.   Location: Five minute walk from town centre, adjacent to railway station.   Map Ref: 33

Central, East & Northeast Scotland

Barrie's Birthplace

9 Brechin Road, Kirriemuir DD8 4BX   Tel: 01575 572646

The upper floors of this two-storeyed house are furnished as they may be been when Barrie lived here. The adjacent house contains an exhibition - 'The Genius of J M Barrie' - Barrie's literary and theatrical works.

Opening Times: 1 Apr to 30 Jun & 1 to 30 Sep Fri to Tue 12:00-17:00, 1 Jul to 31 Aug daily 12:00-17:00.   Admission: Adult £5.00, Concession £3.75, Family £13.50.   Location: A90/A926, in Kirriemuir, six miles north west of Forfar.   Map Ref: 34

Kirriemuir Gateway to the Glens Museum

The Town House, 32 High Street, Kirriemuir DD8 4BB   Tel: 01575 575479
Email: kirriegateway@angus.gov.uk   Web: www.angus.gov.uk/history.htm

Social history of Kirriemuir and the Western Angus Glens including wildlife and archaeology. Museum of the Year in 2001.

Opening Times: Mon to Wed, Fri & Sat 10:00-17:00, Thu 13:00-17:00.   Admission: Free.
Location: In town centre.   Map Ref: 34

Maud Railway Museum

Maud Station, Maud AB42 5LY   Tel: 01224 664228

Housed in the former Maud Railway Station buildings, this museum illustrates the history of north east railways from the GNSR period, through LNER days into the era of British Rail.

Opening Times: Easter to Sep Sat, Sun & BH 14:00-16:30.   Admission: Free.   Location: In centre of Maud Village, at old railway station site.   Map Ref: 35

Methil Heritage Centre

The Old Post Office Building, 272 High Street, Lower Methil, Methil KY8 3EQ   Tel: 01333 422100   Fax: 01333 422101   Web: www.methilheritage.co.uk

A lively local history museum and gallery located in the town of Methil. The museum features an exciting new permanent display 'Levenmouth Lives' as well as a temporary exhibition programme and associated events.

Opening Times: Tue to Thu 11:00-16:30, Sat 13:00-16:30.   Admission: Free.   Map Ref: 13

Montrose Museum & Art Gallery

Panmure Place, Montrose DD10 8HE   Tel: 01674 673232
Email: montrose.museum@angus.gov.uk   Web: www.angus.gov.uk/history.htm

Montrose's maritime and social history. The wildlife of Angus Gallery covering from sea to mountain top. Art Gallery with constantly changing exhibitions.

Opening Times: Mon to Sat 10:00-17:00.   Admission: Free.   Location: Two minutes walk from town centre, ten minutes walk from railway station.   Map Ref: 36

William Lamb Sculpture Studio

Market Street, Montrose DD10 8NB   Tel: 01674 673232
Email: montrose.museum@angus.gov.uk   Web: www.angus.gov.uk/history.htm

Bronze, plaster and stone sculpture, wood carvings, watercolours and etchings by William Lamb (1893-1951) who was commissioned by the Royal Family. The studio collection includes heads of the Queen Mother, and our present Queen and Princess Margaret as children.

Opening Times: Jul to early Sep Mon to Sun 14:00-17:00.   Admission: Free.   Location: In secluded close between High Street and Market Street, in town centre.   Map Ref: 36

Central, East & Northeast Scotland

Laing Museum

High Street, Newburgh KY14 6DX   Tel: 01337 840223   Fax: 01334 413214
Email: museums.east@fife.gov.uk

First opened in 1896 to house Alexander Laing's Museum Collection and Reference Library, now a fascinating local history museum. It still displays Laing's material alongside the history of Newburgh.

Opening Times: Apr to Sep 11:00-17:00. Oct to Mar Wed, Sat & Sun 12:00-16:00.
Admission: Free.   Location: Town centre, High Street.   Map Ref: 37

PERTH

Black Watch Museum

Balhousie Castle, Perth PH1 5HR   Tel: 0131 310 8530
Fax: 0131 310 8525
Email: museum@theblackwatch.co.uk   Web: www.theblackwatch

Over 260 years of history of Scotland's oldest Highland Regiment: on display are paintings, uniforms, silver medals, weapons and memorabilia which brings the past alive, also displays from today. Well stocked gift shop with souvenirs, replica badges etc, on sale.

Opening Times: Oct to Apr Mon to Fri 10:00-15:30. Closed last Sat in Jun. May to Sep Mon to Sat 10:00-16:30.   Admission: Free. Donations welcome.   Location: Hay Street next to Bells Sports Centre.   Map Ref: 38

The Black Watch at Quatre Bras

Fergusson Gallery

Marshall Place, Perth PH2 8NU   Tel: 01738 441944   Fax: 01738 621152
Email: museum@pkc.gov.uk   Web: www.pkc.gov.uk/ah

Houses the most extensive collection of the work of J D Fergusson, one of the leading figures in 20th century Scottish art.

Opening Times: Mon to Sat 10:00-17:00. Closed Sun, Xmas to New Year.   Admission: Free.
Location: On southern edge of town centre, five minute walk from railway and bus stations.
                                                                                 Map Ref: 38

Perth Museum & Art Gallery

George Street, Perth PH1 5LB   Tel: 01738 632488   Fax: 01738 443505
Email: museum@pkc.gov.uk   Web: www.pkc.gov.uk/ah

One of Britain's oldest museums, founded in 1784, now houses wide-ranging collections of local history, archaeology, art and natural history. Changing displays throughout the year.

Opening Times: Mon to Sat 10:00-17:00. Closed Sun, Xmas to New Year.   Admission: Free.   Location: In city centre.   Map Ref: 38

Scone Palace

Perth PH2 6BD   Tel: 01738 552300   Fax: 01738 252588   Email: visits@scone-palace.co.uk
Web: www.scone-palace.co.uk

Family home of the Earls of Mansfield. Housing a magnificent and varied collection of works of art. Set in mature and historic grounds, once the crowning place of the Kings of Scotland, Scone Palace offers a fascinating day out for all the family.

Opening Times: 09:30-17:30. Last entry 16:45.
Admission: Adult £6.35, Child £3.75, OAP/Concession £5.50.   Map Ref: 38

The State Drawing Room

Central, East & Northeast Scotland

Aberdeenshire Farming Museum

Aden Country Park, Mintlaw, Peterhead AB42 5FQ   Tel: 01771 622906

The main museum exhibitions cover the story of farming in north east Scotland and the life of an estate before the First World War. The working farm illustrates life in the 1950s.

Opening Times: Apr & Oct Sat, Sun & school holidays 12:00-16:30. May to Sep daily 11:00-16:30. Admission: Free. Location: In Aden Country Park, one mile west of A952/A950 crossroads at Mintlaw.   Map Ref: 39

Arbuthnot Museum

St Peter Street, Peterhead AB42 1QD   Tel: 01779 477778

Fishing, shipping and whaling displays. Local history, coins and Inuit art. Temporary exhibitions gallery.

Opening Times: Mon to Tue, Thu to Sat 11:00-13:00 & 14:00-16:30, Wed 11:00-13:00. Closed BH. Admission: Free. Location: In town centre, at St Peter Street/Queen Street crossroads, above Peterhead Library.   Map Ref: 40

Peterhead Maritime Heritage Visitor Centre

South Road, Lido, Peterhead AB42 0YP   Tel: 01779 47778

Award-winning building presenting aspects of Peterhead's maritime heritage. Interactive displays on fishing, whaling, navigation and the oil industry. AV presentation on maritime life.

Opening Times: Jun to Aug, please phone for opening times. Admission: Phone for details. Location: One mile south of Peterhead Town Centre on South Road (A952).   Map Ref: 40

Fordyce Joiners Workshop & Visitor Centre

Fordyce, Portsoy AB45 2SL   Tel: 01224 664228

Late 19th/early 20th century rural joiner's workshop. Displays of hand tools and workshop machinery and AV presentation. See a craftsman at work and relax in a Victorian-style garden.

Opening Times: Apr to Sep Thu to Mon 10:00-18:00. Admission: Free. Location: In Church Street, one minute from car park beside Fordyce Parish Church.   Map Ref: 41

British Golf Museum

Bruce Embankment, St Andrews KY16 9AB   Tel: 01334 460046   Fax: 01334 460064   Email: hilarywebster@randagc.org   Web: www.britishgolfmuseum.co.uk

A visit to the British Golf Museum will transport you down a pathway of surprising facts and striking feats from 500 years of golf history. Using diverse displays and exciting exhibits, the Museum traces the history of the game, both in Britain and abroad, from the middle ages to the present day. A must for golfers and non-golfers alike.

Opening Times: Apr to Oct 9:30-17:30. For winter opening times call the museum. Admission: Adult £4.00, Child £2.00, OAP £3.00, Student £3.00, Group (10+) 50p off all charges.(2002 charges). Location: Ten minute walk from town centre, five minute walk from bus station. R/A Clubhouse, beside beach.   Map Ref: 42

Fun in the 18th Hole Gallery

Crawford Arts Centre

93 North Street, St Andrews KY16 9AD   Tel: 01334 474610   Fax: 01334 479880
Email: crawfordarts@crawfordarts.free-online.co.uk   Web: www.crawfordarts.free-online.co.uk

Independent arts centre with a programme of regularly changing exhibitions of all kinds of visual art and craft; also art activities organised; artist's studio; theatre.

Opening Times: Mon to Sat 10:00-17:00, Sun 14:00-17:00. Closed Xmas & New Year. Admission: Free to galleries. Location: Near town centre, opposite Police Station on North Street.   Map Ref: 42

Central, East & Northeast Scotland

St Andrews Museum

Kinburn Park, Doubledykes Road, St Andrews KY16 9DP   Tel: 01334 412690   Fax: 01334 413214   Email: museums.east@fife.gov.uk

Telling the history of this ancient town and showing changing exhibitions about the local environment and Fife as a whole. This museum always has something new to see and do.

Opening Times: Apr to Sep 10:00-17:00. Oct to Mar 10:30-16:00.   Admission: Free.
Location: On western edge of town centre, near bus station.   Map Ref: 42

St Andrews Preservation Trust Museum

12 North Street, St Andrews KY16 9PW   Tel: 01334 477629
Web: www.standrewspreservationtrust.co.uk

This charming 16th century house contains a wealth of fascinating material on the history of St Andrews and its people. There are displays depicting a variety of old shops and businesses - a grocers, chemists, dentists workroom and much more.

Opening Times: May to Sep, Easter week, last week Nov daily 14:00-17:00.   Admission: Free.
Location: Near the Cathedral.   Map Ref: 42

St Andrews University Museum Collections

University of St Andrews, St Andrews KY16 9AL   Tel: 01334 462417   Fax: 01334 462401
Email: hcr1@st-andrews.ac.uk   Web: www.st-andrews.ac.uk/services/muscoll/museum.html

Founded in 1411, St Andrews is Scotland's oldest university. The University's collections date from its earliest years to the present and illustrate its history, personalities and teaching practices.

Opening Times: By appointment only.   Map Ref: 42

Scotland's Secret Bunker

Crown Buildings, Troywood, St Andrews KY16 8QH   Tel: 01333 310301   Fax: 01333 312040
Email: mod@secretbunker.co.uk   Web: www.secretbunker.co.uk

Hidden beneath a Scottish Farmhouse, a tunnel leads to Scotland's Secret Bunker. 24,000 square feet of secret accommodation on two levels, 100 feet underground. Discover the twilight world of the Government Cold War, and take the opportunity to discover how they would have survived and you wouldn't!!! One of Scotland's DEEPEST and best kept secrets.

Opening Times: Apr to Oct daily 10:00-17:00.

Operations Room   Map Ref: 42

Argyll & Sutherland Highlanders Regimental Museum

Stirling Castle, Stirling FK8 1EH   Tel: 01786 475165   Fax: 01786 446038
Email: museum@argylls.co.uk   Web: www.argylls.co.uk

The Museum, containing displays of silver, paintings and medals, provides visitors with tales of those who have served Britain in the ranks of the Regiment. See displays from events in the Regiment's history, from Crimea, where the Regiment formed the famous Thin Red Line, Lucknow where six Victoria Crosses were won and from both World Wars, Korea, Malaya, Cyprus, Aden and peace keeping in Northern Ireland.

The Thin Red Line at Balaklava

Opening Times: Easter to Sep Mon to Sat 10:00-17:45, Sun 11:00-16:45. Oct to Easter daily 10:00-16:15.
Admission: Free, although there is a Castle entry fee.
Location: Within Stirling Castle.   Map Ref: 43

Bannockburn Heritage Centre

Glasgow Road, Stirling FK7 0LG   Tel: 01786 812664   Fax: 01786 810892

The Bannockburn Heritage Centre is situated at one of the most important historic sites in Scotland. On the battlefield nearby, in June 1314, King Robert the Bruce won freedom for the Scots.

Opening Times: 1 Feb to 31 Mar & 1 Nov to 24 Dec daily 10:30-16:00, 1 Apr to 31 Oct daily 10:00-17:30.   Admission: Adult £3.50, Concession £2.60, Family £9.50.   Location: Junction 9 of M80/M9, on A872 two miles south of Stirling.   Map Ref: 43

National Wallace Monument

Abbey Craig, Hillfoots Road, Stirling FK9 5LF   Tel: 01786 472140

Visit the spectacular National Wallace Monument, tribute to Scotland's national hero, Sir William Wallace - inspiration for the Hollywood blockbuster 'Braveheart'. Learn about the turbulent events leading up to the Battle of Stirling Bridge before stepping into a recreation of Westminster Hall to become one of the observers at Wallace's trial in London.

Listen to a talking head of Sir William Wallace recounting his patriotism and fight for Scotland's freedom, and wonder at the sight of Wallace's mighty two-handed broadsword. On your way to the top of the monument visit the vaulted chamber housing the Hall of Heroes where you'll meet other great Scots sculpted in marble. The third floor of this magnificent monument gives you outstanding views of the surrounding countryside and a feeling of total 'freedom' as you learn about its history. If you feel a little wilted after all this, revive yourself in the coffee house before browsing in the souvenir gift shop for that special reminder of your visit.

Opening Times: Jan to Feb & Nov to Dec daily 10:30-16:00, Mar to May & Oct 10:00-17:00, Jun 10:00-18:00, Jul & Aug 09:30-18:30.   Admission: Adult £3.95, Child/OAP £2.75, Student £3.00, Family £10.75.   Location: Ten minutes from Stirling Town Centre.   Map Ref: 43

Stirling Old Town Jail

St John Street, Stirling FK8 1EA   Tel: 01786 450050   Fax: 01786 471301
Email: otvc@aillst.ossian.net   Web: www.visitscottishheartlands.org.uk

Lock yourself into the past, explore life in a 19th century jail. Living history performances, original cells, spectacular roof top views. Meet jailors and inmates. Gift shop.

Admission: Adult £3.95, Child/OAP £2.75, Student £3.00, Family £10.75.   Location: Situated in Stirling Old Town. Five minute walk from bus and railway station.   Map Ref: 43

Stirling Smith Art Gallery & Museum

Dumbarton Road, Stirling FK8 2RQ   Tel: 01786 471917   Fax: 01786 449523
Email: elspeth.king@smithartgallery.demon.co.uk
Web: www.smithartgallery.demon.co.uk

Founded in 1874, the Smith has a collection of Scottish and European paintings and a collection of artefacts illustrating the story of Stirling. These include the world's oldest football (c.1540) and curling stone (1511), the Stirling Jug of 1457, and artefacts relating to the story of Wallace and Bruce. The Smith is an ideal place from which to explore the rest of Stirling.

Opening Times: Tue to Sat 10:30-17:00, Sun 14:00-17:00. Closed Mon.   Admission: Free.   Location: Dumbarton Road, 200 metres from Albert Hall and Tourist Information Centre.   Map Ref: 43

Smith Art Gallery & Museum

Central, East & Northeast Scotland

University of Stirling Art Collection
University of Stirling, Stirling FK9 4LA   Tel: 01786 466050

The Collection comprises over 300 works including paintings, prints, sketches, tapestries, sculpture and silver. There is a sculpture trail through the beautiful university grounds.

Opening Times: Daily 09:00-22:00. Closed Xmas & New Year.   Admission: Free.
Location: Ten minutes from bus/railway stations.   Map Ref: 43

STONEHAVEN *Aberdeenshire*

Tolbooth Museum
The Harbour, Stonehaven AB39 2JU   Tel: 01224 664228

Stonehaven's oldest building - the Earl Marischal's 16th century storehouse which served as the County Tolbooth of Kincardineshire 1600-1767. Displays of local bygones and the building's links with the Scottish Episcopal Church.

Opening Times: Jun to Sep Wed to Mon 13:30-16:30. Please phone 01771 622906 for May & Oct times. Admission: Free. Location: On Stonehaven Harbourfront.   Map Ref: 44

TOMINTOUL *Moray*

Tomintoul Museum & Visitor Centre
The Square, Tomintoul AB37 9ET   Tel: 01309 673701   Fax: 01309 675863
Email: museum@moray.gov.uk   Web: www.moray.org/museums

Displays on local history and wildlife.

Opening Times: Mar to May & Oct Mon to Fri 09:30-16:00, Jun to Aug Mon to Sat 09:30-16:30, Sep Mon to Sat 09:30-16:00. Admission: Free.   Map Ref: 45

TURRIFF *Aberdeenshire*

Fyvie Castle
Fyvie, Turriff AB53 8JS   Tel: 01651 891266   Fax: 01651 891107

Fyvie was once a royal stronghold, one of a chain of fortresses throughout medieval Scotland. A rich portrait collection includes works by Batoni, Raeburn, Romney, Gainsborough, Opie and Hoppner. Also a fine collection of arms and armour.

Opening Times: 1 Apr to 30 Jun & 1 to 30 Sep Fri to Tue 12:00-17:00, 1 Jul to 31 Aug daily 11:00-17:00. Admission: Adult £7.00, Concession £5.25, Family £19.00. Location: Off A947, eight miles south east of Turriff.   Map Ref: 46

Highlands & Islands

The Highlands and Islands present a back cloth of awesome mountains and majestic coastal scenery. The Western Isles are a 130 mile long chain of islands rich in culture. The Orkney Islands have the remains of a Stone Age fishing village preserved from 3000 BC.

There are fascinating museums scattered throughout the region capturing the Highland heritage illustrating the local archaeology, geology, and natural, social and local history

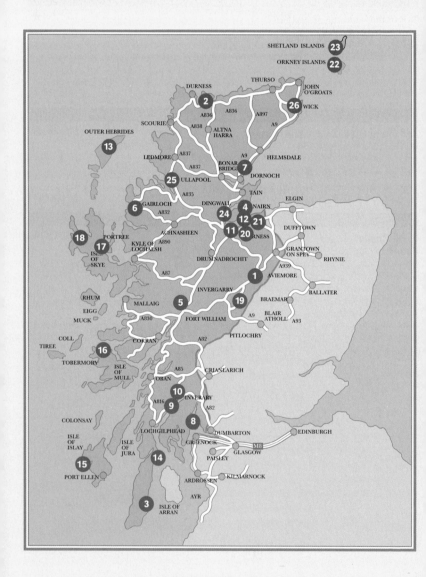

The Red Map References should be used to locate Museums etc on the pages that follow

Highlands & Islands

Strathspey Railway

Aviemore Station, Dalfaber Road, Aviemore PH22 1PY   Tel: 01479 810725
Email: information@strathspeyrailway.co.uk   Web: www.strathspeyrailway.co.uk

Boat of Garten Station

Scotland's 'Steam Railway in The Highlands', operating from Aviemore to Boat of Garten and Broomhill (Nethy Bridge and Dulnain Bridge close by). Splendid views of the Cairngorm Mountain range and the River Spey can be had from the carriage windows. While on board the train you can enjoy tea, coffee, or something stronger, along with light snacks.

Opening Times: 16 to 23 Apr & Jun to Sep 09:00-17:30, Apr Sun & Wed 09:00-17:30, May & Oct Sat, Sun, Wed & Thu 09:00-17:30. Admission: Adult £8.40, Child £4.20, OAP £6.30, Family £21.00. Location: In centre of

Aviemore and Boat of Garten. Bromhill Station is off A95 approx three and a half miles west of Grantown-on-Spey.   Map Ref: 1

Strathnaver Museum

Bettyhill by Thurso KW14 7ST   Tel: 0164 521418   Email: strathnavermus@ukonline.co.uk

Strathnaver Museum is a locally run museum which first opened in 1976. It is housed in what was St Columba's Parish Church at the eastern end of Bettyhill. The Strath area abounds with archaeological sites; finds may be seen in the museum.

Opening Times: Apr to Oct Mon to Sat 10:00-13:00 & 14:00-17:00. Admission: Adult £1.90, Child 50p, OAP £1.20, Student £1.00, Group £1.00 per person. Location: Half a mile from village.   Map Ref: 2

Campbeltown Museum

Hall Street, Campbeltown PA28 6BS   Tel: 01586 552366   Fax: 01369 705797
Email: mvhelmond@abc-museums.demon.co.uk

Good display of local archaeology, geology and natural history. Programme of small temporary exhibitions in foyer of the Public Library.

Opening Times: Tue to Sat 10:00-13:00 & 14:00-17:00, Tue & Thu 17:30-19:30.
Admission: Free. Location: Near town centre, five minute walk from Tourist Information Centre, in the building of the Public Library.   Map Ref: 3

Hugh Millers Cottage

Church Street, Cromarty IV11 8XA   Tel: 01381 600245

Home of eminent geologist, stonemason, editor and writer Hugh Miller. The furnished thatched cottage, built c1698 by his great-grandfather, contains an exhibition and captioned video programme on his life and work.

Opening Times: Good Friday to 30 Sep daily 12:00-17:00, 1 to 31 Oct Sun to Wed 12:00-17:00.
Admission: Adult £2.50, Concession £1.90, Family £7.00. Location: Via Kessock Bridge and A832 in Cromarty.   Map Ref: 4

Highlands & Islands

Treasures of the Earth

    ♿ ❖ 🚚

Road of the Isles A830, Corpach, Fort William PH33 7JL   Tel: 01397 772283
Fax: 01397 772133

A stunning collection of gemstones and crystals, displayed in fascinating simulation of cave, cavern and mining scenes. Priceless gemstones, beautiful crystals and exotic minerals light your path as they glisten and sparkle in cavities set against the scene back drop of ancient forest and tumbling waterfalls. Nuggets of gold, silver, aqua-marines, rubies and opals.

Opening Times: 1 Feb to 2 Jan 10:00-17:00 (Jul, Aug & Sep 09:30-19:00). Admission: Adult £3.00, Child £2.00, OAP £2.75. Location: At Corpach four miles from Fort William on the A830.   Map Ref: 5

The West Highland Museum

⁅ ♿ ❖

Cameron Square, Fort William PH33 6AJ   Tel: 01397 702169   Fax: 01397 701927

Old fashioned, traditional museum, world famous for its Jacobite collections. Excellent social and local history collections including the Alexander Carmichael collection and exhibitions on charms, costume, etc. Usually there is a temporary exhibition.

Opening Times: Oct to May Mon to Sat 10:00-16:00. Jun to Sep 10:00-17:00. Sun Jul & Aug 14:00-17:00. Admission: Adult £2.00, Child 50p, Concession £1.50. Location: Central Square in town, next door to Tourist Office.   Map Ref: 5

Gairloch Heritage Museum

❖ 🗨 ❖ 🚚

Achtercairn, Gairloch IV21 2BP   Tel: 01445 712287
Email: info@gairlochheritagemuseum.org.uk   Web: www.gairlochheritagemuseum.org.uk

Reflects the history of the parish of Gairloch: its people, their life and work, customs, the landscape, local skills such as spinning, fishing etc. Also to be seen is the light from the Rubha Reidh Light House. Children welcome.

Opening Times: Apr to Sep Mon to Sat 10:00-17:00, Oct Mon to Fri 10:00-13:30. Closed Nov to Mar. Open during winter by appointment only. Admission: Adult £3.00, Child 50p, Under 5s Free, OAP £2.00. Location: Situated five minutes walk from the shores of the loch, within easy reach of shops and hotels.   Map Ref: 6

Dunrobin Castle Museum

❖ 🗨 🚚

Dunrobin Castle, Golspie KW10 6SF   Tel: 01408 633177   Fax: 01408 634081
Email: info@dunrobincastle.net   Web: www.highlandescape.com

Pictish stones. Collection of natural history. Sutherland family artefacts.

Opening Times: Apr to 15 Oct Mon to Sat 10:30-16:30, Sun 12:00-16:30. Admission: Adult £6.25, Child £4.50, OAP £5.00, Family £17.00. Group rates available. Location: One and a half miles from Golspie.   Map Ref: 7

Hill House

❖ 🗨 🚚

Upper Colquhoun Street, Helensburgh G84 9AJ   Tel: 01436 673900   Fax: 01436 674685

The finest of Charles Rennie Mackintosh's domestic creations, The Hill House sits high above the Clyde commanding fine views of the river estuary. Walter Blackie commissioned not only the house and garden but much of the furniture and all the interior fittings and decorative schemes. Displays include work of new designers, demonstration of the effects of the wonderful stained glass, and a selection of original fabrics.

Opening Times: 1 Apr to 31 Oct daily 13:30-17:30. Admission: Adult £7.00, Concession £5.25, Family £19.00, Groups must book. Location: Eastern side of Helensburgh.   Map Ref: 8

INVERARAY *Argyllshire*

Auchindrain Township: Open Air Museum
By Inveraray PA32 8XN Tel: 01499 500235

A restored original farming village, furnished and equipped to provide a fascinating glimpse of Highland life in bygone days.

Opening Times: Apr to Sep daily 10:00-17:00. Admission: Adult £3.80, Child £1.80, OAP £3.00.
Map Ref: 9

Inveraray Maritime Museum
The Pier, Inveraray PA32 8UY Tel: 01499 302213

Displays, artefacts and archive film of Clyde and West Scotland maritime history. Hands-on activities and special displays of Highland Clearances and author Neil Munro of Para Handy fame.

Opening Times: Apr to Sep 10:00-18:00, Oct to Mar 10:00-17:00. Admission: Adult £3.60, Child £2.00, OAP £2.60, Family £10.00. Location: Near town centre at Pier.
Map Ref: 10

INVERNESS

Culloden Visitor Centre
Culloden Moor, Inverness IV2 5EU Tel: 01463 790607 Fax: 01463 794294

Scene of the last major battle fought on mainland Britain. The final Jacobite uprising ended here on 16 April 1746. Turf and stone dykes, which played a crucial part in the battle, have been reconstructed on their original site.

Opening Times: 1 to 28/29 Feb & 1 Nov to 24 Dec daily 11:00-16:00, 1 to 31 Mar daily 10:00-16:00, 1 Apr to 30 Jun & 1 Sep to 31 Oct daily 09:00-18:00, 1 Jul to 31 aug daily 09:00-19:00.
Admission: Adult £5.00, Concession £3.75, Family £13.50. Location: B9006, five miles east of Inverness.
Map Ref: 11

Inverness Museum & Art Gallery
Castle Wynd, Inverness IV2 3EB Tel: 01463 237114

Enjoy real Highland heritage in displays, exhibitions and events - an extravaganza of archaeology, art, natural and local history. Discover silver and taxidermy from Inverness, weapons and bagpipes from the Highlands and Scottish contemporary art. The ever-changing temporary exhibitions gallery presents a range of events and displays which reflect the cultural activity of the city. Progamme of talks, events and recitals. Activities for children and adults. Public enquiry service, identifying objects and providing information. Roll up your sleeves and discover the Highlands in

Archaeology Gallery

the brand new interactive discovery centre, with hundreds of interesting artefacts to see and handle. Video macroscope to project objects onto a large screen, computer controlled roof top camera and satellite weather reports from around the world. Museum shop with a range of gifts, books and Highland souvenirs.

Opening Times: Mon to Sat 09:00-17:00. Closed Sun.
Admission: Free. Location: In city centre, five minutes walk from car parks, railway station and bus station. Exhibitions & Events 2003 : For Exhibitions and Events please telephone for details.
Map Ref: 11

Regimental Museum, Queens Own Highlanders
Fort George, Ardersier, Inverness IV2 7TD Tel: 01463 224380

Unique collection of uniform, medals, paintings, prints, weapons of Queen's Own Highlanders, Seaforth Highlanders, The Queen's Own Cameron Highlanders, Lovat Scouts, includes regular militia, territorial battalions. Comprehensive library and archive collection, available by appointment.

Opening Times: Apr to Sep daily 10:00-18:00. Oct to Mar Mon to Fri 10:00-16:00.
Admission: Free. (Visitors to Fort George must pay entrance fee to Historic Scotland)
Location: Within Fort George, 12 miles east of Inverness.
Map Ref: 12

Highlands & Islands

ISLAND OF BENBECULA

Museum Nan Eilean
Sgoil Lionacleit, Lionacleit, Island of Benbecula HS7 5PJ Tel: 01870 602864 Fax: 01870 602817 Email: danamacphee@cne-siar.gov.uk Web: www.cne-siar.gov.uk

Artefacts, photographs illustrating archaeology, local history and way of life in the Uists. Programme of temporary exhibitions.

Opening Times: Mon, Wed & Thu 09:00-16:00. Tue, Fri & Sat 11:00-13:00 & 14:00-16:00.
Admission: Free. Location: Centrally situated on Island of Benbecula. Map Ref: 13

ISLE OF BUTE *Argyllshire*

Bute Museum

Stuart Street, Rothesay, Isle of Bute PA20 0EP Tel: 01700 505067

Illustrative of the natural history, archaeology and social history of the Islands of Bute and Inchmarnock.

Opening Times: Apr to Sep Mon to Sat 10:30-16:30, Sun 14:30-16:30. Oct to Mar Tue to Sat 14:30-16:30. Admission: Adult £1.50, Child 50p, OAP £1.00. Location: In town centre behind castle. Map Ref: 14

ISLE OF ISLAY *Argyllshire*

Museum of Islay Life

Daal Terrace, Port Charlotte, Isle of Islay PA48 7UA Tel / Fax: 01496 850358
Email: imt@islaymuseum.freeserve.co.uk Web: www.islaymuseum.freeserve.co.uk

The collection covers Islay life from earliest times, including archaeological artefacts. Domestic items are displayed in room settings. Traditional industries - whisky, joinery, crafting and fishing are well represented.

Opening Times: Apr to Oct Mon to Sat 10:00-17:00, Sun 14:00-17:00. Nov to Mar opening times advertised locally/by appointment for Groups. Admission: Adult £2.00, Child £1.00, Concession £1.20, Family £5.00. Coach reduction - 20%. Location: At edge of small village - good parking, one minute from bus stop. Map Ref: 15

ISLE OF LEWIS

Museum Nan Eilean

Francis Street, Stornaway, Isle of Lewis HS1 2NF Tel: 01851 709266 Fax: 01851 706318
Email: rlanghorne@cne-slar.gov.uk Web: www.cne-siar.gov.uk

The collections feature local archaeology, objects and photographs relating to local history, domestic life, crofting, agriculture, crafts and fishing.

Opening Times: Apr to Sep Mon to Sat 10:00-17:30. Oct to Mar Mon to Fri 10:00-17:00, Sat 10:00-13:00. Admission: Free. Location: Short walk from town centre. Map Ref: 13

ISLE OF MULL *Argyllshire*

Isle of Mull Museum

Main Street, Tobermory, Isle of Mull PA75 6NY

Historical artefacts and informative displays about the Isle of Mull from its geological beginnings to the present day.

Opening Times: Mon to Fri 10:00-16:00. Admission: Adult £1.00, Child 20p. Location: On Tobermory Main Street next to Clydesdale Bank. Map Ref: 16

ISLE OF SKYE *Highland*

Dualchas-Skye & Lochalsh Area Museums & Heritage Service
The Highland Council, Park Lane, Portree, Isle of Skye IV51 9GP Tel: 01478 613857/613855
Fax: 01478 613751 Web: www.highland.gov.uk/cl/default.htm

The Heritage Service provides detailed information on the history and culture of the area through its varied and extensive collections including the Dualchas Collection, The Archives and the Dualchas Library.

Opening Times: Mon to Fri 10:00-17:00. Closed Sat, Sun & BH. Admission: Free.
Location: Portree, Isle of Skye. Map Ref: 17

Highlands & Islands

Dunvegan Castle

Dunvegan, Isle of Skye IV55 8WF   Tel: 01470 521206   Fax: 01470 521205
Email: info@dunvegancastle.com   Web: www.dunvegancastle.com

The stronghold of the Chiefs of MacLeod for nearly 800 years and it remains their home. Built on a rock once surrounded entirely by salt water, it is unique in Scotland as the only house of such antiquity to have retained its family and its roof throughout the centuries, surviving the extremes of feast, famine and the intermittent periods of warring with neighbouring clans.

Opening Times: Daily mid Mar to Oct 10:00-17:30, Nov to mid Mar 11:00-16:00.   Admission: Adult £6.00, Child £3.50, OAP/Student/Group £5.50.   Location: One and a half miles from village of Dunvegan, follow signposts.

Romantic & Historic Dunvegan Castle

Map Ref: 18

KINGUSSIE *Highland*

Highland Folk Museum

Duke Street, Kingussie PH21 1JG   Tel: 01540 661307   Fax: 01540 661631
Email: highland.folk@highland.gov.uk   Web: www.highlandfolk.com

Award winning museum on two sites recreating the social history of the Scottish Highlands with a reconstructed 18th century farming township, Victorian water-powered sawmill, pre-war school and Isle of Lewis Blackhouse. Art Gallery features local artists.

Opening Times: Easter to Oct, please phone to confirm times.   Admission: Adult £5.00, Child/OAP £3.00.   Location: Kingussie Museum is five minutes from bus stop and railway station. Newtonmore Museum is 15 minutes from railway station.

Map Ref: 19

NAIRN *Highland*

Cawdor Castle   🗽 Cawdor Castle

Cawdor Castle, Nairn IV12 5RD
Tel: 01667 404615   Fax: 01667 404674
Email: info@cawdorcastle.com   Web: www.cawdorcastle.com

Cawdor Castle, the most romantic Castle in the Highlands, has a magical name linked with Macbeth by Shakespeare. The medieval tower and drawbridge are intact and generations of art lovers are responsible for the eclectic collections of paintings, tapestries, furniture and books in the castle. Beautiful gardens, nature trails, 9-hole golf course and putting green.

Opening Times: May to mid Oct daily 10:00-17:00.
Admission: Adult £6.30, Child £3.50, OAP £5.30, Family £18.60. Groups of 20+ £5.50.   Location: Situated between Inverness and Nairn on the B9090 off the A96.

Cawdor Castle from the flower garden

Map Ref: 20

Nairn Museum

Viewfield House, Viewfield Drive, Nairn IV12 4EE   Tel: 01667 456791   Fax: 01667 455399
Email: manager@nairnmuseum.freeserve.co.uk   Web: www.nairnmuseum.co.uk

The two Nairn museums amalgamated in 2000. Our permanent displays cover fishermen and farmers, adventures and Nairnshire notables. Changing monthly exhibitions. Children's area. Family and local history research facilities.

Opening Times: Easter to end Oct Mon to Sat 10:00-16:30.   Admission: Adult £1.50, Child 50p, Family £2.50. Groups discount available.   Location: Near town centre, three minute walk from bus station.

Map Ref: 21

Guided or Private Tours	Disabled Access	Gift Shop or Sales Point	Café or Refreshments	Restaurant	Car Parking

Highlands & Islands

Orkney Museum, Tankerness House
Broad Street, Kirkwall, Orkney KW15 1DH   Tel: 01856 873191   Fax: 01856 875160
Email: museum@orkney.gov.uk   Web: www.orkneyheritage.com

The story of Orkney, from the Stone Age to modern times. Vivid displays, including the Picts and Vikings. Internationally important artefacts housed in a historic 16th century laird's town house.

Opening Times: Oct to Apr Mon to Sat 10:30-12:30 & 13:30-17:00. May to Sep Mon to Sat 10:30-17:00, Sun 14:00-17:00.   Admission: Free.   Location: Opposite St Magnus Cathedral.
Map Ref: 22

Orkney Wireless Museum
Kiln Corner, Junction Road, Kirkwall, Orkney KW15 1ES   Tel: 01856 871400
Web: www.owm.org.uk

Wartime communications equipment from Scapa Flow, history of domestic radio, working crystal set and valve set, Gimmick transistor radios, Orkney Wartime Photographic Archive.

Opening Times: Apr to Sep Mon to Sat 10:00-16:30, Sun 14:30-16:30.   Admission: Adult £2.00, Child £1.00.   Location: Next to harbour.
Map Ref: 22

The Pier Arts Centre
Stromness, Orkney KW16 3AA   Tel: 01856 850 209   Fax: 01856 851 462

A permanent collection of 20th century British art including work by Ben Nicholson, Barbara Hepworth, Terry Frost, Roger Hilton, Alfred Wallis and Peter Lanyon and temporary exhibition programme of contemporary art by international and local artists.

Opening Times: Tue to Sat 10:30-12:30 & 13:30-17:00.   Admission: Free.   Location: One minute walk from bus station.
Map Ref: 22

Scapa Flow Visitor Centre & Museum
Lyness, Hoy, Orkney KW16 3NT   Tel: 01856 791300   Fax: 01856 875160
Email: museum@orkney.gov.uk   Web: www.orkneyheritage.com

The history of Scapa Flow, Britain's main naval base in both World Wars and the grave of the German High Seas Fleet. Historic buildings, photographs and artefacts.

Opening Times: Oct to May Mon to Fri 09:00-16:30. Jun to Oct daily 09:00-16:30.
Admission: Free.   Location: Lyness, Hoy.
Map Ref: 22

Stromness Museum
52 Alfred Street, Stromness, Orkney KW16 3DF   Tel: 01856 850025

Orkney maritime and natural history, including ships and fishing, Hudsons Bay log, Arctic whaling, German fleet in Scapa Flow, birds, seashells, moths and butterflies, fossils and ethnology.

Opening Times: Apr to Sep Sun to Sat 10:00-17:00. Oct to Mar Mon to Sat 11:00-15:30 .
Admission: Adult £2.50, Child 50p, OAP £2.00. Schools Free.   Location: 15 minute walk from town centre.
Map Ref: 22

Böd of Gremista
Gremista, Lerwick, Shetland   Tel: 01595 695057   Web: www.shetland-museum.org.uk

Renovated late 18th century house and fishing booth. Three-storey, stone-roofed bulding. Restored rooms with period furniture. Displays on line fishing and merchant marine trade. Biography of A Anderson, co-founder of P & O.

Opening Times: Jun to mid Sep Tue to Sun 10:00-13:00 & 14:00-17:00.   Admission: Free - donations welcome   Location: Outskirts of town, one mile from ferry terminal.
Map Ref: 23

Shetland Croft House Museum
Voe, Dunrossness, Shetland   Tel: 01595 695057   Fax: 01595 696729   Web: www.shetland-museum.org.uk

Restored mid-19th century steading, comprising house, byre, barn and mill. Stone walls and straw thatched traditional building with authentic contents. Locally-made furniture and agricultural implements.

Opening Times: May to Sep 10:00-13:00 & 14:00-17:00.   Admission: Free - donations welcome.   Location: Near Boddam, five miles from airport.
Map Ref: 23

Highlands & Islands

Shetland Museum

Lower Hillhead, Lerwick, Shetland ZE1 0EL   Tel: 01595 695057   Fax: 01595 696729
Email: tommy.watt@sic.shetland.gos.uk   Web: www.shetland-museum.org.uk

Comprehensive history of Shetland, geology, archaeology from Stone Age to medieval, including Iron Age farm finds and Early Christian treasure. Agriculture and fisheries 18th to 20th century. Social history, textiles.

Opening Times: Mon Wed & Fri 10:00-19:00, Tue, Thu & Sat 10:00-17:00.   Admission: Free.
Location: Town centre, one minutes walk from Town Hall.   Map Ref: 23

STRATHPEFFER *Highland*

Highland Museum of Childhood

The Old Station, Strathpeffer IV14 9DH   Tel / Fax: 01997 421031
Email: info@hmoc.freeserve.co.uk   Web: www.hmoc.freeserve.co.uk

Discover the customs and traditions of Highland childhood through audio-visual displays, childhood treasures and a fascinating doll and toy collection. Hands-on activities for children. Gift shop and coffee shop.

Opening Times: Mon to Sat 10:00-17:00, Sun 14:00-17:00.   Admission: Adult £1.50,
Concession £1.00, Family £3.50.   Location: Strathpeffer, Ross & Cromarty, Highlands.
                                                                          Map Ref: 24

ULLAPOOL *Highland*

Ullapool Museum & Visitor Centre

7/8 West Argyle Street, Ullapool IV26 2TY   Tel / Fax: 01854 612987
Email: ulmuseum@waverider.co.uk

Discover the Loch Broom Story! Award-winning Highland Museum, within a former Telford Parliamentary Church. Insight into a Highland community. Audio-visual, photos, touchscreens. Local archives, records. Exhibitions.

Opening Times: Apr to Oct, Mon to Sat 09:30-17:30. Nov to Feb, Thu & Sat 11:00-15:00. Mar
Mon to Sat 11:00-15:00.   Admission: Adult £3.00, Child 50p, Concession & Group £2.00,
School Group Free.   Location: Near centre of village.   Map Ref: 25

WICK *Highland*

Wick Heritage Centre

20 Bank Row, Wick KW1 5EY   Tel / Fax: 01955 605393

Contains a restored fisherman's house, tableaux of fossils, 19th century fashion, fish kiln, cooperage, complete blacksmith's shop and foundry, a working lighthouse, the famous Johnston collection of photographs of 115 years history.

Opening Times: Jun to Sep Mon to Sat 10:00-17:00.   Admission: Adult £2.00, Child 50p.
Location: Near the harbour.   Map Ref: 26

Wales has a strong tradition of music, literature and art, and this tradition is well represented in the museums and galleries of South Wales. Cardiff and Swansea have exceptional museums and galleries - Welsh heritage, the social history of coal mining, steam railways and maritime history are the focus of museums throughout this region.

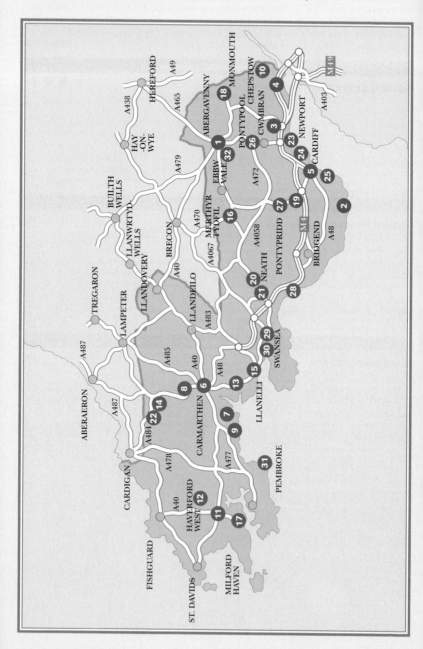

The Red Map References should be used to locate Museums etc on the pages that follow

South & Southwest Wales

Abergavenny Museum & Castle

Castle Street, Abergavenny NP7 5EE   Tel: 01873 854282   Fax: 01873 736004
Email: abergavennymuseum@monmouthshire.gov.uk

The history of Abergavenny from prehistoric to present, housed in a Regency hunting lodge amid the ruins of the Norman Castle. Displays include 1950s shop interior, farm kitchen, saddlers shop. Regular exhibitions and events.

Opening Times: Open all year.   Admission: Adult £1.00, Children Free, Concession 75p.
Location: Near town centre, parking nearby.   Map Ref: 1

Vale of Glamorgan Railway Co

The Station, Barry Island CF62 5TH   Tel: 01446 748816   Fax: 01446 749018

Operating steam railway between Barry Island and Barry Waterfront. Museum of South Wales Railways, rolling stock viewing at Plymouth Road Depot. Please contact the Station for information on special events.

Opening Times: Easter to mid Sep Sat, Sun & BH 11:00-16:00   Admission: Adult £3.00, Child £2.00, Family £8.00.   Location: Barry Island Railway Station - one minute walk from beach.
Map Ref: 2

Roman Legionary Museum

High Street, Caerleon NP18 1AE   Tel: 01633 423134   Fax: 01633 422869
Web: www.nmgw.ac.uk

Discover what made the Romans such a formidable force. See how they lived, slept and ate, how they marched and prepared for battle and which gods they worshipped.

Opening Times: Mon to Sat 10:00-17:00, Sun 14:00-17:00.   Admission: Free.   Location: On Caerleon High Street, in town centre.   Map Ref: 3

Caldicot Castle

Caldicot Castle, Church Road, Caldicot NP26 4HU   Tel: 01291 420241   Fax: 01291 435094
Email: caldicotcastle@monmouthshire.gov.uk   Web: www.caldicotcastle.co.uk

Founded by the Normans, developed in Royal hands as a medieval stronghold and restored as a Victorian family home, the castle has a colourful and romantic history.

Opening Times: Mar to Oct daily 11:00-17:00.   Admission: Adult £3.00, Concessions and Family rates available.   Location: Five minutes from Caldicot Centre, between Chepstow and Newport.   Map Ref: 4

Cardiff Castle

Cardiff Street, Cardiff CF10 3RB   Tel: 029 2087 8100   Fax: 029 2023 1417
Email: cardiffcastle@cardiff.gov.uk   Web: www.cardiff.gov.uk/castle

Discover 2000 years of history in the heart of the city from the arrival of the Romans, through the Norman Conquest to lavish Victorian design - all have left their mark on the castle for you to explore. Plus traditional Welsh banquets for a great night out (booking essential).

Opening Times: Mar to Oct daily 09:30-18:00, Nov to Feb daily 09:30-17:00.   Admission: Adult £5.50, Child/Concession £3.30, Student £4.40, Family £15.50. (2002 prices)   Location: Cardiff City Centre. Quarter mile from central bus and train station.   Map Ref: 5

Guided or Private Tours	Disabled Access	Gift Shop or Sales Point	Café or Refreshments	Restaurant	Car Parking

South & Southwest Wales

Museum of Welsh Life

St Fagans, Cardiff CF5 6XB   Tel: 029 2057 3500   Fax: 029 2057 3490
Web: www.nmgw.ac.uk

One of Europe's most outstanding open air museums. See how we have lived, worked, played and worshipped in over 40 buildings that have been moved from all over Wales.

Opening Times: Daily 10:00-17:00. Admission: Free. Location: In the village of St Fagans, approx six miles from Cardiff City Centre.

Map Ref: 5

National Museum & Gallery Cardiff

Cathays Park, Cardiff CF10 3NP   Tel: 029 2039 7951   Fax: 029 2037 3219
Web: www.nmgw.ac.uk

The National Museum and Gallery Cardiff

The National Museum & Gallery Cardiff is unique amongst British museums and galleries in its range of arts and science displays. The elegant Art Galleries house dazzling works of art by French Impressionists while the Evolution of Wales takes you on an amazing journey through 4600 million years of history. Don't miss the interactive Glanely Gallery where you can enjoy a changing programme of hands-on activities.

Opening Times: Tue to Sun 10:00-17:00, open BH Mon.
Admission: Free. Location: In Cardiff's Civic Centre, approx five minutes walk from Cardiff City Centre.

Map Ref: 5

Techniquest

Stuart Street, Cardiff Bay, Cardiff CF10 5BW   Tel: 029 2047 5475   Fax: 029 2048 2517
Email: info@techniquest.org   Web: www.techniquest.org

Techniquest - the UK's most visited science centre with over 150 hands-on exhibits and puzzles, science theatre, planetarium, discovery room and The Hub.

Opening Times: Mon to Fri 09:30-16:30, Sat, Sun, BH & school holidays 10:30-17:00.
Admission: Adult £6.30, Child £4.30, Family £17.40. Group rates available. Location: Cardiff Bay, waterfront location - five minutes from Cardiff Bay Station.

Map Ref: 5

Welch Regiment Museum (41st/69th Foot) of the Royal Regiment of Wales

The Black and Barbican Towers, Cardiff Castle, Cardiff CF10 2RB   Tel: 029 2022 9367
Email: welch@rrw.org.uk   Web: www.rrw.org.uk

The museum commemorates the service of the Infantry of South Wales namely the Welch Regiment (41st/69th Foot), also associated militia, volunteer and territorial forces, 1719-1969. Also the Royal Regiment of Wales 24th/41st Foot 1969 to date.

Opening Times: Mar to Oct daily 10:00-18:00, closed Tue. Nov to Feb daily 10:00-16:30, closed Tue. Closed Xmas & New Year. Admission: Museum: Free. Castle: Adult £2.60, Child/OAP £1.60, Student £2.10, Family £7.40. Subject to change. Location: The Museum is situated within Cardiff Castle and is within ten minutes walking time of the main train and bus station, also city centre multi-storey car parks.

Map Ref: 5

Carmarthen Heritage Centre

The Quay, Carmarthen SA31 3AN   Tel: 01267 223788   Fax: 01267 223830
Email: cdelaney@carmarthenshire.gov.uk   Web: www.carmarthenshire.gov.uk

Exploring the history of the River Tywi and its importance for Carmarthenshire. On show are coracles made for fishing on the river and other displays.

Opening Times: Easter, May to Oct Mon to Sat 10:00-17:00. Nov to Easter Sat 11:00-16:00.
Admission: Free. Location: Two minutes from bus station.

Map Ref: 6

Carmarthenshire County Museum

Abergwili, Carmarthen SA31 2JG   Tel: 01267 231691   Fax: 01267 223830
Email: cdelaney@carmarthenshire.gov.uk   Web: www.carmarthenshire.gov.uk

One of Wales' finest regional museums housed in the one-time Palace of the Bishop of St Davids.

CARMARTHEN *(continued)*

On show are paintings, furniture, Roman archaeology and much more. Set in own parkland with walks and picnic sites.

Opening Times: Mon to Sat 10:00-16:30. Closed Xmas & New Year. Admission: Free.
Location: At Abergwili - one and a half miles from Carmarthen on the A40. Public transport - buses for Llandeilo. Map Ref: 6

Dylan Thomas Boathouse

Dylans Walk, Laugharne, Carmarthen SA3 4SD Tel: 01994 427420

The Boathouse, where Dylan and Caitlin lived with their children from 1949-1953 is now a heritage centre. The house now contains audio visual presentations, original furnishings and memorabilia, a themed bookshop, tea room, viewing platform and terrace.

Opening Times: May to Oct and Easter weekend daily 10:00-17:30, Nov to Apr daily 10:30-15:30. Admission: Adult £2.75, Under 7s Free. Map Ref: 7

Gwili Steam Railway

Bronwydd Arms Station, Bronwydd, Carmarthen SA33 6HT Tel: 01267 230666
Email: gwili@talk21.com Web: www.gwili-railway.co.uk

A two and a half mile working standard gauge steam railway running through the Gwili Valley. Visit the working signalbox. Miniature railway, gift shop, riverside picnic site and refreshments.

Admission: Adult £4.50, Child/OAP/Concession £3.00, Under 2s Free, Family £12.50. Group rates available. Special fares for special events eg. Thomas and Santa trains. Location: Three miles from Carmarthen on A484 road, at Bronwydd. Follow the tourist 'Steam Railway' signs.
Map Ref: 8

Museum of Speed

Pendine, Carmarthen SA33 4NY Tel: 01994 453488 Fax: 01267 223830
Email: cdelaney@carmarthenshire.gov.uk Web: www.carmarthenshire.gov.uk

Explores the history of Pendine's role in racing. The main exhibition, July and August is the car 'Babs', record breaking and fast vehicles and bikes at other times.

Opening Times: Easter to Sep daily 10:00-13:00 & 13:30-17:00. Oct Fri to Mon 10:00-13:00 & 13:30-17:00. Closed Nov to Easter. Admission: Free. Location: On the seafront at Pendine A4066 from the A40. Map Ref: 9

CHEPSTOW *Monmouthshire*

Chepstow Museum

Bridge Street, Chepstow NP16 5EZ Tel: 01291 625981

Museum reveals the rich and varied past of this ancient Wye Valley port and market centre. Wine trade, ship building and salmon fishing feature in displays which also recall Wye tourism and local social history.

Opening Times: Mon to Sat, Sun afternoon. Admission: Adult £1.00, Child Free, Concession 75p. Location: In lower town, opposite Chepstow Castle. Map Ref: 10

HAVERFORDWEST *Pembrokeshire*

Haverfordwest Town Museum

Castle House, The Castle, Haverfordwest SA61 2EF Tel: 01437 763087
Web: www.haverfordwest-town-museum.org.uk

The Haverfordwest Town Museum is situated in the Old Prison Governor's House in the grounds of Haverfordwest Castle. It reflects on the history of Haverfordwest from Norman times to the present day. The museum contains a wide variety of artefacts, photographs, paintings and uses multi-media computer facilities with touch screen. The oldest letter box in Wales, fully restored, is in the museum. Each room in the museum reflects on a distinct theme. The castle and reception room informs visitors about the history of the castle and its use as a prison. The Civic Room has old mayoral robes, information on town development and archaeological finds. The Religion Room has finds from the

The exterior of Haverfordwest Town Museum

South & Southwest Wales

excavations at Haverfordwest Priory, woodcarvings from St Mary's Church and the town stocks. The landing area has fascinating Victorian views of Haverfordwest and an oil portrait of Lord Kensington. The People Room upstairs has portraits of famous people associated with the town including Augustus John, Sir Thomas Picton and Sir John Perrot. The Trade and Industry Room has interesting artefacts like the old Llewellin churn, billheads, token coinage and old tills. The Institutions Room focuses on schools, police, fire brigade, military units and the workhouse.

Opening Times: Easter to Oct Mon to Sat 10:00-16:00.
Admission: Adults £1.00, Child/OAP/Student £0.50, Family £3.00
Location: In the grounds of Haverfordwest Castle, in the Old Governor's House. Signposted from town centre.   Map Ref: 11

A butter churn at Haverfordwest Town Museum

Picton Castle

Haverfordwest SA62 4AS   Tel / Fax: 01437 751326
Email: pct@pictoncastle.freeserve.co.uk   Web: www.pictoncastle.co.uk

Picton, built in the 13th century by Sir John Wogan, is still the family home of his direct descendants the Philippses. The medieval castle was remodelled above the undercroft in the 1750s providing fine Georgian interiors. Around 1790 a new wing was added which included a dining room and drawing room. The 40 acres of gardens are part of The Royal Horticultural Society access scheme for beautiful gardens. The woodland gardens have a unique collection of rhododendrons, azaleas, mature trees, unusual shrubs, wild flowers, a new fern walk, and a recently restored dewpond. The walled garden has a fishpond with a fountain, fernery, herbaceous borders and a large collection of herbs labelled with their herbal remedies. Children can enjoy the maze and the nature trail.

Opening Times: 1 Apr to 30 Sep Tue to Sun (open BH Mon) 10:30-17:00. Castle: by guided tour only between 12:00-16:00. Gardens only: daily 10:30 to dusk. Admission: Castle, Garden & Gallery: Adult £4.95, OAP £4.75, Child £1.95. Garden & Gallery: Adult £3.95, OAP £3.75, Child £1.95. Group reductions available please phone for details. Location: Four miles east of Haverfordwest, just off the A40. Exhibitions & Events 2003 : The Gallery has regular art exhibitions. Events including garden lectures and plant sales are held throughout the season. Please telephone for details.   Map Ref: 11

Scolton Manor Museum

Spittal, Haverfordwest SA62 5QL   Tel: 01437 731328   Fax: 01437 779500

Manor house built 1842 furnished to around 1900, also with costume and art galleries. Stable block also featuring blacksmith and carpenter's workshops. Railway area with signal box and 'Margaret' locomotive. Exhibition Hall displaying agricultural machinery and other local industries, World War II and railway galleries.

Opening Times: Apr to Oct Tue to Sun & BH 10:30-17:30. Admission: Adult £2.00, Child £1.00, Concession £1.50. Location: Five miles outside Haverfordwest on the B4329 (Cardigan Road).   Map Ref: 12

Kidwelly Industrial Museum

Broadford, Kidwelly SA17 4LW   Tel: 01554 891078   Fax: 01267 223830
Email: cdelaney@carmarthenshire.gov.uk   Web: www.carmarthenshire.gov.uk

A unique opportunity to see how tinplate was made. The museum has buildings and machinery of the tinplate industry, coal mining and much more, in a delightful rural setting.

Opening Times: Easter BH, Spring BH to 31 Aug Mon to Fri 10:00-17:00, Sat & Sun 14:00-17:00. Admission: Free. Location: Signposted from the A484 on the outskirts of Kidwelly.
    Map Ref: 13

South & Southwest Wales

Museum of the Welsh Woollen Industry

Dre-fach Felindre, Llandysul SA44 5UP   Tel: 01559 370929   Fax: 01559 371592
Web: www.nmgw.ac.uk

The Museum of the Welsh Woollen Industry tells the fascinating story of the most traditional of rural industries and still houses a thriving, working woollen mill, producing for the modern market.

Opening Times: Please phone for details, re-opening in mid-spring following re-developments.
Admission: Free. Location: Four miles east of Newcastle Emlyn, 16 miles north west of
Carmarthen, four miles off A484, in village of Dre-Fach Felindre.   Map Ref: 14

LLANELLI *Carmarthenshire*

Parc Howard Museum & Art Gallery

Felinfoel Road, Llanelli SA15 3LJ   Tel: 01554 772029   Fax: 01267 223830
Email: cdelaney@carmarthenshire.gov.uk   Web: www.carmarthenshire.gov.uk

Situated in a fine public park, Parc Howard has the largest collection of Llanelly Pottery, paintings and other items from Llanelli's past.

Opening Times: Apr to Sep Mon to Fri 11:00-13:00 & 14:00-18:00, Sat & Sun 14:00-18:00. Oct
to Mar Mon to Fri 11:00-13:00 & 14:00-16:00, Sat & Sun 14:00-16:00. Admission: Free.
Location: Half a mile north of Llanelli town on the A476.   Map Ref: 15

MERTHYR TYDFIL *Rhondda*

Cyfarthfa Castle Museum & Art Gallery

Brecon Road, Merthyr Tydfil CF47 8RE   Tel / Fax: 01685 723112
Email: museum@cyfarthfapark.freeserve.co.uk

Georgian castellated mansion, originally Crawshay family home, set in 160 acre park. Collection includes: local history, fine art, porcelain, costume collection, brass instruments, Egypt collection, several temporary exhibitions.

Opening Times: Apr to Sep daily 10:00-17:30. Oct to Mar Tue to Fri 10:00-16:00, Sat & Sun
12:00-16:00. Closed Mon. Admission: Free. Location: Cyfarthfa Park on Brecon Road, one
mile north of Merthyr Town Centre.   Map Ref: 16

Joseph Parrys Ironworkers Cottage

4 Chapel Row, Georgetown, Merthyr Tydfil CF48 1BN   Tel / Fax: 01685 723112
Email: museum@cyfarthfapark.freeserve.co.uk

1840s ironworkers cottage, direct contrast to Cyfarthfa Castle. Home to Parry family and birthplace of Joseph Parry, musician and composer of Myfanwy. Ground floor recreates 1841; upper floor, exhibition of Parry's life and local industry.

Opening Times: Apr to Sep Thu to Sun 14:00-17:00. Other times by appointment.
Admission: Free. Location: Town centre, five minutes from bus station.   Map Ref: 16

MILFORD HAVEN *Pembrokeshire*

Milford Haven Maritime & Heritage Museum

The Old Custom House, Sybil Way, The Docks, Milford Haven SA73 3AF   Tel: 01646 694496
Fax: 01646 699454

Building of Milford from early whaling to fishing, oil refining to marina. Television shows on history of town and docks. Brass rubbing, hands-on and off exhibits.

Opening Times: Mon to Sat 11:00-17:00, Sun, BH & school holidays 11:00-17:00. Also group
booking in advance outside these times. Admission: Adult £1.20, Child/OAP 60p, Under 5s
Free. Location: Near town centre, on Milford Haven Marina.   Map Ref: 17

MONMOUTH

Castle & Regimental Museum

The Castle, Monmouth NP25 3BS   Tel: 01600 772175
Email: curator@monmouthcastlemuseum.org.uk   Web: www.monmouthcastlemuseum.org.uk

The regimental museum of the Royal Monmouthshire Royal Engineers, and of the preceding

South & Southwest Wales

onmouthshire Militia. With some history of Monmouth Castle and Henry V. Also a small medieval-style herb garden.

Opening Times: Apr to Oct daily 14:00-17:00, Nov to Easter Sat & Sun 14:00-16:00.
Admission: Free - donations welcome. Location: At the highest point of the town centre.

Map Ref: 18

Nelson Museum & Local History Centre   ♿ ❀

Priory Street, Monmouth NP25 3XA   Tel: 01600 713519   Fax: 01600 775001
Email: nelsonmuseum@monmouthshire.gov.uk

The life, loves, death and commemoration of the famous admiral in one of Britain's major Nelson collections. In the same building Monmouth's history is displayed, including a section on Charles Rolls, co-founder of Rolls Royce.

Opening Times: Mon to Sat 10:00-13:00, 14:00-17:00. Sun 14:00-17:00. Admission: Adult £1.00, Child Free, Concession 75p, Local residents Free. Location: Town centre, parking nearby.   Map Ref: 18

Nantgarw China Works Museum   ✑ ❀ ⛟

Tyla Gwyn, Nantgarw CF15 7TB   Tel: 01443 841703   Fax: 01443 841826
Email: cvm@rhondda-cynon-taff.gov.uk   Web: www.friendsofncwm.org

Dedicated to William Billingsley, the 19th century porcelain manufacturer and decorator, and the Pardoe family, domestic earthen utilityware manufacturers. Grounds contain remains of factory buildings and bottle kilns, some restored.

Opening Times: Please ring or email for details. Admission: Please ring or email for details.
Location: Ten miles north of Cardiff, five miles south of Pontypridd.   Map Ref: 19

Cefn Coed Colliery Museum   ♿ ❀ ⛟

Neath Road, Crynant, Neath SA10 8SN   Tel / Fax: 01639 750556

The museum is located on the site of the former Cefn Coed Colliery. It tells the story of life and work in what was once the deepest anthracite mine in the world.

Opening Times: Apr to Oct daily 10:30-17:00. Admission: Free. Location: Four miles north of Neath, south of Crynant on A4109.   Map Ref: 20

Neath Museum   ♿ ❀

Gwyn Hall, Orchard Street, Neath SA11 1DT   Tel: 01639 645726

It is a small but lively museum of local history, displaying Neath's rich history from prehistoric times through Roman, medieval, Victorian and on. It also houses an art gallery for temporary art and photographic exhibitions.

Opening Times: Tue to Sat 10:00-16:00. Closed Sat, Sun & BH & Xmas week.
Admission: Free Location: Centre of town, one minute walk from the Bus Station, five minutes walk from Train Station.   Map Ref: 21

The National Coracle Centre   ✑ ♿ ❀ ☕ ⛟

Cenarth, Newcastle Emlyn SA38 9JL   Tel: 01239 710980
Email: martinfowler@coraclecentre.fsnet.co.uk   Web: coraclecentre.co.uk

A unique collection of coracles from Wales and around the world, set in the grounds of a 17th century flour mill, overlooking the salmon leap.

Opening Times: Easter to Oct Sun to Fri 10:30-17:30 and by appointment. Admission: Adult £3.00, Child £1.00, OAP £2.50. Location: Centre of Cenarth village, beside the river and falls.

Map Ref: 22

✑	♿	❀	☕	❀	⛟
Guided or Private Tours	Disabled Access	Gift Shop or Sales Point	Café or Refreshments	Restaurant	Car Parking

South & Southwest Wales

NEWPORT

Newport Museum & Art Gallery
John Frost Square, Newport NP20 1PA   Tel: 01633 840064

Houses fascinating displays of the natural and human history of Newport. Archaeology displays including important material from this Roman town of Caerwent; social history displays including the chartists; natural history displays including local geology; art exhibitions of watercolours, oils and prints, John Wait teapot display and Fox collection of contemporary art. There is a temporary exhibition programme.

Opening Times: Mon to Thu 09:30-17:00, Fri 09:30-16:30, Sat 09:30-16:00.   Admission: Free.
Location: Town centre, near car parks and bus station.   Map Ref: 23

PENARTH *Glamorgan*

Turner House Gallery
Plymouth Road, Penarth CF64 3DH   Tel: 029 2070 8870   Web: www.nmgw.ac.uk

Elegant gallery for a changing and varied programme of visual art.

Opening Times: Tue to Sun 10:00-17:00 & BH Mon. Only during exhibition showings.
Admission: Free.   Location: Near town centre, five minutes walk from Penarth Train Station.
Map Ref: 25

PONTYPOOL *Torfaen*

Pontypool Museum
Park Buildings, Pontypool NP4 6JH   Tel: 01495 752036

The museum has a collection of different displays including art and craft, a new art gallery and a Japanware display. Telling the history of the Torfaen area - industrial and social, and is set in a Georgian stable block.

Opening Times: Mon to Fri 10:00-17:00, Sat & Sun 14:00-17:00. Closed Xmas & New Year.
Admission: Adult £1.20, Concession 60p, Family £2.40. Group bookings 10% discount.
Location: Close to town centre and Pontypool Park.   Map Ref: 26

PONTYPRIDD *Rhondda*

Rhondda Heritage Park
Lewis Merthyr Colliery, Coed Cae Road, Trehafod, Pontypridd CF37 7NP   Tel: 01443 682036
Fax: 01443 687420   Email: reception@rhonddaheritagepark.com
Web: www.rhonddaheritagepark.com

The former Lewis Merthyr Colliery now offers a fascinating insight into the rich character of the Rhondda Valleys in an unique entertaining and educational environment for all ages.

Opening Times: Daily 10:00-18:00 (last underground tour 16:30). Closed Mon Oct to Easter.
Closed Xmas to New Year.   Admission: Adult £5.60, Child £4.30, OAP £4.95, Family £16.50.
Location: 15 minute drive from junction 32 of M4. Trehafod Village located three miles from
Pontypridd.   Map Ref: 27

PORT TALBOT

South Wales Miners Museum

Afan Argoed Countryside Centre, Cynonville, Port Talbot SA13 3HG   Tel: 01639
850564   Fax: 01639 850446

Set in the beautiful Afan Valley, The South Wales Miners Museum, gives information on the social history of coal mining. It tells us of the communities, family life and leisure activities.

Opening Times: Summer Mon to Fri 10:30-17:00, Sat & Sun 10:30-18:00. Winter Mon to Fri 10:30-16:00, Sat & Sun 10:30-17:00. Closed Xmas.   Admission: Adult £1.20, Child/OAP 60p.
Location: Approx six miles from nearest town. The South Wales Miners Museum is in Afan Argoed in Afan Forest Park.   Map Ref: 28

SWANSEA

Egypt Centre
University of Swansea, Singleton Park, Swansea SA2 8PP   Tel: 01792 295960

The largest collection of Egyptian antiquities in Wales. Includes coffins, jewellery, tools and weapons etc.

Opening Times: Tue to Sat 10:00-16:00. Closed Sun, Mon & BH.   Admission: Free.
Location: On University Campus, ten minutes by car from Swansea.   Map Ref: 29

Glynn Vivian Art Gallery

Alexandra Road, Swansea SA1 5DZ   Tel: 01792 655006
Fax: 01792 651713   Email: glynn.vivian.gallery@swansea.gov.uk
Web: www.swansea.gov.uk

A changing exhibition programme of contemporary visual arts. Plus a broad spectrum of visual arts form the original bequest of Richard Glynn Vivian (1835-1910) which includes work by Old Masters as well as an international collection of porcelain and Swansea china. The 20th century is also well represented with modern painting and sculpture by Hepworth, Nicholson, Nash alongside Welsh artists such as Ceri Richards, Gwen John and Augustus John.

Opening Times: Tue to Sun 10:00-17:00. Closed Mon except BH.
Admission: Free. Location: One minute walk from railway station.

Sculpture Court with David Nash Sculpture

Map Ref: 29

Gower Heritage Centre

Parkmill, Gower, Swansea SA3 2EH   Tel: 01792 371206   Fax: 01792 371471
Email: info@gowerheritagecentre.sagehost.co.uk
Web: www.gowerheritagecentre.sagehost.co.uk

Crafts and heritage centre based around working 12th century water-powered corn and sawmill. Daily demonstrations of wood-turning, flour making, smithing and jewellery making. Regular historical, musical and schools events throughout the year.

Opening Times: Daily 10:00-17:30. Admission: Adult £2.95, Child/OAP £1.95, Family £8.50.
Group rates available. Location: Eight miles west of Swansea in seaside village, on bus route.

Map Ref: 30

Swansea Maritime & Industrial Museum

Museum Square, Maritime Quarter, Swansea SA1 1SN   Tel: 01792 650351/470371/653004
Fax: 01792 654200   Email: swansea.maritime.museum@swansea.gov.uk

The museum features a fully functional Welsh woollen mill which demonstrates carding, spinning and weaving on a daily basis. The museum also has exhibitions which tell the stories of the town's industrialisation and the maritime trade which enabled it to happen. The museum has a collection of three ships which are open during the summer months.

Opening Times: Tue to Sun & BH 10:00-17:00. Closed Xmas & New Year. Admission: Free. Location: Central location close to Leisure Centre, five minutes from city centre.

Map Ref: 29

Pulling & sailing lifeboat, John & Naomi Beattie.

Key to Classifications
see Classifications Index on page 413

Anthropology	Jewellery	Railway
Archaeological	Literature & Libraries	Religion
Art Galleries	Maritime	Roman
Arts, Crafts & Textiles	Military & Defence	Science - Earth
China, Glass & Ceramics	Mills - Water & Wind	& Planetary
Communications	Multicultural	Sculpture
Egyptian	Music & Theatre	Sporting History
Fashion	Natural History	Stately Homes
Geology	Oriental	Toy & Childhood
Health & Medicine	Palaces	Transport
Horticultural	Police, Prisons & Dungeons	Victoriana

South & Southwest Wales

Swansea Museum

Victoria Road, Maritime Quarter, Swansea SA1 1SN   Tel: 01792 653763
Email: swansea.museum@swansea.gov.uk

Diverse range of collection reflecting the passions of the Victorian founders. The museum displays an exceptional collection of Swansea China. A quirky collection of artefacts provides infinite variety in the 'Cabinet of Curiosities'.

Opening Times: Tue to Sun & BH 10:00-17:00. Closed Xmas & New Year. Admission: Free. Location: Central location, five minutes from city centre.   Map Ref: 29

TENBY *Pembrokeshire*

Tenby Museum & Art Gallery

Castle Hill, Tenby SA70 7BP   Tel / Fax: 01834 842809   Email: tenbymuseum@hotmail.com
Web: www.tenbymuseum.free.online.co.uk

Two art galleries with regularly changing exhibitions, works by Gwen John and Augustus John. Local history, maritime, archaeology, geology and natural history. Activities for children.

Opening Times: Daily Easter to end Oct 10:00-17:00, Nov to Easter Mon to Fri 10:00-17:00.
Admission: Adult £2.00, Child £1.00, Concession £1.50, Family £4.50. Location: Centre of town, above the harbour.   Map Ref: 31

TORFAEN

Big Pit National Mining Museum

Big Pit, Blaenafon, Torfaen NP4 9XP   Tel: 01495 790311
Fax: 01495 792618   Web: www.nmgw.ac.uk

In the heart of the recently declared World Heritage Site at Blaenafon, Big Pit offers an experience unparalleled in Britain and unique to Wales. Guided by an ex-miner, you will descend 300 feet to the very depths of the mine and experience the inky blackness that the miners worked in day after day. Complete your visit on the surface and explore the colliery buildings, pit head baths and winding engine house.

Opening Times: Mid Feb to 30 Nov daily 09:30-17:00
Admission: Free. Location: In the town of Blaenafon, approx 16 miles north of Newport. Signposted from junction 25A of M4.   Map Ref: 32

Glorious unspoilt border country with little traffic and described as 'one of the lost wildernesses of Britain'. The Brecon Beacons National Park offers a wide variety of majestic sights including the Black Mountains.

Museums and galleries are not exactly prolific and generally focus on local history, and the arts and crafts of the region.

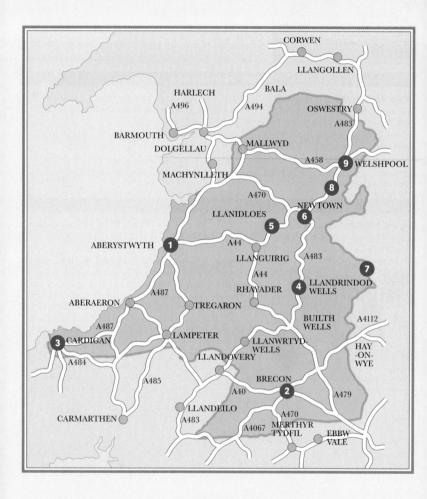

The Red Map References should be used to locate Museums etc on the pages that follow

Mid-Wales

Ceredigion Museum & Gallery   ⌖ ● ▢

Coliseum, Terrace Road, Aberystwyth SY23 2AQ Tel: 01970 633088 Fax: 01970 633084
Email: museum@ceredigion.gov.uk Web: www.ceredigion.gov.uk/coliseum

Local history museum in a restored Edwardian Theatre with exhibitions on archaeology, seafaring, agriculture, furniture etc. Changing temporary exhibition. Art Gallery.

Opening Times: Mon to Sat 10:00-17:00. Admission: Free. Location: Town centre, next to Tourist Information Centre.   Map Ref: 1

School of Art Gallery & Museum : Ceramics Collection   ✑ ⌖ ● ▢ ◕ ⏚

Arts Centre, Penglais, Aberystwyth SY23 3DE Tel: 01970 622460 Fax: 01970 622461
Email: mov@aber.ac.uk Web: www.aber.ac.uk/ceramics

Contemporary British, European, American and Japanese studio pottery; 18th and 19th century Welsh and English slip ware; Swansea and Nantgarw porcelain; Art Pottery and Oriental ceramics; and an outstanding collection of early 20th century British pioneer studio pottery. Changing displays.

Opening Times: Mon to Sat 09:30-17:00, also most evenings. Closed Sun, Easter & Xmas.
Admission: Free. Location: On University Campus, one mile from town centre and railway station.   Map Ref: 1

School of Art Gallery & Museum   ✑ ⌖ ● ⏚

University of Wales, Buarth Mawr, Aberystwyth SY23 1NG Tel: 01970 622460 Fax: 01970 622461 Email: neh@aber.ac.uk Web: www.aber.ac.uk/art/ or /museum

University's collection of fine and decorative art: watercolours, drawings, and European prints from 15th century to present; art in Wales since 1945; contemporary Welsh and post-war Italian photography. Changing exhibitions from the collection, touring shows and exhibitions by invited artists. Study collection by appointment. Housed in magnificent Edwardian building overlooking Cardigan Bay.

Opening Times: Mon to Fri 10:00-17:30. Closed Sat, Sun Easter & Xmas. Admission: Free.
Location: Near town centre, four minute walk from railway station and town centre.   Map Ref: 1

Brecknock Museum & Art Gallery   ⌖ ● ⏚

Captains Walk, Brecon LD3 7DW Tel: 01874 624121 Fax: 01874 611281
Email: brecknock.museum@powys.gov.uk

Located in the centre of Brecon Beacons National Park it explores the past, natural environment and art of Brecknockshire. A Victorian Assize Court is interpreted with figures, sound and light. A lively exhibition programme features contemporary art and crafts from Wales.

Opening Times: Mon to Fri 10:00-17:00. Apr to Sep Sun 12:00-17:00, 4 Nov to Feb Sat 10:00-13:00 & 14:00-17:00. Admission: Adult £1.00, Child Free, Concession 50p, Residents of Powys Free. Location: Near town centre.   Map Ref: 2

South Wales Borderers & Monmouthshire Regimental Museum   ✑ ⌖ ●

The Barracks, Brecon LD3 7EB Tel: 01874 613310 Fax: 01874 613275
Email: swb@rrw.org.uk Web: www.rrw.org.uk

The Royal Regiment of Wales Museum with artefacts from the 1879 Anglo-Zulu War and equipment and war mementoes spanning 300 years.

Opening Times: Apr to Sep daily 09:00-17:00, Oct to Mar Mon to Fri 09:00-17:00.
Admission: Adult £3.00, Child Free. Group rates available. Location: The Museum is adjacent to the Barracks in Brecon in The Walton (B4601)   Map Ref: 2

Cardigan Heritage Centre   ⌖ ● ▢ ⏚

Teifi Wharf, Castle Street, Cardigan SA43 3AA Tel: 01239 614404

A Heritage Centre situated on the ground floor of an 18th Century warehouse on the Teifi river. There are collections on the history of Cardigan from Norman times to the present day. Also a Café, Craft/Book Shop and riverside terrace.

Opening Times: Easter to Oct 10:00-17:00 daily. Admission: Adults £2.00, Child £1.00, Family £5.00 plus concessions. Location: On the Riverside by Cardigan Bridge.   Map Ref: 3

Mid-Wales

Radnorshire Museum

Temple Street, Llandrindod Wells LD1 5DL   Tel: 01597 824513   Fax: 01597 825781

An unrivalled collection of photographs of Llandrindod from Victorian times to the present day. Archaeological collections from Castal Collen (site of main defence of Roman times), Capel Maelog and a unique Sheela-na-Gig.

Opening Times: Tue to Thu 10:00-17:00, Fri 10:00-16:30, closed between 13:00-14:00. Weekends - winter Sat 10:00-13:00, summer Sat 10:00-17:00, Sun 13:00-17:00. Closed Mon.
Admission: Adult £1.00, Child Free, OAP 50p, Powys Residents Free.   Location: Next to Tourist Information, two minute walk from train station.   Map Ref: 4

Llanidloes Museum

The Town Hall, Great Oak Street, Llanidloes   Tel: 01686 413777

Three display areas reflecting the nature and type of the collections including local history, Victorian life and a Natural History Gallery.

Opening Times: Mon & Tue, Thu & Fri 11:00-13:00 & 14:00-17:00. May to Sep Sat & Sun 11:00-13:00 & 14:00-17:00. Oct to Apr Sat 10:00-13:00.   Admission: Adult £1.00, Child/Residents of Powys Free, Concession 50p.   Location: In the Town Hall.   Map Ref: 5

Newtown Textile Museum

5/7 Commercial Street, Newtown   Tel: 01686 622024

The museum is housed in a typical early 19th century weaving shop, it focuses on the history of the woollen industry in Newtown from 1790 to the beginning of the 20th century.

Opening Times: May to Sep Tue to Sat & BH 14:00-17:00.   Admission: Free.   Location: Near town centre, five minutes walk from central bus station.   Map Ref: 6

W H Smith Museum

24 High Street, Newtown SY16 2NP   Tel: 01686 626280

An engrossing collection of models and memorabilia telling how a small family business flourished over two centuries, to become one of today's biggest British companies and a household name.

Opening Times: Mon to Sat 09:00-17:30, closed Sun and BH.   Admission: Free.   Location: In town centre, five minutes walk from main car park and bus station.   Map Ref: 6

Key to Classifications
see Classifications Index on page 413

Anthropology	Jewellery	Railway
Archaeological	Literature & Libraries	Religion
Art Galleries	Maritime	Roman
Arts, Crafts & Textiles	Military & Defence	Science - Earth
China, Glass & Ceramics	Mills - Water & Wind	& Planetary
Communications	Multicultural	Sculpture
Egyptian	Music & Theatre	Sporting History
Fashion	Natural History	Stately Homes
Geology	Oriental	Toy & Childhood
Health & Medicine	Palaces	Transport
Horticultural	Police, Prisons & Dungeons	Victoriana

Mid-Wales

The Judge's Lodging

Broad Street, Presteigne LD8 2AD   Tel: 01544 260650   Fax: 01544 260652
Email: info@judgeslodging.org.uk   Web: www.judgeslodging.org.uk

Stunningly restored 1860s judge's apartments, servants' quarters, courtroom and cells with displays on the Radnor borders region, local history and the Radnorshire Constabulary. A totally hands-on, national award-winning historic house.

Opening Times: 1 Mar to 22 Dec daily from 10:00. Closed Mon & Tue in Nov & Dec.
Admission: Adult £3.95, Child/Concession £2.95, Family £12.00, Group rates available.

Map Ref: 7

Andrew Logan Museum of Sculpture

Berriew, Welshpool SY21 8PJ   Tel: 01686 640689   Fax: 01686 640764
Email: info@andrewlogan.com   Web: www.andrewlogan.com

Enter the glittering, fantasy wonderland where horses fly, butterflies are larger than birds and a throne is a velvet lily. 17th in The Independent's Guide to Top 50 Small Museums.

Opening Times: Easter to Oct Wed to Sun 12:00-18:00. Nov & Dec Sat & Sun 12:00-16:00.
Admission: Adult £2.50, Concession £1.50.

Map Ref: 8

Powis Castle & Garden

THE NATIONAL TRUST

Welshpool SY21 8RF   Tel: 01938 5544338

Powis Castle.
Photo credit National Trust/Andrew Butler

Laid out under the influence of Italian and French styles, the garden retains its original lead statues, an orangery and an aviary on the terraces. In the 18th century an informal woodland wilderness was created on the opposing ridge with fine views over the Severn Valley. Perched on a rock above the garden terraces, the medieval Castle contains one of the finest collections of paintings and furniture in Wales.

Opening Times: Castle, Garden & Museum: 23 Mar to 30 Jun, 1 Sep to 3 Nov Wed to Sun, Jul & Aug Tue to Sun & BH. Castle & Museum: 13:00-17:00, Garden 11:00-18:00. Admission: All inclusive tickets: Adult £7.50, Child £3.75, Family £18.75, Group Rates available. National Trust Members Free. Location: One miles south of Welshpool, signposted off A483 . One mile from railway station.

Map Ref: 9

Powysland Museum & Montgomery Canal Centre

The Canal Wharf, Welshpool SY21 7AQ   Tel: 01938 554656

The museum is housed in a restored 19th century warehouse by the Montgomery Canal. It illustrates the history of the county from pre-historic settlers to the 21st century population.

Opening Times: Mon & Tue Thu & Fri 11:00-13:00 & 14:00-17:00. May to Sep Sat & Sun 10:00-13:00 & 14:00-17:00. Oct to Apr Sat 14:00-17:00. Admission: Adult £1.00, Child/Resident of Powys Free, Concession 50p. Location: Near town centre, five minutes walk from railway station.

Map Ref: 9

North Wales

North Wales contains Snowdonia National Park including the highest mountains in England and Wales. The north coast boasts the queen of the Welsh resorts, Llandudno, the town retaining much of its Victorian charm. The Isle of Anglesey is a delight with fine beaches and a remarkable number of Neolithic ruins.

There is a fine selection of museums and galleries throughout the region which cover both social history and local history as well as subjects as diverse as tramways, steam railways, Roman remains, the style and times of David Lloyd George and Maritime history.

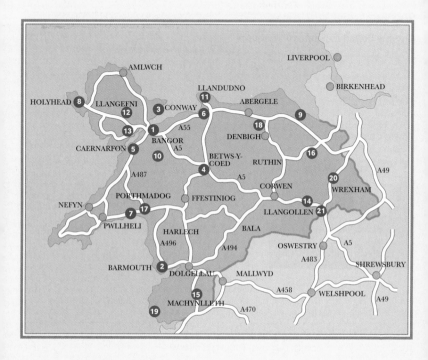

The Red Map References should be used to locate Museums etc on the pages that follow

North Wales

BANGOR *Gwynedd*

Gwynedd Museum & Art Gallery

Ffordd Gwynedd, Bangor LL57 1DT   Tel: 01248 353368   Email: patwest@gwynedd.gov.uk
Web: www.gwynedd.gov.uk/museums

Gwynedd's only general museum where you can learn about the ways of life led by previous generations which helps us to place our own experiences in the context of an unfolding story.

Opening Times: Tue to Fri 12:30-16:30, Sat 10:30-16:30.   Admission: Free.   Location: By the main bus stop near the town centre.   Map Ref: 1

Penrhyn Castle

Bangor LL57 4HN   Tel: 01248 353084   THE NATIONAL TRUST

Built on the profits of Jamaican sugar and Welsh slate, Penrhyn is a massive 19th century neo-Norman castle crammed with fascinating things including a one-ton slate bed made for Queen Victoria and a spectacular grand staircase that took ten years to build. It houses one of the best art collections in Wales, including paintings by Rembrandt, Gainsborough and Canaletto. The castle's interiors are decorated with elaborate carvings, hand-made wallpapers and stained glass, and its furniture collection includes many original pieces made of Penrhyn oak and designed by the architect Thomas Hopper. Penrhyn is

surrounded by 45 acres of grounds, including parkland, wooded walks and semi-tropical areas. Its Victorian walled garden contains exotic plants and shrubs from all over the world. Taking full advantage of its location, the castle offers stunning views of the mountains of Snowdonia and the Menai Strait. The stable block houses an Industrial Railway Museum with full-sized locomotives, rolling stock and track, and the Railway Model Museum. Displayed in the Doll Museum are over 500 dolls from around the world, The stable block's two exhibition galleries hold high quality temporary art exhibitions by local and internationally renowned artists.

Opening Times: 23 Mar to 3 Nov Wed to Mon Castle open 12:00-17:00 (Jul & Aug 11:00-17:00), Grounds, stable block, tearoom open one hour earlier.   Admission: National Trust Members Free. Castle ticket: Adult £6.00, Child £4.00, Family £15.00, Group (15+) £5.00. Grounds & Stable block: Adult £4.00, Child £2.00.   Location: Two miles east of Bangor at junction of A5 and A55, brown tourist signposted.   Exhibitions & Events 2003 : There is a wide programme of exhibitions and events. Please telephone for details.   Map Ref: 1

BARMOUTH *Gwynedd*

Ty Gwyn & Ty Crwn & Barmouth Sailors' Institute

The Quay, Barmouth LL42 1ET   Tel: 01341 241333

The presentations of photographs and pictures in all buildings portray Barmouth's maritime heritage since the Tudor period. The reading room in the Sailors' Institute dates from 1890 and is the last example of its kind in Wales.

Opening Times: Ty Gwyn & Ty Crwn: Apr to Sep daily 09:00-19:00. Barmouth Sailors' Institute: Mon to Sat 09:00-18:00 all year round.   Admission: Free.   Location: On the Quay, five minutes walk from town centre.   Map Ref: 2

BEAUMARIS *Anglesey*

Beaumaris Gaol & Courthouse

Beaumaris LL58 8ED   Tel: 01248 810921

Crime and punishment related collections including prison and court furniture, legal robes, chains, police equipment.

Opening Times: Easter to end Sep daily 10:30-17:00.   Admission: Adult £3.50, Child/OAP £2.50.   Location: Court House, opposite Castle in Main Street, gaol two minute walk from Main Street.   Map Ref: 3

North Wales

Museum of Childhood Memories

1 Castle Street, Beaumaris LL58 8AP   Tel: 01248 712498   Email: bryn.brown@amserve.net
Web: www.aboutbritain.com/museumofchildhoodmemories.htm

A independent museum located in a Georgian house. The nine rooms each display a different theme showing the happier side of family life over the past 150 years.

Opening Times: Mar to Oct 10:30-17:00. Closed Nov to Feb.   Admission: Adult £3.25, Child £2.00, OAP/Student £2.75.   Location: Opposite Beaumaris Castle, Anglesey.   Map Ref: 3

BETWS-Y-COED

Conwy Valley Railway Museum

The Old Goods Yard, Betws-y-Coed LL24 0AL   Tel: 01690 760568   Fax: 01690 710132

Dioramas featuring LNW Railway by the late Jack Nelson quarter full size working model 15' gauge steam locomotive 'Britannia'. Exhibits and working layouts London and North Western Railway.

Opening Times: Apr to Oct daily 10:15-17:30, Nov to Mar daily 10:00-16:00.   Admission: Adult £1.00, Child/OAP 50p, Family £2.50.   Location: Adjacent to railway station, four minute walk from town centre.   Map Ref: 4

CAERNARFON *Gwynedd*

Caernarfon Maritime Museum

Victoria Dock, Caernarfon   Tel: 01248 752083

The museum illustrates the rich maritime and industrial history of the port and town of Caernarfon, including its seafarers. A display illustrates the operation of the dredger Seiont II through a recreation of parts of the bridge and engine room, and another the training ship HMS Conway (including an anchor outside the museum).

Opening Times: Sun to Fri 11:00-16:00. Closed Sat.   Admission: Adult £1.00, Child Free.
Location: Near town centre, just outside town walls on Victoria Dock.   Map Ref: 5

Royal Welch Fusiliers Regimental Museum

Queens Tower, Caernarfon Castle, Caernarfon LL55 2AY   Tel: 01286 673362

Extensive collection of uniforms, paintings, weapons and memorabilia displayed in five refurbished galleries. Outstanding collection of medals and works relating to Great War poets and authors, Siegfried Sassoon, Robert Graves, David Jones, Dr J C Dunn and Frank Richards.

Opening Times: 09:30-17:00 daily in summer. Please phone for details of winter opening.   Admission: Free, within entry to Caernarfon Castle.   Location: Town centre, five minute walk from central bus station.

Mounting the Queen's Guard in London, September, 1975

Map Ref: 5

Segontium Roman Museum

Beddgelert Road, Caernarfon LL55 2LN   Tel: 01286 675625   Fax: 01286 678416
Web: www.nmgw.ac.uk

A small museum neighbouring the remains of one of Britain's most famous forts.

Opening Times: 1 Nov to Mar Mon to Sat 10:00-16:00, Sun 14:00-16:00. 1 Apr to Oct Mon to Sat 10:00-17:00, Sun 14:00-17:00.   Admission: Free.   Location: On the A4085, just out of the centre of Caernarfon.   Map Ref: 5

CONWY

Aberconwy House

2 Castle Street, Conwy LL32 8AY   Tel: 01492 592246

This 14th century house is the last remaining medieval merchant's house in Conwy. The house has been restored and each room shows a different moment in time.

Opening Times: 23 Mar to 3 Nov Wed to Mon 11:00-17:00. Closed Tue.   Admission: Adult £2.00, Child £1.00, Family £5.00. National Trust Members Free. Group Rates available.   Map Ref: 6

North Wales

Royal Cambrian Academy

Crown Lane, Conwy LL32 8AN   Tel / Fax: 01492 593413   Email: rca@rcaconwy.org
Web: www.rcaconwy.org

Nine temporary art exhibitions per year. A variety of contemporary and historical work from the best Welsh artists.

Opening Times: Tue to Sat 11:00-17:00, Sun 13:00-16:30. Closed Mon.   Admission: Adult £1.00, Child Free, Concession 50p.   Location: One minute walk from railway station and bus stop, just off Conwy High Street, behind 'Plas Mawr'.   Map Ref: 6

CRICCIETH Gwynedd

Lloyd George Museum & Highgate Cottage

Llanystumdwy, Criccieth LL52 0SH   Tel / Fax: 01766 522071
Email: nestthomas@gwynedd.gov.uk   Web: www.gwynedd.gov.uk/museums

The Museum traces the life and times of David Lloyd George featuring freedom caskets and scrolls, medals, paintings, photographs and documents such as the Treaty of Versailles. A visit to Highgate, the Victorian cottage where he lived as a child is included, which also features a Victorian garden and shoemaker's workshop.

Opening Times: Easter, May Mon to Fri 10:30-17:00. Jun Mon to Sat 10:30-17:00. Jul to Sep daily 10:30-17:00. Oct Mon to Fri 11:00-16:00.   Admission: Adult £3.00, Child/Over 65's/Concession £2.00, Family £7.00.   Location: Centre of the village, opposite Moriah Chapel.
                                                                                                    Map Ref: 7

HOLYHEAD Anglesey

Holyhead Maritime Museum

8 Llainfain Estate, Llaingoch, Holyhead LL65 1NF   Tel / Fax: 01407 769745
Email: johncave4@AOL   Web: geocities.com/dickburnel

The Museum, located at the old Lifeboat House (c.1858) facing the famous breakwater, displays models, photographs and artefacts relating to the maritime history of Holyhead and district from Roman times until the present.

Opening Times: Spring to autumn daily 13:00-17:00. Closed Mon except BH.
Admission: Adult £2.00, Child 50p, OAP £1.50, Family £5.00.   Location: Newry Beach, Holyhead.   Map Ref: 8

HOLYWELL Flintshire

Greenfield Valley Museum

Basingwerk House, Greenfield Valley Heritage Park, Holywell CH8 7GH   Tel: 01352 714172
Fax: 01352 714791   Email: info@greenfieldvalley.com   Web: www.greenfieldvalley.com

Museum and farm complex within a 70 acre heritage park. Period buildings including Victorian cottage, 17th century cottage, Victorian schoolroom as well as farming exhibitions, adventure playgound, small animals and weekend events.

Opening Times: Apr to Oct daily 10:00-16:30. Nov to Mar by arrangement only for Groups.
Admission: Adult £2.65, Child £1.60, Under 5s Free, Concession £2.20, Saver Ticket (2 adults and 2 children) £7.00. Group rates available.   Location: Close to Basingwerk Abbey and St Winefride's Holy Well. Follow brown signs from A55 through Holywell or A548 coast road.
                                                                                                    Map Ref: 9

LLANBERIS Gwynedd

Welsh Slate Museum

Welsh Slate Museum, Gilfach Ddu, Llanberis LL55 4TY   Tel: 01286 870630   Fax: 01286 871906   Web: www.nmgw.ac.uk

A living, working piece of history, the museum tells the story of the slate industry in Wales, from nurturing traditional crafts and skills to the harsh realities of quarrying life for over 15,000 men (and boys) of Gwynedd.

Opening Times: 1 Nov to Easter Sun to Fri 10:00-16:00, Easter to End Oct daily 10:00-17:00.
Admission: Free.   Location: In the middle of Padarn Country Park, Llanberis, on the A4086.
                                                                                                    Map Ref: 10

North Wales

Great Orme Tramway

Victoria Station, Church Walks, Llandudno   Tel: 01492 575275   Fax: 01492 513664
Email: enq@greatormetramway.com   Web: www.greatormetramway.com

The 100 year old Great Orme Tramway is the only cable hauled tramway in Britain, an amazing way to reach the top of Llandudno's famous mountain. The tramway journey takes in the wonderful panorama of the resort, the Great Orme Country Park and a 4000 year old copper mine. From the summit, views of the Lake District mountains and the Isle of Man can be seen on a clear day.

Opening Times: Late Mar to late Oct daily 10:00-18:00.
Admission: Adult Return £3.95, Child Return £2.80,
Family Tickets and Group discounts available.   Location: Five minutes walk from town centre,
two minute walk from Pier entrance.   Map Ref: 11

Llandudno Museum

17/19 Gloddaeth Street, Llandudno LL30 2DD   Tel / Fax: 01492 876517
Email: llandudno.museum@lineone.net

Painting and sculptures, objets d'art, local history from archaeology, Roman objects, town resort, war memorabilia and Welsh kitchen, etc. Temporary exhibitions from art to local history.

Opening Times: Easter to Oct Tue to Sat 10:30-13:00 & 14:00-17:00, Sun 14:15-17:00. Nov to Easter Tue to Sat 13:30-16:30. Open BH. Closed Xmas.   Admission: Adult £1.50, Child 75p, Concession £1.20, Family £2.25/£3.50.   Location: Near town centre, three minute walk from pier/promenade.   Map Ref: 11

Anglesey Heritage Gallery/Oriel Ynys Mon

Rhosmeirch, Llangefni LL77 7TQ   Tel: 01248 724444   Fax: 01248 750282

Oriel Ynys Mon comprises a museum depicting the culture and history of Anglesey, encompassing archaeology, art, history, industry and agriculture. A separate art gallery presents a changing programme of arts exhibitions by local, regional and nationally acclaimed artists. The museum's core collection includes art works by such artists as Charles Tunnicliffe and Kyffin Williams, social history and archaeology collection.

Opening Times: Tue to Sun 10:30-17:00. Closed Mon except BH.   Admission: Art Gallery: Free. Museum:
Adult £2.25, Child/OAP £1.25.   Location: Close to town centre, on main bus route.   Map Ref: 12

Plas Newydd

THE NATIONAL TRUST

Plas Newydd, Llanfairpwll, Llangefni LL61 6DQ   Tel: 01248 714795
Fax: 01248 713673   Email: ppnmsn@smtp.ntrust.org.uk   Web: www.nationaltrust.org.uk

An impressive 18th century house by James Wyatt housing Rex Whistler's largest painting and an exhibition about his work. Military museum, garden, parkland, shop and tearoom.

Opening Times: House: Sat to Wed 12:00-17:00. Garden: Sat to Wed 11:00-17:30.   Admission: Adult £4.60, Child £2.30, Family £11.50, Group rates available, National Trust Members Free.   Location: Two miles south of Llanfairpwll and A5.   Map Ref: 13

The east front, viewed across the Menai Strait from the Faenol Estate

North Wales

Llangollen Motor Museum

Pentrefelin, Llangollen LL20 8EE   Tel: 01978 860324
Web: www.llangollenmotormuseum.co.uk

Sixty plus vehicles from 1910 to 1970, a 50s garage village scene complete with owner's quarters, toys, tools, motor reference library and a small exhibition showing the history and development of our canal network.

Opening Times: Mar to Oct Tue to Sun 10:00-17:00.   Admission: Adult £2.50, OAP £2.00, Family £6.00.   Location: One mile outside Llangollen.   Map Ref: 14

Plas Newydd

Hill Street, Llangollen LL20 8AW   Tel: 01978 861314   Fax: 01824 708258
Email: heritage@denbighshire.gov.uk   Web: www.denbighshire.gov.uk

The romantic home of the famous Ladies of Llangollen between 1750 and 1832. Eloping to live together in this rural retreat, their gothicisation of a once humble cottage and grounds still fascinates.

Opening Times: 1 Apr to 31 Oct daily 10:00-17:00.   Admission: Adult £2.50, Child £1.25, Family (2 adults and 2 children) £6.00.   Location: Ten minute walk from the centre of Llangollen.   Map Ref: 14

Museum Of Modern Art, Wales

Heol Penrallt, Machynlleth SY20 8AJ   Tel: 01654 703355   Fax: 01654 702160
Email: momawales@tabernac.dircon.co.uk   Web: www.tabernac.dircon.co.uk

Museum Of Modern Art, Wales

The Museum Of Modern Art, Wales has grown up alongside The Tabernacle, a former Wesleyan chapel which in 1986 reopened as a centre for the performing arts. MOMA Wales has six beautiful exhibition spaces which house, throughout the year, Showcase Wales (Wales' top artists), The Tabernacle Collection and The Brotherhood of Ruralists. Individual artists are spotlighted in a series of temporary exhibitions. In July workshops are given for adults and children, while in August expert judges and then the public choose the winners of the Tabernacle Art Competition. Many works of art in MOMA Wales are for sale. The adjacent auditorium has perfect acoustics and pitch-pine pews to seat 350 people. It is ideal for chamber and choral music, drama, lectures and conferences. Translation booths, recording facilities and a cinema screen have been installed; the oak-beamed Foyer has a bar; and extensive access for disabled people is made possible by a lift and a ramped approach.

Augustus John: Portrait of William McElroy

Opening Times: Mon to Sat 10:00-16:00. Closed Xmas & New Year. Admission: Free.
Location: In town centre, five minutes walk from railway station.   Exhibitions & Events 2003
: Showcase Wales and Exhibitions throughout the year.   Map Ref: 15

Daniel Owen Museum & Heritage Centre

Mold Library,Museum and Gallery, Earl Road, Mold CH7 1AP   Tel: 01352 754791

Displays reflect the development of the market town, the industrial heritage, the social and cultural life including the work of local poets and composers, Richard Wilson, the painter, and Daniel Owen, father of the Welsh of Novel.

Opening Times: Mon, Tue, Thu & Fri 09:30-19:00, Wed 09:30-17:30, Sat 09:30-12:30. Closed BH. Admission: Free. Location: Town centre.   Map Ref: 16

North Wales

Porthmadog Maritime Museum

Oakley Wharf No 1, The Harbour, Porthmadog LL49 9LU   Tel: 01766 513736

Models, paintings, drawings, charts, navigation instruments, shipbuilding tools and personal property - all relating to shipbuilding industry and the export of slates quarried at Blaenan Ffestiniog.

Opening Times: Easter week and from May BH to end Sep daily 11:00-17:00.
Admission: Adult £1.00, Child/OAP 50p, Family £2.50. Groups by arrangement.   Location: On wharf near bridge, opposite Harbour Station, behind Tourist Centre.   Map Ref: 17

Bodelwyddan Castle

Bodelwyddan, St Asaph LL18 5YA   Tel: 01745 584060
Fax: 01745 584563   Email: enquiries@bodelwyddan-castle.co.uk   Web: www.bodelwyddan-castle.co.uk

The Welsh home of the National Portrait Gallery. New galleries open April 2003 - interactive displays of Victorian portraiture. Sculpture from the Royal Academy of Arts. Victorian games gallery. Free audio tour.

Opening Times: Open daily 10:30-17:00. Closed Mon & Fri Nov to Mar. Admission: Adult £4.50, Child £2.00, OAP £4.00, Family £12.00. Location: Junction 25 of A55 expressway.   Map Ref: 18

Narrow Gauge Railway Museum

Talyllyn Railway, Wharf Station, Tywyn LL36 9EY   Tel: 01654 710472   Fax: 01654 711755
Email: enquiries@ngrm.net   Web: www.talyllyn.co.uk

A representative selection of predominately Welsh narrow gauge exhibits ranging from photographs to locomotives, adjacent to the Talyllyn Railway.

Opening Times: All year 09:30-17:00, longer between 23 Mar and 2 Oct when trains run daily.
Admission: Train tickets, Day Rover: Adult £9.50, Child £2.00, Concession £8.50. Intermediate fares available. Location: Five minutes from Tywyn station (Wales and Borders), five minutes from town centre.   Map Ref: 19

Key to Classifications

see Classifications Index on page 413

Anthropology	Jewellery	Railway
Archaeological	Literature & Libraries	Religion
Art Galleries	Maritime	Roman
Arts, Crafts & Textiles	Military & Defence	Science - Earth
China, Glass & Ceramics	Mills - Water & Wind	& Planetary
Communications	Multicultural	Sculpture
Egyptian	Music & Theatre	Sporting History
Fashion	Natural History	Stately Homes
Geology	Oriental	Toy & Childhood
Health & Medicine	Palaces	Transport
Horticultural	Police, Prisons & Dungeons	Victoriana

North Wales

Talyllyn Railway

Wharf Station, Tywyn LL36 9EY   Tel: 01654 710472   Fax: 01654 711755   Email: enquiries@talyllyn.co.uk   Web: www.talyllyn.co.uk

Narrow gauge steam trains running seven and a half miles into Snowdonia National Park. Walks from all stations, museum, cafés, shops, waterfalls, wheelchair accommodation on all trains. The first preserved railway in the world. Original 1865 train still runs on summer Sundays. Daily service varies from two to nine trains depending on season.

Opening Times: Apr to Oct daily 09:30-17:30.   Admission: Fares available to all stations. Full round trip Adult £9.50, Child (accompanied) £2.00, Concession £8.50.   Location: Tywyn Central Railway Station 100 yards.
Map Ref: 19

WREXHAM

Bersham Ironworks & Heritage Centre

Bersham, Wrexham LL14 4HT   Tel: 01978 261529   Fax: 01978 361703   Email: bershamheritage@wrexham.gov.uk   Web: www.wrexham.gov.uk

Exhibitions and collections largely based on the iron, steel and coal industries, particularly John Wilkinson and nearby Bersham Ironworks. Also temporary exhibition programme.

Opening Times: Heritage Centre: Easter to Oct Mon to Fri 10:00-16:30, Sat & Sun 12:00-16:30 (Oct to Mar closing 15:30). Ironworks: Easter & summer school holidays Thu to Mon 12:00-16:30.   Admission: Free.   Location: Two miles from town centre.
Map Ref: 20

Erddig

Wrexham LL13 0YT   Tel: 01978 355314   Fax: 01978 313333
Email: erddig@smtp.ntrust.org.uk   Web: www.nationaltrust.org.uk

THE NATIONAL TRUST

Erddig is a first class example of a complete country house collection featuring fine and decorative arts. 18th century furniture and textiles, paintings/servants portraits and silver. The garden is one of the most significant surviving examples of a formal garden of the 18th century in Britain with some later features such as the Victorian Porterre, the Irish Yew Walk and a newly restored glasshouse.

Opening Times: 23 Mar to 3 Nov Sat to Wed 12:00-16:00 (Jul & Aug 12:00-16:00, 7 Oct to 3 Nov 12:00-15:00). Open Good Friday.   Admission: Adult £6.60, Child £3.30, Family £16.50, Group 15+ £5.30.   Location: Two miles south of Wrexham.
Map Ref: 20

Minera Lead Mines

Wern Road, Minera, Wrexham LL11 3DU   Tel: 01978 261529
Email: mineraleadmines@wrexham.gov.uk   Web: www.wrexham.gov.uk

Displays relating to lead mining including a small museum, reconstructed pumping engine, ore processing etc.

Opening Times: Easter & summer school holidays, Thu to Sun 12:00-16:30. Closed Tue and Wed.   Admission: Free.   Location: Five miles from town centre.
Map Ref: 21

Wrexham County Borough Museum

County Buildings, Regent Street, Wrexham LL11 1RB   Tel: 01978 317970   Fax: 01978 317982   Email: museum@wrexham.gov.uk   Web: www.wrexham.gov.uk

Mainly social history collections, exhibitions include 'Brymbo Man - A Bronze Age Burial', The Welsh National Football Collection and exhibitions about the town and surrounding area. Also two temporary exhibition galleries and A N Palmer Centre for archives global studies.

Opening Times: Mon to Fri 10:00-16:30, Sat 10:30-15:00.   Admission: Free.   Location: In town centre.
Map Ref: 20

Northern Ireland

A country steeped in history with its capital city of Belfast and its beautiful sandstone castle. To the west is Londonderry encircled by a 17th century stone wall considered to be the best preserved fortification in Europe. Omagh in the 'wild' county of Tyrone has an outstanding variety of landscapes - mountains, rivers and moorlands. County Fermanagh is the 'Lakeland County' including Devenish Island with its sixth century monastery. To the east in County Armagh the 'Garden of Ulster', and finally County Down with the Mourne Mountains cannot be rivalled for its history and wildlife.

There are 35 interesting Museums and heritage sites depicting Northern Ireland's history, culture, folklife, emigration, archaeology, geology, and natural environment.

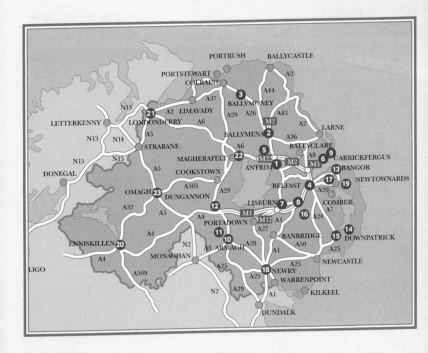

The Red Map References should be used to locate Museums etc on the pages that follow

Northern Ireland

Clotworthy Arts Centre

Antrim Castle Gardens, Randalstown Road, Antrim BT41 4LH   Tel: 028 9442 8000
Email: clotworthy@antrim.gov.uk

Arts Centre with three galleries and a small theatre. Housed in former coach yard of Antrim Castle and set within 17th century Antrim Castle gardens.

Opening Times: Mon to Fri 09:30-21:30, Sat 10:00-17:00, Sun Jul & Aug 14:00-17:00.
Admission: Free. Guided Tours £2.00 per person - must be pre-booked.   Location: Five minute walk from town centre via Market Square. By road off A6 to Randalstown, 150 metres from junction with A26 to Ballymena.   Map Ref: 1

Ballymena Museum

3 Wellington Court, Ballymena BT43 6EG   Tel: 028 25 642166   Fax: 028 25 638582
Email: jayneolphert@btconnect.com   Web: www.ballymena.gov.uk

Mixed social history/local collection providing an insight into the rich local cultural heritage of Mid-Antrim. Temporary exhibitions and events, permanent displays, community outreach and historical enquiry service.

Opening Times: Mon to Fri 10:00-13:00 & 14:00-17:00, Sat 10:00-13:00. Closed Sun & BH.
Admission: Free.   Location: Town centre, between Wellington Street and Church Street.
                                                                                                    Map Ref: 2

Royal Irish Regiment Museum

HQ The Royal Irish Regiment, St Patrick's Barracks, Ballymena BT43 7NX   Tel: 028 2566 1383
Fax: 028 2566 1378

Collection takes the visitor on a journey from the formation of the regiment in 1689 to the present day.

Opening Times: Wed & Sat 14:00-17:00. Also by prior arrangement.   Admission: Adult £2.00, Child/OAP £1.00.   Location: In St Patrick's Barracks.   Map Ref: 2

Ballymoney Museum

33 Charlotte Street, Ballymoney BT53 6AY   Tel: 028 2766 2280   Fax: 028 2766 7659
Email: keith.beattie@ballymoney.gov.uk   Web: www.1798ballymoney.org.uk

Ballymoney Museum has a collection of fascinating artefacts with local historical significance dating back to the earliest human settlements in Ireland. The museum also has a programme of temporary exhibitions.

Opening Times: Tue to Sat 13:00-17:00. Closed Jan.   Admission: Free.   Location: Off Main Street, ten minutes from railway station.   Map Ref: 3

Leslie Hill Open Farm

Ballymoney BT53 6QL   Tel: 028 276 63109/66803

Comprehensive collection of horse-drawn farm implements, carts, mobile threshers, barn threshres and hand tools, governess cart, jaunting car and travelling coach. Household items of the past.

Opening Times: Apr & May Sun & BH 14:00-18:00. Jun Sat & Sun 14:00-18:00, Jul & Aug Mon to Sat 11:00-18:00, Sun 14:00-18:00.   Admission: Adult £2.90, Child £1.90. Group rates available.   Location: One mile north west of Ballymoney.   Map Ref: 3

Fernhill House 'The Peoples Museum'

Fernhill House, Glencairn Park, Belfast BT13 3PT   Tel: 028 9071 5599   Fax: 028 9071 3810

Fernhill House is a community museum which explores the history of the Geater Shankill and tells the story of the people from the early 19th century until the present day.

Opening Times: Mon to Sat 10:00-16:00, Sun 13:00-16:00.   Admission: Adult £2.00, Child £1.00, OAP 50p, Student £1.50, Family £4.00.   Location: 15 minute drive from Belfast City Centre.   Map Ref: 4

Ormeau Baths Gallery

18A Ormeau Avenue, Belfast BT2 8HQ   Tel: 028 9032 1402   Fax: 028 9031 2232

The Gallery is dedicated to the presentation of innovative exhibitions of contemporary visual art

Northern Ireland

across a wide range of disciplines, by leading Irish and international artists.

Opening Times: Tue to Sat 10:00-18:00. Admission: Free. Location: Five minutes from Belfast City Hall via Bedford or Linenhall Street. Map Ref: 4

Royal Ulster Rifles Regimental Museum

5 Waring Street, Belfast BT1 2EW   Tel / Fax: 028 9023 2086   Email: rurmuseum@yahoo.co.uk
Web: www.rurmuseum.tripod.com/

Over 4000 artefacts on show in the museum, including uniforms, trophies, badges, medals and other interesting items for the military historian, such as photograph albums, war diaries, pictures and muniments.

Opening Times: Mon to Thu 10:00-12:30 & 14:00-16:00, Fri 10:00-12:30. Admission: Adult £1.00, Child/OAP Free. Free to former Members of the Regiment. Location: City centre location, five minute walk from Laganside Bus Station. Convenient parking nearby. Map Ref: 4

Ulster Museum

Botanic Gardens, Belfast BT9 5AB   Tel: 028 9038 3000

The museum holds collections of art, history, botany and zoology, geology, antiquities and ethnography. The fine art collection of the Ulster Museum embraces a wide range of periods and schools; British painting from the 17th century to the present day, including works by Gainsborough, Reynolds and Turner; a small but significant collection of Dutch, Flemish and Italian Old Masters; an extensive holding of Irish art from the 17th century to the present; and 20th century British, European and American art.

Opening Times: Mon to Fri 10:00-17:00, Sat 13:00-17:00, Sun 14:00-17:00. Closed 12 Jul and Xmas. Admission: Free.
Location: One mile from city centre, beside Queen's University. Map Ref: 4

Bellaghy Bawn

Castle Street, Bellaghy BT45 8LA   Tel: 028 79 386812   Fax: 028 90 543111

Library of living poets of Northern Ireland including films, audio and art prints of Seamus Heaney. History displays from 17th to 19th century.

Opening Times: Daily 10:00-17:00. Admission: Adult £1.50. Location: At top of Castle Street. Map Ref: 5

Flame: The Gasworks Museum of Ireland

44 Irish Quarter West, Carrickfergus BT38 8AT   Tel: 028 93369575
Web: www.gasworksflame.com

The site contains one only surviving coal-gas manufacturing plant in Ireland and the largest set of horizontal retorts in western Europe. Collection of gas-related appliances and extensive research library.

Opening Times: Mar & Oct Sat & Sun 14:00-18:00, Jul & Aug daily 10:00-18:00, Apr, May, Jun & Sep daily 14:00-18:00. All other times by appointment. Admission: Adult £2.50, Child/OAP £1.50, Under 5s Free. Groups £2.00 per person. School groups £1.00 per person. Family group £7.00. Location: Near town centre, four minute walk from Tourist Office and Castle. (signposted) Map Ref: 6

Ballance House

118A Lisburn Road, Glenavy BT29 4NY   Tel: 02892 648492   Fax: 02892 648098
Email: ballancen3@aol.com   Web: www.johnballance.com

Artefacts relating to the life of New Zealand Prime Minister, John Ballance (1839-93) Liberal politician and welfare state reformer. Also illustrating the history of emigration from Ireland to New Zealand.

Opening Times: Apr to Sep Tue to Fri 11:00-17:00, Sat & Sun 14:00-17:00, BH 11:00-17:00. Closed Mon. Other times by appointment. Admission: Adult £3.00, Child 50p. Group rates available. Location: On the A30, seven miles from Lisburn, two miles from Glenavy. Map Ref: 7

CO ANTRIM *(continued)*

Irish Linen Centre & Lisburn Museum
Market Square, Lisburn BT28 1AG Tel: 028 9266 3377 Fax: 028 9267 2624
Email: irishlinencentre@lisburn.gov.uk

Permanent exhibition on the history of Irish linen including demonstrations of spinning and weaving. Variety of local history and cultural exhibitions.

Opening Times: Mon to Sat 09:30-17:00. Admission: Free.   Map Ref: 8

Railway Preservation Society of Ireland
Castleview Road, Whitehead BT38 9NA Tel / Fax: 028 2826 0803
Email: rpsitrains@hotmail.com Web: www.rpsi-online.org

Steam train rides and preserved examples of Irish main line steam locomotives and vintage carriages.

Opening Times: Jul Sun 14:00-17:00 & Xmas. Admission: £1.50. Location: Whitehead two minute walk from railway/bus.   Map Ref: 9

CO ARMAGH

Armagh County Museum
The Mall East, Armagh BT61 9BE Tel: 028 375 23070
Web: www.magni.org.uk

The collections of the museum reflect the lives of the people who live, work and are associated with County Armagh. The museum has an extensive reference library. A range of special exhibitions are held throughout the year. Armagh County Museum is part of the Museums & Galleries of Northern Ireland (MAGNI).

Opening Times: Mon to Fri 10:00-17:00, Sat 10:00-13:00 & 14:00-17:00. Closed Sun. Admission: Free. Location: On the Mall, an area of urban parkland a few minutes walk from the céntre of the city. Exhibitions & Events 2003 : Jan to Mid Apr: Doll's Story - An exhibition tracing the history of dolls and similar toys through the ages, 2 May to 17 Jun: Japanese Prints - An exhibition of Japanese woodcuts by artist Yoko Omomi, Jul to Aug: Armagh Art Club Annual Exhibition - A display of paintings by member of the local art club.   Map Ref: 10

Royal Irish Fusiliers Museum
Sovereigns House, The Mall, Armagh BT61 9DL Tel / Fax: 02837 522911
Email: rylirfusiliermus@cs.com Web: www.rirfus-museum.freeserve.co.uk

Housed in a Georgian listed building, the collection is dedicated to the history of the regiment from 1793 to 1968. An extensive medal display includes two Victoria Crosses from the Great War.

Opening Times: Mon to Fri & BH 10:00-12:30 & 13:30-16:00. Closed Xmas & New Year.
Admission: Free. Location: Beside The Mall, near town centre and two minute walk from bus station.   Map Ref: 10

St Patrick's Trian
40 English Street, Armagh BT61 7BA Tel: 028 3752 1801 Fax: 028 3752 8329

The exhibition 'the least of all the faithful', examines the life and work of our patron Saint and his connections with Armagh as found in the ancient manuscript - the Book of Armagh.

Opening Times: Mon to Sat 10:00-17:00, Sun 14:00-17:00. Admission: Adult £3.75, Child £2.00, Concession £2.75, Family £9.50. Location: Town centre location.   Map Ref: 10

Cardinal Ó Fiaich Heritage Centre (Áras an Chairdinéil Ó Fiaich)
Slatequarry Road, Cullyhanna BT35 0JH Tel: 028 3086 8757 Email: info@ofiaichcentre-cullyhanna.com Web: www.ofiaichcentre-cullyhanna.com

Exhibition includes audio-visuals of interviews and conversations, photographs, archaeological models and artefacts, personal memorabilia. The display tells the story of Tomás Ó Fiaich - student, priest, professor, scholar and Cardinal-Primate of All-Ireland.

Opening Times: Oct to Mar Mon to Fri 13:00-17:00, BH 10:00-17:00. Sat & Sun by appointment. Apr to Oct Mon to Fri 10:00-17:00, BH 10:00-17:00. Sat & Sun by appointment. Admission: Adult £2.50, Under 11s Free, OAP £2.00, Student & Group rates available.   Map Ref: 11

Northern Ireland

The Argory

🖉 ⚅ 🐾   **THE NATIONAL TRUST**

Moy, Dungannon BT71 6NA   Tel: 028 8778 4753   Fax: 028 8778 9598
Email: uagest@smtp.ntrust.org.uk   Web: www.ntni.org.uk

The Argory is a treasure trove, where the clock ticks but time stands still, and where nothing has been thrown away for 100 years. A guided tour will take you deep into this handsome Aladdin's Cave of Victorian and Edwardian taste and interests. Watch out for the musical tours when the Bishop's cabinet barrel organ is played.

Opening Times: House: 15 Mar to May Sat, Sun & BH 12:00-18:00, Jun daily 13:00-18:00, Jul & Aug daily 12:00-18:00, Sep Sat & Sun 12:00-18:00. Grounds: Oct to Apr daily 10:00-16:00, May to Sep daily 10:00-20:00.

The Argory ©NT

Admission: House & Grounds - Adult £4.10, Child £2.10, Family £10.40, Group £3.40. Grounds only - Car £2.10.   Exhibitions & Events 2003 : 6 Apr: Lady Ada Reveals - House tour 14:00-18:00, 21 Apr: Easter Eggstravaganza - 13:00-18:00, 26 Apr: Vintage & Classic Vehicle Rally - 12:00 onwards, 22 Jun: Viva La France - 14:00-18:00, 17 Aug: A Victorian Sunday at The Argory - 14:00-18:00, 6 & 7 Dec: Victorian Christmas Fair - 13:00-17:00.   Map Ref: 12

North Down Heritage Centre

🐾

Town Hall, Bangor BT20 4BT   Tel: 028 9127 1200   Fax: 028 9127 1370
Email: bangor_heritage_centre@yahoo.com   Web: www.northdown.gov.uk/heritage

Concentrates on the glorious Early Christian monastery, the heyday of seaside holidays and local archaeology. Unique collection relating to Irish entertainer Percy French.

Opening Times: Tue to Sat 10:30-16:30, Sun 14:00-16:30, Jul & Aug closed 17:30.
Admission: Free.   Location: Rear of Town Hall, Castle Park.   Map Ref: 13

Castle Ward

🖉 ⚅ 🐾   **THE NATIONAL TRUST**

Strangford, Downpatrick BT30 7LS
Tel: 028 4488 1204   Fax: 028 4488 1729
Email: castleward@ntrust.org.uk   Web: www.ntni.org.uk

Castle Ward is full of personality. Situated in a stunning location overlooking Strangford Lough, the lawns roll up to one of the curios of the 18th century. Discover the full story on a house tour, which unravels the mystery to why the intriguing mansion was built, inside and out, in two distinct architectural styles, Classical and Strawberry Hill Gothik.

Opening Times: House: 15 Mar to Apr Sat, Sun & BH 12:00-18:00. May Mon & Wed to Fri 13:00-18:00, Sat & Sun 12:00-18:00. Jun daily 13:00-18:00. Jul & Aug daily 12:00-18:00. Sep & Oct Sat & Sun 12:00-18:00. Grounds: Oct to Apr daily 10:00-16:00, May to Sep daily 10:00-18:00.   Admission: House & Grounds: Adult

Castle Ward, Gothik Boudoir. © NT

£4.70, Child £1.80, Family £9.90, Group £3.70. Grounds only: Adult £3.10, Child £1.30, Family £7.30, Group £2.10.   Exhibitions & Events 2003 : 17 May: St Patrick's Day Event, 10 May: Piano recital with Nina Vinogradova-Biek - 19:30, 13 Jul: My Castle Ward - A personal insight into the estate from Hugh Lennon, 15:00, 31 Jul to 4 Aug: Castle Ward International Country Festival Week.   Map Ref: 14

Down County Museum

🖉 ⚅ 🐾

The Mall, Downpatrick BT30 6AH   Tel: 028 44 615218   Fax: 028 44 615590
Email: lmckenna@downclc.gov.uk   Web: www.downcountymuseum.com

Collections relating to the history of County Down from early times to today. Museum is located in restored 18th century gaol of Down.

Opening Times: Mon to Fri 10:00-17:00, Sat & Sun 13:00-17:00. Admission: Free.
Location: Located between Downpatrick Courthouse and Down Cathedral. Follow brown signs.
Map Ref: 15

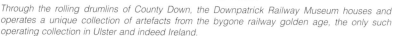

CO DOWN *(continued)*

Downpatrick Railway Museum

The Railway Station, Downpatrick BT30 6LZ Tel: 028 44 61 5779
Email: burkewalmae@cs.com Web: www.downrail.icom43.net

Through the rolling drumlins of County Down, the Downpatrick Railway Museum houses and operates a unique collection of artefacts from the bygone railway golden age, the only such operating collection in Ulster and indeed Ireland.

Opening Times: Jul to Sep Sat & Sun 14:00-17:00, also 17 Mar, Easter Sun & Mon, Halloween weekend & 2nd and 3rd weekend Dec 14:00-17:00. Admission: Tours: Adult £1.50, Child 50p. Train: Adult £4.50, Child/OAP £2.50.   Location: In Downpatrick Town Centre, adjacent to Ulsterbus Station.
Map Ref: 15

The Saint Patrick Centre

Downpatrick BT30 6LZ Tel: 028 4461 9000 Fax: 028 4461 9111
Email: director@saintpatrickcentre.com Web: www.saintpatrickcentre.com

The New World Centre for Saint Patrick is located beside Saint Patrick's Grave within the ancient town of Downpatrick, medieval capital of County Down. The centre is just 30 minutes from Belfast and provides a great family day out. It is an important destination for visitors interested in saints, scholars and the early christian church. Enjoy a 'virtual' helicopter ride over Ireland 'in the footsteps of St Patrick'.

Opening Times: Jun to Aug Mon to Sat 09:30-18:00, Sun 10:00-18:00. Apr, May & Sep Mon to Sat 09:30-17:30, Sun 13:00-17:30. Oct to Mar Mon to Sat 10:00-17:00, Sun on request. Admission: Adult £4.50, Child £2.25, Concession £3.00, Family £11.00, Groups 25+: Adult £3.00, Child £2.00, OAP £2.50.
Map Ref: 15

The Art Gallery

34 Lisburn Street, Hillsborough BT26 6AB Tel: 02892 689896 Fax: 02892 688433
Email: bill@theartgallery.freeserve.co.uk

Commercial art gallery selling contemporary work.

Opening Times: Mon to Sat 11:00-17:00 or by appointment. Admission: Free.
Location: Centre Hillsborough Village.
Map Ref: 16

Ulster Folk & Transport Museum

Cultra, Holywood BT18 0EU Tel: 028 9042 8428

ULSTER FOLK AND TRANSPORT MUSEUM

Take time to explore one of Ireland's foremost visitor attractions, recapturing a disappearing way of life, preserving traditional skills and celebrating transport history. Just minutes from Belfast the Ulster Folk & Transport Museum is situated in over 177 acres of park and grassland. At the Open Air Folk Museum 60 acres are devoted to illustrating the way of life of people in Northern Ireland in the early 1900s. Visitors can stroll through yesteryear's countryside with its farms, cottages, crops and livestock and visit a typical 1900s Ulster town with its shops, churches, and terraced

The Corner Shop

Street Scene

housing. Indoors the Folk Gallery features a number of exhibitions. The indoor Transport Museum boasts the most comprehensive transport collection in Ireland. The Irish Railway Collection is displayed in an award-winning gallery, explaining the history and impact of both standard and narrow gauge railways in Ireland. The Road Transport Galleries boast a fine collection of vehicles ranging from cycles, motorcycles, trams, buses, fire engines and cars. The Museum also has a varied programme of major events and activities from Vehicle Days to the Rare Breeds Show and sale. Skills once commonly practised such as lace sampler making, spinning, weaving, woodturning and forge work, and basket making are among many demonstrated and taught at the Museum.

Opening Times: Mar to Jun Mon to Fri 10:00-17:00, Sat 10:00-18:00, Sun 11:00-18:00. Jul to Sep Mon to Sat 10:00-18:00, Sun 11:00-18:00. Oct to Feb Mon to Fri 10:00-16:00, Sat 10:00-18:00, Sun 11:00-17:00. Admission: Adult £4.00, Child £2.50, Under 5s Free, Concession £2.50, Family £11.00. Group Rates available. Location: On the main Belfast to Bangor Road, just ten minutes outside Belfast with excellent access by road, rail and bus. Exhibitions & Events 2003 : For Exhibitions and Events please telephone for details.　　Map Ref: 17

Newry Museum

1A Bank Parade, Newry BT35 6HP　Tel: 028 3026 6232　Fax: 028 3026 6839

The museum incorporates architectural features from a now demolished Georgian house including a fully furnished panelled room. Highlights of the collection include a table reputed to have been on HMS Victory, an Order of St Patricks Robe and a Gelston Clock dating from 1770.

Opening Times: Mon to Fri 10:30-13:00 & 14:00-16:30. Closed BH. Admission: Free.
Location: Located in Newry Arts Centre. Two minute walk from bus station on the Mall. In town centre.　　Map Ref: 18

Mount Stewart House, Garden & Temple of the Winds

THE NATIONAL TRUST

Newtownards BT22 2AS　Tel: 028 4278 8387/8487　Fax: 028 4278 8569
Email: mountstewart@ntrust.org.uk　Web: www.ntni.org.uk

Situated on the tranquil shores of Strangford Lough, the impressive house and gardens of Mount Stewart have a unique story to tell. This year you will enjoy seeing and hearing many new stories about the Londonderry family, their home, their prominent guests and the people who have worked there over the centuries.

Mount Stewart south front Spanish Garden. © NT

Opening Times: House: 15 Mar to Apr Sat, Sun & BH 12:00-18:00. May to Jun Mon & Wed to Fri 13:00-18:00, Sat & Sun 12:00-16:00. Jul to Aug daily 12:00-18:00. Sep daily (except Thu) 12:00-18:00. Oct Sat & Sun 12:00-18:00. Admission: House & Gardens: Adult £4.95, Child £2.35, Family £10.15, Group £4.15. Exhibitions & Events 2003 : 29 & 30 Mar: Life Below Stairs - explores the life of servants in Victorian era, 6 Apr & 3 May: Murder Mystery Evening - 19:30, 27 Apr: Jazz in the Garden with the Gerry Rice Quartet - 15:00-17:30, 23 Aug: An afternoon of 18th century delight - 12:30-17:00, 13 Sep: 'Hang Him High' A Georgian Highway Robbery, 29 Nov: Masquerade Ball - 19:30.　　Map Ref: 19

The Somme Heritage Centre

233 Bangor Road, Newtownards BT23 7PH　Tel: 028 91 823202　Fax: 028 91 823214
Email: sommeassociation@dnet.co.uk　Web: irishsoldier.org

The centre has a collection of around 5000 pieces related to Irish participation in the First World War. The centre is also starting to collect World War Two material.

Opening Times: Apr to Jun & Sep Mon to Thu 10:00-16:00, Sat 12:00-16:00. Jul to Aug Mon to Fri 10:00-17:00, Sat & Sun 12:00-17:00. Oct to Mar Mon to Thu 10:00-16:00. Admission: Adult £3.75, Child/Concession £2.75, Family £10.00.　　Map Ref: 19

Northern Ireland

Castle Coole ✎ ♿ ❖ ☕ 🚜

Enniskillen BT74 6JY   Tel: 028 6632 2690   THE NATIONAL TRUST
Fax: 028 6632 5665   Email: castlecoole@ntrust.org.uk
Web: www.ntni.org.uk

If you are looking for stately grandeur then Castle Coole is a rare treat. Situated in a stunning landscaped parkland on the edge of Enniskillen this majestic 18th century house built by James Wyatt was built to impress. Soak up the opulent Regency interior with rich decoration and furnishings, including the ornate state bedroom prepared for George IV in 1821.

Opening Times: House: 15 Mar to May Sat, Sun & BH 12:00-18:00. Jun daily (except Thu) 12:00-18:00. Jul to Aug daily 12:00-18:00. Sep Sat & Sun 12:00-18:00. Grounds: Oct to Apr daily 10:00-16:00, May to Sep daily 10:00-20:00.   Admission: House & Grounds: Adult £4.00, Child £2.00, Family £10.00, Group £3.00.   Exhibitions

Castle Coole lobby with gallery. © NT

& Events 2003 : 14 Mar: Castergneri String Quartet - 20:00, 3 Aug: Musical Picnic - 15:00, 19 to 21 Jun: Coolefest - 20:00, 27 Sep: Opera at Castle Coole - 19:30.   Map Ref: 20

Fermanagh County Museum ♿ ❖ 🚜

Enniskillen Castle, Castle Barracks, Enniskillen BT74 7HL   Tel: 028 6632 5000
Fax: 028 6632 7342   Email: castle@fermanagh.gov.uk
Web: www.enniskillencastle.co.uk

Fermanagh County Museum collections represent Fermanagh's history, folklife, archaeology and environment. There are a variety of permanent displays relating to these topics as well as a rich and varied programme of events, education programmes and temporary exhibitions on subjects such as art, literature, music and history.

Opening Times: All year Mon 14:00-17:00, Tue to Fri 10:00-17:00. May to Sep Sat 14:00-17:00, Jul & Aug Sun 14:00-17:00.   Admission: Adult £2.25, Child £1.25, OAP/Student £1.75, Under 5s Free, Family (2 adults and

Enniskillen Castle

2 children) £5.50.   Location: Near town centre, two minute walk from Ulster Bus Station and Tourist Information Centre.   Map Ref: 20

Florence Court ✎ ♿ ❖ ☕ ◐ 🚜

Enniskillen BT92 1DB   Tel: 028 6634 8249   Fax: 028 6634 8873   THE NATIONAL TRUST
Email: florencecourt@ntrust.org.uk   Web: www.ntni.org.uk

Florence Court is a truly welcoming home. Since the recent return of much of the Enniskillen family belongings to this fine mid 18th century house and estate, it has recaptured its warm and gentle atmosphere. House tours take you inside the heart of the house, and as each new door opens you discover more about family and the staff.

Opening Times: House: 15 Mar to May Sat, Sun & BH 12:00-18:00. June Mon to Fri 13:00-18:00, Sat & Sun 12:00-18:00. Jul & Aug daily 12:00-18:00. Sep daily 12:00-18:00. Grounds: Oct to Apr daily 10:00-16:00, May to Sep daily 10:00-20:00.   Admission: House & Grounds: Adult £4.00, Child £2.00, Family £10.00, Group £3.00.

Florence Court East Front. © NT

Grounds only: Car £2.50.   Exhibitions & Events 2003 : 25 May: Country Fair - 13:00-18:00, 26 Oct: Halloween Craft Fair - 13:00-17:00, 1 Nov: Putting the House to Bed tour - 14:00-16:00.
Map Ref: 20

Guided or Private Tours	Disabled Access	Gift Shop or Sales Point	Café or Refreshments	Restaurant	Car Parking

Northern Ireland

Harbour Museum

Harbour Square, Derry BT48 6AF   Tel: 028 7137 7331   Fax: 028 7137 7633
Email: museums@derrycity.gov.uk

A traditional museum, with emphasis on the city's maritime connections - temporary exhibitions are regularly displayed.

Opening Times: Mon to Fri 10:00-13:00, 14:00-16:30.   Admission: Free.   Location: City centre location - one minute from central bus station.   Map Ref: 21

Tower Museum   ☜ 占 ▣

Union Hall Place, Derry BT48 6LU   Tel: 028 7137 2411   Fax: 028 7136 6018
Email: museums@derrycity.gov.uk

The Tower Museum looks at the history of Derry from its geological formation through to the present day. There are special features on the Plantation of Ulster, the Siege of Derry and the 'Troubles'.

Opening Times: Sep to Jun Tue to Sat & BH 10:00-17:00, Jul to Aug Mon to Sat 10:00-17:00, Sun 14:00-17:00.   Admission: Admission charged.   Location: City centre location - just inside the City Walls.   Map Ref: 21

Workhouse Museum   ☜ 占 🚂

Glendermott Road, Waterside, Derry BT47 6BG   Tel: 028 7131 8328
Email: museums@derrycity.gov.uk

First Floor - World War II display on Derry's part in protecting Atlantic convoys. Video presentations plus two rooms for temporary exhibitions. Second Floor - display on Irish and African famines. Also dormitory display.

Opening Times: Mon to Thu & Sat 10:00-16:30. Closed Fri & Sun. Jul to Aug Fri 10:00-16:00, Sun 14:00-16:30.   Admission: Free.   Location: One mile from city centre, on main bus route.
Map Ref: 21

Key to Classifications

see Classifications Index on page 413

Anthropology	Jewellery	Railway
Archaeological	Literature & Libraries	Religion
Art Galleries	Maritime	Roman
Arts, Crafts & Textiles	Military & Defence	Science - Earth
China, Glass & Ceramics	Mills - Water & Wind	& Planetary
Communications	Multicultural	Sculpture
Egyptian	Music & Theatre	Sporting History
Fashion	Natural History	Stately Homes
Geology	Oriental	Toy & Childhood
Health & Medicine	Palaces	Transport
Horticultural	Police, Prisons & Dungeons	Victoriana

Northern Ireland

Springhill

🖼 ♿ 📷 ♿

THE NATIONAL TRUST

20 Springhill Road, Magherafelt BT45 7NQ   Tel / Fax: 028 8674 8210
Email: springhill@ntrust.org.uk   Web: www.ntni.org.uk

Springhill has a beguiling spirit that captures the heart of every visitor. Its welcoming charm has much to do with the lovely gardens, its very pretty 'Plantation' house and 300 years of intriguing history. The stunning collection of colourful haute couture and day-to-day clothing and accessories is a mirror of history, with some pieces dating back to the 17th century.

Opening Times: Mar to 15 Jun Sat, Sun & BH 12:00-18:00. Jul & Aug daily 12:00-18:00. Sep Sat & Sun 12:00-18:00. Admission: House & Costume Collection: Adult £3.65, Child £1.80, Family £7.55, Group £3.00.

Springhill. © NT

Exhibitions & Events 2003 : 20 Apr: Easter Eggcentricities - 14:00-17:00, 7 Jun: Vintage Vehicle Rally - 13:00-17:00, 14 Jun: Teddy Bear's Picnic - 14:00-17:00, 24 & 31 May: The Untold Story, 3 Aug: Springhill Supersleuths - 14:00-17:00.   Map Ref: 22

CO TYRONE

US Grant Ancestral Homestead

🖼 ♿ 🎁 📷 ♿

Dergenagh Road, Dungannon BT70 1TW   Tel: 028 8776 7259/028 855 57133
Email: killymaddy@nihc.net   Web: www.dungannon.gov.uk

Explore the cottage of the Simpson family with close ties to Ulysses Simpson Grant, the Commander of the victorious Union troops in the American Civil War.

Opening Times: Apr to Sep Tue to Sat 12:00-17:00, Sun 14:00-18:00. Closed Mon.
Admission: Adult £1.50, Child/OAP 75p.   Location: Off main A4, 13 miles west of Dungannon.
Map Ref: 12

Ulster American Folk Park

🖼 ♿ 🎁 📷 🎟 ♿

Mellon Road, Castletown, Omagh BT78 5QY   Tel: 028 8224 3292

A museum of Emigration and Folk Life telling the story of the floods of Emigrants who left these shores in the 18th and 19th centuries. Visit the Old and New Worlds joined by a full-sized Emigrant Sailing Ship. Explore 28, mainly original exhibit buildings from both sides of the Atlantic. Costumed interpreters tell the emigrant's story and demonstrate a wide range of traditional crafts daily. Emigrants exhibition explores related themes and the Centre for Migration Studies allows for further research. Facilities include Residential Centre, Educational programmes, shop and restaurant. Voted Visitor Attraction of The Year.

Opening Times: Apr to Sep Mon to Sat 10:30-18:00, Sun & BH 11:00-18:00. Oct to Apr Mon to Fri 10:30-17:00. Admission: Adult £4.00, Child £2.50, OAP £3.50. Location: A5 - three miles from Omagh on Strabane Road. Exhibitions & Events 2003 : For Exhibitions and Events please telephone for details.   Map Ref: 23ef: 12

Ireland

Ireland is a country with a unique history and is renowned for its music and literature, particularly Dublin with its narrow cobbled streets and the superb collections in its museums and art galleries. Wherever one travels in Ireland there are castles, heritage centres and sites, abbeys and in many towns museums that together provide a fascinating record of the local history and crafts, maritime history and military history and indeed the Irish way of living and their culture.

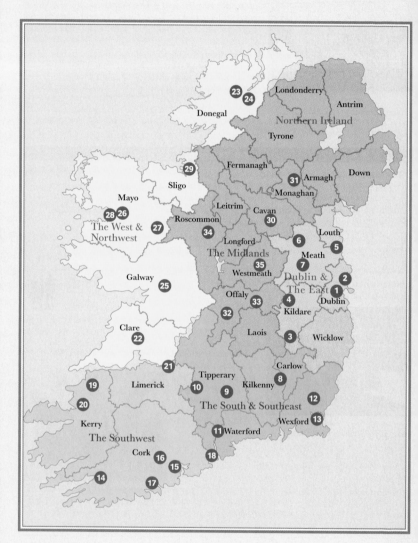

The Red Map References should be used to locate Museums etc on the pages that follow

Ireland - Dublin & The East

Dalkey Castle & Heritage Centre

Castle Street, Dalkey Tel: +353 (0)1 285 8366
Fax: +353 (0)1 284 3141 Email: diht@indigo.ie
Web: www.heritagetowns.com/dalkey

HERITAGE TOWNS
of Ireland

Dalkey has an award-winning Visitor Centre, Dalkey Castle & Heritage Centre. Theatrical animation and living history re-enactments brings the past to colourful life. Guides lead heritage trails and historical walks of Dalkey daily from the Heritage Centre.

Opening Times: Apr to Oct Mon to Fri 09:30-17:00, Sat, Sun & BH 11:00-17:00. Nov to Mar Mon to Sun 11:00-17:00.
Admission: Adult €2.50, Child €1.50, OAP/Student €2.00, Family €8.00. Location: Beside Queens Pub. Five minutes from DART Station. Map Ref: 1

Dalkey Castle

Archaeology & History Museum

Kildare Street, Dublin 2 Tel: +353 (0)1 677 7444
Email: marketing@museum.ie Web: www.museum.ie

Opened in 1890, the National Museum of Ireland, Kildare Street contains artefacts dating from 7000BC to the 20th century including outstanding examples of Celtic and Medieval art and the finest collection of prehistoric gold artefacts in Europe.

Opening Times: Tue to Sat 10:00-17:00, Sun 14:00-17:00. Closed Mon. Admission: Free. Location: Neareest DART Station, Pearse Street. Map Ref: 1

Archaeology & History Museum

Chester Beatty Library

Dublin Castle, Dublin 2 Tel: +353 (0)1 407 0750 Fax: +353 (0)1 407 0760
Email: info@cbl.ie Web: www.cbl.ie

The exhibition galleries open a window on the artistic treasures of the great cultures and religions of the world. The Library's rich collection of manuscripts, prints, icons, miniature paintings, early printed books and objets d'art represent numerous cultures and countries. European Museum of the Year 2002.

Opening Times: May to Sep Mon to Fri 10:00-17:00, Oct to Apr Tue to Fri 10:00-17:00, every Sat 11:00-17:00, every Sun 13:00-17:00. Closed BH Mon, 24-26 Dec, 1 Jan & Good Friday.
Admission: Free. Location: Ten minutes walk from Trinity College/Grafton Street. Map Ref: 1

Decorative Arts & History Museum

Collins Barracks, Dublin 7 Tel: +353 (0)1 677 7444
Email: marketing@museum.ie Web: www.museum.ie

The beautiful restored Collins Barracks on the banks of the River Liffey is now home to the national collection of Decorative Arts & History. On display are artefacts ranging from weaponry, furniture, costume to silver and glassware.

Opening Times: Tue to Sat 10:00-17:00, Sun 14:00-17:00. Closed Mon. Admission: Free. Location: Opposite Heuston Station on Wolfe Tane Quay. Map Ref: 1

Decorative Arts & History Museum

Guided or Private Tours	Disabled Access	Gift Shop or Sales Point	Café or Refreshments	Restaurant	Car Parking

The Douglas Hyde Gallery

🖉 ♿ ● **DH9**

Trinity College, Nassau Street, Dublin 2   Tel: +353 (0)1 608 1116
Fax: +353 (0)1 670 8330   Email: dhgallery@tcd.ie   Web: www.douglashydegallery.com

The Gallery has a diverse programme of exhibitions, embracing both Irish and international contemporary art. A wide range of gallery activities - tours, lectures, discussion groups - encourages audience participation and evaluation of the work on exhibition. An information leaflet accompanies every show. The Gallery has a small bookshop which stocks a wide range of art magazines, including Artforum, Frieze and Circa.

Opening Times: Mon to Fri 11:00-18:00, Thu 11:00-19:00, Sat 11:00-16:45. Closed Xmas, Easter and BH.
Admission: Free. Location: Trinity College, Nassau Street, Dublin 2.

Keith Edmier mixed media exhibition installation, 1998

Map Ref: 1

Dublin Civic Museum

City Assembly House, 58 South William Street, Dublin 2 Tel: +353 (0)1 679 4260

Experience aspects of life in Dublin through the ages. Collections include: streets and buildings of Dublin, traders, industry, transport, political history, maps and views.

Opening Times: Tue to Sat 10:00-18:00, Sun 11:0-14:00. Closed Mon. Admission: Free.

Map Ref: 1

Dublin Writers Museum

🖉 ● ☕ ◐ 🚭

18 Parnell Square, Dublin 1   Tel: +353 (0)1 872 2077   Fax: +353 (0)1 872 2231
Email: writers@dublintourism.ie   Web: www.visitdublin.com

The collection features the lives and works of Dublin's literary celebrities over the past 200 years. Swift, Sheridan, Shaw, Wilde, Yeats, Joyce and Beckett are among those presented through their books, letters, portraits and personal items.

Opening Times: Jan to Dec Mon to Sat 10:00-17:00, Sun & BH 11:00-17:00. Late opening Jun, Jul & Aug Mon to Fri 10:00-18:00. Admission: Adult €6.00, Child €3.50, Concession €5.00, Family €16.50. Location: In Dublin City Centre, five minute walk from O'Connell Street.

Map Ref: 1

Dublin's City Hall
- The Story of the Capital

🖉 ♿ ● ☐

Dublin City
Baile Átha Cliath

City Hall, Dame Street, Dublin 2   Tel: +353 (0)1 672 2204 Fax: +353 (0)1 672 2620 Email: cityhall@dublincity.ie
Web: www.dublincity.ie/cityhall

This multi-media exhibition traces the evolution of the city from 1170 to the present day with particular emphasis on the development of civic governance. The Civic Regalia, including the Great City Sword and Great Mace are on display along with computer interactives, archive films, models and costumes. Located in City Hall, one of Dublin's finest neo-classical buildings, which dates from 1779, this exhibition brings to life the changes in the city over the centuries.

Opening Times: Mon to Fri 10:00-17:15, Sun & BH 14:00-17:00.
Admission: Adult €4.00, Child €1.50, Students/OAPs, Family €10.00. Exhibitions & Events 2003 : 5 to 14 Sept: Pat Liddy and the Changing Face of Dublin.

Map Ref: 1

Guinness Storehouse

St James's Gate, Dublin 8   Tel: +353 (0)1 408 4800

Set in the centre of one of the world's most famous breweries, which has been on site since Arthur Guinness founded it in 1759, the Guinness Storehouse has rapidly become Dublin's 'must see' visitor attraction. The Guinness Storehouse is a dramatic story that begins over 250 years ago and ends in Gravity, the bar in the sky, with a complimentary pint of Guinness, and an astonishing view of Dublin. Often surprising, always entertaining, the adventure begins

the moment you walk through the door and into the buildings giant, pint shaped heart of glass. As you wander up through Guinness Storehouse, you'll discover what goes into making the black stuff - the ingredients, the processes, the passion. You'll meet Arthur Guinness and find out how the drink that carries his name has been transported around the world. You'll see how Guinness has been advertised over the years and visit Guinness, at Home and Abroad. If you'd like a souvenir to remind you of your trip to the home of Guinness, there's plenty to choose from in Store, which stocks an exclusive range of merchandise.

Opening Times: 09:30-17:00. Closed Xmas & New Year, St Stephen's Day and Good Friday.
Admission: Adult €12.00, Family (2 adults and 4 children) €26.00, Student over 18 €8.00, Student under 18 €5.00. Group Rates available.   Location: Bus 51B/78A from Aston Quay or 123 from O'Connell Street.   Map Ref: 1

Hugh Lane Municipal Gallery of Modern Art

Charlemont House, Parnell Square North, Dublin 1   Tel: +353 (0)1 874 1903
Fax: +353 (0)1 872 2182   Email: info@hughlane.ie   Web: www.hughlane.ie

The collection includes Impressionist masterpieces by Renoir, Monet, Degas and Morisot. A fine collection of 20th century Irish art and works by contemporary Irish and international artists. The Gallery also houses Francis Bacon's reconstructed studio accompanied by an audio visual room, a micro gallery with touch screen terminals and an exhibition gallery with works by Francis Bacon.

Opening Times: Tue to Thu 9:30-18:00, Fri & Sat 9:30-17:00, Sun 11:00-17:00. Closed Mon and Xmas.
Admission: Free to permanent collection. Admission to

Interior Francis Bacon Studio. Photo Perry Ogden

Francis Bacon Studio - Adult €7.50, Child €2.50,
Concession €3.50, Under 12s Free.   Location: City centre, at the end of O'Connell Street, on the north side of Parnell Square. A ten minute walk Tara Street or Connolly Street Railway Station.   Map Ref: 1

Kilmainham Gaol

Inchicore Road, Dublin 8   Tel: +353 (0)1 453 5984

Access to the Gaol is by guided tour only. The tour lasts approx one hour and 15 minutes and includes the social and political history of the Gaol. In addition to the tour the public have an opportunity to visit the museum at their own convenience. The museum is on three levels it is the only museum that deals with modern Irish and political history spanning from 1796-1924. Among the highlights of the collection there are artefacts from the 1798 Rebellion, the last letters of the leaders of the 1916 Rebellion, along with documents and artefacts from the Irish War of Independence and Civil War. The Gaol also plays host to a wide range of temporary exhibitions, including art and historical exhibitions etc.

Opening Times: Oct to Mar Mon to Sat 09:30-17:30, Sun 10:00-18:00, Apr to Sep Mon to Sun 09:30-18:00. Closed Xmas. Admission: Adult €4.40, Child/Student €1.90, OAP/Group €3.10, Family €10.10.   Location: Three miles from city centre. Bus 79, 51B, 78A from Aston Quay.
Exhibitions & Events 2003 : Please phone for details.   Map Ref: 1

CO DUBLIN *(continued)*

National Gallery of Ireland

Merrion Square West, Dublin 2   Tel: +353 (0)1 661 5133   Fax: +353 (0)1 661 5372
Email: artgall@eircom.net   Web: www.nationalgallery.ie

The National Gallery of Ireland has a superb collection of western European art, from the Middle Ages to the 20th century. It also holds the most important collection of Irish art in the world including the National Portrait Gallery and the Yeates Museum. Artists on display include Caravaggio, Canova, Vermeer, Rembrant, Poussin, Monet, Velazquez, Picasso, Goya, Turner, Gainsborough and all the major painters of Irish school, including the Yeates family.

Opening Times: Mon to Sat 09:30-17:30, Thur 09:30-20:30, Sun 12:00-17:30. Closed Good Friday and Xmas.

Architects Model of the New Millennium Wing opened in January 2002

Admission: Free.   Location: City centre, five minutes from DART. Meter parking available.   Map Ref: 1

Natural History

Merrion Street, Dublin 2   Tel: +353 (0)1 677 7444
Email: marketing@museum.ie   Web: www.museum.ie

The Natural History Museum opened in 1857 just two years before Charles Darwin published his work 'The Origin of Species'. Packed with diverse animals from all walks of life, the museum is a place where Darwin's theories of evolution and natural selection can be studied and understood.

Opening Times: Tue to Sat 10:00-17:00, Sun 14:00-17:00. Closed Mon. Admission: Free.   Location: Nearest DART Station, Pearse Street.   Map Ref: 1

Royal Hibernian Academy

Gallagher Gallery, 15 Ely Place, Dublin 2   Tel: +353 (0)1 661 2558   Fax: +353 (0)1 661 0762
Email: rhaygallery@eircom.net   Web: www.royalhibernianacademy.com

Established in 1823, the Royal Hibernian Academy is an artist led organisation run by artists for artists. It presents an innovative exhibition programme of leading Irish and international artists. Commercial shows are in the Ashford Gallery which represents emerging artists and Academicians.

Opening Times: Tue to Sat 11:00-17:00, Thu 11:00-20:00, Sun 14:00-17:00. Closed Mon.
Admission: Free.   Location: City Centre, one minute from St Stephen's Green.   Map Ref: 1

Key to Classifications
see Classifications Index on page 413

Anthropology	Jewellery	Railway
Archaeological	Literature & Libraries	Religion
Art Galleries	Maritime	Roman
Arts, Crafts & Textiles	Military & Defence	Science - Earth
China, Glass & Ceramics	Mills - Water & Wind	& Planetary
Communications	Multicultural	Sculpture
Egyptian	Music & Theatre	Sporting History
Fashion	Natural History	Stately Homes
Geology	Oriental	Toy & Childhood
Health & Medicine	Palaces	Transport
Horticultural	Police, Prisons & Dungeons	Victoriana

Shaw Birthplace

33 Synge Street, Dublin 8   Tel: +353 (0)1 475 0854   Fax: +353 (0)1 872 2231
Email: shawhouse@dublintourism.ie   Web: www.visitdublin.com

The first home of the Shaw family and the renowned playwright, restored to its Victorian elegance and charm. The house contains photographs, original documents and letters that throw light on G B Shaw's long and impressive career.

Opening Times: May to Sep Mon to Sat 10:00-13:00 & 14:00-17:00, Sun & BH 11:00-17:00 (closed 13:00-14:00).   Admission: Adult €6.00, Child €3.50, Concession €5.00, Family €16.50.
Location: Ten minute walk from St Stephen's Green.   Map Ref: 1

Trinity College Library

Trinity College Library, College Street, Dublin 2   Tel: +353 (0)1 677 2941   Fax: +353 (0)1 671 9003

The Old Library is home to the famous 19th gospel manuscript the Book of Kells. Also on view is The Book of Kells 'Turning Darkness into Light' Exhibition which explains the background of the Book of Kells and other related manuscripts, the Book of Armagh, the Book of Durrow, the Book of Mulling and the Book of Dimma.

Opening Times: Mon to Sat 09:30-17:00, Sun (Oct to May) 12:00-16:30, Sun (Jun to Sep) 09:30-16:30. BH Oct to May 12:00-16:30. Closed Xmas & New Year. Admission: Adult €7.00, Child Free, Student/OAP €6.00, Family (2 adults and 4 children) €14.00.   Trinity
College Library Dublin   Location: City centre.   Map Ref: 1

Fry Model Railway

Malahide Castle Demesne, Malahide Tel: +353 (0)1 846 3779   Fax: +353 (0)1 846 3723
Email: fryrailway@dublintourism.ie   Web: www.visitdublin.com

This is a unique collection of hand-made models of Irish trains, from the beginning of rail travel to modern times. One of the world's largest miniature railways. The exhibition is unique in that it is a working railway covering an area of 2500 sq ft.

Opening Times: Apr to Sep Mon to Sat 10:00-13:00 & 14:00-17:00 Sun & BH 14:00-18:00.
Admission: Adult €6.00, Child €3.50, Concession €5.00, Family €16.50. Location: Eight miles north of Dublin City Centre, four miles from Dublin Airport.   Map Ref: 2

Malahide Castle

Malahide Tel: +353 (0)1 846 2184   Fax: +353 (0)1 846 2537
Email: malahidecastle@dublintourism.ie   Web: www.visitdublin.com

The Talbot family lived here for nearly 800 years. The Castle is furnished with beautiful Irish period furniture together with an extensive collection of Irish portrait paintings, mainly from the National Gallery of Ireland.

Opening Times: Jan to Dec Mon to Sat 10:00-17:00. Apr to Oct Sun & BH 11:00-18:00, Nov to Mar Sun & BH 11:00-17:00, (closed 13:00-14:00).   Admission: Adult €6.00, Child €3.50, Concession €5.00, Family €16.50. Location: Eight miles north of Dublin City, four miles from Dublin Airport.   Map Ref: 2

James Joyce Museum

Joyce Tower, Sandycove Tel / Fax: +353 (0)1 280 9265   Email: joycetower@dublintourism.ie
Web: www.visitdublin.com

The collection includes letters, photographs, portraits and personal possessions of Joyce. There are first editions of his work including his early broadsides and the celebrated edition of 'Ulysses' illustrated by Henri Matisse.

Opening Times: Apr to Oct Mon to Sat 10:00-17:00 (closed 13:00-14:00), Sun & BH 14:00-18:00.   Admission: Adult €6.00, Child €3.50, Concession €5.00, Family €16.50.
Location: Eight miles south of Dublin City.   Map Ref: 1

CO KILDARE

Athy Museum

HERITAGE TOWNS *of Ireland*

Town Hall, Athy   Tel: +353 (0)507 33075   Fax: +353 (0)507 33076
Email: oriordanmargaret@eircom.net   Web: www.kildare.ie/athyonline

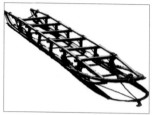

Athy Heritage Centre holds Ireland's only permanent exhibition on polar explorer, Sir Ernest Shackleton who was born locally. It includes a faithful 5th scale replica model of his ship Endurance and various artefacts from his expeditions including a sledge and harness. The centre also relates the history of the town with an exhibition on the 1903 Gordon Bennett Race, the precursor to todays Grand Prix racing.

Opening Times: Jan to Dec Mon to Sat 10:00-18:00, Sun & BH 14:00-18:00. Nov to Feb closed Sun. Admission: Adult €2.00, Child €1.00, OAP/Student €1.50, Family (2 adults & 2 children) €5.00.   Map Ref: 3

The Steam Museum

Straffan   Tel: +353 (0)1 627 3155   Fax: +353 (0)1 627 3477   Email: info@steam-museum.ie
Web: www.steam-museum.ie

The Steam Museum houses two complementary collections. The Richard Guiness Hall houses 20 prototype locomotive models and the Power Hall contains full size 'live steam' stationary engines which work at the weekends. The Museum building is rebuilt from the Church of St Jude moved from Dublin. Lodge Park Walled Garden (also open) is beside the Museum, also the Steaming Kettle Tearoom and the gift and garden shop.

Opening Times: Easter Sun to end May & Sep Sun & BH 14:30-17:30. Jun, Jul & Aug Tue to Sun & BH 14:00-18:00.   Admission: Adult €4.00, Child/OAP/Student €3.00, Family €13.00, Groups 10+ less 10%.
Map Ref: 4

CO LOUTH

Millmount Museum & Tower

Millmount, Drogheda   Tel: +353 (0)41 983 3097   Fax: +353 (0)41 984 1599
Email: info@millmount.net   Web: www.millmount.net

The museum is housed in the former officers' mess of a military complex built in 1808 and contains a wide variety of local and national artefacts. Perhaps its most prized possessions are the three large banners of the 18th century broguemakers, carpenters and weavers guilds. These are the only surviving Guilds' banners in the country. The beautifully woven drapes are wonderfully rich in detail and have been recognised by the National Museum as being of special significance. One of the most popular exhibits is the authentic Folk Kitchen which accurately recreates a 19th century Irish kitchen with items that include vintage utensils, a traditional dresser, a settle bed, examples of the earliest washing

---

Key to Classifications

see Classifications Index on page 413

Anthropology	Jewellery	Railway
Archaeological	Literature & Libraries	Religion
Art Galleries	Maritime	Roman
Arts, Crafts & Textiles	Military & Defence	Science - Earth
China, Glass & Ceramics	Mills - Water & Wind	& Planetary
Communications	Multicultural	Sculpture
Egyptian	Music & Theatre	Sporting History
Fashion	Natural History	Stately Homes
Geology	Oriental	Toy & Childhood
Health & Medicine	Palaces	Transport
Horticultural	Police, Prisons & Dungeons	Victoriana

machines, fire utensils and a range of butter churns and all the equipment needed for butter making. Many visitors are intrigued by the Curiosities Section which contains unique early cinema posters, vintage typewriters and many other weird and wonderful objects. The Industrial Room of the museum explores Drogheda's industrial heritage, highlighting industries that flourished here during the 19th and 20th centuries - spinning, weaving, brewing, pipe and shoemaking, iron works and shipbuilding. St Oliver Plunkett spent much of his time as Primate of Armagh living in Drogheda and his story is detailed in the Religious Exhibition along with local penal crosses and other religious artefacts. The museum is especially proud of its Geological Collection which contains more than 300 examples of granites and marbles from around the world. Local rock types and an exotic exhibit of an iron meteorite from Australia are displayed alongside naturally occurring diamonds, amethyst and gold rocks.

Opening Times: Mon to Sat 10:00-18:00, Sun & BH 14:30-17:30. Admission: Please phone for details.   Location: Five minute walk from town centre.   Map Ref: 5

CO MEATH

Kells Heritage Centre

The Courthouse, Headfort Place, Kells   Tel /
Fax: +353 (0)46 47840
Email: info@meathtourism.ie
Web: www.meathtourism.ie/kellsheritagecentre

HERITAGE TOWNS
→═ of Ireland ═←

This is the home of the Book of Kells - an exhibition entitled 'The Splendour of Ireland' gives an insight into the crafts and culture of monastic Ireland. Relics of St Columcille and a facsimile copy of the Book of Kells.

Opening Times: May to Sep Mon to Sat 10:00-18:00, Sun & BH 13:30-18:00. Oct to Apr Tue to Sat 10:00-18:00. Admission: Adult €3.00, Child/OAP/Student €1.50, Family (2 adults and 2 children) €8.00. Location: On Navan Road N3.   Map Ref: 6

The Book of Kells

Trim Visitor Centre

Mill Street, Trim   Tel: +353 (0)46 37227   Fax: +353 (0)46 38053
Email: info@meathtourism.ie   Web: www.meathtourism.ie

HERITAGE TOWNS
→═ of Ireland ═←

Trim has one of the largest collection of medieval buildings in Ireland and these are easily accessible to the public. The castle the largest Anglo-Norman castle in Europe, has undergone extensive conservation work. Also available in the Visitor Centre is the Power & Glory, an audio-visual show, explaining the fascinating history of this area.

Opening Times: Mon to Sat 10:00-17:00, Sun & BH 12:00-17:30. Closed 12:30-13:30 for lunch.
Admission: Adult €2.00, Child €1.00, OAP/Student €1.25, Family €5.00. Group Rates on request.
Location: Mill Street, close to town centre, five minutes from Castle.   Map Ref: 7

CO KILKENNY

Butler Gallery
The Castle, Kilkenny   Tel: +353 (0)56 61106

Public funded gallery. Exhibitions include Tony Cragg, Bill Woodrow, Sol le Wit, James Turrell, Petah Coyne, Jean Scully and Roman Signer. Collection contains contemporary sculpture, paintings and photography.

Opening Times: Oct to Mar daily 10:30-17:00, Apr to Sep daily 10:00-19:00.   Admission: Free.
Map Ref: 8

Rothe House Museum
Parliament Street, Kilkenny   Tel: +353 (0)56 22893   Email: rothehouse@eircom.net

Rothe House was built by prosperous merchant John Rothe in 1594. The Kilkenny Archaeological Society bought and restored the house. Within the house are various exhibitions from folk to costume and accessories.

Opening Times: Mon to Sat 10:30-17:00, Sun 15:00-17:00. Opening hours may vary off-season.
Location: City centre - five minutes from rail/bus station.
Map Ref: 8

CO TIPPERARY

Bolton Library
GPA Building, John Street, Cashel   Tel / Fax: +353 (0)62 61944
Email: boltonlibrary@oceanfree.net   Web: www.heritagetowns.com/cashel

HERITAGE TOWNS
of Ireland

A unique collection of two Archbishops over 12,000 volumes. Manuscript collections, early printing from 12th century. 20 titles prior to 1500, spectacular copy of Nuremburg Chronicle (1493) and many more. Visit the Georgian Cathedral in grounds and Cashel City walls 14th century.

Opening Times: Mar to Oct Tue to Sat 09:30-17:30, Oct to Feb Mon to Fri 09:30-17:30. Admission: Adult €1.50, Child €0.50, OAP/Student €1.00.
Map Ref: 9

Excel Heritage Centre & Art Gallery
Mitchell Street, Tipperary
Tel: +353 (0)62 33466   Fax: +353 (0)62 31067
Email: info@tipperary-excel.com   Web: www.tipperary-excel.com

HERITAGE TOWNS
of Ireland

This multicultural centre houses an art gallery, heritage centre, tourism office, cinema, coffee shop and craft shop. Multimedia exhibition explores Tipperary today, sport, the land, the town and hear about the song 'Its a long way to Tipperary'.

Opening Times: Daily 09:00-18:00. Closed Good Friday, Xmas & New Year. Admission: Adults €3.00. Location: Beside town car park, Market Square.
Map Ref: 10

Excel Heritage Centre & Art Gallery

Museums • Galleries • Historic Houses

Please let us know of any collections that are not listed in this guide that you feel should be listed. E-mail us on *editor@tomorrows.co.uk* or return the Report Form on page 448

CO WATERFORD

The Lismore Experience

The Courthouse, Lismore   Tel: +353 (0)58 54975   Fax: +353 (0)58 53009
Email: lismoreheritage@eircom.net   Web: www.lismoreIreland.eom

A 30 minute Lismore Experience will transport you through 1400 years of history. Guided tours of the town can be arranged, learn about Sir Robert Boyle 'Father of Modern Chemistry', Boyles Law - from Lismore, artefacts and new exhibition.

Opening Times: Apr to May Mon to Sat 09:30-17:30, Sun 10:00-17:30. Jun to Aug Mon to Sat 09:30-18:00, Sun 10:00-17:30. Sep to Oct Mon to Sun 09:30-17:30. Nov to Jan Mon to Fri 10:00-17:30.
Admission: Adult €3.00, Child/OAP €2.00, Student €2.50, Family €6.00, Group €2.50.   Location: In town centre.   Map Ref: 11

CO WEXFORD

Wexford County Museum

The Castle, Enniscorthy   Tel / Fax: +353 (0)54 35926
Email: wexmus@iol.ie

The County Museum is in four main sections which illustrate in a dramatic way the stories and history of County Wexford through the centuries - military, agriculture, writing, crafts, industrial and ecclesiastical. The museum is a veritable treasure house of information for anyone interested in Irish ways of living, culture and heritage.

Opening Times: Mar to Sep 10:00-17:30, Sun 14:00-17:30.
Admission: Adult €4.50, Student/Senior €3.00, Child €1.00, Family €11.00.   Location: Town centre.   Map Ref: 12

Irish Agricultural Museum

Johnstown Castle Old Farmyard, Wexford   Tel: +353 (0)53 42888   Fax: +353 (0)53 42213

Extensive displays on rural transport, farming and the activities of the farmyard and the farmhouse. Nationally important collection of Irish country furniture - over 100 pieces. Also Famine Exhibition and Ferguson System display.

Opening Times: Mon to Fri 09:00-17:00, Apr to Nov also Sat & Sun 14:00-17:00.
Admission: Adult €5.00, Child €3.00, Family €15.00. Group rates available.   Location: Four miles south west of Wexford Town.   Map Ref: 13

CO CORK

Bantry House

🎨 🖼 📷 🚂

Bantry   Tel: +353 (0)27 50047   Fax: +353 (0)27 50795   Email: info@bantryhouse.ie
Web: www.bantryhouse.ie

Bantry House and Gardens has been home to the White family since 1739, and is one of the finest stately homes in Ireland. The house contains a unique collection of tapestries, furniture, carpets and art treasures, collected mainly by the second Earl in the 19th century. These include Russian icons, 18th century French, Flemish and Irish furniture, Gobelin tapestries and Aubusson carpets.

Opening Times: Mid Mar to end Oct daily 09:00-17:00.
Location: Near town centre on N71, ten minute walk.
Exhibitions & Events 2003 : 28 Jun to 6 Jul: West Cork Chamber Music Festival. Other concerts throughout the year. Enquiries to West Cork Chamber Music, telephone +353 27 52788 or email westcorkmusic@eircom.ie.

Map Ref: 14

Cobh Museum

🖼

Scots Church, High Road, Cobh   Tel: +353 (0)21 481 4240   Fax: +353 (0)21 481 1018
Email: cobhmuseum@eircom.net

The museum is housed in the former Scots Presbyterian Church. Exhibitions reflect the social and cultural history of the town of Cobh (Queenstown), the Great Island and the harbour.

Opening Times: Easter to Oct Mon to Sat 11:00-13:00 & 14:00-18:00, Sun 15:00-18:00.
Admission: Adult €1.50, Child/OAP €0.75, Family €3.75.   Location: Five minutes walk from town centre, near Tourist Office and station.

Map Ref: 15

Cobh - The Queenstown Story

♿ 🖼 🅾 🚂

Cobh Railway Station, Deepwater Quay, Cobh   Tel: +353 (0)21 481 3591
Fax: +353 (0)21 481 3595   Email: info@cobhheritage.com
Web: www.cobhheritage.com

HERITAGE TOWNS
of Ireland

Discover Cobh's maritime history and connections with the Lusitania, Titanic and Irish emigration. Collection of memorabilia including letters, menus and personal belongings.

Opening Times: Apr to Nov 10:00-18:00, Dec to Mar 10:00-17:00, last admission 1 hour before closing.
Admission: Adult €5.00, Child €2.50, OAP €4.00.
Location: Adjacent to Cobh Railway Station in Cobh Town.

Map Ref: 15

Cork City Gaol/Radio Museum Experience

🎨 ♿ 🖼 🚂

Convent Avenue, Sunday's Well, Cork   Tel: +353 (0)21 430 5022   Fax: +353 (0)21 430 7230
Email: corkgaol@indigo.ie   Web: www.corkcitygaol.com

19th century life in Cork inside and outside prison walls. Lifelike figures, furnished cells, sound effects and A.V. Also Radio Museum Experience - restored 1927 radio studio, broadcasting history and RTE Museum collection.

Opening Times: Daily 10:00-17:00.   Admission: Adult €5.50, Student/OAP €4.50, Family €15.00.   Location: Two kilometres north west of main thoroughfare.

Map Ref: 16

Cork Public Museum

🖼

Fitzgerald Park, Mardyke, Cork   Tel: +353 (0)21 427 0679   Fax: +353 (0)21 427 0931
Email: museum@corkcorp.ie

General collection outlining the history of Cork from earliest times to present day, includes archaeology, geology, history - social and political. Cork silver and glass.

Opening Times: Mon to Fri 11:00-13:00 & 14:15-17:00 (Jun & Aug to 18:00), Sun 15:00-17:00.
Closed Sat and BH weekends.   Admission: Free Mon to Fri. Sun - Adult €1.50, Family/Group €3.00.   Location: Ten minute walk from town centre, two minute walk from number 8 bus stop on Western Road.

Map Ref: 16

CO CORK *(continued)*

Crawford Municipal Art Gallery

Emmet Place, Cork   Tel: +353 (0)21 427 3377   Fax: +353 (0)21 480 5043
Email: crawfordgallery@eircom.net   Web: www.crawfordartgallery.com

In a collection of (mostly) Irish art from the last three centuries, highlights include works by James Barry, Daniel Maclise, Walter Osborne, Sean Keating, Jack B Yeats, Louis le Brocquy, Paul Seawright and Kathy Prendergast.

Opening Times: Mon to Sat 10:00-17:00. Closed Sun & BH.   Admission: Free.   Location: City centre.   Map Ref: 16

International Museum of Wine

Desmond Castle, Cork Street, Kinsale   Tel: +353 (0)21 477 4853
Email: info@heritageireland.ie   Web: www.heritageireland.ie

HERITAGE TOWNS
of Ireland

Exhibition which documents the intriguing story of Ireland's wine links with Europe and under world from early modern period to present day.

Opening Times: Mid Apr to mid Jun Tue to Sun 10:00-18:00, open BH. Mid Jun to late Oct daily 10:00-18:00. Admission: Adult €2.00, Child/Student €1.00, Group/OAP €1.50, Family €5.00.   Location: 600 metres from Guard Well along Cork Street.   Map Ref: 17

International Museum of Wine

Youghal Heritage Centre

Tourism House, Youghal   Tel: +353 (0)24 20170   Fax: +353 (0)24 20171
Email: youghal@eircom.net

HERITAGE TOWNS
of Ireland

A visit to this centre is essential. Walking tours of the town depart at 11:00 each day during summer period. Learn about Sir Walter Raleigh who was based in Youghal.

Opening Times: Oct to May Mon to Fri 09:30-17:30. Jun to Sep daily 09:00-19:00.   Admission: Adult €2.50, Child/Student €2.00, Group €1.00.   Location: On N25, beside Quays/Clock Tower.   Map Ref: 18

CO KERRY

Listowel Literary Museum

24 The Square, Listowel   Tel: +353 (0)68 22212   Fax: +353 (0)68 22217
Email: info@seanchai-klcc.com   Web: www.seanchai-klcc.com

HERITAGE TOWNS
of Ireland

The literary and Cultural Capital of Ireland, Listowel is the birthplace of two of Ireland's most distinguished writers, Dr Bryan MacMahon & Dr John B Keane. The town features an attractive Square, similar to Covent Garden in London, which includes the remains of Listowel Castle overlooking the River Feale. Adjacent to the Castle is located Seanchai - Kerry Literary & Cultural Centre, honouring the literary tradition of Listowel & County Kerry through an audio-visual interpretative experience. Listowel is a hive of activity throughout the year from the many performances in St John's Theatre, to pub theatre, traditional music sessions and a heritage trail of the town, taking in the many attractive shop fronts and buildings of architectural & historical interest. Listowel is celebrated for its September Horse Racing Festival and Literary Festival Writers' Week.

Opening Times: Mar to Oct daily 10:00-18:00. Nov to Feb by appointment.   Admission: Adult €4.00, Child/OAP/Student €2.00, Family (2 adults and 3 children) €10.00.   Location: Located in town square.   Map Ref: 19

Ireland - The Southwest

Kerry County Museum

Ashe Memorial Hall, Denny Street, Tralee   Tel: +353 (0)66 712 7475/712 7777

Kerry County Museum, Tralee is Ireland's most visited regional museum. Located in the splendidly restored Ashe Memorial Hall in Tralee Town Centre it traces the history and archaeology of Kerry from earliest times. The Museum comprises four elements: Kerry in Colour - a widescreen audio-visual presentation on Kerry's spectacular scenery, its heritage sites and traditions. Permanent Museum Galleries - with the Treasures of Kerry divided into ten sections chronologically from the Stone Age to the Present Day. The majority of the artefacts on display are on loan from the National Museum of Ireland. There are special sections on Daniel O'Connell (1775-1847), called The Liberator, after whom O'Connell Street in Dublin is named, on Gaelic Football - Ireland's premier sporting passion, and a fascinating newsreel collection on life and political developments in Ireland from 1916-66. Geraldine Tralee Medieval Experience - a reconstruction of Tralee in 1451 when it was headquarters of the Munster Geraldines. Visitors sit in time cars and are transported back in time and experience a day in the life of an Irish Medieval town complete with sounds and smells. Commentaries are provided in a choice of seven languages. Temporary Exhibition Area - that houses major international temporary exhibitions in conjunction with overseas institutions.

Opening Times: Daily 17 Mar to 21 Dec. Mar to Oct 09:30-17:30, Nov to Dec 11:30-16:30.
Admission: Adult €8.00, Child €5.00, OAP/Student €6.00, Family €22.00.   Location: In town centre.   Exhibitions & Events 2003 : Please telephone for details.
Map Ref: 20

The Hunt Museum

The Custom House, Rutland Street, Limerick   Tel: +353 (0)61 312833   Fax: +353 (0)61 312834   Email: info@huntmuseum.com   Web: www.ul.ie/~hunt

A magnificent collection of art and antiquity - donated to the 'people of Ireland' by John and Gertrude Hunt. Exhibited in an 18th century Custom House, with gift shop and a restaurant.

Opening Times: 1 Jan to 28 Feb, 1 Mar to 31 Dec, Mon to Sat 10:00-17:00, Sun 14:00-17:00.
Admission: Jan to Feb: Adult €5.30, Child €2.50, Family €12.70. Mar to Dec: Adult €5.70, Child €2.70, Family €14.00.   Location: 2 minute walk from Limerick Tourist Information Office.
Map Ref: 21

Limerick City Gallery of Art

Carnegie Building, Pery Square, Limerick   Tel: +353 (0)61 310633

The permanent collection consists of some 600 works in a wide variety of media and styles dating from the 18th century to contemporary practice, it is mostly Irish or Irish related in origin with exceptional examples of work by leading Irish artists of all periods. The permanent collection also houses the National Collection of Contemporary Drawing with a published catalogue and the Michael O'Connor Poster Collection, which consists of 3,800 works of international design.

Opening Times: Mon to Wed & Fri 10:00-18:00, Thu 10:00-19:00, Sat 10:00-13:00.
Admission: Free.   Location: One minute walk from train and bus station.
Map Ref: 21

A Section of the Display Galleries

Limerick Museum

Castle Lane, Nicholas Street, Limerick
Tel: +353 (0)61 417826   Fax: +353 (0)61 415266
Email: lwalsh@limerickcorp.ie   Web: www.limerickcorp.ie

Regional museum covering all aspects of the past of Limerick City and the region. Principal themes include archaeology, Limerick silver, Limerick lace, numismatics, printing, labour history, manufacturers, national independence movements, topographical paintings, prints, old photographs, postcards, etc.

Opening Times: Tue to Sat 10:00-13:00 & 14:15-17:00.
Closed Sun, Mon and BH.   Admission: Free.   Location: Limerick City, beside King John's Castle.
Map Ref: 21

The West & Northwest

CO CLARE

Clare Museum

Arthur's Row, Ennis Tel: +353 (0)65 682 3382 Fax: +353 (0)65 684 2119
Email: claremuseum@eircom.net Web: www.clarelibrary.ie

The Riches of Clare Exhibition tells 6000 years of Clare's history, using the authentic artifacts, computer inter-actives, and audio-visual presentations. Includes artifacts from the National Museum of Ireland.

Opening Times: Jan to Apr Tue to Sat 09:30-17:30, May to Sep Mon to Sat 09:30-17:30, Sun 14:00-17:30, Oct to Dec Tue to Sat 09:30-17:30. Admission: Adult €3.50, Student €2.50, Family €10.00. Location: Centre of Ennis, off O'Connell Square. Map Ref: 22

CO DONEGAL

Donegal County Museum

High Road, Letterkenny Tel: +353 (0)74 24613 Fax: +353 (0)74 26522
Email: jmccarthy@donegalcoco.ie

The museum is housed in a stone building which was once part of Letterkenny Workhouse built in 1846. The museum houses and displays a fascinating range of artefacts covering all aspects of the history of County Donegal.

Opening Times: Mon to Fri 10:00-12:30 & 13:00-16:30, Sat 13:00-16:30. Admission: Free.
Location: Signposted in Letterkenny, five minute walk from town centre. Map Ref: 23

Glebe House & Gallery

Churchill, Letterkenny Tel: +353 (0)74 37071

Regency house, 1828, set in woodland gardens, decorated with William Morris textiles, Islamic and Japanese art. Collection includes works by leading 20th century artists - Picasso, Kokoshka as well as Irish and Italian artists.

Opening Times: Mid May to end Sep Sat to Thu 11:00-18:30. Admission: Adult €2.50, Child €1.20, OAP/Group €1.90, Family €6.30. Map Ref: 24

CO GALWAY

Athenry Medieval Museum

St Marys Heritage & Art Centre, Athenry
Tel: +353 (0)91 844661
Email: info@athenryheritagetown.com
Web: www.athenryheritagetown.com

HERITAGE TOWNS
⇒ *of Ireland* ⇐

A variety of interactive media - visual and audio model of Athenry. See the Mace of Athenry - original artefacts. Special children's programmes.

Opening Times: Apr to Sep daily 10:00-18:00. Admission: Adult €2.00, Child/OAP/Student €1.50, Groups on request. Map Ref: 25

CO MAYO

Irish Folklife

Turlough Park, Castlebar Tel: +353 (0)94 31628 Email: tpark@museum.ie
Web: www.museum.ie

Turlough Park is the only branch of the Museum outside the capital. It tells the story of people in rural Ireland, emphasising the continuity of traditions of lifestyles, established for several hundred years and lasting well into the 20th century.

Opening Times: Tue to Sat 10:00-17:00, Sun 14:00-17:00.
Closed Mon. Admission: Free. Map Ref: 26

CO MAYO *(continued)*

Knock Folk Museum

Knock   Tel: +353 (0)94 88100   Fax: +353 (0)94 88295   Email: knockmuseum@eircom.net
Web: www.knock-shrine.ie

Knock Folk Museum documents the story of the Knock Apparition of 1879 and places it in the context of life at that time. Permanent displays range from religious to fishing, farming, crafts and skills, education, housing, clothing and transport.

Opening Times: May to Oct daily 10:00-18:00, Jul & Aug 10:00-19:00.   Admission: Adult €3.81, Child €2.54, Under 5s Free, OAP €2.54.   Location: Located in Knock Shrine grounds, south of Basilica.

Map Ref: 27

Westport Heritage Centre

The Quay, Clew Bay, Westport   Tel: +353 (0)98 26852   Email: joyce@anu.ie
Web: www.anu.ie/westport/

HERITAGE TOWNS
➵ of Ireland ➴

The charming town of Westport, situated on the shores of Clew Bay, in the shadow of Croagh Patrick, is one of the few planned towns in the country. It is an estate town, built to the plan of James Wyatt, the well-known architect of the Georgian period. One of its outstanding features is the elegant tree-lined boulevard, known as The Mall. Westport was overall winner of 2001 National Tidy Towns Award. Guided walks of this historic town are conducted twice weekly during the summer months. The history of the development of Westport, from the time it was an O'Mally stronghold in the 16th century, to the present day, is brought alive in the Heritage Centre.

Opening Times: May to Aug daily 10:00-17:00.   Admission: Adult €2.00, Child/OAP/Student €1.00, Group rate on request.   Location: On the Quay - Clew Bay. Ten minutes from town centre.

Map Ref: 28

CO SLIGO

Sligo County Museum

Stephen Street, Sligo   Tel: +353 (0)71 47190   Fax: +353 (0)71 46798
Email: sligolib@sligococo.ie   Web: www.sligococo.ie

There is a Yeats Collection and an accumulation of local artefacts. Yeats Collection comprises photographs, prints, letters, drawings and medals awarded to W B Yeats as Nobel Prize for Literature 1923.

Opening Times: Oct to May Tue to Sat 14:00-17:00. Jun to Sep Tue to Sat 10:00-12:00 & 14:00-17:00.   Admission: Free.   Location: Near town centre.

Map Ref: 29

Ireland - The Midlands

CO CAVAN

Cavan County Museum

Virginia Road, Ballyjamesduff   Tel: +353 (0)49 854 4070   Fax: +353 (0)49 854 4332
Email: ccmuseum@eircom.net   Web: www.cavanmuseum.ie

Cavan County Museum, a magnificent 19th century building, which is beautifully situated amid extensive grounds, houses the material culture of County Cavan and is an ideal starting point for a relaxing family day out.

Opening Times: Tue to Sat 10:00-17:00, also May to Oct Sun & BH 14:00-18:00.
Location: Five minute walk from town centre.   Map Ref: 30

CO MONAGHAN

Monaghan County Museum

1/2 Hill Street, Monaghan   Tel: +353 (0)47 82928   Fax: +353 (0)47 71189
Email: ccmuseum@monaghancoco.ie

The extensive and rapidly growing collections at Monaghan County Museum range from ancient Stone Age right up to modern times. A purpose built gallery houses temporary/travelling exhibitions.

Opening Times: Tue to Fri 10:00-13:00 & 14:00-17:00, Sat 11:00-13:00 & 14:00-17:00. Closed Sun & Mon. Admission: Free. Location: Town centre.   Map Ref: 31

CO OFFALY

Birr Castle Science Museum

Birr Castle, Birr   Tel: +353 (0)509 20336   Fax: +353 (0)509 21583
Email: info@birrcastle.com   Web: www.birrcastle.com

HERITAGE TOWNS
of Ireland

Discover the largest telescope in the world constructed in the 1840s. Travel through the evolution of astronomy from 17th century with Gallileo, Newton and Hershell. Amazing collection of original artefacts, photographs, drawings and letters can be found in the galleries.

Opening Times: Daily 09:00-18:00.   Location: Near town centre.   Map Ref: 32

Giant Telescope, Birr Castle Science Museum

Tullamore Dew Whiskey Museum

Bury Street, Tullamore   Tel: +353 (0)506 25015   Fax: +353 (0)506 25016

HERITAGE TOWNS
of Ireland

Email: tullamoredhc@eircom.net
Web: www.tullamore-dew.org

The centre uses a combination of artefacts, story panels, recordings and slide shows, with a tasting of the world famous whiskey Tullamore Dew or Irish Mist liqueur.

Opening Times: May to Sep Mon to Sat 09:00-18:00, Sun 12:00-17:00. Oct to Apr Mon to Sat 10:00-17:00, Sun 12:00-17:00. Admission: Adult €3.50, Child €2.25, OAP/Student €2.75, Family €9.00, Group €3.00.
Location: Along Canalside in restored warehouse.
Map Ref: 33

CO ROSCOMMON

National Irish Famine Museum

● ◖ 🚜

Strokestown   Tel: +353 (0)78 33013   Fax: +353 (0)78 33712
Email: info@strokestownpark.ie   Web: www.strokestownpark.ie

HERITAGE TOWNS
↦ of Ireland ↤

Famine museum uses original documents from the house estate. The history of the Irish famine is explained and draws parallels to the occurrance of famine today in the developing world.

Opening Times: Apr to Oct daily 11:00-17:30.
Admission: Adult House/Museum/Gardens €9.00, House only/Museum only €3.50, Gardens only €4.50.
OAP/Student/Group discounts available.   Location: In town on N5 main Dublin/Ballina road.   Map Ref: 34

CO WESTMEATH

Belvedere House, Gardens and Park

    🚹 ● ◖ 🚜

Mullingar   Tel: +353 (0)44 49060   Fax: +353 (0)44 49002   Email: info@belvedere-house.ie
Web: www.belvedere-house.ie

One of the finest Irish historic houses, and together with walled garden and landscaped park has been exquisitely restored. Explore 6 kilometres of woodland trails and discover intriguing follies throughout. Remarkable Visitor Centre with multimedia displays and excellent facilities. The gem of the Irish Midlands - where history lives on.

Opening Times: May to Aug Mon to Sat 09:30-18:00, Sun 10:30-19:00. Sep to Oct 10:30-18:00. Nov to Apr 10:30-16:30. Admission: Adult €6.00, Child €3.80, OAP/Student €4.50, Family €16.00, Group rates available. Location: 50 miles from Dublin and five miles from Mullingar on the N52.   Map Ref: 35

Isle of Man

Manx National Heritage

Manx Museum, Kingswood Grove, Douglas IM1 3LY   Tel: 01624 648000
Fax: 01624 648001   Email: enquiries@mnh.gov.im   Web: www.gov.im/mnh

Manx National Heritage is a major award winning and unique organisation in Europe. The portfolio of Heritage responsibilities include:- The National Museum Service, The National Monuments Service, The National Trust Service, The National Archives and The National Art Gallery.

Rushen Abbey

Ballasalla   Tel: 01624 648000   Fax: 01624 648001
Email: enquiries@mnh.gov.im   Web: www.gov.im/mnh

Rushen Abbey is the most substantial and important medieval religious site in the Isle of Man. Discover what life was like for the Cistercian community, walk through the remains of substantial medieval buildings and see where archaeology research has revealed traces of buildings below ground. This is a highlight of a 'Christian Heritage' route around the Island.

Opening Times: 1 Apr to 26 Oct daily 10:00-17:00.

Calf Sound

Calf Sound   Tel: 01624 648000   Fax: 01624 648001
Email: enquiries@mnh.gov.im   Web: www.gov.im/mnh

Visitor centre sited and styled to address this unique setting of beautiful landscape, sea and the Calf. Information and audio visual presentations about history and wildlife in this area.

Opening Times: Daily 10:00-17:00. Closed Xmas & New Year.   Admission: Free.
Location: One and a half miles from Cregneash.

Castle Rushen

Castletown   Tel: 01624 648000   Fax: 01624 648001
Email: enquiries@mnh.gov.im   Web: www.gov.im/mnh

One of Britains best preserved 12th century medieval castles, Castle Rushen is a limestone fortress rising out of the heart of the old capital of the Island, Castletown. Once the fortress of the Kings and Lords of Mann, Rushen is brought alive with rich decorations, sounds and smells of a bygone era.

Opening Times: 1 Apr to 26 Oct daily 10:00-17:00.
Location: In the town centre.

Nautical Museum

10 Bridge Street, Castletown   Tel: 01624 648000   Fax: 01624 648001
Email: enquiries@mnh.gov.im   Web: www.gov.im/mnh

Set at the mouth of Castletown harbour, this museum is home to an 18th century armed yacht. A replica sailmaker's loft, ship model and photographs bring alive Manx maritime life and trade in the days of sail.

Opening Times: 1 Apr to 26 Oct daily 10:00-17:00.

Old Grammar School

Castletown   Tel: 01624 648000   Fax: 01624 648001
Email: enquiries@mnh.gov.im   Web: www.gov.im/mnh

The former capital's first church was built around 1200AD and was a school from 1570 to 1930. The main wing is the oldest roofed structure in the Island.

Opening Times: 1 Apr to 26 Oct daily 10:00-17:00.   Admission: Free.

Isle of Man

Old House of Keys

Parliament Square, Castletown   Tel: 01624 648000   Fax: 01624 648001
Email: enquiries@mnh.gov.im   Web: www.gov.im/mnh

The history of the Old House of Keys building is one chapter in the long, and often turbulent, history of Manx politics which stretches back to the ninth and tenth centuries when the Viking Kings ruled the Isle of Man. It has been restored to its appearance in 1866 and provides an insight into the political life and times of the Island through interactive audio presentations.

Opening Times: 1 Apr to 26 Oct daily 10:00-17:00.
Location: Opposite Castle Rushen in the town centre.

Manx Museum

Kingswood Grove, Douglas IM1 3LY   Tel: 01624 648000   Fax: 01624 648001
Email: enquiries@mnh.gov.im   Web: www.gov.im/mnh

The natural point to begin your exploration of the Island and the fascinating 10,000 year old 'Story of Mann'. Displays of Manx archaeology, history, folk life and natural science. Also houses the National Art Gallery and the Island's national archive and reference library. In a matter of hours you'll discover all kinds of facts and intriguing features that bring the past to life.

Opening Times: Mon-Sat 10:00-17:00. Closed Xmas & New Year. Admission: Free.

The Great Laxey Wheel & Mines Trail

Laxey   Tel: 01624 648000   Fax: 01624 648001   Email: enquiries@mnh.gov.im
Web: www.gov.im/mnh

Built in 1854 and 22 metres in diameter, the Great Laxey Wheel - christened 'Lady Isabella' after the wife of the then Lieutenant Governor of the Isle of Man, is the largest working water wheel in Europe, and has remained one of the Island's most dramatic tourist attractions. It was designed to pump water from the lead and zinc mines and is an acknowledged masterpiece of Victorian engineering.

Opening Times: 1 Apr to 26 Oct daily 10:00-17:00.

Key to Classifications

see Classifications Index on page 413

Anthropology	Jewellery	Railway
Archaeological	Literature & Libraries	Religion
Art Galleries	Maritime	Roman
Arts, Crafts & Textiles	Military & Defence	Science - Earth
China, Glass & Ceramics	Mills - Water & Wind	& Planetary
Communications	Multicultural	Sculpture
Egyptian	Music & Theatre	Sporting History
Fashion	Natural History	Stately Homes
Geology	Oriental	Toy & Childhood
Health & Medicine	Palaces	Transport
Horticultural	Police, Prisons & Dungeons	Victoriana

Isle of Man

House of Manannan

East Quay, Peel Tel: 01624 648000 Fax: 01624 648001
Email: enquiries@mnh.gov.im Web: www.gov.im/mnh

Using reconstructions, interactive displays, audio visual presentations and original material, the House of Manannan explores the Celtic, Viking and Maritime traditions of the Isle of Man. It brings to life themes which are both ancient and modern. Experience two hours of drama, colour and excitement by the harbour in the City of Peel.

Opening Times: Daily 10:00-17:00. Closed Xmas & New Year. Location: By Peel Harbour.

Peel Castle

Peel Tel: 01624 648000 Fax: 01624 648001 Email: enquiries@mnh.gov.im
Web: www.gov.im/mnh

In the 11th century the Castle was the ruling seat of the Norse Kingdom of Mann. Stroll through the remains of the Round Tower, 13th century Cathedral and site of the 90ft long giant's grave.

Opening Times: 1 Apr to 26 Oct daily 10:00-17:00.

Cregneash Village Folk Museum

Cregneash, Port St Mary Tel: 01624 648000 Fax: 01624 648001
Email: enquiries@mnh.gov.im Web: www.gov.im/mnh

Experience what life was really like in a Manx crofting village during the early 19th century. Stroll around this attractive village set in beautiful countryside, call into Harry Kelly's Cottage, The Turner's Shed, a Weaver's House and the Blacksmith's Smithy. Grazing nearby will be the Manx four horned Loghtan sheep along with other animals from the village farm. Home baked refreshments in the village café will complete your visit.

Opening Times: 1 Apr to 26 Oct daily 10:00-17:00.

The Grove Rural Life Museum

Andreas Road, Ramsey Tel: 01624 648000 Fax: 01624 648001
Email: enquiries@mnh.gov.im Web: www.gov.im/mnh

Victorian time capsule, a country house built as a summer retreat for a Liverpool shipping merchant. Rooms are filled with period and often original furnishings and outbuildings house 19th century vehicles and farming tools.

Opening Times: 1 Apr to 26 Oct daily 10:00-17:00.

Channel Islands

Alderney Society Museum

The Old School, Alderney GY9 3TG   Tel: 01481 823222   Fax: 01481 824979
Email: alderney.museum@virgin.net   Web: www.alderneymuseum.org

A museum of local interest. Special features - Iron Age pottery, Elizabethan shipwreck, German occupation and fortifications, 19th century harbour and fortifications.

Opening Times: Easter to end Oct Mon to Fri 10:00-12:00 & 14:00-16:00, Sat & Sun 10:00-12:00.   Admission: Adult £2.00, Child Free.   Location: High Street.

Castle Cornet

St Peter Port   Tel: 01481 721657   Fax: 01481 740719   Email: admin@museum.guernsey.net
Web: www.museum.guernsey.net

Maritime Museum, Royal Guernsey Militia Museum, 'The Story of Castle Cornet', 201 Squadron RAF Museum, four period gardens and a season of storytelling and outdoor theatre.

Opening Times: Apr to Oct daily 10:00-17:00.   Admission: Adult £5.00, Child Free, OAP £3.00.
Location: St Peter Port, ten minute walk from bus station.

Fort Grey Shipwreck Museum

Rocquaine, St Peters GY7 9BY   Tel: 01481 265036   Fax: 01481 236279
Email: admin@museum.guernsey.net   Web: www.museum.guernsey.net

Martello Tower housing objects recovered from the many wrecks off Guernsey's west coast, dating from 1777 to 1973.

Opening Times: Apr to Oct daily 10:00-17:00.   Admission: Adult £2.00, Child Free, OAP £1.00.
Location: South west coast of Guernsey - Rocquaine Bay.

German Occupation Museum

Forest GY8 0BG   Tel: 01481 238205

Unique collection of German occupation items recreated street scene, restored fortifications audio-visual experience. Tearoom and garden.

Opening Times: Apr to Oct daily 10:00-16:30. Nov to Mar daily 10:00-13:00.   Admission: Adult £3.00, Child £1.50, Groups £2.50.   Location: 15 minutes from town centre.

Guernsey Folk Museum

Saumarez Park, Castel GY5 7UJ   Tel / Fax: 01481 255384   Web: www.nationaltrust-gsy.org.gg

Social/agricultural history of Guernsey from Victorian period. Recreated rooms and displays set in old farm complex around central farm courtyard. Original and reproduction period costumes on display.

Opening Times: 25 Mar to 31 Oct daily 10:00-17:30.   Admission: Adult £3.00,
Child/Concession £1.00. Group rates available.   Location: Set in Saumarez Park, public park. On regular bus route.

Guernsey Museum & Art Gallery

Candie, St Peter Port GY1 1UG   Tel: 01481 726518   Fax: 01481 715177
Email: admin@museum.guernsey.net   Web: www.museum.guernsey.net

Museum - 'The Story of Guernsey'. Art Gallery - exhibitions Feb to Dec.

Opening Times: Feb to Dec daily 10:00-17:00. Winter closing 16:00.   Admission: Adult £3.00, Child Free, OAP £2.00.   Location: Candie Gardens, four minute walk from centre of St Peter Port.

Hauteville House & Victor Hugo's House of Exile

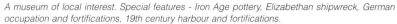

38 Hauteville, St Peter Port GY1 1DG   Tel: 01481 721911   Fax: 01481 715913

The house was bought in 1856 by the famous French writer Victor Hugo and decorated with china, pieces of furniture, tapestries and Delft tiles in a unique and original way. Visit the garden also. 2002 year of the bi-centenary of his birth.

Channel Islands

Opening Times: Apr to Sep Mon to Sat 10:00-12:00 & 14:00-17:00. Jul & Aug 10:00-17:00. Closed Sun & BH. Admission: Adult £5.00. Location: Near town centre, five minutes walk from central bus station.

Sausmarez Manor
St Martins GY4 6SG Tel: 01481 235571 Fax: 01481 235572
Email: peter@desausmarezmanor.co.uk Web: www.artparks.co.uk

Historic house lived in by descendents of Seigneurs going back to c1220. With subtropical garden, sculpture park, dolls house collection, pitch & putt, adventure play area and ride on train.

Opening Times: 10:00-17:00. Admission: Overall admission & carpark free, attractions individually priced.

JERSEY

Channel Islands Military Museum
The Five Mile Road, St Ouen Tel: 01534 723136

The island's finest collection of original military and civilian occupation items to be seen on the island, housed in a restored bunker which formed part of Hitler's Atlantic wall defence.

Opening Times: 25 Mar to 31 Oct daily 10:00-17:00. Admission: Adult £3.00, Child £1.00. Location: At the rear of Jersey Woollen Mills and across from Jersey Pearl.

Elizabeth Castle
St Helier Tel: 01534 723971 Fax: 01534 610338 Email: marketing@jerseyheritagetrust.org Web: www.jerseyheritagetrust.org

A magnificent fortress that hosts a number of fine exhibitions detailing its past and those who have been stationed there. Noon-day gun fired daily.

Opening Times: Apr to Nov daily 10:00-18:00. Closed winter. Admission: Adult £4.95, Concession £4.20, Under 10s Free, 15% Group Discount available. Location: Located in the Bay of St Aubin.

Hamptonne Country Life Museum
Rue de la Patente, St Lawrence Tel: 01534 863955 Fax: 01534 863935
Email: marketing@jerseyheritagetrust.org Web: www.jerseyheritagetrust.org

A unique collection of restored farm houses and buildings tracing 600 years of Jersey's rural past.

Opening Times: Apr to Nov daily 10:00-17:00. Closed winter. Admission: Adult £4.95, Concession £4.20, Under 10s Free, 15% Group Discount available. Location: Centre of Jersey.

Jersey Battle of the Flowers Museum
La Robeline, Mont des Corvees, St Ouen JE3 2ES Tel: 01534 482408

The Battle of Flowers Museum presents the show of the year, so why not come on safari and see a wonderland of animals, meet the zebras, lions, and the 101 dalmations and lots of other interesting animals.

Opening Times: Daily 10:00-17:00. Admission: Adult £3.25, Child £1.00, OAP £3.00. Location: West of island, seven miles from town.

Jersey Museum
The Weighbridge, St Helier JE2 3NF Tel: 01534 633300 Fax: 01534 633301
Email: marketing@jerseyheritagetrust.org Web: www.jerseyheritagetrust.org

The start point to any visit to Jersey. This award winning museum traces Jersey's past from the Ice Age to the present day. Also includes a fine art gallery and three floors of restored Victorian merchant's house.

Opening Times: Apr to Nov daily 10:00-17:00, winter 10:00-16:00. Admission: Adult £4.95, Concession £4.20, Under 10s Free, 15% Group Discount available. Location: Located next to bus office.

Channel Islands

La Hougue Bie Museum
Grouville Tel: 01534 353823 Fax: 01534 866472 Email: marketing@jerseyheritagetrust.org
Web: www.jerseyheritagetrust.org

A loft neolithic mound dominates this site that also includes an extensive geology and archaeology museum, neolithic encampment and memorial bunker to the slave workers of the occupation years.

Opening Times: Apr to Nov daily 10:00-17:00. Closed winter. Admission: Adult £4.95, Concession £4.20, Under 10s Free, 15% Group Discount available. Location: On major bus route from St Helier.

Maritime Museum & Occupation Tapestry Gallery
New North Quay, St Helier Tel: 01534 811043 Fax: 01534 874099
Email: marketing@jerseyheritagetrust.org Web: www.jerseyheritagetrust.org

Interactive fun, discovery and art commissions this museum is ideal for the maritime enthusiast and family alike. The 12 panels of the tapestry movingly record the privation and suffering of occupied people.

Opening Times: Apr to Nov daily 10:00-17:00, Winter 10:00-16:00. Admission: Adult £5.80, Concession £4.95, Under 10s Free, 15% Group Discount available. Location: One minute walk from Jersey Tourism Visitor Centre.

Mont Orgueil Castle
Gorey, St Martin Tel: 01534 853292 Fax: 01534 854303
Email: marketing@jerseyheritagetrust.org Web: www.jerseyheritagetrust.org

A mediaeval castle built in the 13th century, Mont Orgueil dominates the Royal Bay of Granville. It remains one of the most complete castles of its type and commands some of Jersey's finest views.

Opening Times: Apr to Nov daily 10:00-18:00, winter times available on request.
Admission: Adult £4.95, Concession £4.20, Under 10s Free, 15% Group Discount available.
Location: South east coast of Jersey.

Noirmont Command Bunker
Noirmont Point, St Brelade Tel: 01534 746795 Email: m.costard@spoor.co.uk

Built by the German occupying forces during WWII, this impressive artillery command bunker has been restored to a high standard. The adjacent battery and observation tower may also be visited.

Opening Times: Please contact for details. Admission: Adults £1.00, Accompanied Child Free.

Sir Francis Cook Gallery
Augres, Trinity Tel: 01534 863333 Fax: 01534 633301
Email: marketing@jerseyheritagetrust.org Web: www.jerseyheritagetrust.org

Hosting Jersey artists, this venue holds regular exhibitions of their work.

Opening Times: Dependent on exhibitions, please phone for details. Location: Main bus route to north of Jersey.

Classification Index

see Classifications List on page 11

Anthropology

Archaeological

Art Galleries

Art, Crafts & Textiles

China, Glass & Ceramics

Geology

Health & Medicine

Horticultural

Military & Defence

Mills - Water & Wind

Multicultural

Music & Theatre

Natural History

Oriental

Palaces

Police, Prisons & Dungeons

Railways

Religion

Roman

Science - Earth & Planetary

Sculpture

Sporting History

Stately Homes

Toy & Childhood

Transport

Victoriana

Town Index

Index to Entries